ST. MARY'S HIGH SCHOOL
111 – 18TH AVENUE S.W.
CALGARY, ALBERTA
T2S 0B8

ST. MARY'S HIGH SCHOOL

_____

_____

_____

_____

ADDISON WESLEY
SCIENCE *10*

Authors

Lionel Sandner
Curriculum Coordinator
Saanich School District #63
Saanichton, British Columbia
formerly Lead Coordinator
Pan Canadian Science Project

Donald Lacy
Science Department Head
Stelly's Secondary School
Saanich School District #63
Saanichton, British Columbia

Hyacinth Schaeffer
Director of Learning
Science Alberta Foundation
Calgary, Alberta
formerly Supervisor of Science, K-12
Calgary Catholic School District
Calgary, Alberta

Cliff Sosnowski
Science Department Head
Louis St. Laurent Catholic School
Edmonton Catholic Schools
Edmonton, Alberta

Contributing Author
Mary McDougall
Science Consultant
Calgary Catholic School District
Calgary, Alberta

Technology Consultant
Josef Martha
Science Department Head
Onoway Junior-Senior High School
Northern Gateway Schools
Onoway, Alberta

PEARSON
Addison
Wesley

Acknowledgment

The authors and Pearson Education Canada would like to thank Alberta Learning for their guidance in the development of this book.

Advisory Panel

Carmen Berg, *formerly* John G. Diefenbaker High School, Calgary Board of Education

Daryl Chichak, Science Consultant, Edmonton Catholic Schools

Bob Constantin, Bishop McNally High School, Calgary Catholic School Division

Wes Irwin, Grande Prairie Composite High School, Grande Prairie Public School District

Lorraine Lastiwka, Science Consultant, Edmonton Public Schools

Josef Martha, Onoway High School, Northern Gateway Regional Division

Mary McDougall, Science Consultant, Calgary Catholic School Division

Norma Nocente, Faculty of Education, University of Alberta

David Paraschuk, Bishop O'Byrne High School, Calgary Catholic School Division

Ruth Roth, St. Mary's Senior High School, Calgary Catholic School Division

Allan Stewart, Holy Trinity Senior High School, Edmonton Catholic Schools

Thomas Verenka, *formerly* James Fowler High School, Calgary Board of Education

David Warawa, Archbishop O'Leary High School, Edmonton Catholic Schools

Expert Reviewers

Dr. George Bourne, Faculty of Science, University of Calgary

Doug Bright, Ph.D., Royal Roads University, Victoria, BC

Dr. David Cass, Faculty of Science, University of Alberta

Fraser Hunter, Environment Canada

Dr. Ronald A. Kydd, Department of Chemistry, University of Calgary

Bevan Lawson, Environment Canada

Ann Lukey, Black Gold School Division

Dr. David A. Naylor, Department of Physics, University of Lethbridge

Professor Jean-Michel Maillol, Ph.D., Department of Geology and Geophysics, University of Calgary

Brian Waddell, Alberta Environment

Dr. Andrew Weaver, School of Earth and Ocean Sciences, University of Victoria, Victoria, BC

Social Considerations Reviewer

Don Kindt, Consultant, *formerly* Yellowknife Catholic Schools, Yellowknife, NT

Safety Reviewer

Lois M. Browne, Ph.D., Department of Chemistry, University of Alberta

Program Reviewers

Karen Anderson, *formerly* John G. Diefenbaker High School, Calgary Board of Education

Dave Bennett, Calgary Academy, Calgary

Kim Burley, Lindsay Thurber Composite High School, Red Deer Public School District

Jayni Caldwell, Foothills Composite High School, Foothills School Division

John Callegari, M.E. LaZerte High School, Edmonton Public Schools

Mike Craig, William Aberhart High School, Calgary Board of Education

Steven Daniel, Department of Education, Yellowknife, NT

Anthony Green, Austin O'Brian High School, Edmonton Catholic Schools

Lara Keehn, Bert Church High School, Rocky View School Division

Colette Krause, Christ the King School, St. Thomas Aquinas Catholic Schools

Bob Lekivetz, NorQuest College, Edmonton Public Schools

Virginia Lo Pinto, John G. Diefenbaker High School, Calgary Board of Education

Dianne Lohr, William E. Hay Composite High School, Clearview School Division

Cathy MacAdam, Glenmary School, Holy Family Catholic Regional School District

Brian MacConnell, Central Memorial High School, Calgary Board of Education

Dr. Rick Mrazek, Professor of Science Education, University of Lethbridge

Orest Olesky, New Sarepta Community High School, Black Gold Regional Division

Heidi Paterson, Prairie Jr./Sr. High School, Three Hills

Deborah Schroder, Sturgeon Composite High School, Sturgeon School Division

Steve Schultz, Lacombe Composite High School, Wolf Creek School Division

Kandy Songer, Bonnyville Centralized High School, Northern Lights School Division

Greg Voigt, Archbishop O'Leary High School, Edmonton Public Schools

Dwayne Wenaas, George McDougall High School, Rocky View School Division

Cheryl Whipple, Matthew Halton Community High School, Livingstone Range School Division

Henrik Asfeldt, Edwin Par Composite School, Aspen View Regional Division

Danielle Barthel, Edmonton Christian School, Edmonton Public Schools

Allison Belt, Rundle College High School, Calgary

Colin Bulger, Catholic Central High School, Holy Spirit Roman Catholic Separate Regional Division

George Cormie, Leduc Composite High School, Black Gold Regional Division

Carl Davidse, Camrose Composite High School, Battle River Regional School Division

Leno Delcioppo, Harry Ainlay High School, Edmonton Public Schools

Dave Devin, W. P. Wagner School, Edmonton Public Schools

Michael Enyedy, Wm. E. Hay Composite High School, Clearview School Division

Bill Forster, Spruce Grove Composite High School, Parkland School Division

Tracy From, Archbishop Jordan High School, Elk Island Catholic Schools

Ron Fukushima, John G. Diefenbaker High School, Calgary Board of Education

Diane Gee, Camrose Composite High School, Battle River Regional School Division

Amy Hancsicsak, Lester B. Pearson High School, Calgary Board of Education

Morris Heffel, Brooks Composite High School, Grasslands Regional Division

Natasha L. Heron, Henry Wise Wood High School, Calgary Board of Education

K. Jenkins, Harry Ainlay High School, Edmonton Public Schools

Woody Knebel, William Aberhart High School, Calgary Board of Education

Mark Koebel, Consort School, Prairie Land Regional Division

Sharon MacPherson, Earnest Manning High School, Calgary Board of Education

Kevin Manias, Henry Wise Wood High School, Calgary Board of Education

Erin McBride, Henry Wise Wood High School, Calgary Board of Education

T. J. Sadler, Harry Ainlay High School, Edmonton Public Schools

Dave Sherbinin, Glenmary School, Holy Family Catholic Regional District

Shauna Stevens, Harry Ainlay High School, Edmonton Public Schools

Ron Terakita, Kate Andrews High School, Palliser Regional Schools

Trevor Wooff, Innisfail Jr. Sr. High School, Chinook's Edge School Division

Jennifer Yadlowski, Springbank High School, Rocky View School Division

Liane Zutz, Paul Kane High School, St. Albert Protestant Schools

Field-Test Teachers

Curt Blair, St. Albert Catholic High School, Greater St. Albert Catholic Schools

Dave Brecht, Edgerton Public School, Buffalo Trail Public Schools

Richard J. Cadieux, J. A. Williams High School, Northern Lights School Division

Denise Chiles, Forest Lawn High School, Calgary Board of Education

Henry Czarnota, Coronation School, Clearview School Division

Susanne Czentye, Bishop Grandin High School, Calgary Catholic School Division

Nicole Duigou-Jones, Archbishop O'Leary High School, Edmonton Catholic Schools

Barbara Duncan, St. Mary's Senior High School, Calgary Catholic School Division

Nicole Egli, Bassano School, Grasslands Regional Division

Caroline Heppell, Strathcona High School, Edmonton Public Schools

Gail M. Holland, Lethbridge Collegiate Institute, Lethbridge School Division

Judy Huber, Kipohtakaw Education Centre, Morinville

James Kriese, St. Francis Xavier Catholic High School, Edmonton Catholic Schools

Catherine LeBlanc, Ross Sheppard High School, Edmonton Public Schools

Theresa Lema, Austin O'Brien High School, Edmonton Catholic Schools

Philip Lenko, Hilltop High School, Northern Gateway Regional School Division

Ron Pollmann, Sturgeon Composite High School, Sturgeon School Division

Lisa Preston, Sir Winston Churchill High School, Calgary Board of Education

Teraza Real, Holy Trinity Academy, Christ the Redeemer School Division

Harriet Skagen, Leduc Composite High School, Black Gold Regional Division

Dion Skitsko, Bishop McNally High School, Calgary Catholic School Division

Kevin Sommer, St. Jerome's School, Vermilion, East Central Alberta Catholic Separate Schools Regional Division

Shirley Tkachuk, Bev Facey Community High School, Elk Island Public School District

Leanne Dyck, Grande Prairie Composite High School, Grande Prairie Public School District

Claudia Fehres, James Fowler High School, Calgary Board of Education

Dean Johnston, Hunting Hills High School, Red Deer Public School District

Jeannette Kucher, St. Francis Xavier High School, Edmonton Catholic Schools

Carolyn Pawelko, Chestermere High School, Rocky View School Division

Don W. Rogowski, James Fowler High School, Calgary Board of Education

Olof Sandblom, John G. Diefenbaker High School, Calgary Board of Education

Jay Smith, Grande Prairie Composite High School, Grande Prairie Public School District

Pamela Timanson, Victoria School of Performing and Visual Arts, Edmonton Public Schools

Kim Webb, Chestermere High School, Rocky View School Division

The authors and Pearson Education Canada would also like to thank all the students who participated in the field-test.

Contents

Energy and Matter in Chemical Change

Contents

Energy Flow in Technological Systems

UNIT C

Contents

Cycling of Matter in Living Systems

UNIT
D

Contents

Energy Flow in Global Systems

Welcome to Addison Wesley Science 10

You are about to begin a scientific exploration using Addison Wesley Science 10. To assist you in this journey, this book has been designed with the following features.

An Outline gives you an overview of what you will be learning. You may want to use this as a guide to help you study.

Unit Outline

This book is divided into four units. Each unit opens with a large photograph that captures one of the ideas that will be covered in the unit.

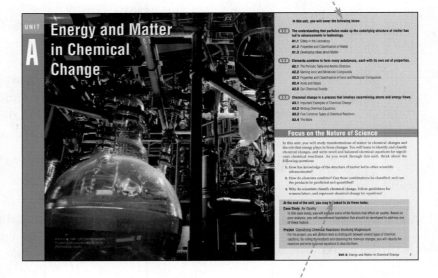

Exploring

This section is an introduction. It has an interesting real-world example to introduce the unit.

The **Focus** section has several questions to help you think about what you learn as you work through the unit. The questions focus on one of three areas or emphases of science: the nature of science, the relationship between science and technology, and the relationship of science and technology to society and the environment.

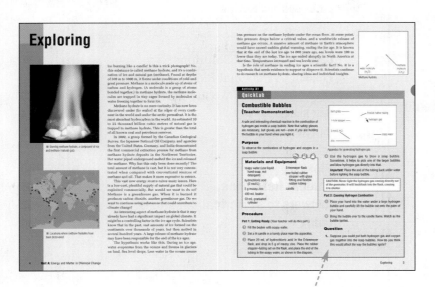

The **QuickLab** is a short, informal hands-on activity that is designed to introduce one of the topics of study in the unit.

The Sections

Each section title summarizes what you will learn in this section. These titles can help you organize your thoughts when you study.

The **Key Concepts** are the main ideas you will learn in this section. By the end of the section, you should be able to describe or explain each concept.

The **Learning Outcomes** are what you should know and be able to demonstrate your understanding of on completing the section.

An **infoBIT** is an interesting fact relevant to the content of the text.

The Lesson

The text is further divided into lessons to make the ideas easier to follow.

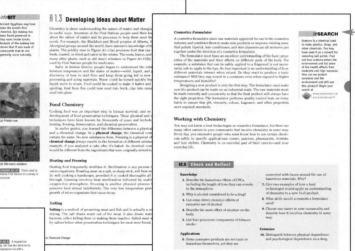

You can further explore and study a topic in **reSEARCH** using the Internet. This may provide an additional way to study the idea of the section or for enrichment.

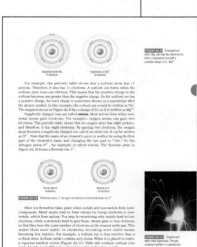

Photos and labelled diagrams help explain or clarify many of the ideas in the unit.

Example Problems show the detailed steps in solving problems.

Practice Problems model the example problem and provide opportunities for further practice. Use these problems to check if you understand the concept being discussed. If you have trouble with a practice problem, you should ask for help before continuing.

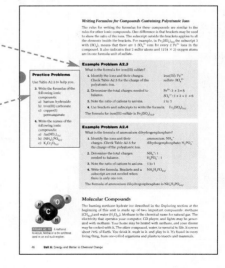

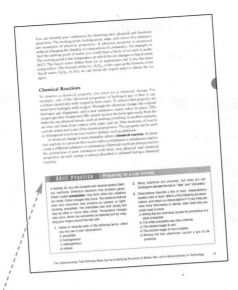

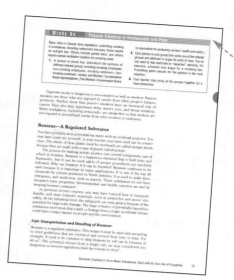

Minds On... activities are designed to stimulate thinking about key aspects of the topic being studied. These activities are usually done in small groups or sometimes by yourself.

A **Skill Practice** reviews or reinforces certain skills necessary for completing some of the lab activities in this course.

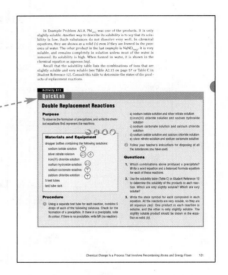

Throughout the book **QuickLabs** help explore specific topics or concepts in a hands-on manner. QuickLabs tend to take less time than the formal labs and do not require the same level of analysis and interpretation. In some situations, your teacher may demonstrate the activity.

Check and Reflect questions allow you to review what you have learned in a lesson and consolidate your understanding.

The **Section Review** provides questions relevant to the whole section. Answering these questions will help you consolidate what you have learned in the various lessons in the section.

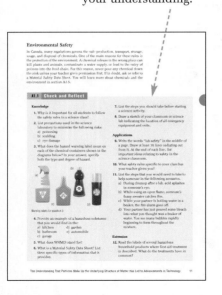

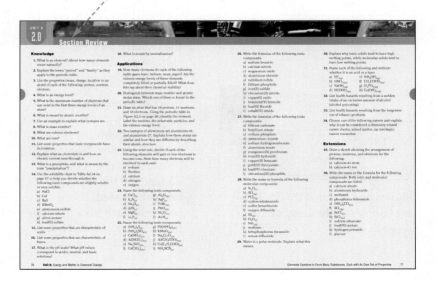

The Lab Activities

There are four main types of lab activities.

Inquiry Lab
These activities provide opportunities for you to work in a lab setting. You will develop scientific skills of predicting, observing, measuring, recording, inferring, analyzing, and much more. In these activities, you investigate many different phenomena that occur in our world.

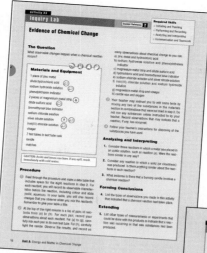

Problem-Solving Investigation
These are open-ended activities that allow you to be creative. You will identify a problem, make a plan, and then construct a solution. These activities usually have more than one solution.

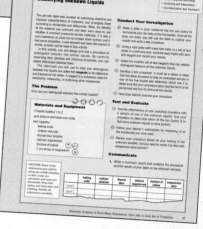

Decision-Making Investigation
These activities present issues or questions related to everyday life. You will analyze the issue and develop a conclusion based on the evidence you collect. Be prepared to present your conclusion to your classmates.

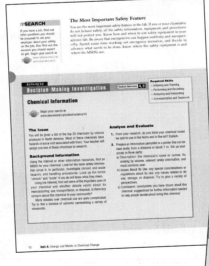

Design a Lab
For this type of lab you are given some criteria that define what a successful result would look like. You then plan an experiment, write the procedure, and perform it. You analyze your data and draw your own conclusions.

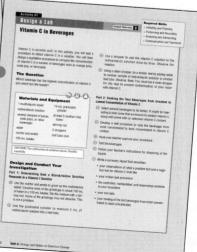

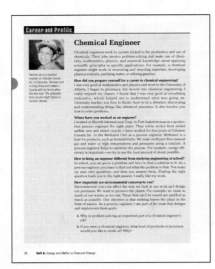

Career and Profile

Here you will find interesting profiles or interviews with people whose careers are related to the science and technology you study in the unit.

The Culminating Tasks

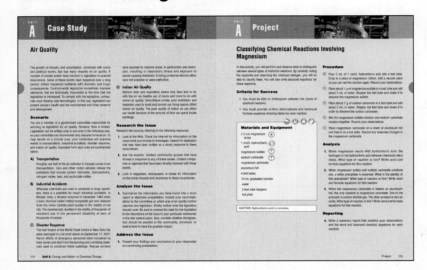

Project

This provides a hands-on opportunity for you to demonstrate what you have learned. The project requires you to apply some of the skills and knowledge that you have acquired to a new situation.

Case Study

This features an issue that may involve several viewpoints or have more than one solution. Here is an opportunity for you to use the different ideas you have learned from the unit or collected from other sources to form your own opinion.

Unit Summary

At a glance, you can find out all the key concepts you have learned within the unit. You can also read the summary of ideas in each section of the unit. This page can help you organize your notes for studying.

Unit Review

The Unit Review presents different categories of questions:

- **Vocabulary**—a chance to demonstrate your understanding of the important terms in the unit
- **Knowledge**—questions to test your basic understanding of the key concepts in each section of the unit
- **Applications**—questions that require you to use the ideas in more than one section in the unit
- **Extensions**—questions that have you apply your learning beyond what you have studied in the unit
- **Skills Practice**—questions that are related to specific skills you have learned in the unit
- **Self Assessment**—opportunities to express your thoughts about ideas you have discovered in the unit

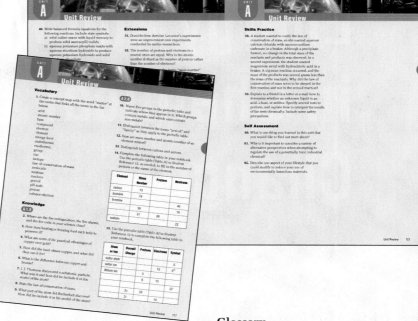

Student Reference

These pages provide references to lab safety and other basic scientific skills that will help you as you do the activities. Refer to these pages when you need a reminder about some of those skills.

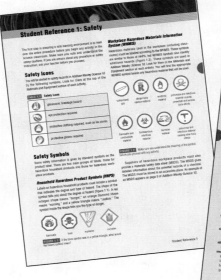

Glossary

The **Glossary** provides a comprehensive alphabetical list of the important terms in the book and their definitions.

Icons

 means you will be working with toxic or unknown materials and should wear safety goggles for protection or as a precaution

 means you should wear a lab apron to protect clothing

 means you should wear rubber gloves for protection when handling the materials

 means you will be working with glassware and you should exercise caution to avoid breakage and possible injury

 means opportunities exist for research on the Internet

Now it's time to begin. We hope you will enjoy your scientific exploration using Addison Wesley Science 10!

Energy and Matter in Chemical Change

A technician (lower right) monitors reactions in a factory that produces chemicals for the pharmaceutical industry.

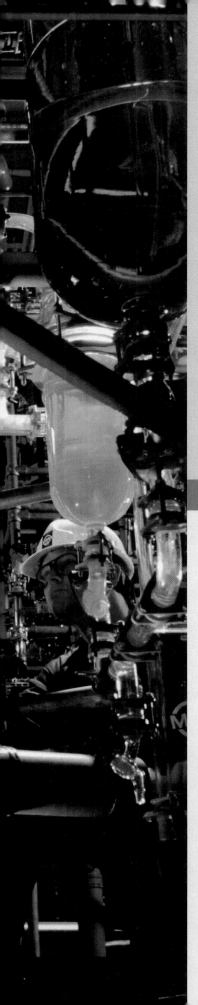

In this unit, you will cover the following ideas:

A 1.0 **The understanding that particles make up the underlying structure of matter has led to advancements in technology.**

A1.1 Safety in the Laboratory

A1.2 Properties and Classification of Matter

A1.3 Developing Ideas about Matter

A 2.0 **Elements combine to form many substances, each with its own set of properties.**

A2.1 The Periodic Table and Atomic Structure

A2.2 Naming Ionic and Molecular Compounds

A2.3 Properties and Classification of Ionic and Molecular Compounds

A2.4 Acids and Bases

A2.5 Our Chemical Society

A 3.0 **Chemical change is a process that involves recombining atoms and energy flows.**

A3.1 Important Examples of Chemical Change

A3.2 Writing Chemical Equations

A3.3 Five Common Types of Chemical Reactions

A3.4 The Mole

Focus on the Nature of Science

In this unit, you will study transformations of matter in chemical changes and the role that energy plays in these changes. You will learn to identify and classify chemical changes, and write word and balanced chemical equations for significant chemical reactions. As you work through this unit, think about the following questions:

1. How has knowledge of the structure of matter led to other scientific advancements?

2. How do elements combine? Can these combinations be classified, and can the products be predicted and quantified?

3. Why do scientists classify chemical change, follow guidelines for nomenclature, and represent chemical change by equations?

At the end of the unit, you may be asked to do these tasks:

Case Study Air Quality

In this case study, you will analyze some of the factors that affect air quality. Based on your analysis, you will recommend legislation that should be developed to address one of these factors.

Project Classifying Chemical Reactions Involving Magnesium

For the project, you will perform tests to distinguish between several types of chemical reactions. By noting the reactants and observing the chemical changes, you will classify the reactions and write balanced equations to describe them.

Exploring

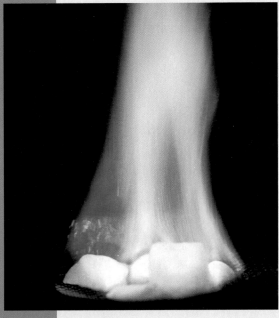

Burning methane hydrate, a compound of ice and methane (natural gas)

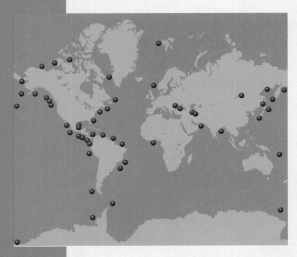

Locations where methane hydrates have been discovered

Ice burning like a candle! Is this a trick photograph? No, this substance is called methane hydrate, and it's a combination of ice and natural gas (methane). Found at depths of 500 m to 3000 m, it forms under conditions of cold and great pressure. Methane is a molecule made up of atoms of carbon and hydrogen. (A molecule is a group of atoms bonded together.) In methane hydrate, the methane molecules are trapped in tiny cages formed by molecules of water freezing together to form ice.

Methane hydrate is no mere curiosity. It has now been discovered under the seabed at the edges of every continent in the world and under the arctic permafrost. It is the most abundant hydrocarbon in the world. An estimated 10 to 25 thousand billion cubic metres of natural gas is trapped in methane hydrate. This is greater than the total of all known coal and petroleum reserves.

In 2002, a group formed by the Canadian Geological Survey, the Japanese National Oil Company, and agencies from the United States, Germany, and India demonstrated the first commercial extraction process for methane from methane hydrate deposits in the Northwest Territories. Hot water piped underground melted the ice and released the methane. Why has this only been done recently? The total amount of methane is vast, but it is not very concentrated when compared with conventional sources of methane and oil. That makes it more expensive to extract.

This vast new energy source raises many issues. Here is a low-cost, plentiful supply of natural gas that could be exploited commercially. But would we want to do so? Methane is a greenhouse gas. When it is burned it produces carbon dioxide, another greenhouse gas. Do we want to continue using substances that could contribute to climate change?

An interesting aspect of methane hydrate is that it may already have had a significant impact on global climate. It might be a controlling factor in the ice age cycle. Scientists know that in the past, vast amounts of ice formed on the continents over thousands of years, but then melted in several hundred years. A large release of methane hydrate may have been responsible for the end of the ice ages.

The hypothesis works like this. During an ice age, water evaporates from the oceans and freezes in glaciers on land. Sea level drops. Less water in the oceans means less pressure on the methane hydrate under the ocean floor. At some point, this pressure drops below a critical value, and a worldwide release of methane gas occurs. A massive amount of methane in Earth's atmosphere would have caused sudden global warming, ending the ice age. It is known that at the end of the last ice age 14 000 years ago, sea levels were 100 m lower than they are today. The ice age ended abruptly in North America at that time. Temperatures increased and sea levels rose.

Is the role of methane in ending ice ages a scientific fact? No, it is a hypothesis that needs evidence to support or disprove it. Scientists continue to do research on methane hydrate, sharing ideas and individual insights.

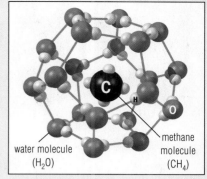

water molecule
(H_2O)

methane molecule
(CH_4)

Methane hydrate

Activity A1

QuickLab

Combustible Bubbles
(Teacher Demonstration)

A safe and interesting chemical reaction is the combustion of hydrogen gas inside a soap bubble. Note that safety glasses are necessary, but gloves are not—even if you are holding the bubble in your hand when you light it.

Purpose

To observe the combustion of hydrogen and oxygen in a soap bubble

Materials and Equipment

soapy water (use liquid dishwashing soap)

hydrochloric acid (3 mol/L)

5 g mossy zinc

400-mL beaker

50-mL graduated cylinder

Erlenmeyer flask

one-holed rubber stopper with glass fitting and flexible rubber tubing

candle

Procedure

Part 1: Getting Ready (Your teacher will do this part.)

1. Fill the beaker with soapy water.

2. Set a lit candle in a handy place near the apparatus.

3. Place 20 mL of hydrochloric acid in the Erlenmeyer flask, and drop in 5 g of mossy zinc. Place the rubber stopper–tubing set on the flask, and place the end of the tubing in the soapy water, as shown in the diagram.

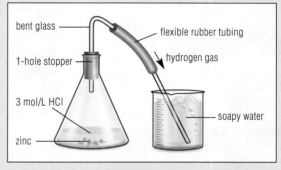

bent glass

flexible rubber tubing

1-hole stopper

hydrogen gas

3 mol/L HCl

soapy water

zinc

Apparatus for generating hydrogen gas

4. Use the hydrogen gas to blow a soap bubble. Sometimes, it helps to pick one of the larger bubbles and blow hydrogen gas directly into that.

   Important: Place the end of the tubing back under water before lighting the soap bubble.

   CAUTION: Never light the hydrogen gas coming directly out of the generator. It will backflash into the flask, causing it to shatter.

Part 2: Causing Hydrogen Combustion

5. Place your hand into the water under a large hydrogen bubble and carefully lift the bubble out onto the palm of your hand.

6. Bring the bubble over to the candle flame. Watch as the bubble ignites.

Question

1. Suppose you could put both hydrogen gas and oxygen gas together into the soap bubbles. How do you think this would affect the way the bubbles ignite?

The understanding that particles make up the underlying structure of matter has led to advancements in technology.

Key Concepts

In this section, you will learn about the following key concepts:

- Workplace Hazardous Materials Information System (WHMIS) and safe practices

- evidence of chemical change

- how chemical substances meet human needs

Learning Outcomes

When you have completed this section, you will be able to:

- illustrate an awareness of WHMIS guidelines, and demonstrate safe practices in the handling, storage, and disposal of chemicals in the laboratory and at home

- identify examples of how early humans worked with chemical substances to meet their basic needs

- outline the role of evidence in the development of the atomic model consisting of nucleons (protons and neutrons) and electrons through the work of Dalton, Thomson, Rutherford, and Bohr

- describe evidence for chemical change

FIGURE A1.1 All the materials we wear and use result from the various ways that atoms combine. These combinations form substances with different properties.

Our world is full of a rich and complex variety of materials, both natural and manufactured. Cotton and wool fabrics clothe us. Precious jewels decorate our bodies. Metal and concrete form skyscrapers. Plastics are everywhere. We wear them; we eat off them; and we drive in them. They are one of the most commonly used materials in the world today.

People have discovered and taken advantage of different properties of materials for thousands of years. To do this, they have invented a variety of chemical technologies.

In this section, you will begin by reviewing lab safety rules and safety symbols. Then you will review the differences between physical and chemical properties of substances and how to recognize chemical reactions. You will also read about various ways in which early human societies discovered and used naturally occurring materials. Finally, you will learn how an understanding of matter developed gradually over the centuries, and how experimental evidence led to changing models of the atom.

A1.1 Safety in the Laboratory

Safety must be an essential part of all your science studies. Your safety and the safety of your classmates and your teacher are of the highest importance.

Safety depends on awareness, knowledge, and action. You must be aware of known hazards and alert to the possibility of unforeseen ones. You must know how to use the right equipment and what to do in an emergency. But knowing isn't enough. Ultimately, it's what you *do* that makes the difference to your being an asset or a liability to others. Fooling around is forbidden. Everyone in the class must act safely and responsibly.

Working in the science laboratory involves taking precautions and minimizing hazards. For example, to avoid poisoning, we take the precaution of never eating in the lab. We also minimize the chance of poisoning by washing our hands. We avoid scalding by keeping far enough away from beakers with boiling water so that, even if they break, the water will not reach us. If we must move a beaker of hot water, we make sure to inform others so they can stay out of the way, and we use the correct kind of tongs for lifting.

Eye safety, in particular, is critically important. The eye's surface is very fragile tissue, and damaging it can have life-long consequences. Regular eyeglasses are not enough protection. Eyewear approved by your teacher will have side shielding and other safety features.

*info*BIT

According to the Alberta Department of Human Resources and Employment, workers with less than six months of experience are three times more likely to be injured than those with a year or more of experience. Young workers are 33% more likely to be injured on the job than older workers.

Understanding the Rules

Safety rules also help you minimize the risks of working in the lab. It's important to understand and follow the list of safety rules below. Your teacher will discuss any other specific rules that apply to your classroom. For more information on lab safety, see Student Reference 1: Safety.

Science Laboratory Safety Rules

1. Read all written instructions carefully before doing an activity.
2. Listen to all instructions and follow them carefully.
3. Wash your hands thoroughly after each activity and after handling chemicals.
4. Wear safety goggles, gloves, or an apron as required.
5. Think before you touch. Equipment may be hot and substances may be dangerous.
6. Smell a substance by fanning the smell toward you with your hand. Do not put your nose close to the substance.
7. Do not taste anything in the lab.
8. Tie back loose hair and roll up loose sleeves.
9. Never pour liquids into containers held in your hand. Place a test tube in a rack before pouring substances into it.
10. Clean up any spilled substances immediately as instructed by your teacher.
11. Never look into test tubes or containers from the top. Always look through the sides.
12. Never use cracked or broken glassware. Make sure you follow your teacher's instructions when getting rid of broken glass.
13. Label any container you put chemicals in.
14. Report all accidents and spills immediately to your teacher.
15. Read the WHMIS (Workplace Hazardous Materials Information System) safety symbols on any chemical you will be using and make sure that you understand all the symbols. See Student Reference 1 at the back of this book.

flammable

toxic

explosive

corrosive

FIGURE A1.2 Hazard symbols indicate both the type of hazard and the degree of hazard.

Safety Hazard Symbols

The first step in doing any science activity is to read the procedures all the way through to make sure you understand them. Carefully note any "Caution" boxes containing specific safety warnings. All activities in this text that require special precautions have safety icons next to the "Materials and Equipment" heading. These icons will alert you when you need to wear safety goggles, gloves, or an apron, and when you must be careful handling glassware.

The next step before beginning an activity is to check the warning symbols in the list of materials you will be using. Also check for hazard symbols on the containers of these materials. All hazardous materials have a label showing a hazard symbol. You may have seen these labels on chemical substances in your kitchen or garage. For example, window cleaner may contain ammonia, which is toxic and corrosive. Spray paint cans show labels warning that they are flammable and explosive.

Each hazard symbol shows two pieces of information:

- the degree of hazard, indicated by the shape and colour of the border. The degree increases from a yellow triangle meaning "caution," to an orange diamond meaning "warning," to a red octagon meaning "danger."
- the type of hazard, indicated by a symbol inside the border

Examples of these hazard symbols are shown in Figure A1.2. Figure A1.3 shows an example of hazard symbols on a common household product.

WHMIS

The **Workplace Hazardous Materials Information System (WHMIS)** is another system of easy-to-see warning symbols on hazardous materials, shown in Figure A1.4. These eight symbols are designed to help warn and protect people who use hazardous materials at work. You will see the symbols for dangerously reactive material, corrosive material, and poisonous material next to the names of some of the chemicals you will be using in this unit. Follow your teacher's instructions in carefully handling and disposing of all chemicals.

FIGURE A1.3 This spray paint is both flammable and explosive.

compressed gas

dangerously reactive material

oxidizing material

poisonous and infectious material causing immediate and serious toxic effects

flammable and combustible material

biohazardous infectious material

corrosive material

poisonous and infectious material causing other toxic effects

FIGURE A1.4 WHMIS symbols

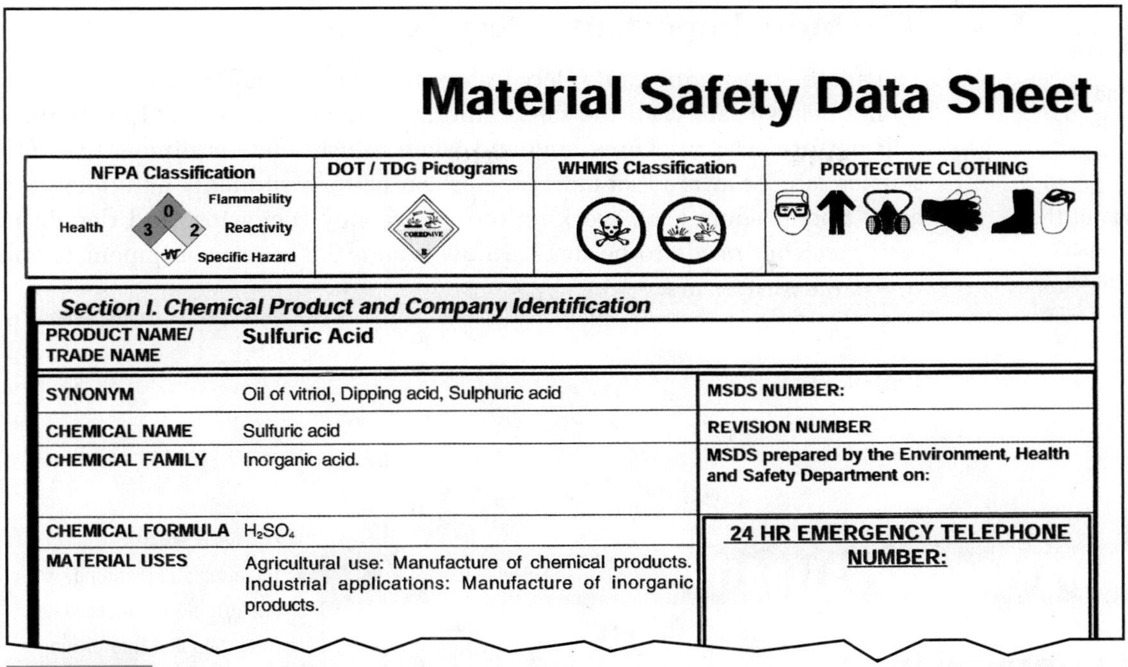

Material Safety Data Sheet

NFPA Classification	DOT / TDG Pictograms	WHMIS Classification	PROTECTIVE CLOTHING
Health 3 / 0 Flammability / 2 Reactivity / W Specific Hazard	CORROSIVE 8	☠ ⚗	👓 ↑ 😷 🧤 👢 🗑

Section I. Chemical Product and Company Identification		
PRODUCT NAME/ TRADE NAME	**Sulfuric Acid**	
SYNONYM	Oil of vitriol, Dipping acid, Sulphuric acid	**MSDS NUMBER:**
CHEMICAL NAME	Sulfuric acid	**REVISION NUMBER**
CHEMICAL FAMILY	Inorganic acid.	**MSDS prepared by the Environment, Health and Safety Department on:**
CHEMICAL FORMULA	H_2SO_4	**24 HR EMERGENCY TELEPHONE NUMBER:**
MATERIAL USES	Agricultural use: Manufacture of chemical products. Industrial applications: Manufacture of inorganic products.	

FIGURE A1.5 An MSDS provides information about a specific chemical.

Material Safety Data Sheets

In Canada, manufacturers of all hazardous products used in workplaces, including schools, must provide information sheets about their products. The **Material Safety Data Sheet (MSDS)** identifies the chemical and physical hazards associated with each substance. It includes physical data, such as melting point and boiling point, toxicity, health effects, first aid, and spill and leak cleanup procedures. WHMIS regulations require employers to make these sheets available to employees who use hazardous substances in their work. Figure A1.5 shows an example of an MSDS for a substance that you might use in a science activity.

Minds On ... Reading an MSDS for Household Bleach Solution

Your teacher will give you a copy of an MSDS for bleach solution. Use this MSDS to answer the following questions.

1. List three synonyms for the name "bleach."

2. Bleach solution has two ingredients. What are they? Which of these ingredients are hazardous?

3. Find the hazard identification section. Under "Emergency Overview," there is a short summary. Find the summary and record it.

4. Read the list of potential health effects. Copy down the potential health effect caused by eye contact.

5. Find the section under "First Aid Measures" and record the instructions for what to do in case of eye contact.

6. If a fire were to break out near bleach, should the bleach itself be considered a fire hazard? What special equipment is required to fight a fire in which bleach is present?

7. Suppose someone drank bleach. Should the first aid procedure include inducing vomiting to get the solution out of the person? What other treatments are possible?

8. Find out what is meant by the term "chronic exposure."

 re**SEARCH**

If you have a job, find out what questions you should be prepared to ask your employer about your safety on the job. Also find out the answers you should expect to get. Begin your search at

www.pearsoned.ca/
school/science10

The Most Important Safety Feature

You are the most important safety feature in the lab. If you or your classmates do not behave safely, all the safety information, equipment, and procedures will not protect you. Know how and when to use safety equipment in your science lab. Be aware that emergencies can happen suddenly and unexpectedly. Spend some time working out emergency scenarios, and decide in advance what needs to be done. Know where the safety equipment is and where the MSDSs are.

Activity A2
Decision-Making Investigation

Student Reference **4, 9**

Required Skills
- Initiating and Planning
- Performing and Recording
- Analyzing and Interpreting
- Communication and Teamwork

Chemical Information

 Begin your search at
www.pearsoned.ca/school/science10

The Issue

You will be given a list of the top 20 chemicals by volume produced in North America. Most of these chemicals have hazards of some sort associated with them. Your teacher will assign you one of these chemicals to research.

Background Information

Using the Internet or other information resources, find an MSDS for your chemical. Look for the basic safety information about it. In particular, investigate chronic and acute hazards, and handling procedures. Look up the terms "chronic" and "acute" if you do not know what they mean.

Using the Internet, find out some of the important uses of your chemical and whether debate exists about its manufacturing, use, transportation, or disposal. Is there any concern about this chemical in your community?

Many debates over chemical use are quite complicated. Try to find a balance of opinions representing a variety of viewpoints.

Analyze and Evaluate

1. From your research, do you think your chemical would be safe to use in the home and in the lab? Explain.

2. Prepare an information pamphlet or a poster that can be read easily from a distance of about 1 m. Set up your poster in three parts:
   a) Description: the chemical's name or names, its ranking by volume, relevant safety information, and most common uses
   b) Issues About Its Use: any special considerations or regulations about its use; any issues related to its use, storage, or disposal. Try to give a variety of perspectives.
   c) Conclusion: conclusions you have drawn about this chemical; suggestions for further information needed to help people decide about using this chemical

Environmental Safety

In Canada, many regulations govern the safe production, transport, storage, usage, and disposal of chemicals. One of the main reasons for these rules is the protection of the environment. A chemical release in the wrong place can kill plants and animals, contaminate a water supply, or lead to the entry of poisons into the food chain. For this reason, never pour any chemical down the sink unless your teacher gives permission first. If in doubt, ask or refer to a Material Safety Data Sheet. You will learn more about chemicals and the environment in section A2.5.

A1.1 Check and Reflect

Knowledge

1. Why is it important for all students to follow the safety rules in a science class?

2. List precautions used in the science laboratory to minimize the following risks:
   a) poisoning
   b) scalding
   c) eye damage

3. What does the hazard warning label mean on each of the chemical containers shown in the diagrams below? In your answer, specify both the type and degree of hazard.

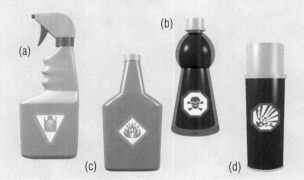

Warning labels for question 3

4. Provide an example of a hazardous substance that you would find in the:
   a) kitchen   d) garden
   b) bathroom   e) automobile
   c) garage

5. What does WHMIS stand for?

6. What is a Material Safety Data Sheet? List three specific types of information that it provides.

7. List the steps you should take before starting a science activity.

8. Draw a sketch of your classroom or science lab indicating the location of all emergency equipment and exits.

Applications

9. Write the words "lab safety" in the middle of a page. Draw at least 10 lines radiating out from it. At the end of each line, list important ideas relating to safety in the science classroom.

10. What safety rules specific to your class has your teacher given you?

11. List the steps that you would need to take to help someone in the following scenarios.
    a) During cleanup after a lab, acid splashes in someone's eye.
    b) While using an open flame, someone's fuzzy sweater catches fire.
    c) While your partner is boiling water in a beaker, the fire alarm goes off.
    d) Your partner has just poured some bleach into what you thought was a beaker of water. You see many bubbles rapidly beginning to form throughout the mixture.

Extension

12. Read the labels of several hazardous household products where first aid treatment is described. What do the treatments have in common?

A1.2 Properties and Classification of Matter

How many dogs are there in the world? Even if you could find an accurate answer to this question, it would not tell you very much about dogs. You can learn much more about dogs by looking at their different classifications. Breeders have classified dogs into several hundred breeds. Each breed has unique markings, physical attributes, and personality types (Figure A1.6). The various breeds can be combined into a smaller number of groups that identify what they are used for, such as companion dogs or hunting dogs. Other ways of classifying dogs are based on their size or geographic origin.

Similarly, scientists use classification systems to help them work with the millions of compounds that have been discovered or synthesized. No one can possibly know more than a small fraction of them in detail. Chemists get around this problem by classifying compounds by their characteristics. They use several different classification systems, depending on which is most useful at the time. For example, all matter at room temperature (25°C) can be classified as solid, liquid, or gas. However, this system has limited usefulness. For example, bromine, mercury, and water are all liquids, but they have very few other properties in common. A more useful way to classify compounds is by their physical and chemical properties.

FIGURE A1.6 Organizing dogs into breeds helps to classify them. Each breed is recognized by certain characteristics.

Minds On... Classification

Sometimes, mixtures need to be separated into pure substances. The first step is to classify the components of the mixture according to their physical properties. The differences between these properties can be used to separate the substances. For example, in a mixture of water and sand, one is a solid and the other is a liquid, and they have different densities. Separating them is easy: simply let the mixture sit until the sand settles out. Working with your partner, develop a procedure to separate each of the following mixtures.

a) sugar, water, sand
b) table salt, aluminium filings, iron filings
c) vegetable oil, aluminium filings, table salt, water
d) water, table salt, sugar

Properties Used to Classify Substances

Physical properties describe the physical appearance and composition of a substance. Table A1.1 lists common physical properties used for classifying substances.

TABLE A1.1 Common Physical Properties Used for Classifying Substances

Physical Property	Description
boiling point or condensation point	temperature of boiling or condensing
melting point or freezing point	temperature of melting or freezing
malleability	ability to be beaten or rolled into sheets without crumbling
ductility	ability to be stretched without breaking
colour	colour
state	solid, liquid, gas
solubility	ability to dissolve
crystal formation	crystalline appearance (Figure A1.7)
conductivity	ability to conduct heat or electricity
magnetism	magnetic attraction between objects (iron, cobalt, and nickel, and electromagnets)

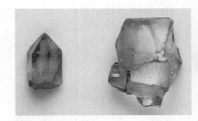

FIGURE A1.7 The formation of crystals is a physical property that can be used to classify substances. On the left is a typical crystal formed by the mineral quartz ($SiO_{2(s)}$). Glass (right) is an amorphous substance: it never forms crystals.

  Chemical properties describe the reactivity of a substance. For example, calcium reacts vigorously when placed in water (Figure A1.8). This is one of calcium's chemical properties. Table A1.2 lists some common chemical properties used for classifying substances.

TABLE A1.2 Common Chemical Properties Used for Classifying Substances

Chemical Property	Description
ability to burn	combustion (flame, heat, light)
flash point	temperature needed to ignite a flame
behaviour in air	tendency to degrade, react, or tarnish
reaction with water	tendency to corrode or dissolve
reaction with acids	corrosion, sometimes bubble formation
reaction to heat	tendency to melt or decompose
reaction to red and blue litmus	red—acid; blue—base; no colour change—neutral

FIGURE A1.8 Calcium reacts vigorously with water.

FIGURE A1.10 Paint is a heterogeneous mixture.

Pure Substances and Mixtures

Recall from science classes in other grades that matter can be classified as pure substances and mixtures (Figure A1.9). In a **pure substance**, all the particles that make up the substance are identical, so its chemical and physical properties are constant. A pure substance may be an **element** or a **compound**. Recall from grade 9 science that an element is a pure substance that cannot be broken down into other substances. It is a substance made up of only one type of atom. For example, both gold and helium are elements. A compound is a chemical combination of two or more elements in a specific ratio. For example, water is a pure substance made up of water molecules. Each water molecule consists of two hydrogen atoms and one oxygen atom. Its formula is $H_2O_{(l)}$. Water's properties are constant: it is a liquid at 25°C. It freezes at 0°C, and it boils at 100°C at sea level.

A **mixture** is a combination of pure substances. The proportions of the pure substances in a mixture vary, so the properties of the mixture vary as well. For example, the sweetness of lemon juice increases as the proportion of sugar in it increases. In a **mechanical mixture**, such as soil, the different substances are visible. It is also called a **heterogeneous** mixture. (The prefix "hetero-" means "different.") A **suspension** is another kind of mechanical mixture, where the components are in different states. For example, mud is a suspension of dirt in water, and a sandstorm is a suspension of sand in air. A **colloid** is similar to a suspension but the suspended substance cannot be easily separated from the other substance.

In some mixtures, the separate components are not visible. These are **solutions**. They are called **homogeneous** mixtures because they look the same throughout. (The prefix "homo" means "same.") In a solution, one substance is dissolved in another. For example, a soft drink is a solution composed mainly of sugar dissolved in water.

Mixtures such as paint, glue, and motor oil are important materials. However, they can be difficult to classify because they are not pure substances and do not have constant properties. Pure substances are much easier to classify. Elements are classified in the periodic table, and many compounds can be classified either as ionic or molecular. Another important method of grouping compounds is as acids, bases, or neutral solutions. You will learn more about acids and bases in section A2.4.

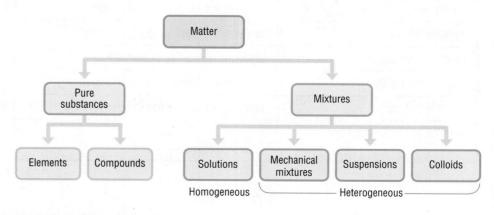

FIGURE A1.9 Classification of matter

You can identify pure substances by observing their physical and chemical properties. The melting point, boiling point, state, and colour of a substance are examples of physical properties. A physical property is measured without changing the identity or composition of a substance. For example, to find the melting point of water, you could heat a block of ice until it melts. The melting point is the temperature at which the ice changes to liquid water (0°C). The liquid water differs from ice in appearance, but it has the same composition. The formula of the ice, $H_2O_{(s)}$, is the same as the formula of the liquid water, $H_2O_{(l)}$. In fact, we can freeze the liquid water to obtain the ice again.

Chemical Reactions

To observe a chemical property, you must see a chemical change. For example, one of the chemical properties of hydrogen gas is that it can combine chemically with oxygen to form water. To observe this property, we must burn hydrogen with oxygen. Through the chemical change, the original hydrogen gas disappears, and a new substance, water, takes its place. (The oxygen gas also disappears.) We cannot recover the hydrogen easily from the water by any physical means, such as melting or boiling. In another example, an iron nail rusts from contact with water and air. This tendency of iron to corrode when wet is one of its chemical properties. This property can be used to distinguish iron from less reactive metals, such as platinum.

A chemical change is more formally called a **chemical reaction**. A chemical reaction is a process that occurs when a substance or substances react to create a different substance or substances. Chemical reactions always involve the production of new substances with their own physical and chemical properties. As well, energy is always absorbed or released during a chemical reaction.

Skill Practice — Preparing for a Lab Activity

In Activity A3, you will complete and observe several chemical reactions. Chemical reactions may produce gases. Solids (called **precipitates**) may form when two solutions are mixed. Colour changes may occur. Two solutions that are clear and colourless may produce an opaque, or light-blocking, precipitate. The precipitate may look cloudy and may be white or some other colour. Temperature changes may occur, which can sometimes be detected just by wrapping your fingers around the test tube.

1. Define or describe each of the following terms, which you may use in your observations:
   a) precipitate
   b) homogeneous
   c) heterogeneous
   d) opaque

2. Many solutions are coloured, but many are not. Distinguish between the terms "clear" and "colourless."

3. Observations describe a fact or facts. Interpretations explain a fact or facts. Which of the following are observations, and which are interpretations? If you think you need more information to decide, state what else you would need to know.
   a) Mixing the two chemicals caused the production of a white precipitate.
   b) The white precipitate was silver chloride.
   c) The solution began to boil.
   d) The solution began to form bubbles.
   e) Mixing the two chemicals caused a gas to be produced.

Evidence of Chemical Change

The Question

What observable changes happen when a chemical reaction occurs?

Materials and Equipment

1 piece of zinc metal

dilute hydrochloric acid

sodium hydroxide solution

phenolphthalein indicator

2 pieces of magnesium metal strip

dilute sulfuric acid

bromothymol blue indicator

sodium chloride solution

silver nitrate solution

iron(III) chloride solution

vinegar

7 test tubes in test tube rack

candle

matches

CAUTION: Acids and bases can burn. If any spill, wash immediately with cold water.

Procedure

1. Read through the procedure and make a data table that includes space for the eight reactions in step 2. For each reactant, you will record its observable characteristics before the reaction, including colour and state (solid, aqueous). In your table, you will also record changes that you observe when you mix the reactants. Remember to give your table a title.

2. At the top of the right column is a list of pairs of reactants from (a) to (h). For each pair, record your observations about each reactant. For (a) to (g), carefully mix each pair in its own test tube. For (h), carefully light the candle. Observe the results, and record as

many observations about chemical change as you can.

a) zinc metal and hydrochloric acid

b) sodium hydroxide solution and phenolphthalein indicator

c) magnesium metal strip and dilute sulfuric acid

d) hydrochloric acid and bromothymol blue indicator

e) sodium chloride solution and silver nitrate solution

f) iron(III) chloride solution and sodium hydroxide solution

g) magnesium metal strip and vinegar

h) candle wax and oxygen

3. Your teacher may instruct you to add some tests by mixing any two of the substances in the materials section in combinations that were not tried in step 2. Do not mix any substances unless instructed to by your teacher. Record observations that may indicate that a reaction, if any, has occurred.

4. Follow your teacher's instructions for disposing of the substances you have used.

Analyzing and Interpreting

1. Consider those reactions in which a metal was placed in an acidic solution, such as reaction (a). Were the reactions similar in any way?

2. Consider any reaction in which a solid (or cloudiness) was produced. Is there anything similar about the reactants in each reaction?

3. What evidence is there that a burning candle involves a chemical reaction?

Forming Conclusions

4. List the types of observations you made in this activity that indicated that a chemical reaction had taken place.

Extending

5. List other types of measurements or experiments that could be done with the products to indicate that a reaction was occurring or that new substances had been produced.

Recognizing Chemical Reactions

Some chemical reactions are simple, and some are complex. All reactions share certain characteristics. These include:

- All reactions involve the production of new substances with their own characteristic properties. These properties include: state at room temperature, melting point, colour, and density.
- All reactions involve the flow of energy. This may be detected by a change in temperature.
- Many reactions cause a phase change, such as the formation of a gas (bubbles) or of a solid that appears as cloudiness in a previously clear solution.

You will learn more about chemical reactions in section A3.0.

re**SEARCH**

Besides the states of matter you are familiar with, there are less common states, known as "exotic" states. One example is the gas inside a fluorescent light bulb when the light is turned on. Research one of the following exotic states of matter: plasma, liquid crystal, the superconductive state, or other exotic state of your choice. Begin your search at  www.pearsoned.ca/school/science10

A1.2 Check and Reflect

Knowledge

1. Define the following terms:
   a) boiling point
   b) malleability
   c) ductility
   d) solubility

2. State the observations that would lead to the following conclusions:
   a) A solid is forming.
   b) A gas is being formed.
   c) The temperature increases.

3. Water freezes at 0°C. At what temperature does it melt?

4. A blue crystal is placed in water. After much stirring, the crystal disappears and the water becomes blue. The liquid is then heated. Eventually, all the water evaporates and many small blue crystals appear. Has a chemical reaction taken place? Explain.

5. List two features common to all chemical reactions.

Applications

6. A waxy material is heated very slowly. Rather than melting at a particular temperature, it melts gradually over a range of temperatures starting at 52°C and finishing at 65°C. Is this material a pure substance or a mixture?

7. A black solid with a constant melting point is heated to a high temperature, producing a gas, and a shiny brown metal. The boiling point of the gas is measured at −183°C, and the melting point of the metal at 1085°C. Is the black solid an element, a compound, or a mixture? Explain.

8. Diamond is a pure substance and an element (carbon). Water is a pure substance and a compound. Suppose a number of diamonds are placed in water, and the water is then frozen. How should this material be classified?

9. Fresh milk separates spontaneously into cream, which floats to the surface with a watery layer below. Homogenized milk is made by breaking the cream into tiny droplets and mixing them into the rest of the milk. This prevents the cream from separating. Is homogenized milk homogeneous or heterogeneous?

Extensions

10. Find out whether homogenized milk is a suspension, a colloid, or a solution.

11. The formation of bubbles in a liquid may mean that the liquid is boiling. Or it may mean that a chemical reaction is producing a gas. List two ways to determine which is occurring: boiling or a chemical reaction.

(a) Prickly rose

(b) Old man's whiskers

FIGURE A1.11 Plants used by Alberta First Nations for a variety of purposes

A 1.3 Developing Ideas about Matter

Chemistry is about understanding the nature of matter and changing matter in useful ways. Ancestors of the First Nations people used their knowledge about the nature of matter and its processes to help them meet their basic needs. For example, the Blackfoot and Blood peoples of Alberta, like most Aboriginal groups around the world, have extensive knowledge of the use of plants. The prickly rose in Figure A1.11(a) produces fruit that can be eaten fresh, roasted, or dried and eaten in the winter. The roots, leaves, and seeds of many other plants, such as old man's whiskers in Figure A1.11(b), are also used by First Nations people for medicines.

Early in human history, people began to understand the relationship between temperature and the states of matter—solid, liquid, and gas. The discovery of how to start fires and keep them going led to new ways of processing and using materials. Water could be turned quickly from ice to liquid water to steam. Food could be cooked to make it tastier and to delay spoiling. Heat from fire could turn mud into brick, clay into ceramic, and sand into glass.

Food Chemistry

Cooking food was an important step in human survival, and so was the development of food preservation techniques. These physical and chemical techniques have been known for thousands of years and include drying, heating, freezing, fermentation, and chemical preservation.

In earlier grades, you learned the difference between a physical change and a chemical change. In a **physical change**, the chemical components remain the same. No new substances form. Freezing is a physical change. A **chemical change** always results in the formation of different substances. For example, if you analyzed a cake after it's baked, its chemical composition would be different from the ingredients that were originally mixed to make it.

Heating and Freezing

Heating food temporarily sterilizes it. Sterilization is any process that kills micro-organisms. Roasting meat on a spit, or sharp stick, will heat sterilize it. So will cooking a hamburger, provided it is cooked thoroughly all the way through. Canning involves heat sterilization followed by sealing in an oxygen-free atmosphere. Freezing is another physical process that can preserve food almost indefinitely. The very low temperature prevents the growth of micro-organisms that cause decay.

Salting

Salting is a method of preserving meat and fish and is actually a method of drying. The salt draws water out of the meat. It also draws water out of bacteria, either killing them or making them inactive. Salted meat was used by sailors before other preservation techniques for meat were found.

Fermentation

Unfortunately, certain nutrients, such as vitamin C, were not always retained when food was preserved. The absence of vitamin C in sailors' diets caused the disease known as scurvy. Captain Cook, who explored much of the eastern Pacific Ocean for Great Britain, brought pickled cabbage on his voyages because it was known to prevent scurvy. Pickled cabbage (sauerkraut) has a high vitamin C content, and was produced through a process called **fermentation**. Wine and beer are also made by a process of fermentation.

You may be surprised that ancient peoples knew how to preserve vegetables for very long periods without the need for canning machines or freezers. One way this was done was through fermentation. Fermentation is a biochemical preservation technique involving bacteria called *lactobacilli*. These bacteria are present on the surfaces of all living things. They convert starches and sugars present in fruits and vegetables into a chemical called lactic acid. Lactic acid is a preservative that prevents the growth of bacteria that cause food to rot. The lactobacilli bacteria are beneficial to food because they make it more digestible and increase vitamin levels. Think about that the next time you bite into a pickle!

Smoking was also a common means of chemical food preservation and is still used today. Bacon and smoked fish are common examples. Smoking introduces chemicals called antioxidants that slow the rotting process. Wood smoke contains some formaldehyde, which acts as a preservative.

Metallurgy—An Early Branch of Chemistry

Another early branch of chemistry was metallurgy, the science of producing and using metals. Until 3000 B.C., the only known metals were gold, copper, silver, lead, and iron. Gold was used extensively in ancient times as jewellery, because it is soft and easy to work with. But its softness—and its rarity—meant it was not suitable for weapons or equipment for hunting or farming.

Copper has many practical advantages over gold. Because it is harder, it can be made into tools and weapons, as well as jewellery. The Inuit used copper found in the Coppermine River, which flows into the Arctic Ocean. This is often referred to as "native" copper because it occurs naturally in pure form. Besides spears, arrows, and knife blades (Figure A1.12), early Inuit also formed the copper into handles for pots, staples, and rivets.

When people first began using copper, they hammered it into shapes, but this caused it to become brittle. Tools made from copper broke easily. A process called "annealing" solved this problem. Annealing is the heating of copper before it is hammered. Annealing changed the metal so it was no longer brittle when hammered. With this discovery, copper could be hammered into sheets and made into stronger tools and weapons.

FIGURE A1.12 Harpoon head with a point made of copper and a holder made of antler. Inuit used it for hunting about 800 years ago.

These early uses of copper relied on native copper. However, copper occurs this way only in small amounts. It is much more common in compounds with other elements. But copper in compounds was unusable until smelting technology was developed. Smelting is the process of separating a metal from the other elements in a compound by melting. Copper was being smelted in Egypt by 4000 B.C.

Later, the discovery of tin ores caused a revolution in metallurgy. By 2500 B.C., the Sumerians, in the Middle East, had begun smelting tin ores with copper ore. They found that the metal produced from this combination was much easier to cast than pure copper because it flowed more easily and was much stronger. The copper and tin formed an alloy called bronze. An alloy is any mixture of metals. Bronze made much stronger tools and weapons than either copper or tin alone.

When people first began using metals, they thought iron was very rare. The only source seemed to be meteorites. Like copper, iron occurred more widely in mineral compounds. Eventually, a process for smelting iron became common at around 1200 B.C., and the Iron Age began. The production of iron tools revolutionized agriculture, and iron weapons did the same thing for warfare. When iron and carbon were combined in the right way, steel was produced. Steel was much stronger than iron alone. It was especially useful for hunting knives, armour, and swords.

During early times, people discovered many ways of changing and using matter but still had no basic understanding of what it was. Greater understanding was needed for the development of more advanced applications.

Aristotle's Description of Matter

What is matter? As early as 400 B.C., Greek philosophers were attempting to answer this question. They considered the idea that fundamental types of matter or elements could be combined to produce the incredible variety of substances that we see around us. The philosopher Aristotle believed that all matter was composed of combinations of fire, earth, water, and air.

Another question was whether matter could be divided into infinitely smaller and smaller pieces. Or did it become indivisible at some point? Aristotle thought fire, earth, water, and air were all continuous, which meant that there was no such thing as a smallest piece. Democritus, another Greek philosopher, had a different idea. He proposed that matter was made up of tiny particles that could not be divided into smaller pieces. He called them *atomos*, meaning "indivisible." The Greeks did not perform experiments to test their ideas, and it may not have occurred to them to try. Scientific investigation, based on experimentation, did not yet exist.

Democritus's idea of matter being made up of tiny particles was closer to what we know of the structure of matter today. However, Aristotle was better known and well respected at the time. His idea of matter being made up of fire, earth, air, and water was accepted for the next 2000 years.

Alchemy

A scientific process of investigation did not exist, but that did not mean that no one was doing experiments. Alchemists like the one in Figure A1.13 were experimenting with matter. Alchemy was a combination of science and magic. Many alchemists hoped to get rich quickly by turning cheap metals, such as lead, into gold. Because of this, alchemists were secretive about their work. This meant that scientific knowledge was slow to develop, because people did not work together or share information about their discoveries. When an alchemist died, his knowledge disappeared with him. The same information had to be discovered again by others. Sometimes, this information was not rediscovered for hundreds of years.

Alchemy was not a real science, but it did contribute to the development of chemistry. Many important scientific advances were made during this period. Mercury was discovered, and procedures for making mineral acids, such as hydrochloric acid, were developed. Alchemists also developed or improved laboratory equipment, such as glassware and the distillation apparatus.

In the late 1500s, people began to ask questions about how to investigate the natural world. They wondered if there was a specific procedure that could lead to a better understanding of the world. This procedure would help to ensure that results and conclusions were meaningful and true. Gradually, the scientific process that involves experimentation, observation, and forming conclusions developed. Student Reference 2: The Inquiry Process will help you use this process in your own investigations.

Like the Greek philosophers, early scientists were interested in the question: What is matter? They began to debate if the "atomos" proposed by Democritus thousands of years earlier existed. They called these tiny particles **atoms**.

FIGURE A1.13 Alchemists developed many experimental techniques used later by chemists to make important discoveries. Chemistry developed very slowly during this early period.

Developing Hypotheses about Matter

Many scientists contributed evidence that led to our understanding of atoms. One of the first was the Irish scientist Robert Boyle, who lived from 1627 to 1691. Boyle measured relationships between volume and pressure of gases. From his experiments, he concluded that gases are made up of tiny particles that group together to make different substances. This is similar to today's theories, but we have a much better idea of what these basic particles are.

The French scientist Antoine Lavoisier (1743–1794) measured the masses of the substances that reacted together and the substances produced in many chemical reactions. He discovered that mass is neither produced nor lost during a chemical reaction. He called this the **law of conservation of mass**. You will learn more about this law in section A3.0.

During this early period, many scientists were investigating matter, and many models of atoms were proposed. However, four classic models are always discussed because they are examples of the scientific process at its best. Each model is founded on an experiment. Although each model is attributed to one person, all the scientists applied their own insights to pre-existing ideas. The works of Dalton, Thomson, Rutherford, and Bohr illustrate the role of evidence in the development of the model of the atom.

As you read about the different models of the atom, record the development in the understanding of the atom by showing the *differences* from one model to the next. Compare Dalton's model to Aristotle's ideas, which were replaced by Dalton's work.

John Dalton

John Dalton (1766–1844) was an English chemist and physicist who made many contributions to chemistry. He based his model of the atom on experiments he did in combining elements.

Dalton imagined that all atoms were like small spheres, but that they could have different properties. They varied in size, mass, or colour. Figure A1.14 shows how Dalton imagined atoms to look.

Dalton used the following model to explain matter:

- All matter is made of small, indivisible particles called atoms.
- All the atoms of an element are identical in properties such as size and mass.
- Atoms of different elements have different properties.
- Atoms of different elements can combine in specific fixed ratios to form new substances.

FIGURE A1.14 Dalton described atoms as tiny balls. The atoms of different elements were different in size and mass.

J. J. Thomson

Joseph John Thomson (1856–1940) was an English physicist who discovered the **electron**.

In the 1890s, Thomson was experimenting with beams of particles produced in a vacuum tube like the one shown in Figure A1.15. Thomson's experiments showed that the beam was made of negative charges. By testing many different elements, he showed that they all produced the same type of beam. This suggested that atoms of different elements contained smaller particles that were identical.

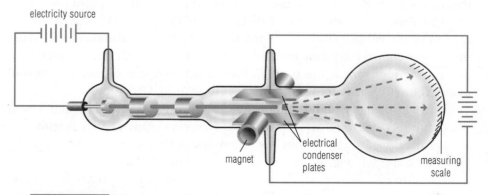

electricity source

magnet

electrical condenser plates

measuring scale

FIGURE A1.15 J. J. Thomson used this apparatus to produce beams of particles.

Thomson used his experimental evidence to develop a new model of the atom (Figure A1.16). His model stated that all atoms are made of smaller subatomic particles put together in different combinations to make the different elements. He suggested that an atom was a sphere of positive charge in which negative particles were imbedded. The negatively charged particles were called electrons. The Japanese scientist H. Nagaoka proposed a different model in 1904. He placed the electrons on the outside of the sphere. There they travelled around the central sphere in a pattern like the rings around the planet Saturn. Both models were useful explanations but neither one remained acceptable for very long.

FIGURE A1.16 In Thomson's model, the atom was made up of a positively charged sphere with negative particles embedded in it.

Ernest Rutherford

Ernest Rutherford (1871–1937) began working with radioactive substances in England with J. J. Thomson. Radioactive substances release energy or charged particles. Later, Rutherford did research at McGill University in Montreal, where he performed an experiment that led to the discovery of the nucleus of the atom. He had a radioactive material encased in lead with one small opening. This material released positively charged particles which he aimed at a thin sheet of gold foil (Figure A1.17). Using Thomson's model of the atom, he predicted that all the high-speed particles would pass right through the foil. The gold atoms would either have no effect on the particles or would deflect them slightly. This is exactly what happened to most of the particles. However, a few—about 1 in 10 000—bounced back, and a few others were sharply deflected. This was entirely unexpected.

Rutherford compared this result to firing a cannon ball at tissue paper, and seeing the cannon ball bounce back occasionally! Rutherford knew that even though the unexpected results happened rarely, they still meant that Thomson's model was wrong. Rutherford developed his own model (Figure A1.18). He suggested that an atom is mainly empty space through which the positive particles could pass, but that each atom had a tiny, positively charged core. This dense core of positive charge was so strong that it was causing some of the positively charged high-speed particles to bounce back. Electrons move through the rest of the atom's volume. Rutherford called the small dense centre the **nucleus**. He calculated the size of the nucleus to be about 1/10 000 of the size of the atom. This is like the size of an ant in a football field. Rutherford received the Nobel Prize in chemistry in 1908 for his work on radioactivity.

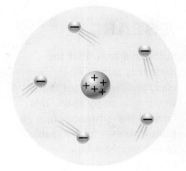

FIGURE A1.18 Rutherford's model of the atom had a tiny positively charged nucleus.

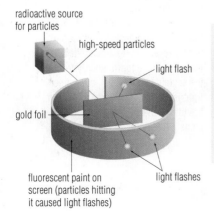

radioactive source for particles

high-speed particles

light flash

gold foil

fluorescent paint on screen (particles hitting it caused light flashes)

light flashes

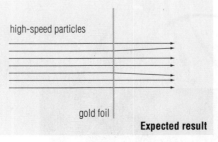

high-speed particles

gold foil

Expected result

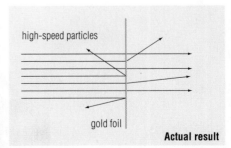

high-speed particles

gold foil

Actual result

FIGURE A1.17 Rutherford was surprised when all the particles did not go straight through the gold foil. He realized that each atom must have a dense core of positive charge.

Neils Bohr

Neils Bohr (1885–1962) was a Danish physicist who worked under Rutherford in England. He proposed that electrons surrounded the nucleus in specific energy levels (Figure A1.19). He found evidence for these energy levels by examining the light released by hydrogen atoms when they are made to glow in a tube.

Figure A1.20 shows the different colours of light emitted by hydrogen atoms. The individual bands of light correspond to gaps between the energy levels of the electrons. When electrons fall from higher energy levels to lower energy levels, they release a particular colour of light. From these colours, it is possible to identify the energy levels in atoms of all the elements in the periodic table. Figure A1.21 shows the relationship between the colours of the hydrogen emission spectrum and energy levels in atoms.

Bohr's experiments also partly explained why the negatively charged electrons do not merge with the positively charged nucleus. The reason is that electrons cannot fall below the lowest energy level. Thus an electron cannot fall into a nucleus under normal circumstances.

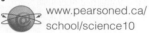
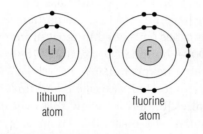

FIGURE A1.19 Bohr's model of the atom shows electrons at different energy levels orbiting the nucleus.

FIGURE A1.20 The hydrogen emission spectrum. Bohr used the range of light emitted by hydrogen atoms in his studies of the atom.

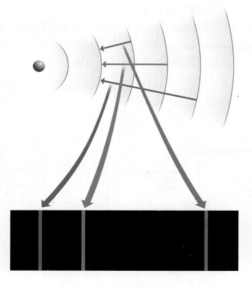

FIGURE A1.21 Electron energy levels and the hydrogen emission spectrum. When an electron falls from the third energy level to the second energy level, red light is emitted. When it falls from the fourth energy level to the second energy level, blue-green light is emitted. Similarly, a fall from the fifth to the second energy level emits violet light.

The Quantum Mechanical Model of the Atom

Today's model of the atom (Figure A1.22) is based on a theory called quantum mechanics. This abstract model is difficult to visualize. It uses mathematical probability to describe how electrons exist in atoms. Each electron can be thought of as a "cloud" of negative charge, instead of a tiny negative particle. Rather than thinking of the electron as a small particle moving quickly through a space, as Bohr originally did, the whole idea of electron movement is abandoned. Instead, electrons "occupy" the whole space all at once at different energy levels.

The electron cloud surrounds a nucleus containing two types of particles called **nucleons: protons** and **neutrons**. Protons have a positive electrical charge, and neutrons have no electrical charge. This model of the atom could change in the future as scientists learn more about the atom and subatomic particles.

FIGURE A1.22 In the model of the atom that scientists use today, electrons form a cloud around the nucleus.

A1.3 Check and Reflect

Knowledge

1. List three methods for preserving food. For each method, state if it is a physical process or a chemical process.

2. Of the five metals known to early peoples, iron was the rarest. Why?

3. How did the discovery of tin ores affect the smelting of copper?

4. List three examples of advances in chemistry made by the alchemists.

5. List the four basic ideas proposed by Dalton in describing the nature of matter.

6. What particle did J. J. Thomson discover? Where did this particle fit in his model of the atom?

7. Describe the evidence that led Rutherford to the discovery of the nucleus.

8. How did Bohr use light emitted from atoms to decide that electrons existed in specific energy levels?

Applications

9. The First Nations people of North America used copper extensively. However, there is no evidence that they developed smelting technology. Why do you think they did not need to develop this technology?

10. Sketch four diagrams of models of the atom proposed by Dalton, Thomson, Rutherford, and Bohr. Label the important parts of each.

11. Think about the quantum mechanical model of the atom. Why is it incorrect to think of the electrons in the atom as being like planets that move around the Sun?

Extensions

12. Write a conversation between Democritus and Aristotle in which they debate their different ideas about the composition of matter.

13. Rutherford was a student in J. J. Thomson's laboratory. Write a letter from Rutherford to Thomson in which he explains his new experiments that seem to make Thomson's model of the atom obsolete.

Chemical Engineer

Pauline Lee is a chemical engineer at Celanese Canada Inc. in Edmonton. She was born in Hong Kong and moved to Canada with her family when she was eight. She graduated from Innisfail High School in Innisfail, Alberta.

Chemical engineers work in careers related to the production and use of chemicals. Their jobs involve problem-solving and make use of chemistry, mathematics, physics, and practical knowledge about applying scientific principles to specific applications. For example, a chemical engineer might work in recovering and recycling materials, developing pharmaceuticals, purifying water, or refining gasoline.

How did you prepare yourself for a career in chemical engineering?

I was very good at mathematics and physics and went to the University of Alberta. I began in pharmacy, but moved into chemical engineering. I really enjoyed my classes. I found that I was very good at visualizing molecules, which helped me to understand what was going on. University teaches you how to think—how to be a detective discovering and understanding things like chemical processes. It also teaches you how to solve problems.

Where have you worked as an engineer?

I worked at Sherritt International Corp. in Fort Saskatchewan as a production process engineer for eight years. They refine nickel from nickel sulfide ores and nickel recycle. I have worked for four years at Celanese Canada Inc. in the Methanol Unit as a process engineer. Methanol is a base for products, such as formaldehyde. We make methanol from natural gas and water at high temperatures and pressures using a catalyst. A process engineer helps to optimize the process. For example, energy efficiency is important—we try to use the least amount of steam possible.

How is being an engineer different from studying engineering at school?

In school, you are given a problem and have to find a solution to it. As a process engineer, you have to find out what the problem is first. You make up your own questions, and then you answer them. Finding the right question leads you to the right answer. I really like my work.

How important are environmental concerns to you?

Environmental concerns affect the way we look at our work and design our processes. We want to preserve the planet. For example, we reuse as much of our wastes as we can. Those that can't be reused are purified as much as possible. Our objective is that nothing leaves the plant in the form of wastes. As a process engineer, I am part of the team that designs and implements these goals.

1. Why is problem-solving an important part of a chemical engineer's job?

2. If you were a chemical engineer, what kind of products or processes would you like to work on? Why?

Knowledge

1. How many fire extinguishers are in your science class and where are they?

2. Explain why standard eye glasses are not enough eye protection in the science lab.

3. Hazard symbols specify degree of hazard using three borders of different shape and colour. What are the name, shape, and colour of each degree of hazard?

4. List four of the most important safety rules in your class.

5. Explain what is meant by the term "chemical reaction." List two characteristics common to chemical reactions.

6. What is fermentation? How is it used to preserve food?

7. What is bronze? How is it made?

8. What basic law of nature did Antoine Lavoisier discover by making careful measurements of the masses of the chemicals in his experiments?

9. How did the discovery of the electron by J. J. Thomson change Dalton's model of the atom?

10. Dalton imagined that all atoms are like small spheres. In what ways did he imagine the spheres could vary?

11. How did Bohr's model of the atom begin to explain why the negatively charged electrons don't simply fall into the positively charged nucleus?

12. In the modern theory of an atom, do the electrons move within an energy level? How is an electron thought to exist in an atom?

Applications

13. What type of hazard symbol would you expect to see used for each of the following?
    a) bleach   d) pesticide
    b) drain cleaner   e) solid fertilizer
    c) lube oil   f) gasoline

14. Imagine that you have discovered a new hazardous chemical. Describe your chemical, give it some characteristics, and then write a one-page MSDS for it.

15. Classify each as a compound or a mixture:
    a) hot tea   d) a cookie
    b) methanol, $CH_3OH_{(l)}$ e) sugar in water
    c) $NaCl_{(aq)}$

16. A radioactive material is placed in a lead shielding block with one hole leading to the outside, as shown below. What tests would you use for the following?
    a) Determine whether any radiation is coming out of the hole.
    b) Determine whether the particles of radiation have a positive charge, a negative charge, or no electric charge at all.

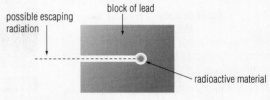

Diagram for question 16

17. Rutherford concluded from his gold foil experiment that the nucleus of the atom was positively charged and most of the volume of the atom was negatively charged. The opposite conclusion would have been that the nucleus was negative and most of the volume of the atom was positive. Explain why this opposite conclusion was not made.

18. Write a letter to John Dalton explaining why some of the four points in his model of the atom are not correct.

Extensions

19. Create a model of an atom that illustrates the nucleus and the location of surrounding electrons in their energy levels.

20. Create a Web page or other electronic presentation that explains the development of the model of the atom from Dalton to Bohr.

Elements combine to form many substances, each with its own set of properties.

FIGURE A2.1 The brightly coloured fabrics we wear are the result of advances in chemistry over hundreds of years.

Think of the many different styles of clothing that people wear and how bright and varied the many colours are (Figure A2.1). There are red and yellow hues, deep blues, and dark, solid blacks. Most of the pigments used to make the dyes for these fabrics were not available as recently as 100 years ago.

At first, clothing was coloured with dyes from natural sources, such as plants. Many of these colours were not as bright or intense as the ones we see today. An understanding of the elements and how they combine led to the invention and mass production of chemicals for dyes.

In this section, you will review the elements and the periodic table. You will also review and learn more about the structure of the atoms that make up the different elements. This will lead to a study of how atoms combine chemically by gaining, losing, or sharing electrons. You will learn how to name substances and how to categorize them based on their properties. At the end of this section, you will consider how toxic and hazardous chemicals affect each of us and the environment.

A 2.1 The Periodic Table and Atomic Structure

We live in a world that contains a vast number of different materials. Yet the components of all these many materials can be separated into about 115 basic building blocks called the **elements**. Recall from earlier science studies that elements are substances that cannot be broken down into other substances. Some of the most familiar elements are carbon, oxygen, and gold.

The Elements

There are about 90 naturally occurring elements, and another 25 synthetic elements. Based on their properties, all the elements can be divided into three classes: metals, non-metals, and metalloids.

Metals

Most of the elements are **metals**. Most are silver or grey in colour and shiny. They are all good conductors of electricity and heat. They are also **malleable** and **ductile**. Malleable means that they can be beaten or rolled into sheets without crumbling. Ductile means they can be stretched into long wires.

Metals have many other properties in common, although there are differences. For example, most metals are solids at room temperature (25°C). Mercury is the exception. It melts at −39°C. Another variable characteristic is how strongly metals react with other substances. Some metals, such as sodium, are highly reactive with air and water. Others such as platinum and gold are **inert**, or unreactive, except with the most corrosive acids.

Non-Metals

Only 17 elements are **non-metals**. They are grouped together mainly because of their lack of resemblance to metals, rather than their similarities to each other. For example, 11 of the non-metals are gases at 25°C, 5 are solids, and 1, bromine, is a red-brown liquid. There is also tremendous variation in colour. Fluorine is pale green, and chlorine is yellow. Iodine is violet. Some non-metals exist in different forms. For example, phosphorus has a red form and a white form. Both forms are stable at room temperature. Carbon can exist in three forms as shown in Figure A2.2.

Some non-metals are highly reactive. Fluorine, for example, can etch glass. Noble gases, such as helium, are generally unreactive. About half of the non-metals exist at 25°C as connected groups of atoms called **molecules**, such as oxygen, O_2. Others, such as neon, exist only as individual atoms. You will learn more about molecules in sections A2.2 and A2.3.

Metalloids

The remaining elements are called **metalloids**, and they have properties that are intermediate between metals and non-metals. For example, some metalloids conduct electricity, but not very well. Silicon, used in the manufacture of computer chips, is a metalloid. Boron and arsenic are also metalloids.

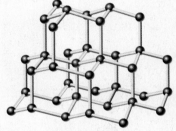

(a) Diamond has a three-dimensional web of bonds, which makes it very hard.

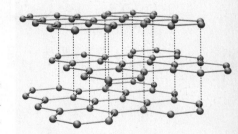

(b) Graphite has a two-dimensional network of bonds. It is very soft.

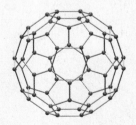

(c) Buckminsterfullerene forms spheres. It is also soft.

FIGURE A2.2 Carbon exists in three common forms.

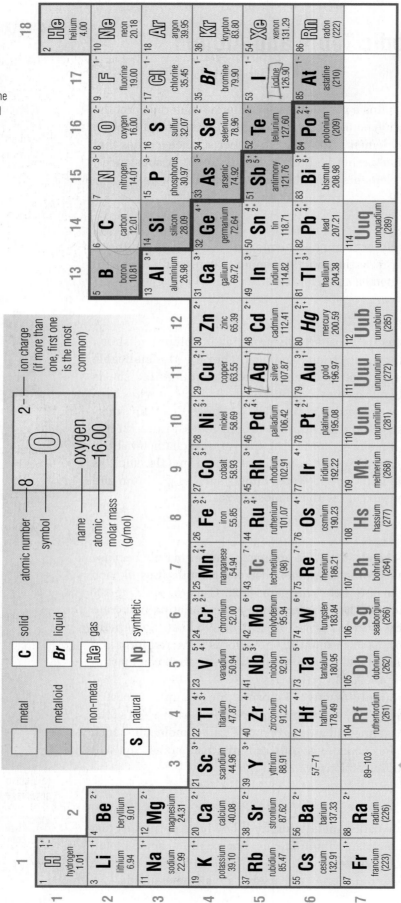

The Periodic Table

The periodic table organizes all the elements according to their chemical properties (Figure A2.3). Notice that the metals are located on the left side and centre of the table, and the non-metals are on the far right. In between are the metalloids. One exception is hydrogen. It is a non-metal, but it is located at the left side because it often behaves like a metal in chemical reactions.

Each box in the table shows the name and symbol for each element. The symbol is often an abbreviation derived from the element's name. You can see that carbon's symbol is C. Some of the metals have been known for thousands of years. Their symbols are derived from their original Latin names. For example, the symbol for lead is Pb. It is derived from the Latin word for lead, *plumbum*. The English word "plumber" is also derived from *plumbum* because Roman plumbers used lead piping.

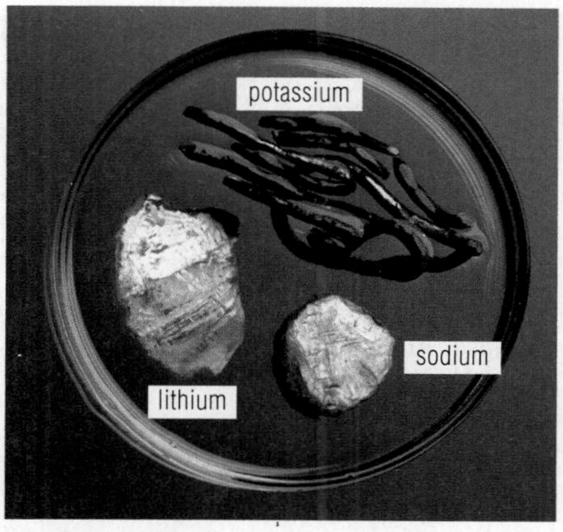

Periods and Families

The periodic table is organized into rows and columns. Each horizontal line or row is called a **period**. The periods are numbered from 1 to 7. Hydrogen and helium make up the first period. Each vertical column forms a **group** or **family** of elements, numbered from 1 to 18.

Chemical families are groups of elements that have similar chemical and physical properties. For example, group 1 is located in the column at the far left of the table, and includes lithium, sodium, and potassium (Figure A2.4). Called the **alkali metals**, they are all soft, shiny, and silver in colour, and very reactive with water. Their compounds tend to be white solids that are soluble in water. Recall that a compound is a chemical combination of two or more elements in a specific ratio. Next to them is group 2, which includes magnesium and calcium (Figure A2.5). They are called the **alkaline-earth metals**. They are shiny and silver but are not as soft as the alkali metals. Their compounds tend to be white, but they are less soluble than compounds formed by the alkali metals.

Moving to the right side of the periodic table, group 18 is a column that contains helium, neon, and argon. These are the **noble gases**. They are very unreactive. Helium has a very low density, which is why helium-filled balloons float, and its non-reactivity means it cannot catch fire. Floating party balloons are filled with helium.

The elements in group 17, just to the left of the noble gases, are called the **halogens.** This family of non-metals consists of the elements fluorine, chlorine, bromine, and iodine (Figure A2.6). These elements are poisonous and react readily with the alkali metals to form **salts**, such as sodium chloride (table salt). Salts are compounds produced in neutralization reactions between acids and bases. You will learn more about salts, acids, and bases in section A2.4.

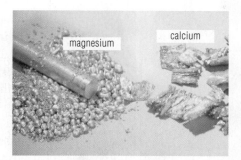

FIGURE A2.4 Lithium, sodium, and potassium are alkali metals. The alkali metals are group 1 on the periodic table.

FIGURE A2.5 Magnesium and calcium are alkaline-earth metals. They are group 2 in the periodic table.

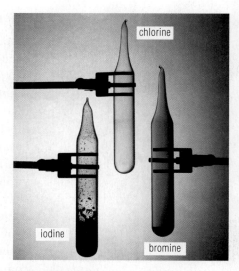

FIGURE A2.6 Iodine, chlorine, and bromine are halogens. The halogens are group 17 on the periodic table.

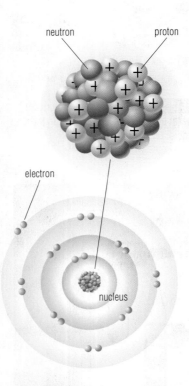

FIGURE A2.7 Electrons occupy most of the volume of an atom. Most of the mass is in the nucleus. A calcium atom (shown here) has 20 electrons, 20 protons, and 20 neutrons.

Atomic Theory

When you write with a pencil, tiny flakes of graphite break off to form the pencil mark. Each flake is pure carbon—made up of millions of carbon atoms. The smallest possible piece of graphite is a single carbon atom. An **atom** is the smallest part of an element that still has the properties of the element. A typical atom is very small—only about 10^{-10} m in diameter. This size is hard to imagine, but an analogy can help. An orange contains many carbon atoms as well as other atoms. Imagine that all the atoms in an orange increase in size until a single atom becomes the size of the original orange. How big is the whole orange after all its atoms have expanded? If a carbon atom became the size of an orange, then the orange that contained it would become the size of the whole Earth!

Subatomic Particles

Three kinds of subatomic particles are: electrons, protons, and neutrons. Recall that electrons are negatively charged particles, and protons are positively charged particles. Neutrons are neutral particles. They have no electrical charge. All the protons and neutrons are gathered together in a tiny region at the atom's centre called the nucleus. The nucleus is so small that 10 000 nuclei (plural of nucleus) in a row would fit once across the diameter of an atom.

Despite their small size, protons and neutrons account for more than 99.9% of the total mass of an atom. This was the amazing fact that Ernest Rutherford discovered with his gold foil experiment. For example, a piece of iron metal, such as a fork, feels very solid, and its mass is detectable when you pick it up. However, more than 99.9% of the volume has virtually no mass at all. Imagine a room the size of a typical classroom filled completely with a huge block of iron. Then imagine taking all the nuclei out of all the iron atoms and placing them side by side, and touching. How big would the volume of all the nuclei be? It would be about the size of the period at the end of this sentence. Yet its mass would be almost equal to the mass of the room full of iron!

Energy Levels

Electrons take up most of the volume of an atom (over 99.9%), and they occupy specific energy levels. An **energy level** can be thought of as a region of space near a nucleus that may be empty or may contain electrons. Electrons in energy levels nearest the nucleus have the lowest energy. Electrons in energy levels farther away from the nucleus have more energy. Electrons in the lowest energy levels are the most tightly held in the atom because they are closest to the positively charged nucleus.

The number of electrons that can exist in the different energy levels varies. The lowest energy level is the one closest to the nucleus. It can hold only 2 electrons. The next energy level is larger and farther from the nucleus. It can hold up to 8 electrons. Think of these energy levels as being like spheres that add new layers to the outside of the atom, just as an onion has layers. The third energy level also has room for up to 8 electrons. It is common to discuss the electron arrangement in atoms up to 20 electrons, which is calcium. Beyond that, the pattern is more complicated. For calcium, the electron distribution is 2, 8, 8, 2, as shown in Figure A2.7.

An energy level can be empty, partly filled, or completely filled. Partly filled energy levels from two different atoms can overlap, and a pair of electrons can exist in both of them at once. This is the basis for chemical bonding, which you will study later in this section.

Electrons and protons are attracted to each other because they have opposite charges. However, they cannot completely come together under normal circumstances. This is fortunate, because it means that atoms cannot collapse. Some of the properties of these particles are summarized in Table A2.1.

TABLE A2.1   Properties of Protons, Neutrons, and Electrons

Particle	Symbol	Charge	Mass	Location
proton	p^+	1+	1.7×10^{-24} g	nucleus
neutron	n^0	0	1.7×10^{-24} g	nucleus
electron	e^-	1−	9.1×10^{-28} g	surrounding the nucleus

Atomic Number

All atoms of an element have the same number of protons. For example, all hydrogen atoms have exactly one proton. Atoms of helium, the next element in the periodic table, have two protons—never more, never less. The **atomic number** of an element indicates the number of protons it has. This number can be used to specify an element.

Look at the periodic table in Figure A2.3 on page 30. Notice that the elements in a period are arranged according to increasing atomic number. The element with atomic number 3 is lithium. Therefore, all atoms of lithium have three protons. Beryllium has atomic number 4. All atoms of beryllium have four protons. To the right of beryllium is boron with five protons. As you move from left to right in a period, each element has one more proton in its atom.

Mass Number and Atomic Molar Mass

Atoms of the same element that contain different numbers of neutrons are called **isotopes**. For example, the most common form of hydrogen has one proton and no neutrons at all. However, about 1 in 10 000 hydrogen atoms contains one proton and one neutron. This isotope of hydrogen is called deuterium. It is sometimes also called "heavy hydrogen" because the neutron increases the mass of the atom. Deuterium is used in the production of heavy water for Canadian nuclear reactors. Hydrogen has a third isotope, called tritium, that has 1 proton and 2 neutrons.

To help distinguish between the isotopes of an element, each isotope is given a number called the **mass number**. The mass number is an integer equal to the total number of protons and neutrons in the nucleus of an atom. Electrons are not included in the mass number because their mass is so small. Oxygen has three naturally occurring isotopes. They all have the same number of protons, so they have the same atomic number (8). The most common isotope has a mass number of 16: it has 8 protons and 8 neutrons. The other two isotopes have mass numbers of 17 (8 protons and 9 neutrons) and 18 (8 protons and 10 neutrons).

The atomic symbol for an element is sometimes shown with both the mass number and atomic number as follows:

$$_{\text{atomic number}}^{\text{mass number}}\text{element symbol}$$

Using this format, the symbols for the oxygen isotopes are:

$$_{8}^{16}\text{O} \qquad _{8}^{17}\text{O} \qquad _{8}^{18}\text{O}$$

The isotopes and their symbols are shown in Figure A2.8.

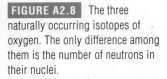

FIGURE A2.8 The three naturally occurring isotopes of oxygen. The only difference among them is the number of neutrons in their nuclei.

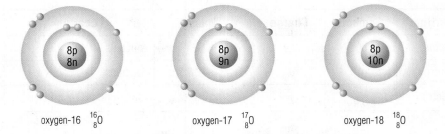

oxygen-16 $_{8}^{16}\text{O}$ oxygen-17 $_{8}^{17}\text{O}$ oxygen-18 $_{8}^{18}\text{O}$

Note that the atomic symbol written this way does *not* give either the number of neutrons or the number of electrons directly. You can determine the number of neutrons in an atom by subtracting the atomic number from the mass number. For example, the oxygen isotope $_{8}^{18}\text{O}$ has a mass number of 18 and an atomic number of 8. The number of neutrons can be determined by subtracting 8 from 18.

mass number (18) − atomic number (8) = number of neutrons (10)

The **atomic molar mass** shown in the periodic table is related to the mass number. The atomic molar mass is the average mass of the element's isotopes. Isotopes of an element do not have exactly the same mass: some have slightly greater masses than others. This is because each isotope has a different number of neutrons in its nucleus.

In general, atoms are neutral, so the number of electrons in an atom equals the number of protons.

Formation of Ions

Under some circumstances, the atoms of most elements will either gain or lose one or more of their outermost electrons. The process of gaining or losing electrons is called **ionization**, and it results in the formation of an **ion**. An ion is an electrically charged atom or group of atoms. Ionization results in metals and non-metals forming compounds.

Positively charged ions are called **cations**. Most cations form when metal atoms lose electrons. When a cation is forming, the lost electrons usually move to another atom. Electrons are negatively charged. When they leave an atom, the ion that remains is positively charged because it now has more protons than electrons.

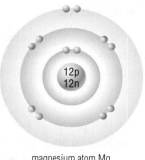

magnesium atom Mg
12 electrons

magnesium ion Mg^{2+}
10 electrons

FIGURE A2.9 A magnesium atom, Mg, can lose two electrons to form a magnesium ion with a positive charge of 2+: Mg^{2+}.

For example, the periodic table shows that a sodium atom has 11 protons. Therefore, it also has 11 electrons. A sodium ion forms when the sodium atom loses one electron. This means that the positive charge in the sodium becomes one greater than the negative charge. So the sodium ion has a positive charge. An ion's charge is sometimes shown as a superscript after the atomic symbol. In this example, the sodium ion would be written as Na$^+$. The magnesium ion in Figure A2.9 has a charge of 2+, so it is written as Mg^{2+}.

Negatively charged ions are called **anions**. Most anions form when non-metal atoms gain electrons. For example, oxygen atoms can gain two electrons. The periodic table shows that an oxygen atom has eight protons, and therefore, it has eight electrons. By gaining two electrons, the oxygen atom becomes a negatively charged ion, called an oxide ion. It can be written as O^{2-}. Note that the name of an element's anion is written by using the first part of the element's name and changing the last part to "-ide." So the nitrogen anion N^{3-}, for example, is called nitride. The fluorine atom in Figure A2.10 forms a fluoride ion, F$^-$.

fluorine atom F
9 electrons

fluoride ion F$^-$
10 electrons

FIGURE A2.10 A fluorine atom, F, can gain one electron to form a fluoride ion, F$^-$.

Most ion formation takes place when metals and non-metals form ionic compounds. Metal atoms tend to form cations by losing electrons to non-metals, which form anions. You may be wondering why metals tend to lose electrons, while non-metals tend to gain them. Atoms gain or lose electrons so that they have the same number of electrons as the nearest noble gas. This makes them more stable. In chemistry, becoming more stable means becoming less reactive. For example, a sodium ion is less reactive than a sodium atom. Sodium metal contains only atoms. When it is placed in water, a vigorous reaction occurs (Figure A2.11). Table salt contains sodium ions (and chloride ions). When it is placed in water, it dissolves quietly.

FIGURE A2.11 Sodium and water react vigorously. The gas produced ignites in a spectacular manner.

Elements Combine to Form Compounds

Recall that elements in the same group or family on the periodic table have similar physical and chemical properties. One of these properties is reactivity. An element's reactivity is related to the number of electrons in its outer energy level. Elements are most stable, or unreactive, when they have filled outer energy levels.

Recall that the noble gases (group 18 on the periodic table) are very stable. They have filled outer energy levels, as shown in Figure A2.12. The noble gases neither gain nor lose electrons. Other elements are not as stable as the noble gases. These elements gain or lose electrons. They become more stable when they have the same number of electrons in their outer energy level as the nearest noble gas does.

The electrons in the outer energy level are called **valence electrons**. The tendency to gain or lose electrons is sometimes called **valence**. The term **valence number** is commonly used to describe the number of electrons an element can gain or lose to combine with other elements. Figure A2.12 shows the number of electrons in each atom in part of the periodic table. It illustrates several striking patterns.

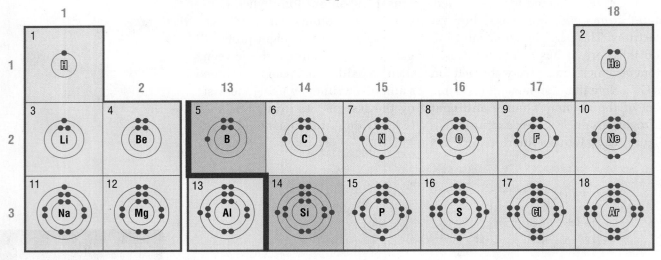

FIGURE A2.12 Part of the periodic table showing electron arrangements for the atoms of each element

Elements in the same family have the same number of valence electrons. This results in similar chemical properties. For example, the alkali metals lithium, sodium, and potassium are all soft, shiny metals that react vigorously with water. Each has one valence electron and is one atomic number away from a noble gas. Each loses one electron to form an ion with a 1+ charge. The loss of one electron gives them a filled outer energy level, just like the nearest noble gas.

Now look at the periods in Figure A2.12. Hydrogen and helium make up the first period, and lithium is the first element in the second period. From left to right across a period, atoms gain one valence electron (and one proton) with each new element. Within a period, electrons are always added to the same energy level. An element in the second period has electrons in two energy levels, and an element in the third period has electrons in three energy levels. The period number indicates the number of occupied energy levels.

Problem-Solving Investigation

Required Skills
- Initiating and Planning
- Performing and Recording
- Analyzing and Interpreting
- Communication and Teamwork

Classifying Unknown Liquids

The periodic table was founded on examining chemical and physical characteristics of materials, and arranging them according to similarities and differences. Often, the identity of the material was unknown and tests were done to see whether it matched previously known materials. If it was a pure substance (it could not be broken down further) and it had novel properties, a new element had been discovered! A similar process will be used in this activity.

In this activity, you will design and test a procedure to distinguish between five similar liquids. By carefully observing their physical and chemical properties, you can detect differences between them.

The chemicals you will use to help you distinguish between the liquids are called test **reagents** in the Materials and Equipment list below. A reagent is a substance used for identifying, measuring, or producing other substances.

The Problem

How can you distinguish between five similar liquids?

Materials and Equipment

5 liquids labelled 1 to 5

spot plate or test tubes and racks

test reagents:
    baking soda
    sodium chloride
    thymol blue solution
    calcium supplement
    tincture of iodine
    1-cm strips of magnesium

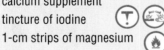

CAUTION: Some of the substances you will be using are mildly irritating to skin; some are corrosive; and some are flammable. Note that iodine will stain skin and clothing. Handle all substances carefully.

Conduct Your Investigation

1. Make a table in your notebook like the one below to summarize your six tests of the five liquids. Once all the tests are done, you will use the table to analyze your results and write a test procedure.

2. Using a spot plate with many test wells or a set of test tubes in a test tube rack, combine each liquid with each test reagent and record your results.

3. Select the smallest set of test reagents that can reliably distinguish between all five unknown liquids.

4. Develop a test procedure. It must be a series of steps that will allow someone to take an unlabelled sample of one of the five liquids and determine which one it is. Make sure that your procedure describes the tests to be performed and how to interpret the results.

5. Have your teacher approve your procedure.

Test and Evaluate

6. Test the effectiveness of your analytical procedure with a sample of one of the unknown liquids. Use your procedure to determine which of the five liquids it is. Test more unknown liquids as time permits.

7. Follow your teacher's instructions for disposing of all the substances you have used.

8. Review your procedure based on your testing of the unknown samples. Did you need to revise it to deal with unexpected observations?

Communicate

1. Write a summary report that contains the procedure and the results of your tests on the unknown samples.

	baking soda	sodium chloride	thymol blue	calcium supplement	tincture of iodine	magnesium strip
Liquid 1						
Liquid 2						

The Octet Rule

Another way to understand the patterns by which atoms gain or lose electrons is to look at their energy levels. All the noble gases have filled energy levels. So it is possible to restate the pattern for ion formation in a new way: Atoms tend to gain or lose electrons so that they end up with completely filled energy levels. Notice in Figure A2.12 that the noble gases neon and argon each have eight electrons in their valence energy levels. The **octet rule** (also called the rule of eight) states that atoms bond in such a way as to have eight electrons in their valence energy level. ("Oct-" means eight, so an octet is a group of eight.) This is just another way to say that atoms tend to be stable with full outer energy levels. However, it is a handy rule for figuring out an element's charge or valence by looking for the octet.

For example, chlorine is just below fluorine in group 17. All atoms in this family have seven valence electrons. By the octet rule, fluorine will have an octet of electrons (eight electrons) in its valence energy level if it gains an electron to form the F^- ion (Figure A2.13). This means that a chlorine atom will also gain one electron, forming the Cl^- ion.

The exceptions to the octet rule are hydrogen, lithium, and beryllium. They each need only two electrons in their valence energy levels because their nearest noble gas, helium, has two electrons.

The situation is more complicated with transition metals. In the periodic table, these are all the metals from scandium to zinc inclusive, and any metals directly below them. All metals tend to lose electrons to become more stable, but it is difficult for atoms to lose more than about three electrons. This is because, every time an electron is lost, the remaining electrons are held more tightly by the nucleus. Gold, for example, can lose at most three electrons, to form Au^{3+}. Depending on the chemical conditions, iron can lose either two or three electrons, to form Fe^{2+} or Fe^{3+}. The elements boron, silicon, and carbon rarely form ions. Predicting the number of electrons transition metals will lose is difficult. Consult the periodic table for the ion charge for these elements. The first charge given is the most common.

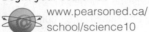

re**SEARCH**

Since 1950, about 20 new elements have been created or discovered. Find out how new elements are created. Begin your search at

www.pearsoned.ca/
school/science10

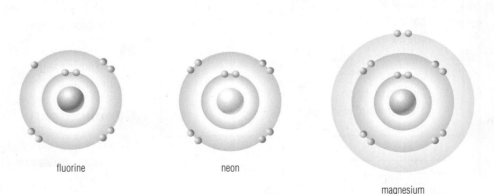

fluorine   neon   magnesium

FIGURE A2.13   Fluorine has seven valence electrons; neon has eight valence electrons; and magnesium has two valence electrons. Using the octet rule, we can determine that fluorine gains one more electron; neon does not gain or lose any; and magnesium loses two to join other elements.

Knowledge

1. List the names of four families in the periodic table. Name three elements in each family.

2. Which subatomic particle determines what the element is?

3. a) What is a valence energy level?
   b) What are valence electrons?

4. What are isotopes?

5. What is an ion? What are the special names for positive and negative ions?

6. How is the number of electrons gained or lost by atoms related to the noble gas nearest them in the periodic table?

7. State the octet rule.

Applications

8. Draw an atom that has six protons, seven neutrons, and six electrons. Using the periodic table, identify the element. Label the nucleus, the subatomic particles, and the valence energy level.

9. Two isotopes of nitrogen are nitrogen-14 and nitrogen-15. Explain how these atoms are similar and how they are different by describing their atomic structure.

10. Refer to the periodic table in Figure A2.3 on page 30 to answer the question.

    Using the octet rule, decide if each of the following elements will gain or lose electrons to become ions. State how many electrons will be involved in each case:
    a) phosphorus
    b) sodium
    c) chlorine
    d) magnesium
    e) iodine

11. Copy and complete the following table in your notebook. Use the periodic table in Figure A2.3 on page 30, as needed, to fill in the number of protons or the name of an element.

Element Name	Mass Number	Number of Protons	Number of Neutrons
calcium	41		
uranium	238		
aluminium			14
	9		5
	19	10	
iron			27

12. Copy and complete the following table in your notebook. Refer to the periodic table in Figure A2.3 on page 30.

Atom or Ion Name	Overall Charge	Number of Protons	Number of Electrons	Symbol	Number of Electrons Lost or Gained
oxygen atom				O	
oxide ion			10	O^{2-}	
potassium ion		19			
		12	10		
				F^-	
	2+	20			
	3+		10		

Extension

13. Using the periodic table on page 30, draw a periodic table from atomic number 1 to atomic number 20. For each element, write its symbol and the number of valence electrons in its atom. In a different colour, write down the value of the electric charge (e.g., 1^+, 3^-) on the ions of that element. Explain the pattern of ion charges either by using the octet rule or by referring to filled valence energy levels.

A 2.2 Naming Ionic and Molecular Compounds

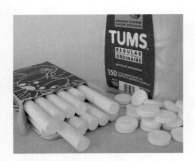

Does your classroom have chalk? You have probably used blackboard chalk. You may also have used another product that contains chalk—the antacid called TUMS. The chalk in TUMS is mixed with sweeteners and flavours so that it can be eaten easily. However, do not eat blackboard chalk for your upset stomach because blackboard chalk and the chalk in TUMS are not the same chemical at all. Blackboard chalk is mainly calcium phosphate, while the antacid chalk is calcium carbonate (Figure A2.14). This is just one example of the confusion that can result from inaccurately naming compounds. It also shows the importance of using names that provide information about the chemical composition of a substance. The term "chalk" gives no hint as to what elements are present in either compound.

The International Union of Pure and Applied Chemistry (IUPAC) is the body responsible for naming compounds. It ensures the use of a consistent, practical way of naming compounds that allows scientists to communicate clearly and precisely. Throughout this unit, you will be using IUPAC names for different types of compounds. First, we will look at ionic compounds.

info**BIT**

We throw salt on the roads in winter. But you don't throw road salt on your food! Road salt is calcium chloride. Table salt is sodium chloride. The term "salt" is not really the name of a compound. It is the name of a class of related compounds.

Ionic Compounds

Table salt—sodium chloride—is one of the most common compounds on Earth. The oceans are salty because of sodium chloride and other salts. Our cells control the amount of water they contain by controlling the concentration of salts, including sodium chloride. A high salt content in our cells draws water into them. Drawing water into the cells in our tissues removes water from our blood, causing the concentration of salts in our blood to increase. A high salt content in our blood triggers a feeling of thirst. We then have the desire to drink, and when we do, we replace the fluid that was originally drawn into the cells of our tissues. Drinking to quench our thirst adds fluids to reduce the salt concentration in our blood.

Salt is also used for electrical messaging in our bodies. Our nervous system, including our brain, is the most complex wiring system known. Salt conducts the electrical signals in our nerves because it forms ions. Recall from section A2.1 that ions are electrically charged atoms or groups of atoms. Salt belongs to a class of substances called ionic compounds.

Ionic compounds form when electrons transfer from one atom to another. For sodium chloride, positively charged sodium ions are attracted to negatively charged chloride ions. The two kinds of ions group together in an organized array called a **crystal lattice**. The lattice is made up of one sodium ion for every one chloride ion (Figure A2.15). Such a neutral unit is called a **formula unit**.

Recall that an atom of sodium has one valence electron, and a chlorine atom has seven valence electrons. When the two elements combine, the sodium atom transfers an electron to the chlorine atom (Figure A2.16). As a result, both atoms now have full outer energy levels. Remember that the most

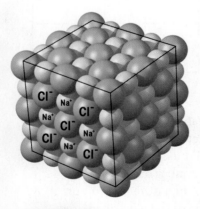

FIGURE A2.15 Table salt (NaCl) is an ionic compound. As a solid, it forms a crystal lattice.

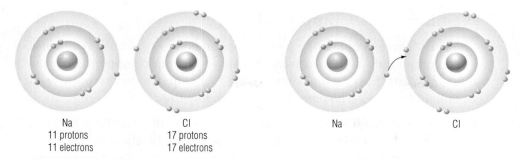

Na
11 protons
11 electrons

Cl
17 protons
17 electrons

Na

Cl

FIGURE A2.16 (a) Sodium has an atomic number of 11, so it has 1 valence electron. Chlorine has an atomic number of 17, so it has 7 valence electrons.

(b) One electron transfers from the sodium atom to the chlorine atom.

stable atoms have full outer energy levels. When sodium transfers an electron to chlorine, sodium's outer energy level is now full. When chlorine receives the electron, its outer energy level is also now full. Both elements are now stable as ions. This type of bonding is called **ionic bonding**. Ionic bonds form between atoms of metals and non-metals (Figure A2.17).

Ionic compounds have many common properties. For example, all of them are solids at room temperature. Table salt can be heated to a very high temperature without decomposing or burning. Its melting point is 800°C, which can be reached only by using a blow torch or a special oven. Ionic compounds also tend to dissolve in water, although some dissolve much better than others. Solutions of ionic compounds always conduct electricity. You will learn more about the properties of ionic compounds in section A2.3.

There are many thousands of different ionic compounds. Some have common names, such as table salt. They also have chemical names that reveal something about the elements in them. Table A2.2 gives examples of the chemical formulas and names of some common ionic compounds. Recall that the state of an element or compound is indicated by a subscript: *(s)* for solid, *(l)* for liquid, and *(g)* for gas. The subscript *(aq)* stands for aqueous. This means that the element or compound is dissolved in water.

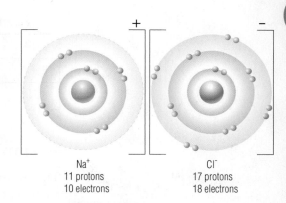

+   −

Na^+
11 protons
10 electrons

Cl^-
17 protons
18 electrons

FIGURE A2.17 Sodium and chlorine form an ionic bond when their ions join to become the compound NaCl.

TABLE A2.2 Names, Formulas, and Uses of Some Common Ionic Compounds

Common Name	Formula	Chemical Name	Application
lye	$NaOH_{(s)}$	sodium hydroxide	unclogs drains
baking soda	$NaHCO_{3(s)}$	sodium hydrogencarbonate	raises breads and cakes by giving off CO_2 when heated
milk of magnesia	$Mg(OH)_{2(s)}$	magnesium hydroxide	works as antacid and laxative
table salt	$NaCl_{(s)}$	sodium chloride	adds salty taste in foods
cream of tartar	$KHC_4H_4O_{6(s)}$	potassium hydrogentartrate	mixes with baking soda to make baked goods rise

Naming Ionic Compounds

The IUPAC system of naming ionic compounds is very simple. All names of ionic compounds have two parts, because all ionic compounds are made from two parts. Every ionic compound is made up of a cation (positive) and an anion (negative). The naming rules work like this:

1. Name the cation first by using the element's name. (It is usually a metal ion.)
2. Name the anion second by using the first part of the element's name and changing the last part to "-ide." (The anion is usually a non-metal ion.)

Table A2.3 gives some examples of how ionic compounds are named.

TABLE A2.3 Examples of How Ionic Compounds Are Named

Formula	Cation	Anion	Name
$NaCl_{(s)}$	Na^+	Cl^-	sodium chloride
$BaF_{2(s)}$	Ba^{2+}	F^-	barium fluoride
$K_3N_{(s)}$	K^+	N^{3-}	potassium nitride

Formulas for Ionic Compounds

The formula of an ionic compound contains element symbols that identify each type of ion present. In some formulas, the symbols are followed by subscript numbers that indicate the ratio of ions in the compound. For example, in Table A2.3, the formula for $BaF_{2(s)}$ contains subscripts. In $BaF_{2(s)}$, there is one barium ion for every two fluoride ions. This represents the formula unit. The formula unit is the smallest amount of a substance with the composition shown by the chemical formula. It consists of positive and negative ions in the smallest whole-number ratio that results in a neutral unit in the crystal lattice of a compound. If there are no subscripts, assume that the compound has one of each ion, so the ratio is one to one in the formula unit (e.g., $NaCl_{(s)}$).

All ionic compounds are composed of an equal number of positive and negative charges. This means that the total charge of the cations must equal the total charge of the anions. In some compounds, the cation has a charge of 1+, and the anion has a charge of 1−. Recall that this is because there has been a transfer of electrons between the atoms. Consider sodium chloride. The sodium ion is Na^+ and the chloride ion is Cl^-. So only one ion of each element is needed to make the positive and negative charges equal. The ratio of sodium ions to chloride ions is one sodium ion to one chloride ion in a formula unit. Therefore, the formula is NaCl. No subscripts are needed because both ions have a charge of one.

Now consider the example of aluminium chloride, $AlCl_3$. All the charges in the formula unit must be equal. So each aluminium atom loses three electrons, and each chlorine atom gains one. The aluminium ion has a charge of 3+. The chloride ion has a charge of 1−. Therefore, every one aluminium ion combines with three chloride ions. The ratio is one cation (Al^{3+}) to three anions (Cl^-), so the formula is $AlCl_3$. Table A2.4 summarizes the two examples we have just worked through.

Steps	Examples	
	sodium chloride	**aluminium chloride**
1. Identify the ions and their charges.	sodium: Na^+ chloride: Cl^-	aluminium: Al^{3+} chloride: Cl^-
2. Determine the total charges needed to balance.	Na^+ : 1 Cl^- : 1	Al^{3+} : 3 Cl^- : 1+1+1 = 3
3. Note the ratio of cations to anions.	1 to 1	1 to 3
4. Use subscripts to write the formula, if needed.	NaCl	$AlCl_3$

The Method of Lowest Common Multiple

The method of lowest common multiple is another way of determining the correct formula for an ionic compound. First, find the lowest common multiple of the charges for the two ions. Then divide by the combining capacity of one ion to get the correct subscript for that ion. Repeat the process for the other ion. This ensures that the number of positive charges equals the number of negative charges, so the formula unit is electrically neutral.

Example Problem A2.1 shows the two ways of working out a formula. With the method of lowest common multiple, find the smallest number that both ion charges divide into evenly. For calcium nitride, calcium has a charge of 2+ and nitride has a charge of 3–. The lowest common multiple of 2 and 3 is 6. To find the subscript for calcium, divide 6 by 2 to get 3. For nitride, divide 6 by 3 to get 2. The formula is $Ca_3N_{2(s)}$.

Example Problem A2.1

What is the formula for calcium nitride?

Calculating the ratio:

1. Identify the ions and their charges.

calcium: Ca^{2+}
nitride: N^{3-}

2. Determine the total charges needed to balance.

Ca^{2+}: 2 + 2 + 2 = 6
N^{3-}:   3 + 3 = 6

3. Note the ratio of cations to anions.

3 to 2

4. Use subscripts to write the formula.

$Ca_3N_{2(s)}$

OR

Using the method of lowest common multiple:

1. Identify the ions and their charges: Ca is 2+, and N is 3–.

2. Find the smallest number that both charges will divide into. For Ca and N it is 6.

3. Divide each charge into the lowest common multiple, and write the numbers as subscripts: Ca: 6 ÷ 2 = 3   N: 6 ÷ 3 = 2 The formula is $Ca_3N_{2(s)}$.

Practice Problem

1. Write formulas for the following ionic compounds:

  a) magnesium chloride

  b) sodium sulfide

  c) calcium phosphide

  d) potassium nitride

  e) calcium fluoride

Compounds with Multivalent Elements

Some metals have more than one stable ion. For example, iron has two stable ions: Fe^{2+} and Fe^{3+}. Elements with more than one stable ion are called **multivalent** elements. Ionic compounds containing multivalent elements must have Roman numerals in their names to indicate which ion is forming that compound. The Roman numeral is written in brackets after the element to indicate the charge. For example, chromium is multivalent, so chromium(III) sulfide indicates that the Cr^{3+} ion forms that compound. Roman numerals are not used in formulas, because you can figure out the charge on the ion by looking at the formula.

You can find the Roman numeral to use in the name of a multivalent ion by using the subscripts in the formula. For example, in $FeBr_2$, the subscript 2 after the Br is a guide to the iron ion's charge. Recall that the positive and negative charges in an ionic compound must be equal. According to this rule, only an Fe^{2+} could pair up with two Br^- to give this formula unit. $FeBr_2$ would be written out as iron(II) bromide. In $FeBr_3$, only an Fe^{3+} could pair up with three Br^- to give this formula unit. $FeBr_3$ would be written out as iron(III) bromide.

Example Problem A2.2

Write the name of the compound that has the formula $Cu_3N_{(s)}$.

1. Identify the ions that form the compound.

   $Cu^?$ copper ion N^{3-} nitride ion

2. Use the charge of the nitride ion (3−) and the rule that the total positive and negative charges in the formula unit must be equal. Three copper ions are present in the formula unit so each must have a charge of 1+.

3. Write the name of the compound.

   The name of the compound is copper(I) nitride.

Practice Problem

2. Write out the name of the following compounds:
   a) $FeCl_{3(s)}$ d) $CuF_{2(s)}$
   b) $PbO_{2(s)}$ e) $Cr_2S_{3(s)}$
   c) $Ni_2S_{3(s)}$

When writing the names of ionic compounds, either recall the charges of anions from memory or use a reference table (Table A in Student Reference 12). Use the anion's charge to find the cation's charge when the cation is multivalent. Remember that the Roman numeral is needed only if the metal element is multivalent. You can use a reference table or periodic table to find out which elements are multivalent. Select the first one listed in the periodic table if you are not given any other information. This is the most common ion for each element.

Polyatomic Ions

Some ions are made up of several non-metallic atoms joined together. These are called **polyatomic ions** ("poly" means "many"). Consider the hydroxide ion, whose formula is given in Table A2.5. In the compound NaOH, for example, the sodium has a charge of 1+. The oxygen and hydrogen together form the polyatomic hydroxide ion, OH^-, with a charge of 1−. Human bones

TABLE A2.5 Some Common Polyatomic Ions

Polyatomic Ion Name	Formula
ammonium	NH_4^+
carbonate	CO_3^{2-}
dihydrogenphosphate	$H_2PO_4^-$
hydrogencarbonate	HCO_3^-
hydroxide	OH^-
nitrate	NO_3^-
permanganate	MnO_4^-
phosphate	PO_4^{3-}
sulfate	SO_4^{2-}

contain calcium phosphate. The phosphate anion, PO_4^{3-}, behaves like a single ion with a charge of $3-$.

Table A2.5 gives some examples of common polyatomic ions. You can find a more extensive list in Table E in Student Reference 12. Note that in the table, the formula is shown with its ion charge. This is the correct way to show polyatomic ions.

Suffixes for Polyatomic Ions

The two most common suffixes used in naming polyatomic ions are "-ate" and "-ite." When a pair of similar ions exist, such as SO_4^{2-} and SO_3^{2-}, "-ate" and "-ite" are used in their names to differentiate them. SO_4^{2-} is sulfate, and SO_3^{2-} is sulfite. As you may have guessed, "-ate" means more oxygen atoms, and "-ite" means fewer oxygen atoms are part of the ion. But these suffixes do not tell you how many oxygen atoms are actually in the formula. If there are more than two similar ions, then other naming variations are used. Consider for example, the series of chlorine and oxygen ions in Table A2.6. It is not necessary at this stage to memorize all the suffix patterns. Use the ion chart of Table A2.5 and Table E in Student Reference 12 as needed.

Naming Compounds Containing Polyatomic Ions

Naming a compound containing polyatomic ions is simple. Look at the formula, and name the cation, followed by the anion. You do not need to change the ending of a polyatomic ion's name. The only difficulty sometimes is recognizing the ions within the formula. Table A2.7 gives some examples of compounds containing polyatomic ions.

TABLE A2.6 Names of Ions Made up of Chlorine and Oxygen

Ion Name	Ion Formula
perchlorate	ClO_4^-
chlorate	ClO_3^-
chlorite	ClO_2^-
hypochlorite	ClO^-

FIGURE A2.18 You probably know that your teeth contain calcium. The calcium is in a calcium phosphate mineral called hydroxyapatite. It includes the polyatomic ion PO_4^{3-}.

TABLE A2.7 Examples of Compounds Containing Polyatomic Ions

Formula	Name	Hints for Writing Names
$Ca(OH)_{2(s)}$	calcium hydroxide	The polyatomic ion is often found inside brackets. Look up OH in Table A2.5 to find its name. It is listed as OH^-, and its name is hydroxide.
$Na_3PO_{4(s)}$	sodium phosphate	Inspect the compound for polyatomic ions. This compound contains the polyatomic ion PO_4^{3-}. Its charge is $3-$, and its name is "phosphate."
$(NH_4)_2SO_{4(s)}$	ammonium sulfate	Look in the brackets to find the polyatomic ion NH_4. Look in Table A2.5 to find its name: ammonium. The ammonium ion is the only common polyatomic cation. Memorize the name and formula of ammonium, NH_4^+. The second half is SO_4 which appears in the table as SO_4^{2-}, with the name "sulfate."
$NH_4HCO_{3(s)}$	ammonium hydrogencarbonate	There are no brackets here. Remember that the formula unit for an ionic compound always consists of positive and negative ions in the smallest whole-number ratio that results in a neutral unit. The cation is ammonium, NH_4^+. The second part is the anion, HCO_3^-. Table A2.5 shows HCO_3^-, the hydrogencarbonate ion.

Writing Formulas for Compounds Containing Polyatomic Ions

The rules for writing the formulas for these compounds are similar to the rules for other ionic compounds. One difference is that brackets may be used to show the ratio of the ions. The subscript outside the brackets applies to all the elements inside the brackets. For example, in $Fe_2(SO_4)_{3(s)}$ the subscript 3 with $(SO_4)_3$ means that there are 3 SO_4^{2-} ions for every 2 Fe^{3+} ions in the compound. It also indicates that 3 sulfur atoms and 12 (4 × 3) oxygen atoms are in one formula unit of sulfate.

Practice Problems

Use Table A2.5 to help you.

3. Write the formulas of the following ionic compounds:
   a) barium hydroxide
   b) iron(III) carbonate
   c) copper(I) permanganate

4. Write the names of the following ionic compounds:
   a) $Au(NO_3)_{3(s)}$
   b) $(NH_4)_3PO_{4(s)}$
   c) $K_2Cr_2O_{7(s)}$

Example Problem A2.3

What is the formula for iron(III) sulfate?

1. Identify the ions and their charges. Check Table A2.5 for the charge of the polyatomic ion.

   iron(III): Fe^{3+}
   sulfate: SO_4^{2-}

2. Determine the total charges needed to balance.

   Fe^{3+}: 3 + 3 = 6
   SO_4^{2-}: 2 + 2 + 2 = 6

3. Note the ratio of cations to anions.

   2 to 3

4. Use brackets and subscripts to write the formula. $Fe_2(SO_4)_{3(s)}$

The formula for iron(III) sulfate is $Fe_2(SO_4)_{3(s)}$.

Example Problem A2.4

What is the formula of ammonium dihydrogenphosphate?

1. Identify the ions and their charges. Check Table A2.5 for the charge of the polyatomic ion.

   ammonium: NH_4^+
   dihydrogenphosphate: $H_2PO_4^-$

2. Determine the total charges needed to balance.

   NH_4^+: 1
   $H_2PO_4^-$: 1

3. Note the ratio of cations to anions.   1 to 1

4. Write the formula. Brackets and a subscript are not needed when there is only one ion.

   $NH_4H_2PO_{4(s)}$

The formula of ammonium dihydrogenphosphate is $NH_4H_2PO_{4(s)}$.

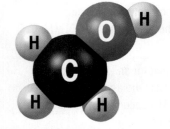

FIGURE A2.19   A methanol molecule. Methanol is the antifreeze used in car and truck engines.

Molecular Compounds

The burning methane hydrate ice described in the Exploring section at the beginning of this unit is made up of two important compounds: methane ($CH_{4(s)}$) and water ($H_2O_{(s)}$). Methane is the chemical name for natural gas. The electricity that operates your computer, CD player, and lights may be generated with methane. Your home may be heated with methane, and your dinner may be cooked with it. The other compound, water, is essential to life. It covers about 74% of Earth. You drink it, wash in it, and play in it. It's found in every living thing, from one-celled organisms and plants to insects and mammals.

Neither of these compounds contains any ions—they are each made up of molecules. A **molecule** forms when two or more non-metallic atoms bond together. It can be made up of atoms of different elements or of atoms of all the same element. For example, $CH_3OH_{(l)}$ (methanol) and $O_{2(g)}$ (oxygen gas) are both molecules. Figure A2.19 shows the structure of a methanol molecule.

Recall that the formula unit of an ionic compound represents a ratio of ions in a crystal lattice. In a solid ionic compound, this lattice extends in all directions. A formula unit is not an independent unit—it is just one part of a crystal lattice. Molecules are independent units made up of fixed numbers of atoms bonded together.

Unlike ionic compounds, molecular subtances can be solid, liquid, or gas at room temperature. They tend to be poor conductors of electricity, even in solution. Many do not dissolve in water very well. You will learn more about the properties of molecular compounds in section A2.3. Table A2.8 describes some common compounds.

TABLE A2.8 Examples of Common Molecular Compounds

Common Name	Formula	Chemical Name	Application
sugar	$C_{12}H_{22}O_{11(s)}$	sucrose	sweetener
alcohol	$CH_3CH_2OH_{(l)}$	ethanol	component of alcoholic beverages
nail polish remover	$CH_3COCH_{3(l)}$	acetone	solvent
natural gas	$CH_{4(g)}$	methane	heating fuel

Sharing Electrons—Covalent Bonds

The atoms in a molecule are joined together by **covalent bonds** that form when atoms share electrons. Each pair of shared electrons forms one covalent bond. Electrons are not transferred from one atom to another as they are in ionic bonds.

Chlorine gas is an example of a substance that has molecules formed of only one element. Each chlorine molecule is made up of two chlorine atoms joined by a covalent bond. Recall that a chlorine atom has seven valence electrons in its outer energy level. For this outer energy level to be filled, an additional electron is needed. A molecule of chlorine gas is created when two atoms of chlorine each share an electron to form a covalent bond. Figure A2.20 shows how sharing an electron forms a covalent bond.

Notice that the electron is not transferred from one atom to another as it would be in an ionic bond. In covalent bonds, atoms share electrons so that their outer energy levels become filled. Other examples of covalent compounds include $H_2O_{(l)}$ (water), $NH_{3(g)}$ (ammonia), and $C_{12}H_{22}O_{11(s)}$ (sugar).

In some covalent compounds, the atoms share more than two electrons. For example, nitrogen gas occurs in the form $N_{2(g)}$. (Nitrogen gas makes up 78% of our atmosphere.) An atom of nitrogen has five valence electrons. To form $N_{2(g)}$, two nitrogen atoms share three pairs of electrons (Figure A2.21). In carbon dioxide ($CO_{2(g)}$), all atoms share two pairs of electrons (Figure A2.22).

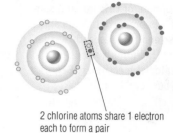

2 chlorine atoms share 1 electron each to form a pair

FIGURE A2.20 A molecule of chlorine gas forms when two chlorine atoms share one pair of electrons to form a covalent bond.

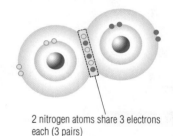

2 nitrogen atoms share 3 electrons each (3 pairs)

FIGURE A2.21 A molecule of nitrogen gas forms when two nitrogen atoms share three pairs of electrons to form covalent bonds. Each atom now has a stable outer energy level of eight electrons.

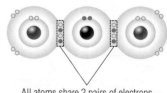

All atoms share 2 pairs of electrons

FIGURE A2.22 A molecule of carbon dioxide gas forms when one carbon atom and two oxygen atoms each share two pairs of electrons to form covalent bonds.

re**SEARCH**

Mercury is unusual because it is a metallic liquid at room temperature. The mercury(I) ion is also unusual in that it exists as a polyatomic ion. Find out the formula of this ion and some of its properties. You can extend this research further by finding out about calomel electrodes. Begin your search at

www.pearsoned.ca/
school/science10

Molecular Elements

Nitrogen is known as a **molecular element** because it forms molecules made up of only one type of atom. Its molecules are **diatomic**, which means each one is composed of only two atoms: $N_{2(g)}$ ("di-" means "two"). Some elements form polyatomic molecules. For example, sulfur forms a ring of eight atoms and has the formula $S_{8(s)}$. Other elements are monatomic. Their atoms can exist on their own. Carbon, for example, is written as $C_{(s)}$, although in both diamond and graphite it is connected to other carbon atoms in very large arrays. Formulas of molecular elements are summarized in Table A2.9.

TABLE A2.9 The Chemical Formulas of Molecular Elements

Monatomic	$C_{(s)}$		noble gases		all metals		
Diatomic	$H_{2(g)}$	$N_{2(g)}$	$O_{2(g)}$	$F_{2(g)}$	$Cl_{2(g)}$	$Br_{2(l)}$	$I_{2(s)}$
Polyatomic	$O_{3(g)}$(ozone)	$P_{4(s)}$	$S_{8(s)}$				

It can be very helpful to have the diatomic elements memorized, particularly when writing chemical reactions, as you will do in the next section. One way to remember them is that the diatomic elements are the "gens": hydro*gen*, nitro*gen*, oxy*gen*, and the halo*gens*.

Molecular Compounds That Do Not Contain Hydrogen

A binary compound contains two elements. Some of these compounds contain hydrogen, and some do not. IUPAC rules for naming binary molecular compounds not containing hydrogen are similar to the rules for naming ionic compounds. For molecules, Greek prefixes are used to indicate how many atoms of each element are present in the compound. For example, $P_4O_{10(s)}$ is called tetraphosphorus decaoxide: "tetra" means "4," and "deca-" means "10." Table A2.10 lists the prefixes used for naming binary compounds.

Any compound that does not have a metal or an ammonium ion in its formula is molecular. The format for naming binary molecular compounds not containing hydrogen is:

prefix + first element *followed by* prefix + second element ending in "-ide"

Note that the prefix "mono-" is not used when the first element is only one atom. When the prefix "mono-" is required before "oxide," the last "o" in the prefix is usually dropped. For example, it is "monoxide," not "monooxide." Table 2.11 shows how the format is used in two examples.

TABLE A2.10 Prefixes Used for Naming Binary Molecular Compounds

Prefix	Number
mono	1
di	2
tri	3
tetra	4
penta	5
hexa	6
hepta	7
octa	8
ennea (nona)	9
deca	10

TABLE A2.11 Examples for Naming Binary Molecular Compounds

Steps	Examples	
	$N_2O_{(g)}$	$PBr_{3(g)}$
1. Name the first element.	nitrogen	phosphorus
2. Name the second element with "-ide" at the end.	oxide	bromide
3. Add prefixes indicating numbers of atoms.	dinitrogen monoxide	phosphorus tribromide

Here are some examples:

$CO_{(g)}$ carbon monoxide
$SO_{2(g)}$ sulfur dioxide
$CS_{2(g)}$ carbon disulfide
$N_2O_{3(g)}$ dinitrogen trioxide
$CCl_{4(l)}$ carbon tetrachloride
$P_4O_{10(s)}$ tetraphosphorus decaoxide

Example Problem A2.5

Write the name of the compound that has the formula $PCl_{5(s)}$.

The rules listed above are applied in order. The first element is phosphorus. The second element is chlorine, so this compound is a chloride. Since only one atom of phosphorus is present, no prefix is used. Five atoms of chlorine are present, so the prefix is "penta."

The name of the compound with the formula $PCl_{5(g)}$ is phosphorus pentachloride.

Practice Problem

5. Write the names or formulas for the following molecular compounds:
   a) $CO_{2(g)}$
   b) $N_2O_{(g)}$
   c) $PCl_{3(g)}$
   d) oxygen difluoride
   e) dinitrogen tetrasulfide
   f) sulfur trioxide

Molecular Compounds That Contain Hydrogen

Hydrogen is unique in many ways, and this is reflected in naming systems. Many compounds containing hydrogen have simply been given names. The name "water," for example, was chosen by IUPAC to be the official name for H_2O. These names have to be memorized or found by referring to a chart like Table A2.12. Note, in particular, that the prefix "mono-" is omitted in $H_2S_{(g)}$, which is named hydrogen sulfide.

Writing the formulas for molecular compounds is easy because the prefixes in the names indicate the number of each element. However, predicting formulas when elements combine is difficult because more than one combination is possible; for example, $CO_{(g)}$ or $CO_{2(g)}$.

TABLE A2.12

Examples of Names of Molecular Compounds Containing Hydrogen

IUPAC Name	Formula and State at 25°C
water	$H_2O_{(l)}$
hydrogen peroxide	$H_2O_{2(l)}$
ammonia	$NH_{3(g)}$
sucrose	$C_{12}H_{22}O_{11(s)}$
methane	$CH_{4(g)}$
propane	$C_3H_{8(g)}$
methanol	$CH_3OH_{(l)}$
ethanol	$C_2H_5OH_{(l)}$
hydrogen sulfide	$H_2S_{(g)}$

For some of the following questions, you may use the periodic table or the table of polyatomic ions in Table E of Student Reference 12.

Knowledge

1. Define each of the following and provide an example of each:
   a) ion
   b) cation
   c) anion
   d) polyatomic ion
   e) multivalent metal

2. List the Greek prefixes corresponding to the numbers from 1 to 10.

3. Write symbols or formulas for the following ions:
   a) sodium ion
   b) calcium ion
   c) silver ion
   d) copper(II) ion
   e) lead(IV) ion
   f) chloride
   g) chlorate
   h) chlorite
   i) acetate
   j) ammonium

4. Name the following ions:
   a) Al^{3+}
   b) K^+
   c) Zn^{2+}
   d) Ni^{3+}
   e) Fe^{2+}
   f) Fe^{3+}
   g) HCO_3^-
   h) OH^-
   i) SCN^-
   j) SO_3^{2-}

5. Name the following molecular compounds containing hydrogen:
   a) $CH_{4(g)}$
   b) $NH_{3(g)}$
   c) $H_2O_{(l)}$
   d) $H_2S_{(g)}$
   e) $HF_{(g)}$

6. Classify the following compounds as molecular or ionic from their names or formulas:
   a) $CuCl_{2(s)}$
   b) $(NH_4)S_{(s)}$
   c) $NH_{3(g)}$
   d) $Fe(NO_3)_{3(s)}$
   e) $CCl_{4(l)}$
   f) $C_6H_{12}O_{6(s)}$
   g) sodium oxide
   h) sulfur hexafluoride
   i) methane
   j) zinc sulfate

7. a) What does IUPAC stand for?
   b) Use an example to explain the need for the IUPAC system of naming chemical compounds.

Applications

8. Name the following ionic compounds:
   a) $AlCl_{3(s)}$
   b) $CaS_{(s)}$
   c) $Na_3N_{(s)}$
   d) $K_2SO_{4(s)}$
   e) $Li_2O_{(s)}$
   f) $FeI_{3(s)}$
   g) $Pb(NO_3)_{4(s)}$
   h) $Cu_3PO_{4(s)}$
   i) $NH_4NO_{2(s)}$
   j) $NaCH_3COO_{(s)}$

9. Write the formulas of the following ionic compounds:
   a) sodium hydroxide
   b) ammonium sulfite
   c) magnesium thiocyanate
   d) calcium hydrogenphosphate
   e) aluminium acetate
   f) chromium(III) chloride

10. Write the formulas for the following molecular compounds:
    a) dinitrogen tetraoxide
    b) phosphorus pentachloride
    c) nitrogen triiodide
    d) carbon monoxide
    e) tetraphosphorus decaoxide
    f) carbon disulfide
    g) sulfur trioxide
    h) methane
    i) ammonia
    j) sucrose

11. Write the name of each of the following molecular compounds:
    a) $CBr_{4(g)}$
    b) $NO_{(g)}$
    c) $OF_{2(g)}$
    d) $IBr_{(g)}$
    e) $SeCl_{2(g)}$
    f) $PCl_{3(g)}$
    g) $N_2O_{3(g)}$
    h) $SCl_{2(g)}$

Extension

12. For each of the following, either write its name or the formula. Both ionic and molecular compounds are listed.
    a) $H_2O_{2(l)}$
    b) $Fe(SCN)_{3(s)}$
    c) ethanol
    d) sodium silicate
    e) ammonium perchlorate
    f) $SF_{6(g)}$

A 2.3 Properties and Classification of Ionic and Molecular Compounds

If someone calls you "the salt of the Earth," you are receiving a compliment. Salt was precious in ancient times, especially in hot climates, where a good supply is essential for life. This type of salt is sodium chloride, but it is not the only kind of salt. Magnesium sulfate and lead(II) iodide are also salts—although they are not meant for the dinner table. Magnesium sulfate is a component in fertilizer, while lead(II) iodide was once used to make a bright yellow paint. Today its use is restricted to specialty artist's paints. Each of these chemicals has its own properties. Sodium chloride is edible. Magnesium sulfate (also called Epsom salts) may be mixed with water and used for soaking tired, dry feet to make the skin feel soft. Lead(II) iodide is a poison.

These properties do not seem similar, yet these compounds have many properties in common. All of them melt above 800°C, which is much hotter than a candle flame, for example. They all form crystals. Their crystals have the interesting property that, if they are ground up and then examined under a microscope, the new tiny crystals look just like the bigger ones, with flat surfaces and well-defined edges. None of these solid compounds conduct electricity but all of their solutions do. All of these compounds are ionic: they are composed of positive ions and negative ions.

Many important compounds are not ionic. Water, methane, wax, caffeine, and glucose are all molecular compounds. At first look, they may not seem to have properties in common. Water is a liquid, while methane is a gas. The others are all solids. But they all melt below 250°C, a relatively low temperature. This temperature can easily be reached in a very hot frying pan. These five compounds are related in many other ways as well. None of them contain any metals. Also, none of them conducts electricity, and neither do the solutions of those that will dissolve in water. In this section, we will examine both ionic and molecular substances to see how their properties are determined.

Both ionic and molecular compounds form crystals. Possibly the most important molecular crystal studied in the last century was DNA. DNA is the molecule responsible for passing genetic information from one generation to the next in all living things. An X-ray photograph of DNA taken by Rosalind Franklin in 1951 led to the understanding that DNA is composed of two long chains twisted into a helix.

Skill Practice   Writing a Hypothesis

In Activity A5, you will be asked to write a **hypothesis**. A hypothesis is a sentence intended as a possible explanation for observations. It is a proposed answer to a question.

Questions in science are usually cause-and-effect questions, such as "How does temperature affect the growth of rose plants?" Notice that the cause, temperature, is the manipulated variable. The effect, plant growth, is the responding variable.

A hypothesis is often written as an "if … then…." statement. For example, *if* the temperature is increased, *then* the plants will not grow as tall. A hypothesis does not have to be the right answer—it's just a possible answer. Scientists test the hypothesis by carrying out an investigation.

Create a cause-and-effect question and a hypothesis for each of the following statements:

1. Plants require light for photosynthesis.

2. Copper loses its brittleness if it is heated before being hammered into tools.

3. Fermentation keeps food from rotting.

4. Hydrocarbon combustion produces carbon dioxide and water.

5. Sodium and chlorine react to produce sodium chloride (table salt).

Inquiry Lab

Student Reference **1, 2, 10**

Required Skills
- Initiating and Planning
- Performing and Recording
- Analyzing and Interpreting
- Communication and Teamwork

Ionic or Molecular?

The Question

How can substances be classified as ionic or molecular based on their properties?

The Hypothesis

Write a hypothesis that answers the question above.

Variables

Identify the manipulated and responding variables.

Materials and Equipment

sodium chloride

sugar

potassium iodide

bees wax

Epsom salts

naphthalene flakes

2 hot plates

6 test tubes

aluminium foil

conductivity meter

CAUTION: Naphthalene gives off toxic fumes when heated. Use the fume hood when heating it. Beware of hot surfaces to avoid burns.

Procedure

1. Copy the data table below into your notebook.

2. Plug in a hot plate and set it to medium heat. This hot plate will be used in step 9. Place another hot plate in the fume hood and plug it in. It will be used in step 10.

3. Obtain a small sample of about 1 g of each substance (an amount the size of a fingernail). Place the samples of the first five substances from the materials list on one piece of aluminium foil. Do not mix them. Place the naphthalene flakes on a separate piece of aluminium foil.

4. Note the appearance of each substance. In particular, do they appear crystalline or waxy?

5. Using a spatula, try to crush a small piece of each substance. Record your observations.

6. Carefully determine whether any of the samples have a characteristic odour. (See Student Reference 1: Safety for information on how to detect odours safely.) Record your observations.

7. Place a few crystals of one substance in a test tube. Add water and note whether any dissolve. The fewer the crystals placed in the test tube, the easier it is to observe if any dissolve. Repeat this step for each substance. Use a clean test tube each time. The same test tube can be used each time, as long as it is washed out between uses.

Substance	Appearance	Hardness	Odour	Solubility in Water	Conductivity	Melting Point
sodium chloride						
sugar						
potassium iodide						
bees wax						
Epsom salts						
naphthalene flakes						

8. (Your teacher may demonstrate this step). Test each sample that appeared to dissolve to see whether it conducts electricity.

9. Place the aluminium foil containing the five samples on the hot plate. Note the order in which the samples melt. Some may not melt at all. Record your observations.

10. Place the aluminium foil holding the naphthalene flakes on the hot plate in the fume hood. Note how long they take to melt.

11. Follow your teacher's instructions for disposing of all the substances you have used.

Analyzing and Interpreting

1. Draw two circles that overlap each other to form a Venn diagram. Make them large enough to write the names of the six test substances inside.

2. Write "bees wax" in one circle and "Epsom salts" in the other.

3. Write the names of other substances that are similar in their properties to bees wax in the same circle where you wrote "bees wax."

4. Write the names of other substances that are similar in their properties to Epsom salts in the same circle where you wrote "Epsom salts."

5. If any substances do not clearly fit into either group, write their names in the overlapped area.

6. Decide which group of compounds are molecular and which are ionic.

Forming Conclusions

7. Identify each compound tested as ionic or molecular. Describe how you used their properties to classify them.

Identifying Ionic Compounds

Recall that ionic compounds always contain positive and negative ions. One is a cation, which is a positive metal ion, such as Fe^{3+}, or the positive ammonium ion NH_4^+. The second ion is always an anion, which is a negative non-metal ion, such as fluoride, F^-, or a negative polyatomic ion, such as the phosphate ion PO_4^{3-}.

You can recognize an ionic compound by inspecting its formula, and noting the presence of a cation. In other words, if the formula of a compound begins with a metal ion or with the NH_4^+ ion, the compound is ionic. Table A2.13 shows examples of some ionic compunds.

TABLE A2.13 Examples of Ionic Compounds and Their Properties

Property	$NaCl_{(s)}$	$MgSO_{4(s)}$	$PbI_{2(s)}$	$NH_4NO_{3(s)}$
colour	white	white	bright yellow	white
state at room temperature (25°C)	solid	solid	solid	solid
melting point/freezing point	801°C	1124°C (decomposes)	400°C	170°C
malleable	no	no	no	no
soluble in water	yes	yes	slightly	yes
conductor as solid	no	no	no	no
conductor in solution	yes; strong	yes; strong	yes; weak	yes; strong

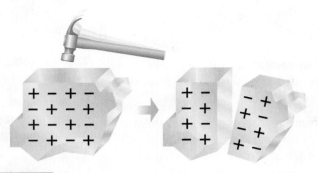

FIGURE A2.23 (a) Before being hit, all ions alternate precisely.

(b) After being hit, the positive ions momentarily move close to positive ions, and negative ions move close to negative ions, causing the crystal to split.

Properties of Ionic Compounds

Ionic compounds share many of the following properties. These properties help to distinguish ionic compounds from molecular compounds.

High Melting Point

Notice that the compounds listed in Table A2.13 all have high melting points. Because of their high melting points, all ionic compounds are solids at room temperature. The attractions between the cations and the anions in a solid ionic compound are so strong that the ions are held in the tight, highly organized crystal lattice. In the lattice, all the negative ions are surrounded by positive ions, and the positive ions are surrounded by negative ions (Figure A2.23(a)). A large amount of energy must be added in the form of heat before the ions can begin to move past each other in the liquid state.

Retention of Crystal Shape

If you examine grains of table salt closely, you can see that each crystal is made up of perfectly flat surfaces. If you grind the salt into a fine powder, and then examine the powder with a microscope, you will see that all the pieces are still little crystals. Each piece still has flat surfaces, just very much smaller. This results from the alternating positive and negative alignments of the ions in the crystal. When the crystal is hit, positive ions line up with each other, and negative ions line up with each other (Figure A2.23(b)). The two parts of the crystal fly apart, producing new perfectly flat surfaces. Ionic compounds retain their crystal shape. Figure A2.24 shows a crystal of table salt ($NaCl_{(s)}$).

Solubility in Water

All ionic compounds dissolve in water to some extent because both cations and anions are strongly attracted to water molecules. This occurs because each water molecule is **polar**. One end has a slightly positive electric charge, and the other end has a slightly negative charge. You will learn more about the polarity of water later in this section. When an ionic crystal is placed in water, some ions on the surface of the undissolved crystal are attracted into the water. There they become surrounded by many water molecules (Figure A2.25). You will learn more about the solubility of ionic compounds later in this section.

FIGURE A2.24 Salt (NaCl) is an ionic compound. Ionic compounds form beautiful crystals when allowed to grow under the right conditions.

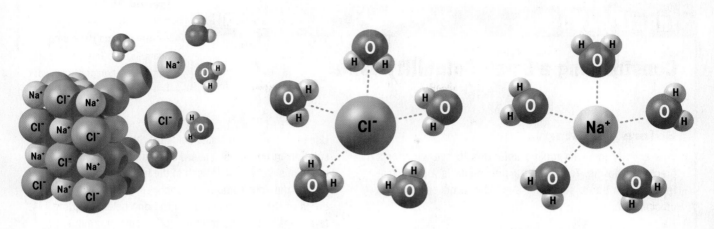

Ions break off the crystal as they dissolve. Water molecules orient themselves around the cations and anions.

Conductivity in Solution

Solutions containing ionic compounds are good conductors of electricity, unlike pure water, which has almost no conductivity. The greater the concentration of ions in solution, the more conductive the solution is. For example, a 1-L solution of 2 g of $NaCl_{(aq)}$ in water is twice as conductive as the same volume containing 1 g of $NaCl_{(aq)}$. The solution with 2 g of $NaCl_{(aq)}$ has twice as many $Na^+_{(aq)}$ and $Cl^-_{(aq)}$ ions as the one with 1 g of $NaCl_{(aq)}$. Figure A2.26 shows that ions in solution can complete a circuit for electric current to light a light bulb.

Solutions of ionic compounds are considered to be excellent **electrolytes**. An electrolyte is any solution that can conduct electricity. If a solution does not contain ions, it will not conduct. For example, a solution of table sugar, $C_{12}H_{22}O_{11(s)}$, contains no charged particles, just neutral molecules of $C_{12}H_{22}O_{11(aq)}$, so it does not conduct electricity. A solution of table sugar is not an electrolyte.

Some molecular compounds, such as $HCl_{(g)}$, become ionic in solution. Hydrogen chloride reacts with water to produce new ions. This is a general characteristic of acids, which will be examined in the next section.

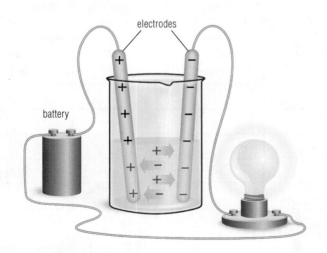

FIGURE A2.26 An electric current is carried by moving electrons in a wire and by moving ions in a solution.

Required Skills
- Initiating and Planning
- Performing and Recording
- Analyzing and Interpreting
- Communication and Teamwork

Constructing a Small Solubility Table

Before You Start...

This activity involves mixing solutions to see whether a precipitate forms. Recall that a precipitate is a solid that forms when some solutions mix. This process is called precipitation.

The Question

What combinations of ions produce a precipitate when their solutions are mixed?

Materials and Equipment

spot plate

5 drops of each of the following solutions:

silver nitrate

strontium nitrate

sodium iodide

sodium sulfate

barium iodide

CAUTION: Some solutions you are using are poisonous or corrosive. Wash your hands thoroughly after handling these chemicals.

Procedure

1. Copy the following table into your notebook.

2. Use the table in step 1 as a guide to where to place each solution in your spot plate. For example, place a few drops of silver nitrate in each of the five wells on the left side of the spot plate. In the top well, add a few more drops of the same solution. In the one below it, add a few drops of strontium nitrate to the silver nitrate, and so on down the column. In the next column of wells, to the right, strontium nitrate should be in all the wells, and other substances added to it.

3. Wait at least two minutes after mixing the solutions before making your final observations.

4. In your table, record whether a precipitate has formed in each well. Where a precipitate has formed, note its colour and appearance.

5. Do not rinse the spot plate in the sink. Some of these chemicals contain metals. They require special disposal procedures. Follow your teacher's instructions for disposing of all the substances you have used.

Analyzing and Interpreting

1. When you mixed a solution with itself, did a precipitate form in any of the solutions?

2. Did the order in which you added solutions to each other make any difference as to whether a precipitate did or did not form? (For example, did it make a difference if you added sodium iodide to sodium sulfate, or if you added sodium sulfate to sodium iodide?) What evidence is there to support this conclusion?

	silver nitrate	strontium nitrate	sodium iodide	sodium sulfate	barium iodide
silver nitrate					
strontium nitrate					
sodium iodide					
sodium sulfate					
barium iodide					

3. When silver nitrate and sodium iodide were mixed, a white precipitate formed. Its identity is either silver iodide or sodium nitrate. Use the results from your experiment to help you decide which of these two substances formed the precipitate.

4. Identify two other substances that formed precipitates in this experiment.

Forming Conclusions

5. List three compounds that form precipitates when their ions are mixed together in a solution. Use the solubility table you constructed as you did the activity to support your conclusion.

Solubility of Ionic Compounds

Some ionic compounds dissolve better than others. A substance that dissolves well is considered very soluble. Recall that its chemical formula would be followed by the subscript "(aq)" when it's in solution. A substance that does not dissolve well is considered slightly soluble. Its chemical formula is followed by the subscript "(s)." Table A2.14 shows the solubility of some common ionic compounds in water. It summarizes the results of many solubility experiments.

TABLE A2.14 Solubility of Some Common Ionic Compounds in Water

Note: Group 1 = Li^+, Na^+, K^+, Rb^+, Cs^+, Fr^+
   Group 2 = Be^{2+}, Mg^{2+}, Ca^{2+}, Sr^{2+}, Ba^{2+}, Ra^{2+}

"all" means "all compounds containing these ions"
"most" means "most compounds containing these ions"
"only with" means "only compounds containing" the ion or ions listed

Ion	Group 1 NH_4^+ H_3O^+ (H^+)	ClO_3^- NO_3^- ClO_4^-	CH_3COO^-	Cl^- Br^- I^-	SO_4^{2-}	S^{2-}	OH^-	PO_4^{3-} SO_3^{2-} CO_3^{2-}
Very Soluble	all	all	most	most	most	only with: Group 1 Group 2 NH_4^+	only with: Group 1 NH_4^+ Sr^{2+} Ba^{2+} Tl^+	only with: Group 1 NH_4^+
Slightly Soluble	none	none	only with: Ag^+ Hg^+	only with: Ag^+ Pb^{2+} Hg^+ Cu^+ Tl^+	only with: Ca^{2+} Sr^{2+} Ba^{2+} Ra^{2+} Pb^{2+} Ag^+	most	most	most

Recall that group 1 elements are the alkali metals, which include the very common metal ions lithium, sodium, and potassium. Table A2.14 shows that any compounds containing these ions are very soluble. Salts containing these ions are common in the ocean. As noted above, the chemical formulas for soluble compounds in solution have the subscript *(aq)*. It stands for "aqueous," meaning that the compound is dissolved in water. For example, sodium chloride in solution is written $NaCl_{(aq)}$. Sodium chloride in your salt shaker is written $NaCl_{(s)}$.

Most compounds that contain chloride ions are also soluble, with a few exceptions. Silver chloride, for example, is only slightly soluble. Most phosphates and carbonates are only slightly soluble. This is fortunate, because these compounds are present in everything from egg shells to clam shells to bones and teeth.

Sometimes, when ionic solutions are mixed, they form a **precipitate**. A precipitate is a solid with low solubility that forms from a solution. Precipitates may form when solutions of two different ionic compounds are mixed. **Precipitation** is the process involved in forming a precipitate. You will learn more about chemical reactions that produce precipitates in section A3.3.

Minds On ...   Using the Solubility Chart

Use the solubility chart in Table A2.14 to help you answer the following questions.

1. Suppose the following compounds were added to water. Indicate the solubility of each one by using the subscript *(aq)* for those that are very soluble and *(s)* for those that are slightly soluble.
   a) $(NH_4)_2S$ f) $Au(NO_3)_3$
   b) $AgCl$ g) PbI_4
   c) $PbSO_4$ h) Na_3PO_4
   d) $Sr(OH)_2$ i) CuS
   e) $Fe(OH)_3$ j) $AgCH_3COO$

2. Suppose the following compounds were added to water. Indicate the solubility of each one by stating whether it is very soluble or slightly soluble.
   a) potassium carbonate
   b) iron(II) nitrate
   c) copper(I) chloride
   d) barium hydroxide
   e) ammonium sulfite
   f) calcium sulfide
   g) lead(IV) bromide

Properties of Molecular Compounds

Recall from section A2.2 that molecular compounds are made up of molecules. Molecules are groups of non-metallic atoms held together by **covalent bonds**. These very strong bonds form when non-metallic atoms share electrons. Each molecule of a compound always has the same number and proportion of atoms in it. For example, every water molecule has two atoms of hydrogen and one atom of oxygen, and its formula is written as $H_2O_{(l)}$ (Figure A2.27).

FIGURE A2.27 Both water and hydrogen peroxide contain hydrogen and oxygen, but in different proportions.

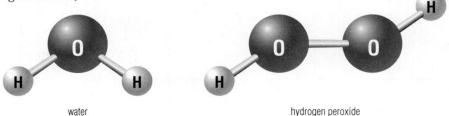

water   hydrogen peroxide

The attraction between individual atoms in a molecule is very strong, but the attraction between neighbouring molecules is weak. For this reason, the melting points of molecular compounds tend to be much lower than the melting points of ionic compounds. In molecular compounds, only a small amount of energy is required for the molecules to begin sliding past one another. Note that the molecule itself does not break up during melting. For this reason, melting is not considered a chemical change. The properties of five common molecular compounds are shown in Table A2.15.

TABLE A2.15 Properties of Five Common Molecular Compounds

Property	$H_2O_{(l)}$ (water)	$CH_{4(g)}$ (methane)	$C_{18}H_{38(s)}$ (wax)	$C_8H_{10}N_4O_{2(s)}$ (caffeine)	$C_6H_{12}O_{6(s)}$ (glucose)
colour	colourless	colourless	colourless	white	white
state at room temperature (25°C)	liquid	gas	solid	solid	solid
melting point/ freezing point	0°C	−183°C	64°C	238°C	150°C
malleable	—	—	no	no	no
soluble in water	—	no	no	slightly	yes
conductor as solid	no	no	no	no	no
conductor in solution	—	—	—	no	no

Molecular substances can form beautiful crystals, such as snowflakes. Snowflakes are simply crystalline water. Unlike crystals of ionic compounds, crystals of molecular compounds crumble easily. The relatively weak attractions between molecules mean that the crystals do not hold their shape. Another difference between ionic and molecular compounds is electrical conductivity. All molecules are electrically neutral, both as solids and in solution, so they do not conduct electricity in either state.

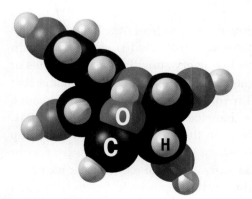

FIGURE A2.28 Molecular substances such as glucose can form crystals. But their crystals break down more easily than those of ionic compounds.

*info*BIT

Methane ($CH_{4(g)}$) is produced by the breakdown of organic materials. Because it is produced in swamps by rotting vegetation, it is known as "swamp gas." It is highly flammable, so some communities recover it from landfill sites for energy production. The fossil fuel natural gas is also methane.

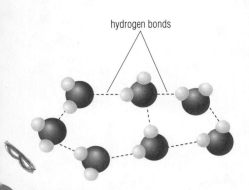

hydrogen bonds

FIGURE A2.29 Liquid water molecules are held together through the attractions caused by each molecule being slightly polar.

Special Properties of Water

One of water's most important properties is that it is polar: each water molecule has a negative end and a positive end. Water has this interesting property because of its bent shape and because of the unequal sharing of electrons in the bonds holding the hydrogen and oxygen together (Figure A2.29). This makes the oxygen end of water slightly negative, and the hydrogen end slightly positive. It also means that water molecules attract each other, just as two bar magnets attract each other if they are lined up with opposite poles together. This attraction makes it easier for water to form a liquid than if it were not polar.

Other properties would also change if water were not polar. Table A2.16 compares water with similar compounds that are not polar. From this comparison, we can see that it's likely water would boil at a much lower temperature if it was not polar, at about −80°C.

TABLE A2.16 Boiling Points of Some Compounds Similar to Water

Compound	Boiling Point
hydrogen selenide, $H_2Se_{(g)}$	−40°C
hydrogen sulfide, $H_2S_{(g)}$	−60°C
water, $H_2O_{(l)}$	100°C

It is hard to overstate the importance of the polarity of water. If water was not polar, all the oceans would boil away even during the coldest winter. Life on Earth would be non-existent or completely different from what we see today. Much of the thermal energy at Earth's surface is held by water in oceans, lakes, and rivers. In summer, the oceans act as a heat sink, absorbing heat from the Sun and the air. In winter, they are a heat source, radiating stored heat. Both of these effects keep Earth's surface temperatures from swinging too high or too low. Living systems depend on this stability.

Formation of Ice

As liquid water turns to ice, the molecules spread out. They line up in a three-dimensional array that contains six-sided rings, as shown in Figure A2.30. This is the reason that every snowflake has six sides or six points. The ordering of water molecules in ice also means that there are fewer molecules in a litre of ice than in a litre of liquid water, so that liquid water is denser than ice. Because of this, ice floats. Would it matter if ice didn't float? In the winter, ice forms at the top surface of a lake because that is where it is coldest. If ice were denser than liquid water, then as a lake froze over, the ice would sink to the bottom and collect there. Eventually, the lake would freeze solid, and all the fish would die. Fish can survive through the winter because ice floats.

*re*SEARCH

The weak interactions between water molecules are called hydrogen bonds. Investigate hydrogen bonding in other substances such as DNA and the plastic used in sandwich wrap. Begin your search at

www.pearsoned.ca/ school/science10

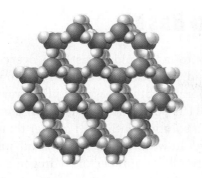

FIGURE A2.30 Water molecules in ice. The origin of the six-sided snowflake can be seen by the honeycomb shape that water molecules form.

Knowledge

1. Explain how to recognize an ionic compound from its chemical formula.

2. Describe four properties of an ionic compound.

3. Explain how to recognize a molecular compound by its chemical formula.

4. Describe four properties of molecular compounds.

5. Water is a polar molecule. What does this mean?

6. Indicate whether each of the following compounds is slightly soluble *(s)* or very soluble *(aq)*. Refer to Table A2.14 on page 57 or Table C in Student Reference 12.
   a) $NaCl$
   b) $PbCl_2$
   c) $PbCl_4$
   d) $BaSO_4$
   e) Cr_2S_3
   f) $CsCH_3COO$
   g) K_2CO_3

Applications

7. Explain how a large body of water can moderate the temperatures of the land around it in both winter and summer.

8. For each substance below, identify it as ionic or molecular. Explain how you came to your conclusion.
   a) Compound 1: melting point: 48°C, low solubility in water, flammable, mild odour, colourless solid easily crushed
   b) Compound 2: melting point: 800°C, highly soluble, solution is highly conductive, hard, white crystals
   c) Compound 3: melting point: 185°C, decomposes at 190°C, highly soluble, solution is not conductive, hard, white crystals
   d) Compound 4: sublimates (goes from solid to gas) at −56°C, moderately soluble in water, colourless, odourless
   e) Compound 5: highly flammable liquid at room temperature, does not mix with water, less dense than water
   f) Compound 6: colourless, odourless liquid, tends to dissolve ionic substances, boils at 100°C

9. All of the compounds in question 8 are common materials. Suggest the identity of each material from the descriptions of the physical properties.

Extension

10. Some well water is considered "hard" because it contains high concentrations of Mg^{2+} and Ca^{2+} ions. Explain how adding a small amount of sodium carbonate to the well water can make the water "soft" by removing these ions.

A 2.4 Acids and Bases

You are already familiar with acids and bases from everyday use and from earlier science studies. Recall that an **acid** is a compound that dissolves in water to form a solution with a pH lower than 7. The vinegar in Figure A2.31 is acidic. A **base** is a compound that dissolves in water to form a solution with a pH greater than 7. The **pH** measurement indicates how acidic or basic a substance is. Recall that pH is a measure of the number of hydrogen ions in a solution.

Acids and Bases in Your Body

Acids and bases are in the foods we eat and the products we use. They are also essential components of your own biochemistry. For example, your saliva is slightly basic so your teeth won't dissolve in acids, such as the citric acid in fruit juices. It also protects you from the acids that the bacteria in your mouth produce as a byproduct of their metabolism.

Your stomach makes hydrochloric acid strong enough to burn, as anyone who has accidentally burped up some stomach acid can confirm. What does this acid do? Some of it dissolves food, but it also has a much more important function. It acts like a chemical switch to turn on an enzyme called pepsin. Pepsin, like all enzymes, speeds up chemical reactions in living systems. The reaction that pepsin speeds up is the digestion of protein into amino acids, which are the building blocks of proteins. Pepsin would be lethal if it passed into the intestine without being deactivated. It would begin to digest the digestive tract itself.

An organ called the pancreas produces sodium hydrogencarbonate (the same chemical as in baking soda) and other bases that neutralize the stomach acid. This deactivates the pepsin. After that, the sodium hydrogencarbonate goes into the bloodstream, making it very slightly basic. Sodium hydrogencarbonate has the amazing property that it can neutralize both acids and bases that enter the blood. When acids and bases are neutralized, they lose their characteristic properties. You will learn more about neutralization later in this section.

Sodium hydrogencarbonate is an example of a **buffer**. It is a substance that can keep the pH of a solution nearly constant despite the addition of a small amount of acid or base.

Acids and bases are all around us and inside us. How can we make sense of this amazing variety of chemicals? We can begin by classifying them as acidic, basic, or neutral according to their chemical and physical properties.

FIGURE A2.31 The pH of vinegar is less than 7, indicating that vinegar is acidic.

Properties of Acids and Bases

You are already an expert at sorting out acids and bases. You were born with this skill—it is hard wired into your sense of taste. The four basic tastes are sweet, sour, salty, and bitter. If you have ever had soap in your mouth, you know the taste of a base—bitter. You know the taste of acid from lemons (citric acid) and vinegar (acetic acid). You probably would not be surprised to find that *acidus* is the Latin word for "sour." Given the commonness of these chemicals, it is no wonder that your tongue is able to detect them.

Acidic and basic solutions even feel different. Bleach, soap, and ammonia cleanser all feel slippery, and all are bases. Bleach, of course, must be washed off quickly because it is corrosive to skin. Acid solutions do not feel slippery.

Remember that taste and touch tests are fine for food in the kitchen, but they should never be performed in the lab. Other tests are needed to classify acids and bases. For example, adding a metal to a solution could help determine if the solution is acidic or basic. Acids react with metals, although some acids, such as nitric acid, react more vigorously with metals than other acids. And some metals, such as copper and gold, are better than other metals at resisting attack by acids. Most bases do not attack metals. Neither does pure water, which is a neutral substance. This ability to react with metals could be used to distinguish acids from bases and neutral substances. But there is an easier way—by determining the pH.

Indicators

Acid–base indicators are chemicals that are used to determine if a solution is an acid or a base. Indicators change colour depending on the pH of a solution. Litmus indicator is a chemical derived from lichen, a plant-like organism. Litmus is usually dried onto paper to make it easier to use in tests. In acid, blue litmus paper turns red, and in base, red litmus paper turns blue. In a neutral solution, such as pure water, litmus paper does not change colour. Red litmus paper stays red, and blue litmus paper stays blue. Litmus is a very common indicator, so it's useful to memorize the colour changes (Figure A2.32).

There are many indicators, and each changes colour at a specific level of acidity. A **universal indicator** is a mixture of several indicators that change colour as the acidity changes (Figure A2.33).

ACID
RED
BASE
BLUE

FIGURE A2.32 This diagram shows a memory trick for remembering the colour of litmus in acid and in base.

FIGURE A2.33 The colour of a universal indicator changes at a variety of pH values.

infoBIT

Understanding the pH scale can help you understand the seriousness of the problem with acid rain. Ordinary rainwater is about pH 6. Acid rainwater can have a pH as low as 3. A difference of 3 units on the pH scale means that acid rain can be as much as 1000 times more acidic than ordinary rain.

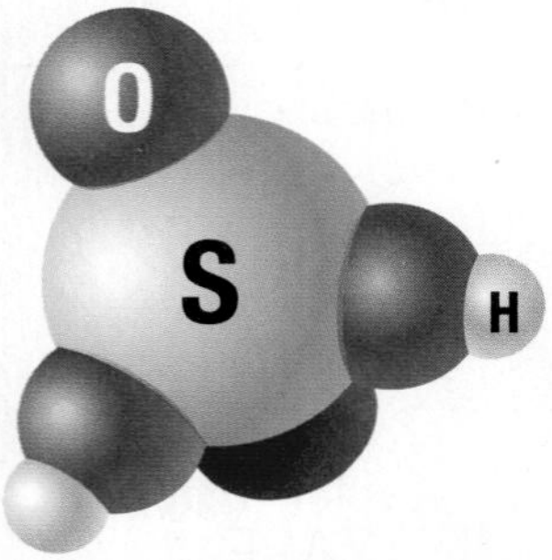

FIGURE A2.34 Sulfuric acid molecule

The pH Scale

Recall that the pH scale is a measure of acidity. Most solutions are between 0 and 14 on the pH scale. A **neutral** substance has a pH of 7 (at 25°C). It is neither acidic nor basic. Acidic substances have pH values below 7. The closer the pH is to 0, the more acidic the substance is. Stomach acid is about pH 1.5. Vinegar is less acidic at about pH 3. Normal rainwater is slightly acidic and has a pH of about 6. Bases have pH values greater than 7. Blood is slightly basic, with a pH of 7.4. Soaps have pH values between 8 and 10.

Every increase of 1 on the pH scale indicates an increase of 10 in how basic a substance is. A solution with a pH of 9 is 10 times more basic than one with a pH of 8. Similarly, a decrease of 1 on the pH scale indicates a 10-times increase in acidity.

Acidic and basic solutions can be classified according to the properties shown in Table A2.17.

TABLE A2.17 Properties of Acids and Bases

Property	Acid	Base
taste	sour	bitter
touch	not slippery	slippery
reaction with metals (e.g., magnesium)	metal corrodes H_2 bubbles form	no reaction
litmus indicator	red	blue
electrical conductivity	conductive	conductive
pH of solution	< 7	> 7

Naming Acids

The formula for a compound can help you determine if it is an acid or a base. H, the symbol for hydrogen, tends to appear one or more times on the left side of the formula of an acid. For example, in hydrochloric acid, $HCl_{(aq)}$, the hydrogen symbol appears on the left. In acetic acid, which is the acid in vinegar, hydrogen appears on the right in a group of symbols known as an organic acid group: -COOH. To identify acids from their formulas, look for H on the left side of the formula or COOH on the right. Some common acids are listed in Table A2.18.

Notice that the acids listed in Table A2.18 are all aqueous. The IUPAC recommends naming acids as aqueous substances containing the IUPAC name of the compound. For example, $HCl_{(aq)}$ is called aqueous hydrogen chloride; and $H_2SO_{4(aq)}$ is called aqueous hydrogen sulfate.

However, acids have been known for thousands of years, and they are very common compounds. Because of this, other naming systems exist that are still popular. For example, the names of acids that contain hydrogen and one other non-metallic element can be written with the prefix "hydro-" and the suffix "-ic." In this system, $HCl_{(aq)}$ is called hydrochloric acid. Following this pattern, $HF_{(aq)}$ is called hydrofluoric acid.

Acids that contain oxygen, such as $H_2SO_{4(aq)}$, follow a different system that is based on the name of the anion. In this naming system, if the anion ends in "-ate," the name of the acid that is derived from it ends in "-ic." For example, $H_2SO_{4(aq)}$ contains the sulfate anion (SO_4^{2-}), an anion whose name ends in the suffix "-ate." In this case, the acid's name begins with "sulfur" (the first element in the anion) and ends with "-ic." It is called sulfuric acid. Another example is $H_3PO_{4(aq)}$. Its IUPAC name is aqueous hydrogen phosphate, but it is also called phosphoric acid. Similarly, $HNO_{3(aq)}$ is called both aqueous hydrogen nitrate and nitric acid. If the anion's name does not end in "-ate," other naming systems are used. You will learn about these naming systems in later courses.

TABLE A2.18 Formulas, Names, and Uses of Some Common Acids

Acid	Name	Common Name	Use
$HCl_{(aq)}$	hydrochloric acid or aqueous hydrogen chloride	muriatic acid	concrete cleaning
$H_2SO_{4(aq)}$	sulfuric acid or aqueous hydrogen sulfate	battery acid	car batteries, fertilizer manufacturing
$HNO_{3(aq)}$	nitric acid or aqueous hydrogen nitrate	—	fertilizer manufacturing, metal refining
$H_3PO_{4(aq)}$	phosphoric acid or aqueous hydrogen phosphate	—	sour taste in soft drinks, fertilizer manufacturing
$HCOOH_{(aq)}$	methanoic acid	formic acid	wool dyeing, leather tanning
$CH_3COOH_{(aq)}$	ethanoic acid	acetic acid	vinegar

Skill Practice   Controlling Variables

In Activity A7, you will qualitatively compare the concentration of vitamin C in several different beverages. To do this, you will have to control a certain variable so you can observe its effects. In previous science studies, you learned that the **manipulated variable** is the condition that is deliberately changed by the experimenter. The **responding variable** is the condition that changes in response to the manipulated variable. The responding variable must be something that can be measured. To test the effect of a manipulated variable, it is important that only that one variable is being changed. All other variables in an experiment must be controlled. In other words, they must be kept exactly the same.

1. A student wants to determine which freezes faster, salt water or fresh water. She adds 10 g of salt to a beaker containing 100 mL of water, 20 g of salt to a beaker containing 150 mL of water, and no salt to a beaker containing 50 mL of water. All of the substances are at room temperature at the beginning of the experiment. All will be placed in a freezer where the temperature is −5.0°C.
   a) Identify the manipulated variable.
   b) Are the other variables being controlled? If they are not, describe how the conditions can be controlled so that only the manipulated variable is changed.

2. You are asked to determine the effect of turbulence on the amount of dissolved oxygen in water. Turbulence is the violent disturbance of a fluid, such as water or air. You will use an indicator that tells you the amount of dissolved oxygen present in a sample. You will use water that has had the oxygen content reduced by being boiled and cooled. You will simulate turbulence by shaking a sample of water.
   a) What is the manipulated variable in this experiment?
   b) What variables must be controlled?

Design a Lab

Vitamin C in Beverages

Vitamin C is ascorbic acid. In this activity, you will test a procedure to detect vitamin C in a solution. You will then design a qualitative procedure to compare the concentration of vitamin C in a number of beverages such as orange juice, soda pop, or lemonade.

The Question

Which beverage has the highest concentration of vitamin C and which has the lowest?

Materials and Equipment

1 multivitamin tablet

iodine/starch solution

several samples of juices, soda pops, or other beverages

water

mortar and pestle

100-mL beaker

10-mL graduated cylinder

at least 6 medium test tubes

stirring rod

2 droppers

test tube rack

CAUTION: The iodine/starch solution stains. Handle carefully.

Design and Conduct Your Investigation

Part 1: Determining How a Starch/Iodine Solution Responds to a Vitamin C Solution

1. Use the mortar and pestle to grind up the multivitamin tablet. Dissolve most of the grindings in about 100 mL of water in a 100-mL beaker. Stir the mixture with a stirring rod. Some of the grindings may not dissolve. This is not a problem.

2. Use the graduated cylinder to measure 5 mL of iodine/starch solution into a test tube.

3. Use a dropper to add the vitamin C solution to the iodine/starch solution drop-by-drop. Observe the reaction.

4. Using a clean dropper, do a similar test by adding water to another sample of iodine/starch solution in another test tube. Observe. Note: You *must* use a clean dropper for this step to prevent contamination of your water with vitamin C.

Part 2: Ranking the Test Beverages from Greatest to Lowest Concentration of Vitamin C

5. Select several beverages to be tested. It might be interesting to test some that are known to contain vitamin C, along with some with an unknown vitamin C content.

6. Develop a test procedure to rank the beverages from most concentrated to least concentrated in vitamin C content.

7. Have your teacher approve your procedure.

8. Test the beverages.

9. Follow your teacher's instructions for disposing of the liquids.

10. Write a summary report that describes:

- your observations of what a positive test and a negative test for vitamin C look like

- your written test procedure

- the controlled, manipulated, and responding variables in your procedure

- your test data

- your ranking of the test beverages from most concentrated to least concentrated

Recognizing Bases by Their Formulas

Bases are more difficult to recognize by their formulas than acids are. The presence of the hydroxide ion (OH^-) with a metal ion or the ammonium ion usually indicates that a substance is basic. For example, $NaOH_{(s)}$ forms a base when dissolved in water. However, substances with other kinds of formulas can also be basic. For example, when ammonia ($NH_{3(g)}$) is dissolved in water, the resulting solution is basic. You will study these bases in more advanced chemistry courses. For now, consider any compound with high solubility and an OH on the right side of the formula to be a base. Some common bases are listed in Table A2.19.

TABLE A2.19 Formulas, Names, and Uses of Some Common Bases

Base	Name	Common Name	Application
$NaOH_{(s)}$	sodium hydroxide	caustic soda	drain cleaner
$KOH_{(s)}$	potassium hydroxide	caustic potash	leather tanning
$NH_4OH_{(aq)}$	ammonium hydroxide	ammonia solution	window cleaner
$Ca(OH)_{2(s)}$	calcium hydroxide	slaked lime	glass, cement, and steel manufacturing
$Mg(OH)_{2(s)}$	magnesium hydroxide	milk of magnesia	laxative, antacid
$Al(OH)_{3(s)}$	aluminium hydroxide	—	antacid, wastewater treatment

Acids and Bases in the Home

We all use acids and bases in the home, often when we are not even aware of it. Lemon juice, vinegar, and some toilet bowl cleaners are acids. Most soaps and cleaners are bases, such as oven cleaner, hand soaps, and many window cleaners. Bases are excellent at dissolving and dislodging oil and grease. Household bleach is also basic, as well as being an oxidizing agent. This means it has the ability to break down stains into colourless compounds. Drinks such as coffee, tea, and soda pop are acidic. Shampoos that are "pH balanced" are often slightly acidic, to make them more gentle on hair than standard soaps, which, being basic, tend to strip out oils. Advertisers came up with the term "pH balanced" so they would not have to try to explain how an acidic product could be good for your hair!

Many efforts have been made to minimize the use of toxic or highly corrosive chemicals in the household. At one time, arsenic and mercury products were commonplace in the kitchen. These have been replaced by much more benign and environmentally friendly chemicals. Even so, many chemicals will react strongly if mixed together. Acids and bases generally react when mixed, and many otherwise-safe household chemicals become dangerous when mixed improperly. Always read the labels of household cleaning products.

The pH of Common Household Materials

Purpose

To test the pH of a variety of household chemicals

CAUTION: Acids and bases can burn. If any spill, wash immediately with cold water.

Materials and Equipment

droppers

spot plate

small beaker

universal indicator, pH test paper, or pH meter

distilled water (if using pH meter)

known and unknown solutions used in the kitchen, bathroom, or laundry

2 Place a few drops of each solution into separate wells of a spot plate. Do not mix them.

3 Add either a few drops of universal indicator or a 1-cm strip of pH paper to each sample. If you are using a pH meter, rinse the probe with distilled water after each test.

4 Record the pH of each solution.

5 Follow your teacher's directions for disposing of the solutions you have used.

Procedure

1 Make a data table with space for recording the following for each test solution:
- its name
- your prediction about whether it is acidic, basic, or neutral
- its measured pH

Questions

1. Draw a vertical line about 15 cm long. Write the number 1 at the top, 7 in the middle, and 14 at the bottom.

2. For each test solution, find the place along the line that matches its pH number, and record its name beside its pH.

3. Decide whether each solution is acidic, basic, or neutral.

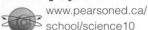

*re*SEARCH

Hydrochloric acid is also known as muriatic acid and is available in hardware stores. Research three ways that it can be used around the home. Begin your search at

www.pearsoned.ca/
school/science10

Neutralization

When acids and bases react together, both acidic and basic properties disappear. This is the process of **neutralization**. Neutralization is the reaction between an acid and a base that produces water and a compound called a salt. It is a very important and common process. For example, the pain of a bee sting is caused by methanoic acid attacking nerves in the skin. The bee secretes the acid, which dissolves the nerve endings in the skin. This causes the nerves to fire continuously, sending pain signals to the brain. Cream containing ammonia can be used to limit the pain. Ammonia is a base so it neutralizes the acid and prevents further damage to the nerve endings. In industry, countless manufacturing processes produce acidic or basic waste that must be neutralized.

Knowledge

1. Use the chemical or physical properties identified below to classify each solution as acidic, basic, or neutral. For example, solution (a) is basic.
   a) feels slippery and conducts electricity
   b) reacts with magnesium to produce bubbles and conducts electricity
   c) red litmus stays red and blue litmus turns red
   d) blue litmus stays blue and red litmus stays red
   e) tastes sour and feels wet but not slippery
   f) does not conduct electricity, and red litmus stays red
   g) has a pH of 3 and turns litmus red
   h) has a pH of 10 and blue litmus stays blue
   i) conducts electricity and has a pH of 7
   j) tastes bitter and does not react with magnesium

2. What is an acid–base indicator?

3. From the following formulas, decide whether the solution is an acid, a base, or neither.
   a) $KOH_{(aq)}$
   b) $H_2SO_{4(aq)}$
   c) $NaCl_{(aq)}$
   d) $CH_3COOH_{(aq)}$
   e) $HCl_{(aq)}$
   f) $Mg(OH)_{2(aq)}$
   g) $C_6H_5COOH_{(aq)}$

4. State the name or the formula for each of the following substances:
   a) aqueous hydrogen nitrate
   b) cesium hydroxide
   c) ethanoic acid
   d) calcium hydroxide
   e) aqueous hydrogen chloride
   f) phosphoric acid
   g) $KOH_{(aq)}$
   h) $HBr_{(aq)}$
   i) $H_2SO_{4(aq)}$
   j) $Mg(OH)_{2(aq)}$

Applications

5. Draw a horizontal line to represent a pH scale. At the left end of the line write 1, in the middle write 7, and at the right end write 14. Use this scale to complete the following tasks.
   a) Place the following three labels at the correct place on the scale: neutral, strongly acidic, strongly basic.
   b) On the acidic end of the scale, write the following four labels in the correct relative order: acid rain, normal rain, lemon juice, stomach juices.
   c) On the basic end of the scale, write the following four labels in the correct relative order: a concentrated solution of baking soda, human blood, oven cleaner ($NaOH_{(aq)}$), window cleaner (ammonia).

6. Why is a universal indicator more useful than litmus paper for measuring pH in some applications?

7. Some hydrochloric acid is placed in a beaker, and a pH meter is set into the solution. It reads pH 1.5.
   a) Describe how the pH will change when NaOH solution is added drop-by-drop to the acid.
   b) Will the conductivity of the solution change during the addition of the $NaOH_{(aq)}$? Why or why not?

Extensions

8. A solution is adjusted from pH 8 to pH 4.
   a) How many times more acidic has the solution become?
   b) How many times less basic has the solution become?

9. Find out the structure of the organic acid group $-COOH$. Build a model of ethanoic acid, CH_3COOH.

*info*BIT

Most jurisdictions regulate the disposal of computer parts and other electronic components as hazardous waste. Many landfills ban old computer parts because internal circuit boards and CPUs contain heavy metals.

A 2.5 Our Chemical Society

All substances, natural and manufactured, are chemicals. Water, gases in the air, the components of our bodies—all are chemicals. Our society relies heavily on manufactured chemicals including paints, plastics, fertilizers, and pesticides. Many of these chemicals are potentially hazardous, but we continue to produce and use them because they have many benefits. Guidelines and regulations, such as environmental laws and WHMIS, reduce the potential for harm to human health and the environment.

Look at the materials in the room where you are sitting. Try to find something in the room that was *not* made using potentially toxic or hazardous chemicals. Paint was toxic when it was wet. Even unpainted wood would have been oiled or stained. Do you see any plastic? There may be more than you realize. Plastic fibres are present in many clothing materials, in your pen, and in carpeting and other flooring materials. Many plastics are produced from compounds that are toxic. However, the final plastic products are generally very stable, unreactive, and non-toxic.

Issues Related to Chemicals

Issues involving the use of hazardous material go beyond whether the material itself is safe. For example, they include concerns about the health of the workers exposed to toxic substances during manufacturing. They also include concerns about poisonous substances escaping into the environment during manufacturing. Many manufacturing processes produce byproducts that must be disposed of. These problems can lead to the final product being safe, while making it is not.

Some products are safe until they are thrown away. For example, some batteries contain mercury. Mercury is a poison, but it is not a problem as long as the battery remains sealed. A battery may be used for mere hours or days, but it may spend a decade in a ditch slowly leaching mercury into groundwater. Proper disposal is essential to protect people and the environment from hazardous chemicals.

Environmental Effects

Some chemicals are safe for people to handle but may cause long-term environmental damage. Chlorofluorocarbons (CFCs) are non-toxic, non-flammable chemicals used mainly in cooling systems. They contain chlorine, which acts as a catalyst in the upper atmosphere and causes the destruction of Earth's ozone layer. It is estimated that CFCs released 50 years ago are still in the upper atmosphere. CFCs are no longer manufactured in Canada or used in new air conditioners and refrigerators. When older appliances are serviced or no longer useful, the CFCs in them must be recycled or destroyed. In Unit D: Energy Flow in Global Systems, you will learn about the Montreal Protocol, an international agreement to phase out the production and use of CFCs.

These changes in the way we use CFCs have paid off. In the 10 years between 1990 and 2000, CFC emissions dropped to one-seventh of their 1990 value. But the effects of these emissions are long lasting. It is predicted that the ozone hole will not be eliminated until about the time your grandchildren are in high school.

Health Concerns

Many people use chemical substances for recreational purposes, and some of these substances can be toxic. The two most commonly used hazardous recreational chemicals are alcohol and nicotine.

Alcohol

Alcohol is an example of a chemical that is toxic when used in large amounts. The alcohol used in beverages is ethanol. Its formula is $CH_3CH_2OH_{(l)}$. Alcohol is considered to be a drug because of its effects on the body. The excessive use of alcohol can lead to destruction of the liver, the kidneys, and brain cells (Figure A2.35). It can cause physical dependence, also called **addiction**. Physical dependence occurs when the body becomes used to a drug and needs it to function. Alcoholism is an addiction to alcohol.

Alcohol abuse can also lead to psychological dependence. In psychological dependence, the use of the drug is linked to certain moods or feelings. When the drug wears off, the feeling disappears. The person drinks more alcohol to try to recapture the mood or feelings. Both physical and psychological dependence prevent people from controlling their drug use, and can seriously damage their health.

*info*BIT

A mother who consumes alcohol during pregnancy can cause permanent damage to her baby. Babies born with fetal alcohol spectrum disorder (FASD) suffer from brain damage, slow growth, heart defects, and mental disabilities. No safe level for alcohol consumption during pregnancy has been determined. Doctors advise pregnant women not to drink alcohol at all.

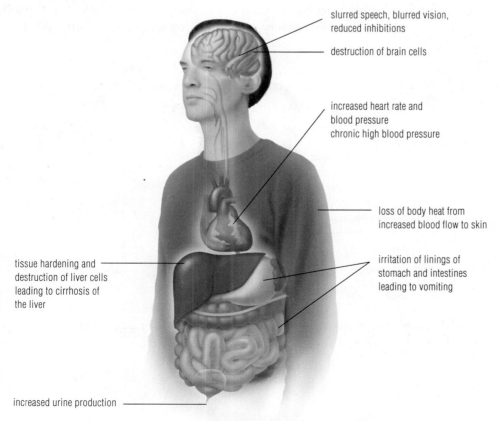

slurred speech, blurred vision, reduced inhibitions

destruction of brain cells

increased heart rate and blood pressure
chronic high blood pressure

loss of body heat from increased blood flow to skin

tissue hardening and destruction of liver cells leading to cirrhosis of the liver

irritation of linings of stomach and intestines leading to vomiting

increased urine production

FIGURE A2.35 Alcohol abuse damages health in many ways.

Alcohol misuse costs lives in other ways by leading to high-risk types of behaviour, three of which are significant killers. The first is driving while drunk. The second dangerous behaviour is binge drinking, where a large amount of alcohol is consumed quickly. The blood alcohol level becomes so high that it affects parts of the brain and nervous system that control breathing and heartbeat. The drinker then dies because breathing stops or the heart stops beating, usually while the drinker is unconscious. A common way to die from alcohol poisoning is to vomit while unconscious, and then inhale the vomit and suffocate. The third dangerous behaviour is the use of alcohol in combination with some other drug—prescription, over the counter, or illegal. This is dangerous because the mixture of drugs affects the body in ways that can cause death at relatively low levels of blood alcohol.

Nicotine and Other Tobacco-Related Chemicals

Nicotine, like alcohol, is a highly addictive drug. It is present in all tobacco products, including cigarettes, cigars, and chewing tobacco. People addicted to nicotine experience both psychological and physical dependence. Most people are unaware of their addiction until they try to stop smoking and cannot.

Cigarettes are the most common source of nicotine. But nicotine is only one of the chemicals that make cigarettes dangerous. Cigarette smoke is many times more harmful than the most polluted air. It contains large amounts of carbon monoxide, a poison that is also released from car exhaust. Thirty percent of cigarette smoke is composed of a mixture called tar, which is made up of over 3000 chemicals including formaldehyde and benzene, a hazardous substance. Cigarette smoking damages both the respiratory system and the circulatory system (Figure A2.37). A heavy smoker has a 20 times greater chance of developing lung cancer than a non-smoker does. About one-third of all cancer deaths in our society are caused by smoking (Figures A2.36 and A2.37).

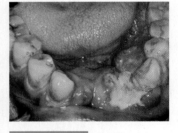

FIGURE A2.36 Smoking can cause mouth cancer.

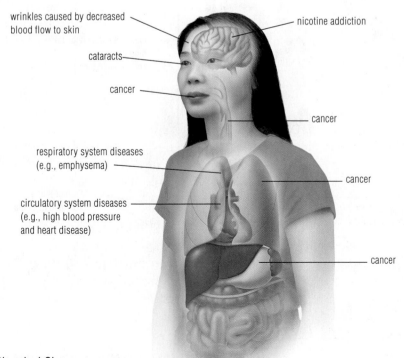

wrinkles caused by decreased blood flow to skin

nicotine addiction

cataracts

cancer

cancer

respiratory system diseases (e.g., emphysema)

cancer

circulatory system diseases (e.g., high blood pressure and heart disease)

cancer

FIGURE A2.37 Cigarette smoking damages health in many ways.

Many cities in Canada have regulations controlling smoking in workplaces, including restaurants and pubs. Some require an outright ban. Others include partial bans; and others require special ventilation systems for smoking areas.

1. In groups of about four, brainstorm the opinions of different interest groups including smoking employees, non-smoking employees, smoking customers, non-smoking customers, owners, and Workers' Compensation Board representatives. (The Workers' Compensation Board is responsible for protecting workers' health and safety.)

2. Each person in your group then picks one of the interest groups and attempts to argue its point of view. You do not need to feel restricted to "expected" opinions. For example, smokers may argue for a smoking ban. Presenting good reasons for the opinion is the main objective.

3. Your teacher may bring all the groups together for a class discussion.

Cigarette smoke is dangerous to non-smokers as well as smokers. Passive smokers are those who are exposed to smoke from other people's tobacco products. Studies show that passive smokers have an increased risk of cancer. They also may experience itchy, watery eyes, and throat irritation. Many workplaces, including restaurants, are smoke-free so that workers are not exposed to secondhand smoke from other workers or customers.

Benzene—A Regulated Substance

You have probably seen presentations made with an overhead projector. You may have used one yourself, or your teacher may have used one in science class. The sheets of clear plastic used for overheads are called acetate sheets because they are made with a type of plastic called acetate.

The process for making acetate plastics uses several compounds, one of which is benzene. Benzene is a hazardous chemical that is both toxic and flammable, but it can be used safely if proper procedures are carefully followed. Why use benzene if it can be harmful? Benzene continues to be used because it is important in many applications. It is one of the top 20 chemicals by volume produced in North America. It is used to make dyes, detergents, and medicines, such as aspirin. These substances do not have benzene's toxic properties. Environmental and health concerns are met by keeping benzene contained.

In previous science courses, you may have learned how to transport, handle, and store domestic materials, such as pesticides and motor oils, safely. At the industrial level, the safeguards are even greater because of the potential for large-scale damage. The huge volumes of potentially hazardous substances used mean that a spill or leakage from a single accidental release could have a major impact on people and the environment.

Safe Transportation and Handling of Benzene

Benzene is a regulated substance. This means it must be used only according to strict guidelines that are reviewed and revised from time to time. For example, it used to be common to ship benzene by rail car in volumes of 80 m^3. The potential release from a single rail car was considered too dangerous, so current regulations limit the volume to 20 m^3.

The guidelines to protect workers who produce, transport, and dispose of benzene are very specific. For example, workers should not be exposed to an average benzene concentration of more than 1 part per million (ppm). At higher concentrations, workers must wear masks with activated charcoal filters. These measures may seem complicated, but they are designed to protect workers and still allow chemical processing to continue.

Good science and technology make it possible to use a potentially hazardous substance like benzene safely and effectively to produce materials that we need and want. We can manage hazardous substances through a combination of:

- understanding the properties of materials;
- using careful and clever design and process engineering;
- placing personal safety and environmental protection as the top priority; and
- enforcing effective regulations.

Chemistry-Related Careers

Our society is so dependent on chemicals that it's not surprising that many different careers involve chemistry. The most obvious ones are chemical engineers and chemistry teachers. But many others require some knowledge of the use and handling of chemicals. Two examples are food technologist and cosmetics formulator.

FIGURE A2.38 Analysis and development of different food products require a detailed knowledge of food chemistry.

Food Technologist

Could you tell the difference between red ketchup and green ketchup in a blind taste test (Figure A2.38)? Does ketchup have nutritional value or is it simply for making food more appetizing to some people? Food technologists use sight, smell, touch, and taste to evaluate existing food products and develop new ones. They study how ingredients, which provide nutrition, interact with additives, which improve colour, texture, taste, and shelf life.

In Alberta, the food production, processing, and distribution sector accounts for over one quarter of all jobs. It is second only to the petrochemicals industry in economic importance. Food science is involved in every part of it.

Cosmetics Formulator

A cosmetics formulator takes raw materials approved for use in the cosmetics industry and combines them to make new products or improve existing ones. Nail polish, lipstick, hair conditioner, and skin cleansers are all mixtures put together under the direction of a cosmetics formulator.

The formulator must have an excellent understanding of the basic properties of the materials and their effects on different parts of the body. For example, a substance that can be safely applied to a fingernail is not necessarily safe to apply to the lips. No less important is an understanding of how different materials interact when mixed. Do they react to produce a toxic substance? Will they stay mixed in a container, even when exposed to higher temperatures and humidity?

Designing a new product is only the first step. The formulator must make sure the product can be made on an industrial scale. The raw materials must be made correctly and consistently so that the final product will always have the right properties. The formulator performs quality control tests on every batch to ensure that pH, viscosity, colour, fragrance, and other properties meet required standards.

*re*SEARCH

Acetone is a chemical used to make plastics, drugs, and other chemicals. You may have used it as a solvent for removing nail polish. Find out how acetone enters the environment and list some of the health effects from moderate and high exposure. How can we protect ourselves and the environment and still use this product? Begin your search at

 www.pearsoned.ca/ school/science10

Working with Chemistry

You may not know a food technologist or cosmetics formulator, but there are many other careers in your community that involve chemistry in some way. Every day, you encounter people who must know how to use certain chemicals safely in specific applications: nurses, painters, pharmacists, dentists, and hair stylists. Chemistry is an essential part of their careers—and your everyday life.

A2.5 Check and Reflect

Knowledge

1. Describe the hazardous effects of CFCs, including the length of time they can remain in the atmosphere.

2. Why is alcohol considered to be a drug?

3. List some direct chemical effects of excessive use of alcohol.

4. Describe the main effect of nicotine on the body.

5. List four poisonous components of tobacco smoke.

Applications

6. Some consumer products are not toxic or hazardous themselves, yet they are connected with issues around the use of hazardous materials. Why?

7. Give two examples of how a food technologist would apply an understanding of chemistry to a new food product.

8. What skills would a cosmetics formulator need?

9. Choose one career in your community and describe how it involves chemistry in some way.

Extension

10. Distinguish between physical dependence and psychological dependence on a drug.

Knowledge

1. What is an element? About how many elements occur naturally?

2. Explain the terms "period" and "family" as they apply to the periodic table.

3. List the properties (mass, charge, location in an atom) of each of the following: proton, neutron, electron.

4. What is an energy level?

5. What is the maximum number of electrons that can exist in the first three energy levels of an atom?

6. What is meant by atomic number?

7. Use an example to explain what isotopes are.

8. What is mass number?

9. What are valence electrons?

10. What are ions?

11. List some properties that ionic compounds have in common.

12. Explain what an electrolyte is and how an electric current runs through it.

13. What is a precipitate, and what is meant by the term "precipitation"?

14. Use the solubility chart in Table A2.14 on page 57 to help you decide whether the following ionic compounds are slightly soluble or very soluble:
    a) NaCl
    b) CuI
    c) BaS
    d) $KMnO_4$
    e) ammonium sulfide
    f) calcium nitrate
    g) silver acetate
    h) lead(II) sulfate

15. List some properties that are characteristic of acids.

16. List some properties that are characteristic of bases.

17. What is the pH scale? What pH values correspond to acidic, neutral, and basic solutions?

18. What is meant by neutralization?

Applications

19. How many electrons do each of the following noble gases have: helium, neon, argon? Are the valence energy levels of these elements completely filled or partially filled? What does this say about their chemical stability?

20. Distinguish between mass number and atomic molar mass. Which one of these is found in the periodic table?

21. Draw an atom that has 10 protons, 11 neutrons, and 10 electrons. Using the periodic table in Figure A2.3 on page 30, identify the element. Label the nucleus, the subatomic particles, and the valence energy level.

22. Two isotopes of aluminium are aluminium-26 and aluminium-27. Explain how these atoms are similar and how they are different by describing their atomic structure.

23. Using the octet rule, decide if each of the following elements will gain or lose electrons to become ions. State how many electrons will be involved in each case:
    a) sodium
    b) fluorine
    c) calcium
    d) nitrogen
    e) oxygen

24. Name the following ionic compounds:
    a) $CsCl_{(s)}$ g) $Al_2O_{3(s)}$
    b) $K_3N_{(s)}$ h) $AgF_{(s)}$
    c) $Na_2O_{(s)}$ i) $FeBr_{2(s)}$
    d) $AlN_{(s)}$ j) $PbCl_{4(s)}$
    e) $MgS_{(s)}$ k) $Ni_2O_{3(s)}$
    f) $Li_3P_{(s)}$ l) $AuN_{(s)}$

25. Name the following ionic compounds:
    a) $(NH_4)_2S_{(s)}$ g) $Pb(HPO_4)_{2(s)}$
    b) $(NH_4)_2SO_{4(s)}$ h) $KMnO_{4(s)}$
    c) $Ca(NO_3)_{2(s)}$ i) $Na_2Cr_2O_{7(s)}$
    d) $Al(HCO_3)_{3(s)}$ j) $Al(CH_3COO)_{3(s)}$
    e) $Na_2SiO_{3(s)}$ k) $Co(C_6H_5COO)_{2(s)}$
    f) $Cr(ClO_2)_{2(s)}$ l) $NH_4SCN_{(s)}$

26. Write the formulas of the following ionic compounds:
    a) sodium bromide
    b) calcium nitride
    c) magnesium oxide
    d) aluminium chloride
    e) rubidium iodide
    f) lithium phosphide
    g) iron(II) sulfide
    h) chromium(II) nitride
    i) copper(I) oxide
    j) titanium(IV) bromide
    k) lead(II) fluoride
    l) cobalt(III) nitride

27. Write the formulas of the following ionic compounds:
    a) lithium carbonate
    b) beryllium nitrate
    c) sodium phosphate
    d) ammonium cyanide
    e) sodium hydrogencarbonate
    f) aluminium borate
    g) manganese(II) perchlorate
    h) iron(III) hydroxide
    i) copper(II) benzoate
    j) gold(III) thiocyanate
    k) lead(IV) chromate
    l) chromium(III) phosphite

28. Write the name or formula of the following molecular compounds:
    a) $N_2O_{(s)}$
    b) $SO_{3(g)}$
    c) $PCl_{5(g)}$
    d) carbon tetrabromide
    e) sulfur hexachloride
    f) oxygen difluoride
    g) $NI_{3(s)}$
    h) $H_2O_{(l)}$
    i) $NH_{3(g)}$
    j) methane
    k) tetraphosphorus decaoxide
    l) xenon difluoride

29. Water is a polar molecule. Explain what this means.

30. Explain why ionic solids tend to have high melting points, while molecular solids tend to have low melting points.

31. Name each of the following and indicate whether it is an acid or a base:
    a) $HF_{(aq)}$ e) $NH_4OH_{(aq)}$
    b) $HNO_{3(aq)}$ f) $CH_3COOH_{(aq)}$
    c) $NaOH_{(aq)}$ g) $H_3PO_{4(aq)}$
    d) $HCOOH_{(aq)}$ h) $Ca(OH)_{2(aq)}$

32. List health hazards resulting from a sudden intake of an excessive amount of alcohol (alcohol poisoning).

33. List health hazards resulting from the long-term use of tobacco products.

34. Choose one of the following careers and explain why it can be considered a chemistry-related career: doctor, school janitor, car mechanic, cancer researcher.

Extensions

35. Draw a sketch showing the arrangement of protons, neutrons, and electrons for the following:
    a) calcium-41 atom
    b) calcium-41 ion

36. Write the name or the formula for the following compounds. Both ionic and molecular compounds are listed.
    a) calcium nitrate
    b) aluminium hydroxide
    c) methanol
    d) phosphorus tribromide
    e) $(NH_4)_2CO_{3(s)}$
    f) $SCl_{2(g)}$
    g) $SnCl_{2(s)}$
    h) $SrCl_{2(s)}$
    i) sodium ethanoate
    j) lead(IV) acetate
    k) hydrogen peroxide
    l) glucose

Chemical change is a process that involves recombining atoms and energy flows.

Key Concepts

In this section, you will learn about the following key concepts:

- how chemical substances meet human needs
- evidence of chemical change
- role and need for classification of chemical change
- writing and balancing equations
- law of conservation of mass
- the mole concept

Learning Outcomes

When you have completed this section, you will be able to:

- provide examples of household, commercial, and industrial processes that use chemical reactions to produce useful substances and energy
- identify chemical reactions that are significant in societies
- describe the evidence for chemical changes (i.e., energy change, formation of a gas or precipitate, colour or odour change, or change in temperature)
- differentiate between endothermic and exothermic chemical reactions
- classify and identify categories of chemical reactions (i.e., formation (synthesis), decomposition, hydrocarbon combustion, single replacement, double replacement)
- translate word equations to balanced chemical equations and vice versa for chemical reactions that occur in living and non-living systems
- predict the products of formation (synthesis) and decomposition, single and double replacement, and hydrocarbon combustion chemical reactions, when given the reactants
- define the mole as the amount of an element containing 6.02×10^{23} atoms (Avogadro's number) and apply the concept to calculate quantities of substances made of other chemical species
- interpret balanced chemical equations in terms of moles of chemical species, and relate the mole concept to the law of conservation of mass

FIGURE A3.1   The space shuttle is driven by two chemical reactions. The main engines use liquid hydrogen and oxygen, and the booster rockets use solid fuel.

The launch of a space shuttle is always dramatic (Figure A3.1). Flames and smoke pour out. The sound of the engines can be heard—and felt—at the viewing stand 5 km away. At the top of the ship, seven astronauts sit in the crew cabin, dependent on the energy unleashed by the violent chemical reactions occurring just below them.

Within the shuttle, liquid oxygen and hydrogen react to produce water. This reaction drives the shuttle's main engines.

The booster rockets are fuelled by a different reaction in what can be described as a "controlled explosion."

The solid fuel used in the space shuttle booster rockets is a mixture of aluminium metal and ammonium perchlorate. These two substances react chemically when the rocket is ignited. The reaction quickly releases a tremendous amount of heat. It also converts the solid fuel into several products, some of which are gases. This chemical reaction is complicated, but like all reactions, it is a process in which substances change to form different substances with different properties. In this reaction, energy is released. In others, energy is consumed.

In this section, you will learn more about chemical reactions, and use the law of conservation of mass to help you write chemical equations. These equations are concise, meaningful statements that describe chemical change. You will also learn how to predict the outcomes of thousands of chemical reactions simply by looking at the names of the starting materials and following some simple patterns. Finally, you will be introduced to Avogadro's number (6.02×10^{23}) and a quantity called the mole, used universally by chemists to measure amounts of chemicals.

A 3.1 Important Examples of Chemical Change

Chemical change occurs when a substance or substances react in a chemical reaction to create a different substance or substances. The substances that react are called **reactants**, and their reaction produces new substances called **products**. The products have completely different properties from the reactants. Chemical changes are always accompanied by energy flows. These flows of energy into or out of systems drive chemical reactions.

> ***info*BIT**
>
> Slicing an onion causes your eyes to sting because of a chemical reaction. Slicing ruptures the onion's cells, allowing substances to mix. A gas is produced and reacts with the water in your eyes—producing dilute sulfuric acid!

Minds On... Energy Flow through Systems

FIGURE A3.2

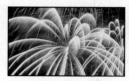

(a) Fireworks (b) Water on a stove (c) Baking (d) A glow stick

Look at each of the photographs in Figure A3.2. With your partner, consider the questions on the right. Then write a statement about each process, outlining whether it represents a chemical or physical change, and whether energy is absorbed or released.

1. Which of these processes involve a release of energy?
2. Which involve the absorption of energy?
3. Which are chemical changes?
4. Which are physical changes?

Chemical reactions are used in a wide variety of applications. A fast chemical change, such as the sudden release of gases from solids, may be needed to make an explosion. But not all chemical reactions are fast. Chemical reactions can be used both to release energy slowly and to store it, as in a rechargeable dry cell battery. One chemical reaction in the battery releases energy to power a flashlight. The reverse chemical reaction recharges the battery when it has run down. Chemical reactions are also used to make starting material for industrial processes and in manufacturing final products. For example, large amounts of the compound ethylene are produced in Alberta. It is a starting material for many products, including polyethylene, used in sandwich wrap.

Chemical reactions also occur naturally in countless biochemical processes. These include photosynthesis in plants, which produces sugars, and cellular respiration in all living things, which breaks the sugars down again. We will look at examples of different kinds of reactions to illustrate some of the ways our society uses chemistry.

Reactions That Form Gases

Reactions that form gases can be sudden and dramatic in an explosion, or slow and steady in a rising cake. An explosion occurs when a small amount of solid or liquid converts quickly to a large volume of gas. Although military uses of explosives may be the first to come to mind, most explosions are commercial.

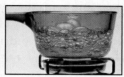

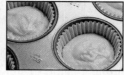

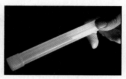

FIGURE A3.3 A very fast chemical reaction produces the gas that inflates the bag.

An automobile air bag is a good example of a commercial use of an explosion in a safety device (Figure A3.3). A solid compound called sodium azide ($NaN_{3(s)}$) is heated and ignited by an electrical signal when a front-end collision occurs. The air bag inflates in about 25 milliseconds, just in time to cushion the body of a person 30 to 50 milliseconds after the collision. In this case, nitrogen gas is produced when a solid suddenly decomposes.

Reactions That Form Solids

A common household application that forms a solid is a popular glue known as five-minute epoxy. The product package contains two chemicals: a resin and a hardener. When you are ready to use the glue, you mix the two chemicals together. You can work with the product for about five minutes before it begins to harden. It fully hardens in one hour. Each of the molecules in the resin has several places where it can join with the molecules in the hardener. A web of links forms, causing the whole mixture to form one large molecule. The result is a solid that will hold its shape and not melt. The bonds are strong and will bind many materials that are otherwise difficult to glue together, such as plastic to steel.

Showing States in Chemical Formulas

You have probably noticed that the states of each substance in a chemical reaction are often provided. These are included to give as much information as possible about a reaction. You can assume that the state subscript refers to the substance's state at room temperature (25°C), unless other information is provided. For example, at 25°C, carbon dioxide is a gas and is written as $CO_{2(g)}$, but "dry ice"—frozen carbon dioxide—is solid carbon dioxide, and should be written as $CO_{2(s)}$. Table salt is a solid ($NaCl_{(s)}$), but when dissolved in water, it is aqueous ($NaCl_{(aq)}$). Here are some guidelines for the states of substances at room temperature.

Elements

- Metals are solid, except mercury, which is a liquid.
- Most of the diatomic elements are gases: $H_{2(g)}$, $N_{2(g)}$, $O_{2(g)}$, $F_{2(g)}$, and $Cl_{2(g)}$. Bromine is a liquid, and iodine is a solid: $Br_{2(l)}$ and $I_{2(s)}$.
- Sulfur, phosphorus, and carbon are solids.

Compounds

- All ionic compounds are solid at room temperature.
- An ionic compound that is very soluble is shown as aqueous when it is dissolved in water. An ionic compound that is slightly soluble is usually shown as a solid, even when it's in water.
- Molecular compounds are very difficult to predict. The smaller the molecules are, the more they tend to be gases. The larger they are, the more they tend to be liquids and then solids. For example, $CH_{4(g)}$ is a gas (natural gas), $C_6H_{14(l)}$ is a liquid (component of gasoline), and $C_{18}H_{38(s)}$ is a solid (bees wax).

info**BIT**

The following symbols are used to indicate states in chemical formulas:

(s) solid
(l) liquid
(g) gas
(aq) aqueous (dissolved in water)

Energy Changes

Energy flow is an essential part of any chemical reaction. In some reactions, energy is released. Earlier in this section, you saw examples of how the rapid release of energy can produce explosions. In other chemical reactions, energy is absorbed.

Exothermic Reactions

Exothermic reactions release energy, usually in the form of heat, light, or electricity. The lead-acid storage battery in Figure A3.4 is an important commercial product. It discharges during ignition and charges while the vehicle is running. While it is discharging, an exothermic reaction occurs. This type of battery has been used in almost every car and truck for over 100 years. It can withstand considerable shaking and is one of the few batteries that can be recharged repeatedly—several thousand times! The battery contains sulfuric acid, which works as an electrolyte to carry an electric current between the solid chemicals inside the battery. The solids are lead and lead(IV) oxide. They react in reversible chemical reactions inside the battery. When the vehicle is started, the battery releases energy in the form of electricity. As the vehicle is running, the battery recharges.

Each discharge and recharge of the battery wears it out as the chemicals gradually break down. Eventually, the battery must be discarded, but the lead, plastic parts, and even the sulfuric acid are recycled. Over 90% of all lead batteries are recycled, making it one of the most recycled products.

Another important exothermic reaction is the combustion of fossil fuels: coal, oil, and natural gas. **Combustion** is a chemical reaction that occurs when oxygen reacts rapidly with a substance to form a new substance and gives off energy. This is called "burning." For example, coal is used to produce electricity. The heat released by coal combustion is used to make steam, which drives turbines that produce electricity. This process also produces carbon dioxide, which is a greenhouse gas that contributes to climate change.

$$C_{(s)} + O_{2(g)} \longrightarrow CO_{2(g)} + energy$$

coal + oxygen $\longrightarrow$ carbon dioxide + energy

Automobiles use gasoline instead of coal for combustion. Gasoline is a mixture of compounds, including hexane ($C_6H_{14(l)}$). The combustion of hexane is shown in the equation below.

$$2\ C_6H_{14(l)} + 19\ O_{2(g)} \longrightarrow 12\ CO_{2(g)} + 14\ H_2O_{(g)} + energy$$

hexane + oxygen $\longrightarrow$ carbon dioxide + water + energy

Endothermic Reactions

Endothermic reactions absorb energy. For example, a cold pack, like the one in Figure A3.5, contains chemicals that absorb energy directly from the environment. When you squeeze the package, you break a container inside the pack that keeps the chemicals separate from each other. When the container breaks, the chemicals mix and react. As they react, they absorb energy, and the whole mixture cools down.

sulfuric acid electrolyte

FIGURE A3.4 Almost every car and truck produced in the last century has used the chemical reaction in a lead-acid battery like this one.

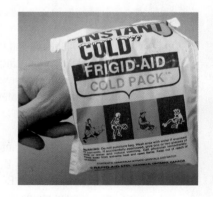

FIGURE A3.5 An athelete cools an injury using a cold pack. The chemicals in the cold pack are reacting in an endothermic reaction.

Biochemical Reactions

The reactions we have looked at so far are important for our society. For example, combustion of fossil fuels produces energy for transportation. The next group of reactions we will look at are biochemical reactions. They are essential to life itself.

Biochemical reactions may be endothermic or exothermic. They happen at an organism's internal temperature, and they are almost always helped by enzymes (biological catalysts). Catalysts are chemicals that speed up a reaction but are not used up by it. One of the most important chemical reactions on Earth is photosynthesis. Life on Earth depends on photosynthesis. In earlier grades, you learned that photosynthesis is a complex process that captures the Sun's light and allows a plant to use this energy to make sugar molecules. It is an endothermic reaction, as shown below. In an endothermic reaction, energy appears on the left side of the equation.

$$\text{energy} + 6\ CO_{2(g)} + 6\ H_2O_{(l)} \longrightarrow C_6H_{12}O_{6(aq)} + 6\ O_{2(g)}$$

energy + carbon dioxide + water $\longrightarrow$ glucose + oxygen

FIGURE A3.6 The chemical reaction of photosynthesis is essential to life on Earth. It takes place in chloroplasts in the cells of green leaves and stems.

Almost all food on Earth begins with this reaction in the leaves of plants (Figure A3.6). The oxygen is a byproduct of the reaction. Most of the oxygen in our atmosphere comes from photosynthesis.

Cellular respiration is the reverse of photosynthesis. Both plants and animals use cellular respiration to release energy that is then used to drive all the chemical reactions in their tissues and organs. The equation for this exothermic reaction is shown below. This is an exothermic reaction so energy appears on the right side of the equation.

$$C_6H_{12}O_{6(aq)} + 6\ O_{2(g)} \longrightarrow \text{energy} + 6\ CO_{2(g)} + 6\ H_2O_{(l)}$$

glucose + oxygen $\longrightarrow$ energy + carbon dioxide + water

Skill Practice   Making Inferences

In Activity A9, you will be making inferences. An inference is a conclusion made by analyzing facts. When you draw conclusions about the observations you make in a scientific investigation, you are making inferences. An inference is a logical analysis of facts, so it can always be justified by those facts.

For example, an advertisement states that 20 out of 25 people prefer Brand A cola over Brand B. Can you infer that 80 percent of all people prefer Brand A cola? No, because you do not know how many people were interviewed or how these people were chosen. Were they chosen at random, or were they all regular buyers of Brand A cola? Without this information, there is not enough data to make an inference.

For each of the following situations, write an inference based on the given data. If there isn't enough data to justify an inference, write a sentence to explain why.

1. The juice stored in the back of the bottom shelf of the refrigerator is frozen. What can you infer about the temperature in the refrigerator?

2. Your cake comes out of the oven looking more like a pancake than a light, fluffy cake. What can you infer about the length of the baking time?

3. Eight in ten dentists recommend Brand X toothpaste for reducing cavities. What can you infer about this toothpaste?

Mass Change in Chemical Reactions

The Question

Does the mass of a system change during a chemical reaction?

The Hypothesis

Read over the procedure and write a hypothesis about what happens to the mass of a system during a chemical reaction.

Variables

Read over the procedure, and identify the manipulated, responding, and controlled variables.

Materials and Equipment

sodium carbonate (T) solution

calcium chloride (T) solution

dilute hydrochloric acid

sodium hydrogencarbonate powder

Erlenmeyer flask with tightly fitting stopper

small test tube

50-mL beaker

scupula

balance

25-mL graduated cylinder

Procedure

Part 1: Reaction in a Sealed Apparatus

1. Test that the equipment fits together by assembling it as follows. Place a small test tube inside the Erlenmeyer flask and seal the flask with the stopper. Verify that the stopper fits snugly and does not fall out when the apparatus is inverted. Take the test tube out again.

2. Use the graduated cylinder to pour 25 mL of the calcium chloride solution into the Erlenmeyer flask. Wipe the outside of the flask to make sure it is dry. Set it aside.

3. Fill the test tube about 80% full with the sodium carbonate solution. Wipe the outside of the test tube to make sure it is dry.

4. Carefully place the filled test tube into the Erlenmeyer flask. Carefully seal the flask with the stopper, ensuring that no mixing of the solutions occurs. Measure the mass of the sealed assembly and record it.

5. Tip the assembly so that the two liquids can mix. Make sure that the stopper does not come off or allow liquid to leak. Observe the reaction and record your observations.

6. Predict whether the mass of the assembly has decreased, stayed the same, or increased. Record your prediction.

7. Measure the mass of the assembly again and record it.

8. Follow your teacher's instructions for disposing of the solutions.

Part 2: Reaction in an Open Apparatus

9. Measure 5 g of sodium hydrogencarbonate powder into a dry 50-mL beaker.

10. Fill a small test tube about 80% full with dilute hydrochloric acid. Wipe the outside of the test tube to make sure it is dry. Place the test tube in the beaker. Carefully measure and record the mass of the whole assembly without spilling any liquid from the test tube.

11. Empty the contents of the test tube into the flask and record your observations.

12. Predict whether the mass of the assembly has decreased, stayed the same, or increased. Record your prediction.

13. Find the mass of the assembly again and record it.

14. Follow your teacher's instructions for disposing of the solutions.

Analyzing and Interpreting

1. What evidence is there that a chemical reaction took place in each case?

2. How did the mass before mixing compare with the mass after mixing in each case? How did the results compare with your predictions of how the mass would change?

3. Usually the two reactions give different results with regard to mass changes. Taking into account the observations that you made, explain why you would expect these results to be different.

Forming Conclusions

4. Use your observations and the data collected to answer the question posed at the beginning of the activity.

Characteristics of Chemical Reactions

At the beginning of this unit, you learned how to recognize chemical reactions. As you work through the unit, you are learning more about them. The following points summarize the characteristics of all chemical reactions.

- All reactions involve the production of new substances with their own characteristic properties. These properties include: state at room temperature, melting point, colour, and density.
- All reactions involve the flow of energy. This may be detected by a change in temperature during the reaction. Endothermic reactions absorb energy from the environment. Exothermic reactions release energy to the environment.
- When new substances form in chemical reactions, sometimes changes of state can be observed, for example, formation of a gas (bubbles) or a solid (precipitate).
- All chemical reactions are consistent with the law of conservation of mass.

Conservation of Mass

In 1789, the French chemist Antoine Lavoisier came to an important conclusion based on the results of many experiments he had done. He concluded that, regardless of the type of chemical reaction, the total mass of the reaction system never changes. The "reaction system" includes both the reactants and the products. Here is another way of saying this: When a system of chemicals reacts completely, the total mass of all of the reactants equals the total mass of the products. A shorter way of saying this is that conservation of mass occurs in all chemical reactions ("to conserve" means to stay constant).

Very quickly, people recognized that Lavoisier's conclusion has many applications. For example, suppose 23.0 g of magnesium metal is burned in pure oxygen, as shown in Figure A3.7. A white powder forms. It is magnesium oxide. When all of the white powder is carefully collected and placed on a scale, its mass is measured as 39.0 g. That is, we have 16.0 g more white powder after the reaction than we had magnesium metal to start: 39.0 g − 23.0 g = 16.0 g.

Does this mean that Lavoisier's conclusion is wrong? No, it isn't wrong. In fact, it's providing us with information. Using Lavoisier's conclusion, we can determine that 16.0 g of oxygen reacted with the 23.0 g of magnesium metal. What if we had not yet discovered oxygen? The difference in mass indicates that there must be a reactant we can't see—some new form of matter. The difference in mass between the magnesium and white powder product also gives us the mass of this unseen compound.

No exceptions to Lavoisier's proposal about the conservation of mass during a chemical reaction are known. Not all situations are testable, of course. A forest fire appears to cause a lot of mass to disappear, as the trees and other organic matter burn up. However, the combustion of wood has been carefully tested in the lab. These tests have shown that the mass of the reactants equals the mass of the products. The mass of the gases produced plus the mass of the ash equals the mass of the wood and the oxygen that were present before combustion began.

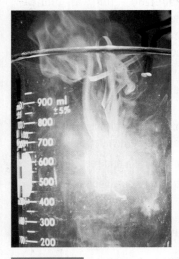

FIGURE A3.7 Magnesium burning in oxygen

In science, observations that have wide application and appear to have no exceptions are given a special status—they are called laws. Antoine Lavoisier's conclusion is called the **law of conservation of mass**. Lavoisier did not know of the existence of atoms because there was very little evidence for them at the time. Recall from section A1.0 that people were still developing different models of matter. However, we do know about atoms today. Using the law of conservation of mass, we can deduce that the total number of atoms present before a reaction is equal to the total number of atoms present after a reaction. This is important in writing chemical equations, as you will be doing later in this section.

*re*SEARCH

Investigate the proportion of greenhouse gases in Alberta that are produced from forest fires, compared with other sources. Begin your search at

www.pearsoned.ca/ school/science10

A3.1   Check and Reflect

Knowledge

1. List five industrial or commercial processes that use chemical reactions.

2. Explain the difference between the meanings of the state symbols *(l)* and *(aq)*.

3. How are the combustion of coal and the combustion of hexane (in gasoline) similar in terms of the products of these reactions?

4. State the law of conservation of mass.

5. What is the difference between an exothermic and an endothermic reaction?

6. Explain how photosynthesis and cellular respiration are related in terms of the chemicals involved and energy.

Applications

7. Many reactions done in laboratories at high temperatures occur in living organisms at much lower temperatures. What do living systems have that allow these reactions to occur at the lower temperatures?

8. List three features of a chemical reaction that would make it suitable for propelling a rocket.

9. What are the environmental impacts of the combustion of fossil fuels?

10. A 20.2-g sample of carbon dioxide contains 5.50 g of carbon. What mass of oxygen is present in the sample?

11. A 100.0-g sample of sugar contains carbon, hydrogen, and oxygen. The sample contains 40.0 g of carbon and 53.3 g of oxygen. What mass of hydrogen is in the sample?

Extensions

12. Iron and sulfur react when heated together. If 50.0 g of iron and 100.0 g of sulfur are mixed together and heated, a product with a mass of 107.4 g is produced. All of the iron reacted, and excess sulfur burned off during the process.
    a) What mass of sulfur combined chemically with the iron?
    b) What mass of sulfur was burned off?

13. In principle, all chemical reactions are reversible; that is, under the right circumstances, the products of a reaction can be used to make the reactants again. Photosynthesis and cellular respiration are related to each other this way. Use this idea to explain why, for every exothermic reaction in the universe, there is a corresponding endothermic one.

FIGURE A3.8 Evidence for the reaction between nitric acid and copper comes from the formation of bubbles, a yellow-brown gas, and a green or blue solution.

FIGURE A3.9 The reaction of magnesium with hydrochloric acid results in an increase in temperature.

A 3.2 Writing Chemical Equations

Recall that a chemical reaction is a process in which one or more substances are transformed into new substances, each with its own properties. The process also involves energy being released or absorbed. In other words, a chemical reaction is a process involving chemical change. Chemists record such a process in a **chemical equation** that uses chemical symbols and formulas. This equation is a shorthand way of showing what happens during a reaction. Other special symbols are also used. You have seen many chemical equations in this unit. Now you will learn how to write them yourself.

Symbolizing Chemical Change

To write a chemical equation, you need to know what substances react (the reactants) and what new substances form (the products). This requires the following:

- careful observations
- knowledge of what substances are present at the start of the reaction
- the ability to analyze the materials produced by the reaction

The first step in writing a chemical equation is to recognize that a chemical change has actually occurred. To do this, look for changes in properties and changes in energy.

Consider the reaction between copper and nitric acid in Figure A3.8. The photo shows two substances that were not present in the unmixed reactants: a brown gas and a green solution. The presence of bubbles indicates that a gas is being produced. Closer inspection would reveal that the pennies are corroding, and the mixture has become very hot.

Chemical change is often accompanied by visible events, such as the production of gas (bubbling), the release of heat (increased temperature), a change in colour, or the appearance of a substance that is only slightly soluble (cloudiness).

Writing Word Equations

Consider the chemical reaction of a piece of magnesium metal with hydrochloric acid (Figure A3.9). The corrosion of the magnesium and fizzing of the liquid are evidence that a reaction is taking place. The temperature is elevated above room temperature, showing that this is an exothermic reaction. We can describe the reaction with the following sentence:

Solid **magnesium** metal reacts with aqueous **hydrochloric acid** to produce aqueous **magnesium chloride** and **hydrogen** gas.

The starting materials (in blue) are the reactants. The substances made during the reaction (in red) are the products. The physical states (e.g., solid, gas) of each substance in the reaction are also mentioned. "Aqueous" means that the magnesium chloride is dissolved in water. The word equation for this reaction is:

magnesium + hydrochloric acid ⟶ magnesium chloride + hydrogen gas

A plus sign (+) groups the reactants together. It does not matter what order the reactants are written. Hydrochloric acid could have been written first. The arrow ($\longrightarrow$) separates the reactants from the products and is read "produces." The products are also joined by a "+" sign.

The use of word equations opens the door to easily describing countless examples of chemical change. Figure A3.10 shows another example of a chemical reaction. An iron nail is placed in a solution of copper(II) chloride. The equation for the reaction is:

iron + copper(II) chloride $\longrightarrow$ iron(II) chloride + copper

You may be wondering how it is possible to know what the products of a chemical reaction are. With experience, you will often be able to predict what will happen in a given reaction just by looking at the names of the reactants. This prediction is easier if you use formula equations. Formula equations also help you describe chemical changes more precisely.

Writing Balanced Formula Equations

The bus in Figure A3.11 runs on electricity produced by a fuel cell. The electricity comes from a reaction between hydrogen and oxygen to form water. The reaction can be described with the following word equation:

hydrogen + oxygen $\longrightarrow$ water

A **formula equation** uses the chemical formulas of reactants and products in a chemical equation to represent a chemical reaction. Recall that both oxygen and hydrogen gases exist as diatomic molecules. Their formulas are $O_{2(g)}$ and $H_{2(g)}$. The formula equation for this reaction is:

$$H_{2(g)} + O_{2(g)} \longrightarrow H_2O_{(l)}$$

This equation is called a **skeleton equation**. It shows the identities of the substances involved in the reaction, and which elements are present. A skeleton equation is of limited value, because it does not show the correct proportions of the reactants and the products.

How do we know what these correct proportions are? The law of conservation of mass gives us this information. Recall that the law states that the total mass of the reactants in a reaction equals the total mass of the products. The mass of all the components is represented by the number of atoms of each element in the reactants and products. To show the correct proportions, we need to write a balanced equation. The balanced equation for the formation of water is:

$$2\ H_{2(g)} + O_{2(g)} \longrightarrow 2\ H_2O_{(l)}$$

This equation is also shown in Figure A3.12

FIGURE A3.11 Hydrogen and oxygen gas combine chemically in a fuel cell. The reaction in the fuel cell produces electrical energy to operate the bus.

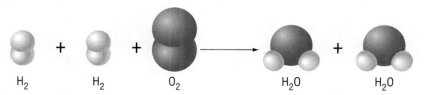

$H_2 \quad\quad H_2 \quad\quad O_2 \quad\quad\quad H_2O \quad\quad H_2O$

FIGURE A3.12 Molecules of hydrogen and oxygen react to form water.

Notice that integers have been placed in front of the formulas for the hydrogen and the water molecules. These are called coefficients. In this case, the coefficient 2 is used to ensure that the number of hydrogen and oxygen atoms in the reactants equals the number of hydrogen and oxygen atoms in the products. Oxygen does not need a coefficient in front of it because only one molecule ($O_{2(g)}$) is needed on the reactant side of the equation to balance the two oxygen atoms in the products.

An equation is properly balanced if the number of each type of atom on the reactants side of an equation is equal to the number of each type of atom on the products side. Consider another reaction involving oxygen, but this time, oxygen is reacting with methane gas (Figure A3.13). The word equation for this reaction is:

oxygen + methane $\longrightarrow$ carbon dioxide + water

To write the skeleton equation, you need to know that oxygen is diatomic ($O_{2(g)}$) and that the formula for methane is $CH_{4(g)}$. You can find formulas for some compounds in Table B of Student Reference 12. The skeleton equation for this reaction is:

$$O_{2(g)} + CH_{4(g)} \longrightarrow CO_{2(g)} + H_2O_{(g)}$$

The balanced equation is:

$$2\ O_{2(g)} + CH_{4(g)} \longrightarrow CO_{2(g)} + 2\ H_2O_{(g)}$$

Note that you balance an equation by making sure that the number of atoms of each element left of the arrow is equal to the number of atoms of each element right of the arrow. Note also that you *cannot* change the formulas of any of the substances, so you cannot balance the hydrogen atoms by removing two from the subscript beside the H in $CH_{4(g)}$. Never change a subscript to balance an equation. Instead, add coefficients. A balanced equation contains coefficients that consist of the lowest whole-number ratios of the substances involved in the reaction.

Table A3.1 shows how atoms are counted.

TABLE A3.1 Number of Atoms in the Equation for the Combustion of Methane

Combustion of Methane: $2\ O_{2(g)} + CH_{4(g)} \longrightarrow CO_{2(g)} + 2\ H_2O_{(g)}$		
Type of Atom	**Number of Reactant Atoms** (coefficient × no. of atoms)	**Number of Product Atoms** (coefficient × no. of atoms)
O	$2 \times 2 = 4$	$1 \times 2 + 2 \times 1 = 4$
C	1	1
H	4	$2 \times 2 = 4$

Example Problem A3.1

Aqueous iron(II) nitrate reacts with aqueous sodium phosphate. The products are aqueous sodium nitrate and solid iron(II) phosphate. Iron(II) phosphate is used as a fertilizer to prevent iron deficiency in trees. This condition prevents trees from making chlorophyll. Write the balanced equation for this reaction, and include symbols showing the states.

1. Write the word equation for the reaction.

iron(II) nitrate + sodium phosphate $\longrightarrow$ sodium nitrate + iron(II) phosphate

2. Write the skeleton equation for the reaction.

$$Fe(NO_3)_{2(aq)} + Na_3PO_{4(aq)} \longrightarrow NaNO_{3(aq)} + Fe_3(PO_4)_{2(s)}$$

3. Count the number of each type of atom or polyatomic ion in the reactants and the products. It may be helpful to use a table like Table A3.2.

TABLE A3.2 Number of Atoms and Polyatomic Ions in the Reaction

Reaction of Iron(II) Nitrate with Sodium Phosphate		
Atom or Polyatomic Ion	**Reactants**	**Products**
Fe	1	3
Na	3	1
NO_3^-	2	1
PO_4^{3+}	1	2

4. Remember that you cannot change the formulas of any of the substances. Treat polyatomic ions as single units. Add coefficients:
- Start with the first element on the left, Fe. It is not balanced. Place a 3 in front of $Fe(NO_3)_2$ in the reactants to balance it with the Fe in the $Fe_3(PO_4)_2$ product.
- NO_3 appears on both sides of the equation. Place a 6 in front of $NaNO_3$ to balance the NO_3 on both sides. This 6 means there are now 6 Na atoms on the product side.
- Place a 2 in front of the Na_3PO_4 to balance the number of Na atoms. The PO_4 polyatomic ions are now also balanced.

5. The result is the balanced equation:

$$3\ Fe(NO_3)_{2(aq)} + 2\ Na_3PO_{4(aq)} \longrightarrow 6\ NaNO_{3(aq)} + Fe_3(PO_4)_{2(s)}$$

*re*SEARCH

Catalysts are chemicals that can speed up a chemical reaction, but are not changed by it. A catalyst is present at the end of a reaction in the same amount as at the start of the reaction. Find out how a catalyst is represented in a balanced chemical reaction. Begin your search at

www.pearsoned.ca/school/science10

Practice Problem

1. Balance the following equations:
  a) $N_{2(g)} + H_{2(g)} \longrightarrow NH_{3(g)}$
  b) $CaC_{2(s)} + H_2O_{(l)} \longrightarrow Ca(OH)_{2(s)} + C_2H_{2(g)}$
  c) $SiCl_{4(s)} + H_2O_{(l)} \longrightarrow SiO_{2(s)} + HCl_{(aq)}$
  d) $H_3PO_{4(aq)} + CaSO_{4(s)} \longrightarrow Ca_3(PO_4)_{2(s)} + H_2SO_{4(aq)}$

Knowledge

1. What is a chemical equation?

2. List four observations that could indicate that a chemical reaction is taking place.

3. List four pieces of information given by a balanced formula equation.

4. What information about chemical reactions is not given by the chemical equation?

5. Which law of nature are we using when we balance a chemical equation?

6. Use the following equation to explain the following terms: reactants, products, state symbols, formulas, coefficients.

$$Zn_{(s)} + 2\ HCl_{(aq)} \longrightarrow ZnCl_{2(aq)} + H_{2(g)}$$

Applications

7. Balance the following equations:
   a) $Al_{(s)} + F_{2(g)} \longrightarrow AlF_{3(s)}$
   b) $K_{(s)} + O_{2(g)} \longrightarrow K_2O_{(s)}$
   c) $C_6H_{12}O_{6(s)} + O_{2(g)} \longrightarrow CO_{2(g)} + H_2O_{(g)}$
   d) $H_2SO_{4(aq)} + NaOH_{(s)} \longrightarrow$
      $$Na_2SO_{4(aq)} + H_2O_{(l)}$$
   e) $Mg(CH_3COO)_{2(aq)} + AgNO_{3(aq)} \longrightarrow$
      $$Mg(NO_3)_{2(aq)} + AgCH_3COO_{(s)}$$
   f) $H_2O_{2(aq)} \longrightarrow O_{2(g)} + H_2O_{(l)}$

8. For each of the following, write skeleton formula equations, and then balance them.
   a) methane + oxygen $\longrightarrow$
      carbon dioxide + water vapour
   b) sodium chloride $\longrightarrow$ sodium + chlorine
   c) calcium nitrate + sodium sulfate $\longrightarrow$
      sodium nitrate + calcium sulfate
   d) hydrogen + carbon monoxide $\longrightarrow$
      carbon + water
   e) sodium + water $\longrightarrow$
      sodium hydroxide + hydrogen
   f) calcium carbonate + sulfur dioxide + oxygen
      $\longrightarrow$ calcium sulfate + carbon dioxide
   g) sulfur + oxygen $\longrightarrow$ sulfur dioxide
   h) calcium phosphate + sulfuric acid $\longrightarrow$
      phosphoric acid + calcium sulfate
   i) potassium chlorate $\longrightarrow$
      potassium chloride + oxygen

9. Write the following equations as balanced formula equations.
   a) Solid calcium metal is placed in a solution of hydrochloric acid, producing aqueous calcium chloride and hydrogen gas.
   b) Solid magnesium nitride is placed in water and stirred. This produces aqueous magnesium hydroxide and ammonia gas.
   c) Aqueous sulfuric acid reacts with solid sodium hydroxide to produce aqueous sodium sulfate and liquid water.
   d) Gaseous nitrogen dioxide reacts with itself to produce gaseous dinitrogen tetraoxide.
   e) Aqueous copper(II) chloride mixes with aqueous sodium hydroxide to produce solid copper(II) hydroxide plus aqueous sodium chloride.

Extension

10. Create a drawing to illustrate the law of conservation of mass by showing how the atoms rearrange during the decomposition of hydrogen peroxide into oxygen and water.

A 3.3 Five Common Types of Chemical Reactions

How many different chemical reactions are possible? There are millions of chemical compounds, and each one can undergo many different kinds of chemical change. It would be impossible to learn all these reactions. Fortunately, chemistry is rich in patterns. Chemists looked at many different reactions and found that some had common characteristics. From the vast array of reactions, a few simple types have emerged. They allow us to predict the outcome of many chemical reactions just by examining the reactants.

Five common types of reactions are: formation, decomposition, hydrocarbon combustion, single replacement, and double replacement. You will explore them in more detail in the rest of section A3.3.

Formation Reactions

In the simplest type of **formation reaction**, two elements combine to form a compound. This type of reaction is also known as a **synthesis reaction**. A general statement for a formation reaction is:

element + element $\longrightarrow$ compound

OR

A + B $\longrightarrow$ AB

When sulfur burns in air, the reaction produces a poisonous gas called sulfur dioxide (Figure A3.14). The equation for this reaction is:

Word equation: sulfur + oxygen $\longrightarrow$ sulfur dioxide

Skeleton equation: $S_{8(s)} + O_{2(g)} \longrightarrow SO_{2(g)}$

Sulfur dioxide can combine with water in the air to form acid rain. That is why as much sulfur as possible is removed from gasoline during production.

Note that in this section, we will often use only skeleton equations and not balanced equations. This allows us to focus on the reaction types.

Another formation reaction involving only non-metals is the synthesis of ammonia from its elements. The formula of ammonia is NH_3, so the reactants must be the elements hydrogen and nitrogen. Both of these elements form diatomic molecules.

Word equation: hydrogen + nitrogen $\longrightarrow$ ammonia

Skeleton equation: $H_{2(g)} + N_{2(g)} \longrightarrow NH_{3(g)}$

Because ammonia is used in the production of explosives and fertilizers, its formation is an important commercial reaction. The reaction is carried out at high temperatures and pressure, in the presence of a catalyst. Note that you cannot always predict the formula of molecular compounds that form because more than one combination of elements is possible. For example, carbon and oxygen can react to form $CO_{(g)}$ or $CO_{2(g)}$.

*info*BIT

The car of the future may operate on hydrogen instead of gasoline. Burning gasoline produces carbon dioxide, a known greenhouse gas. A hydrogen fuel cell produces only water. A hydrogen fuel cell is a device that uses a formation reaction involving hydrogen gas and oxygen gas to produce electrical energy—and water. The electrical energy can be used to drive an electric motor.

FIGURE A3.14 Sulfur burning in air is an example of a formation reaction.

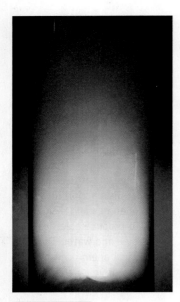

FIGURE A3.15 Burning sodium metal in chlorine gas produces solid sodium chloride.

Many formation reactions occur between metals and non-metals. Table salt can be produced from two highly reactive substances: chlorine gas and sodium metal. Commercial table salt is not prepared this way, since it can easily be mined, but the reaction is possible (Figure A3.15). The equation for the reaction is:

Word equation: sodium + chlorine $\longrightarrow$ sodium chloride

Skeleton equation: $Na_{(s)} + Cl_{2(g)} \longrightarrow NaCl_{(s)}$

Example Problem A3.2

Special high quality grades of magnesium oxide are used in cosmetics, antacids, Sun blocks, and ointments. Write the balanced equation for the formation of solid magnesium oxide from its elements.

1. Write the word equation: From the name of the product compound, you can tell that the elements it is composed of are magnesium, which is a metal, and oxygen, which is a diatomic gas.

   Word equation: magnesium + oxygen $\longrightarrow$ magnesium oxide

2. Write the skeleton equation: Metals are indicated in an equation by their element symbol, and oxygen is a diatomic element. Metals other than mercury are solids at room temperature. Magnesium oxide is an ionic compound. All ionic compounds are solids at room temperature.

   Skeleton equation: $Mg_{(s)} + O_{2(g)} \longrightarrow MgO_{(s)}$

3. Balance the equation: The balanced equation for the formation of solid magnesium oxide is:

   $2\ Mg_{(s)} + O_{2(g)} \longrightarrow 2\ MgO_{(s)}$

Example Problem A3.3

Artists use iron(III) chloride solutions to etch images onto copper. Write the skeleton equation and balanced equation without state symbols for the formation of iron(III) chloride from its elements.

1. Write the word equation: From the name of the product compound, you can tell that it is composed of the elements iron, which is a metal, and chlorine, which is a diatomic gas.

   Word equation: iron + chlorine $\longrightarrow$ iron(III) chloride

2. Write the skeleton equation: Metals are always indicated in an equation by their element symbol, and chlorine is a diatomic element. Iron(III) chloride is an ionic compound.

   Skeleton equation: $Fe_{(s)} + Cl_{2(g)} \longrightarrow FeCl_{3(s)}$

3. Write the balanced equation. The balanced equation for the formation of iron(III) chloride from its elements is:

   $2\ Fe_{(s)} + 3\ Cl_{2(g)} \longrightarrow 2\ FeCl_{3(s)}$

Practice Problems

2. Write the skeleton equation and balanced equation for the formation of lithium oxide from its elements.

3. Write the skeleton equation and balanced equation for the formation of lead(IV) bromide from its elements.

More complex types of formation reactions involve compounds that react to form a single product. For example, carbon dioxide can join with water to make carbonic acid. This happens to about 10% of the carbon dioxide that is forced into soda pop in a process called carbonation, which adds the fizz to the drink (Figure A3.16). The skeleton equation for this reaction is:

$$CO_{2(g)} + H_2O_{(l)} \longrightarrow H_2CO_{3(aq)}$$

When both reactants are compounds, the product of this type of formation reaction can be very difficult to predict. When one reactant is a metal and the other is a non-metal, predict the product by writing the ionic compound that they form.

FIGURE A3.16 **FIGURE A3.16** The bubbles in carbonated beverages are carbon dioxide gas. The carbon dioxide sometimes reacts with water in the beverage to form carbonic acid ($H_2CO_{3(aq)}$).

Example Problem A3.4

The product of this reaction is used in solution to digest wood fibre in the papermaking process. Name and give the formula of the product in the following reaction:
sodium + sulfur $\longrightarrow$

These compounds form the ionic compound sodium sulfide, formula $Na_2S_{(s)}$.

Practice Problem

4. Name and give the formula of the product in each of the following reactions:
   a) calcium + nitrogen $\longrightarrow$
   b) silver + oxygen $\longrightarrow$
   c) aluminium + fluorine $\longrightarrow$

Skill Practice   Formation Reactions

Later in this section, in Activity A10, you will be asked to write the equations for a formation reaction. Before doing that activity, you can practise identifying and predicting products and writing equations by answering the following questions.

1. Name the product in each of the following reactions:
   a) potassium + iodine $\longrightarrow$
   b) magnesium + phosphorus $\longrightarrow$
   c) cesium + chlorine $\longrightarrow$
   d) calcium + oxygen $\longrightarrow$
   e) aluminium + sulfur $\longrightarrow$

2. Complete each equation below. The products are all ionic compounds.
   a) $Na_{(s)} + Br_{2(l)} \longrightarrow$
   b) $Mg_{(s)} + F_{2(g)} \longrightarrow$
   c) $Al_{(s)} + Cl_{2(g)} \longrightarrow$
   d) $K_{(s)} + N_{2(g)} \longrightarrow$
   e) $Ca_{(s)} + P_{4(s)} \longrightarrow$

3. Write balanced chemical equations for the following reactions. Add state symbols. You must predict the products of the last three reactions.
   a) solid lithium + oxygen gas $\longrightarrow$ solid lithium oxide
   b) solid aluminium + liquid bromine $\longrightarrow$ solid aluminium bromide
   c) liquid mercury + solid iodine $\longrightarrow$ solid mercury(II) iodide
   d) solid sodium + chlorine gas $\longrightarrow$
   e) solid magnesium + nitrogen gas $\longrightarrow$
   f) solid nickel + fluorine gas $\longrightarrow$

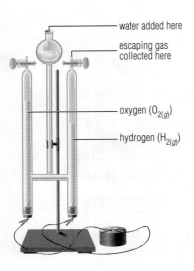

FIGURE A3.17 A Hoffman apparatus separates water into hydrogen and oxygen using electricity, in a process called electrolysis.

Decomposition Reactions

Each of the reactions described in the discussion of formation reactions above is reversible. That is, the products can be broken down to yield the reactants again in a **decomposition reaction**. Sometimes this is difficult, and requires special equipment or the input of energy, but it is possible.

A general statement for this type of reaction is:

compound $\longrightarrow$ element + element

OR

AB $\longrightarrow$ A + B

Decompostion reactions have only one reactant. One example of a decomposition reaction is the breakdown of water into hydrogen and oxygen. Figure A3.17 shows the apparatus used to do this. The balanced equation for the reaction is:

$$2\,H_2O_{(l)} \longrightarrow 2\,H_{2(g)} + O_{2(g)}$$

Example Problem A3.5

Before 1825, pure aluminium metal did not exist. In that year, a few pin-head-sized pieces of aluminium metal were produced through a reaction involving aluminium chloride. Write a balanced equation showing the decomposition of solid aluminium chloride into its elements.

1. Write the word equation: The elements in aluminium chloride are aluminium and chlorine.

   Word equation: aluminium chloride $\longrightarrow$ aluminium + chlorine

2. Write the skeleton equation: Aluminium chloride is an ionic compound. All ionic compounds are solids at room temperature. Metals are indicated by their symbols. Chlorine is diatomic. All metals other than mercury are solids at room temperature, and chlorine is a gas.

   Skeleton equation: $AlCl_{3(s)} \longrightarrow Al_{(s)} + Cl_{2(g)}$

3. Write the balanced equation: The balanced equation for the decomposition of solid aluminium chloride into its elements is:

   $$2\,AlCl_{3(s)} \longrightarrow 2\,Al_{(s)} + 3\,Cl_{2(g)}$$

Practice Problem

5. Write balanced equations for the reactions below.

   a) solid magnesium sulfide $\longrightarrow$ solid magnesium + solid sulfur

   b) solid potassium iodide $\longrightarrow$ solid potassium + solid iodine

   c) solid aluminium oxide $\longrightarrow$ solid aluminium + oxygen gas

   d) solid nickel(II) chloride $\longrightarrow$ solid nickel + chlorine gas

Hydrocarbon Combustion

Hydrocarbons are substances that contain hydrogen and carbon. Common hydrocarbons include the main components of gasoline (which is a mixture of many liquid hydrocarbons), candle wax, and many plastics, such as polyethylene. Methane is the simplest hydrocarbon, with a formula of $CH_{4(g)}$, but there are millions of different hydrocarbon molecules.

One way to write a general formula for a hydrocarbon is C_xH_y. The x and y subscripts are whole numbers that indicate how many carbon and hydrogen atoms are in the molecule. Figure A3.18 shows how to convert the general formula of C_xH_y to the formula for a specific hydrocarbon. Butane has 4 carbon atoms and 10 hydrogen atoms, so its formula is $C_4H_{10(g)}$.

Any reaction with oxygen that is fast and exothermic is a combustion reaction (Figure A3.19). If plenty of oxygen is available to react in hydrocarbon combustions, there will always be only two products: carbon dioxide and water vapour. The general skeleton equation for this type of reaction is:

$$C_xH_y + O_{2(g)} \longrightarrow CO_{2(g)} + H_2O_{(g)}$$

hydrocarbon + oxygen $\longrightarrow$ carbon dioxide + water

Natural gas is used as a fuel for home heating and cooking. Recall that natural gas is methane, with the formula $CH_{4(g)}$. The balanced equation for the combustion of methane is:

$$CH_{4(g)} + 2 O_{2(g)} \longrightarrow CO_{2(g)} + 2 H_2O_{(g)}$$

The following example problem uses hexane as the hydrocarbon in the combustion reaction. Notice that balancing these types of reactions often requires large numbers for the coefficients.

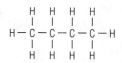

FIGURE A3.18 For butane, x = 4 and y = 10, giving the formula $C_4H_{10(g)}$.

FIGURE A3.19 An oxyacetylene torch cuts through solid steel.

Example Problem A3.6

One of the hydrocarbon components of gasoline is hexane, $C_6H_{14(l)}$. Write word, skeleton, and balanced equations for the combustion of hexane.

1. Write the word equation: Combustion always means reaction with oxygen. Since hexane is a hydrocarbon, the reaction always produces carbon dioxide and water vapour.

   Word equation: hexane + oxygen $\longrightarrow$ carbon dioxide + water vapour

2. Write the skeleton equation: You know from the question that hexane is a liquid (because gasoline is a liquid). The other components are gases. Except for the particular hydrocarbon, the formulas are always the same for hydrocarbon combustion.

   Skeleton equation: $C_6H_{14(l)} + O_{2(g)} \longrightarrow CO_{2(g)} + H_2O_{(g)}$

3. Write the balanced equation:

   Balanced equation: $2 C_6H_{14(l)} + 19 O_{2(g)} \longrightarrow 12 CO_{2(g)} + 14 H_2O_{(g)}$

Practice Problem

6. Complete and balance each equation.

   a) $CH_{4(g)} + O_{2(g)} \longrightarrow$

   b) $C_2H_{6(g)} + O_{2(g)} \longrightarrow$

   c) $C_3H_{8(g)} + O_{2(g)} \longrightarrow$

   d) $C_6H_{6(l)} + O_{2(g)} \longrightarrow$

Single Replacement Reactions

In a **single replacement reaction**, a reactive element reacts with an ionic compound. After the reaction, the element ends up in a compound, and one of the elements in the reactant compound ends up by itself as an element. These reactions often take place in solution. The equation for a single replacement reaction may look like this:

$$A + BC \longrightarrow B + AC$$

In one type of single replacement reaction, a metal atom trades places with a metal ion in a compound. For example, magnesium metal reacts with the compound silver nitrate as follows:

Word equation: magnesium + silver nitrate $\longrightarrow$ silver + magnesium nitrate

Any metal element on its own is present as atoms. Any metal element in a compound is present as an ion. Its ionic charge determines how the compound is written. In this example, silver is a 1+ ion in silver nitrate. In the products, silver is an element and has no charge. In the same reaction, magnesium starts out in the reactants as an element and ends up in the products as a 2+ ion. The skeleton and balanced equations for this reaction are:

Skeleton equation: $Mg_{(s)} + AgNO_{3(aq)} \longrightarrow Ag_{(s)} + Mg(NO_3)_{2(aq)}$

Balanced equation: $Mg_{(s)} + 2\ AgNO_{3(aq)} \longrightarrow 2\ Ag_{(s)} + Mg(NO_3)_{2(aq)}$

Example Problem A3.7

Copper compounds are poisonous. Sometimes, active metals such as iron or aluminium are placed in water contaminated with copper ions. These metals react with the copper ions and remove them from the water. Solid copper metal is produced, which is safe in the water. What reaction occurs when aluminium metal is placed in a solution of aqueous copper(II) chloride? Write the balanced equation.

1. Write the word equation: Aluminium metal replaces copper in the compound. Copper becomes copper metal, and aluminium forms aluminium chloride.

   Word equation: aluminium + copper(II) chloride $\longrightarrow$ copper + aluminium chloride

2. Write the skeleton equation: Copper(II) chloride and aluminium chloride are both ionic compounds.

   Skeleton equation: $Al_{(s)} + CuCl_{2(aq)} \longrightarrow Cu_{(s)} + AlCl_{3(aq)}$

3. Write the balanced equation:

   Balanced equation: $2\ Al_{(s)} + 3\ CuCl_{2(aq)} \longrightarrow 3\ Cu_{(s)} + 2\ AlCl_{3(aq)}$

In another type of single replacement reaction, non-metals trade places. The equation for this reaction may look like this:

$$D + BC \longrightarrow C + BD$$

For example, chlorine reacts with the compound silver bromide to produce bromine and silver chloride. Both chlorine and bromine are diatomic elements. Silver bromide and silver chloride are ionic compounds. The balanced equation for this reaction is:

Balanced equation: $Cl_{2(g)} + 2\ AgBr_{(s)} \longrightarrow Br_{2(l)} + 2\ AgCl_{(s)}$

Example Problem A3.8

Iron(III) bromide is an industrial catalyst. It helps to speed certain chemical reactions used in manufacturing plastics. Liquid bromine is added to a solution of aqueous iron(III) iodide, and the mixture is stirred. This produces aqueous iron(III) bromide and solid iodine. Write the word, skeleton, and balanced equations for this reaction. Include the state symbols in the balanced equation.

1. Write the word equation: Read the question carefully to find the names of the reactants and products.

Word equation: bromine + iron(III) iodide $\longrightarrow$ iodine + iron(III) bromide

2. Write the skeleton equation: Bromine and iodine are both diatomic elements. The state of each substance is given in the question.

Skeleton equation: $Br_{2(l)} + FeI_{3(aq)} \longrightarrow I_{2(s)} + FeBr_{3(aq)}$

3. Write the balanced equation: In balancing, remember not to change any subscripts; just add coefficients where needed.

Balanced equation: $3\ Br_{2(l)} + 2\ FeI_{3(aq)} \longrightarrow 3\ I_{2(s)} + 2\ FeBr_{3(aq)}$

Practice Problems

Write the word, skeleton, and balanced equations.

7. Chlorine gas is added to a solution of aqueous nickel(III) bromide and the mixture is stirred. This produces aqueous nickel(III) chloride and liquid bromine.

8. Zinc metal is placed into a solution of silver nitrate and allowed to sit. This produces aqueous zinc nitrate and solid silver metal.

Skill Practice — Decomposition and Single Replacement Reactions

In Activity A10, you will be asked to write the equations for formation and single replacement reactions. You have already had an opportunity to practise identifying and predicting products and writing equations for formation reactions in the Skill Practice on page 93. You can practise identifying and predicting products and writing equations for decomposition and single replacement reactions by answering the following questions.

1. Name the products in each of the following reactions:
   a) magnesium phosphide $\longrightarrow$
   b) sodium chloride $\longrightarrow$
   c) strontium oxide $\longrightarrow$
   d) zinc + iron(II) chloride $\longrightarrow$
   e) aluminium + copper(II) iodide $\longrightarrow$
   f) magnesium + gold(III) nitrate $\longrightarrow$

2. Complete each skeleton equation.
   a) $CaO_{(s)} \longrightarrow$
   b) $NaF_{(s)} \longrightarrow$
   c) $Mg_3N_{2(s)} \longrightarrow$
   d) $Fe_{(s)} + Cu(NO_3)_{2(aq)} \longrightarrow$
   e) $Cl_{2(g)} + NaI_{(aq)} \longrightarrow$
   f) $Pb_{(s)} + AgNO_{3(aq)} \longrightarrow$

3. Write balanced chemical equations for the following reactions. You must predict the products where indicated.
   a) solid iron(III) chloride $\longrightarrow$ solid iron + chlorine gas
   b) solid copper(I) oxide $\longrightarrow$
   solid copper + oxygen gas
   c) solid lithium bromide $\longrightarrow$?
   d) liquid bromine + aqueous chromium(III) iodide $\longrightarrow$ chromium(III) bromide + solid iodine
   e) aqueous silver nitrate + solid copper $\longrightarrow$?

4. Write the word, skeleton, and balanced equations for the following reactions. Include the state symbols in the balanced equations.
   a) Liquid bromine is added to a solution of aqueous iron(III) iodide and the mixture is stirred. This produces aqueous iron(III) bromide and solid iodine.
   b) Magnesium metal is placed into a solution of gold(III) fluoride and allowed to sit. This produces aqueous magnesium fluoride and gold metal.

Inquiry Lab

Formation, Decomposition, and Single Replacement Reactions

The Question

What chemical changes happen during formation, decomposition, and single replacement reactions?

Materials and Equipment

anhydrous copper(II) sulfate

3% hydrogen peroxide solution

manganese(IV) oxide

15-cm length of copper wire

steel wool

water

balance

test tube

medicine dropper

tongs

Bunsen burner

Erlenmeyer flask

copper(II) sulfate pentahydrate

1-cm² pieces of copper, silver, and magnesium metal

copper(II) nitrate solution

silver nitrate solution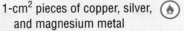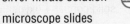

microscope slides

microscopes (preferred), hand lenses, or magnifying glasses

Procedure

Part 1: Formation Reaction: Anhydrous Copper(II) Sulfate + Water

1. Place about 2 g of anhydrous copper(II) sulfate in a test tube. Record the colour.

2. Hold the test tube by curling your fingers around it, so you can detect any temperature changes when you add water.

3. Using a dropper, add 5 drops of water to the anhydrous copper(II) sulfate in the test tube. Record any colour changes and temperature changes in your notebook.

Part 2: Formation Reaction: Iron + Oxygen

4. Light the Bunsen burner. Using the tongs, light one of the pieces of steel wool, and record the result.

5. Place about 1 g of manganese(IV) oxide in an Erlenmeyer flask. Add 5 mL of 3% hydrogen peroxide solution. Observe bubbles forming. This is pure oxygen gas.

6. Using the tongs and the Bunsen burner, light the second piece of steel wool and plunge it into the Erlenmeyer flask. Record the result.

7. Follow your teacher's instructions for disposing of all the chemicals you have used.

Part 3: Decomposition Reaction: Copper(II) Sulfate Pentahydrate

8. Place 5 g of copper(II) sulfate pentahydrate in a test tube.

9. Using tongs, heat the test tube over a Bunsen burner flame. Note particularly the formation of any product on the walls of the test tube at the top. Note any colour changes in the material at the bottom of the test tube. Record your observations.

10. Once the test tube is cool enough to touch, add a few drops of water to the product. Record any changes.

Part 4: Single Replacement Reaction: Metal Ion Solutions with Magnesium and Copper Metals

11. Use a microscope or magnifying glass for the following steps.

12. Put a piece of magnesium on a clean slide, and place the slide under the microscope lens. Focus on the edge of the magnesium.

13. Put a drop of silver nitrate solution on the magnesium. Record your observations. Note whether a reaction is occurring or not. If you are using a microscope, try to describe the growth of the metallic crystals.

14. Repeat steps 12 and 13 with the copper metal and the silver nitrate solution.

15. Repeat steps 12 and 13 using the silver metal with the copper(II) nitrate solution.

16. These solutions contain toxic metal ions. They require special disposal procedures. Follow your teacher's instructions for disposing of all the substances you have used.

Analyzing and Interpreting

Part 1: Formation Reaction: Anhydrous Copper(II) Sulfate + Water

1. What evidence is there that adding water to anhydrous copper(II) sulfate creates a chemical reaction and not just a mixture?

2. Is the reaction of anhydrous copper(II) sulfate with water exothermic or endothermic? Explain.

Part 2: Formation Reaction: Iron + Oxygen

3. Describe the differences between burning steel wool (a source of iron) in air and burning it in pure oxygen.

4. Rewrite the following sentence as a balanced formula equation. Include the state symbols.
Solid iron reacts with oxygen gas to form solid iron(III) oxide.

Part 3: Decomposition Reaction: Copper(II) Sulfate Pentahydrate

5. What evidence is there that water is one of the products of the decomposition of copper(II) sulfate pentahydrate?

6. What is the other product of this decomposition reaction?

Part 4: Single Replacement Reaction: Metal Ion Solutions with Magnesium and Copper Metals

7. Do all the combinations of metals and solutions appear to react in the same way? Include the rate of the reaction and the shape of the crystals in your answer.

8. Translate the following sentences into balanced formula equations, showing state symbols:
   a) Magnesium metal reacts with silver nitrate solution to produce silver metal and magnesium nitrate solution.
   b) Copper(II) nitrate solution reacts with magnesium metal to give magnesium nitrate solution and copper metal.
   c) Silver nitrate solution reacts with copper metal to give silver metal and copper(II) nitrate solution.

Forming Conclusions

9. Write a summary describing the observations that you made that indicate a chemical reaction has occurred for each type of reaction.

Applying and Connecting

10. Drying agents are used to keep humidity low by absorbing moisture from the air. For example, hearing aids are often stored at night in an airtight container that has a drying agent inside it. The drying agent must be regenerated when it has reached its water absorption limit. Use the results of this investigation to suggest a means for producing a drying agent that indicates when it has reached its absorption limit.

Extending

11. Based on your results, which is a more reactive metal: copper or silver? Explain.

Double Replacement Reactions

Double replacement reactions commonly occur between two ionic compounds. Ionic compounds are always solids at room temperature, so these reactions happen in solution (that is, dissolved in a liquid), where the ions have the opportunity to mix. This type of reaction often results in the formation of at least one precipitate.

A general statement for a double replacement reaction is:

$$AB + CD \longrightarrow AD + CB$$

The ions in the first compound join with ions from the second compound. This is called a double replacement reaction because two new ionic compounds are formed.

There are several facts to keep in mind as this double replacement occurs:
- A and C are both positive ions. They will never pair up together because they repel each other.
- A and C will always appear first in formulas because positive ions are always written first.
- B and D are negative ions, so they will combine with any positive ions. They are always written second in formulas.

Practice Problem

9. Write the word, skeleton, and balanced equations for the following reactions.
   a) When aqueous copper(I) nitrate and aqueous potassium bromide are mixed, a precipitate of solid copper(I) bromide forms. Another product also forms.
   b) When aqueous aluminium chloride and aqueous sodium hydroxide are mixed, a precipitate of solid aluminium hydroxide forms. Another product also forms.

Example Problem A3.9

When aqueous lead(II) nitrate and aqueous sodium iodide are mixed, a bright yellow precipitate of solid lead(II) iodide forms (Figure A3.20). Another product also forms. It is aqueous. Write the balanced equation for this double replacement reaction.

1. Write the word equation: The question does not name the second product. However, every ionic compound has two parts to its name. Look at the reactants and switch the parts of their names around.

FIGURE A3.20 The yellow precipitate lead(II) iodide was widely used as a paint pigment in the past. Lead-based paints were popular, and today lead paint dust is a health hazard in very old homes.

Word equation:
lead(II) nitrate + sodium iodide $\longrightarrow$ lead(II) iodide + sodium nitrate

2. Write the skeleton equation: All these substances are ionic. Use the solubility table (Table C) in Student Reference 12 to determine that PbI_2 is only slightly soluble. It appears in the equation as a solid.

Skeleton equation: $Pb(NO_3)_{2(aq)} + NaI_{(aq)} \longrightarrow PbI_{2(s)} + NaNO_{3(aq)}$

3. Write the balanced equation: Remember—do not change any subscripts. Simply add coefficients.

Balanced equation: $Pb(NO_3)_{2(aq)} + 2\ NaI_{(aq)} \longrightarrow PbI_{2(s)} + 2\ NaNO_{3(aq)}$

In Example Problem A3.9, $PbI_{2(s)}$ was one of the products. It is only slightly soluble. Another way to describe its solubility is to say that its solubility is low. Such substances do not dissolve very well. In chemical equations, they are shown as a solid *(s)* even if they are formed in the presence of water. The other product in the last example is $NaNO_{3(aq)}$. It is very soluble, and remains completely in solution unless most of the water is removed. Its solubility is high. When formed in water, it is shown in the chemical equation as aqueous *(aq)*.

Recall that the solubility table lists the combinations of ions that are slightly soluble and very soluble (see Table A2.13 on page 57 or Table C in Student Reference 12). Consult this table to determine the states of the products of replacement reactions.

Activity A11
QuickLab

Double Replacement Reactions

Purpose

To observe the formation of precipitates, and write the chemical equations that represent the reactions

Materials and Equipment

dropper bottles containing the following solutions:

sodium iodide solution

silver nitrate solution

iron(III) chloride solution

sodium hydroxide solution

sodium carbonate solution

calcium chloride solution

5 test tubes

test tube rack

Procedure

① Using a separate test tube for each reaction, combine 5 drops of each of the following solutions. Check for the formation of a precipitate. If there is a precipitate, note its colour. If there is no precipitate, write NR (no reaction).

a) sodium iodide solution and silver nitrate solution
b) iron(III) chloride solution and sodium hydroxide solution
c) sodium carbonate solution and calcium chloride solution
d) sodium iodide solution and calcium chloride solution
e) silver nitrate solution and sodium carbonate solution

② Follow your teacher's instructions for disposing of all the substances you have used.

Questions

1. Which combinations above produced a precipitate? For each reaction that produced a precipitate, write a word equation and a skeleton equation. Then balance the equation.

2. Use the solubility table (Table C) in Student Reference 12 to determine the solubility of the products in each reaction. Which are only slightly soluble? Which are very soluble?

3. Write the state symbol for each compound in each equation. All the reactants are very soluble, so they are all aqueous *(aq)*. One product in each reaction is soluble, and the other is only slightly soluble. The slightly soluble product should be shown in the equation as solid *(s)*.

Predicting the Products of Chemical Reactions

Now that you have become familiar with five simple types of chemical reactions, you have the foundation for predicting the outcome of thousands of chemical reactions. Each reaction type follows a pattern that is different from the others. An examination of the reactants usually makes it possible to predict the identity of the products.

The first step in predicting what will happen in any reaction is to classify the reaction. Then, the products can be determined by following the pattern for that type. Table A3.3 summarizes the types of reactions.

TABLE A3.3 Summary of Types of Reactions

Type of Reaction	Reactants		Products
formation (synthesis)	$A + B$	$\longrightarrow$	AB
decomposition	AB	$\longrightarrow$	$A + B$
hydrocarbon combustion	$C_xH_y + O_2$	$\longrightarrow$	$CO_2 + H_2O$
single replacement	(A is a metal) $A + BC$	$\longrightarrow$	$B + AC$
	(D is a non-metal) $D + BC$	$\longrightarrow$	$C + BD$
double replacement	$AB + CD$	$\longrightarrow$	$AD + CB$

Note that there are many kinds of reactions that do not fit into the five categories that you have just learned. There are even variations of these five types for which the products are difficult to predict.

FIGURE A3.21 Hexane ($C_6H_{14(l)}$), in part (c) of Example Problem A3.10, is one of the components of gasoline.

Example Problem A3.10

Classify each of the following reaction types. Predict the names of the product(s), and write the skeleton equation.

a) $PbBr_{4(s)} \longrightarrow$

b) $Ni(NO_3)_{3(aq)} + Na_2SO_{3(aq)} \longrightarrow$

c) $C_6H_{14(l)} + O_{2(g)} \longrightarrow$ (assume plenty of oxygen is available during the reaction)

d) copper + gold(III) chlorate $\longrightarrow$

e) zinc + sulfur $\longrightarrow$

a) $PbBr_{4(s)} \longrightarrow$
- Classify the reaction: Since there is only one reactant, this must be a decomposition reaction.
- Predict the names of the products: This compound contains the lead(IV) ion, Pb^{4+}, and the bromide ion, Br^-. It can be decomposed into the elements lead and bromine.
- Write the skeleton equation: Lead metal is shown by its element symbol in the products because it is an atom and has no charge. Bromine is diatomic.

Skeleton equation: $PbBr_{4(s)} \longrightarrow Pb_{(s)} + Br_{2(l)}$

b) $Ni(NO_3)_{3(aq)} + Na_2SO_{3(aq)} \longrightarrow$
- Classify the reaction: Two ionic compounds mean this is a double replacement reaction.
- Predict the names of the products: The nickel(III) ion, Ni^{3+}, will combine with the sulfite ion, SO_3^{2-}, to make nickel(III) sulfite. Similarly, the sodium ion, Na^+, will combine with the nitrate ion, NO_3^-, to make sodium nitrate.
- Write the skeleton equation:

Skeleton equation: $Ni(NO_3)_{3(aq)} + Na_2SO_{3(aq)}$
$$\longrightarrow Ni_2(SO_3)_{3(s)} + NaNO_{3(aq)}$$

c) $C_6H_{14(l)} + O_{2(g)} \longrightarrow$
- Classify the reaction: The presence of a hydrocarbon with oxygen indicates that this is a hydrocarbon combustion reaction.
- Predict the names of the products: Assuming that there is plenty of oxygen available during combustion, the products will be carbon dioxide and water vapour.
- Write the skeleton equation:

Skeleton equation: $C_6H_{14(l)} + O_{2(g)} \longrightarrow CO_{2(g)} + H_2O_{(g)}$

d) copper + gold(III) chlorate $\longrightarrow$
- Classify the reaction: An element reacting with a compound is characteristic of a single replacement reaction.
- Predict the names of the products: The element is a metal, so it will replace the gold(III) ion, Au^{3+}. The gold is an element in the products, and since it is in the form of an atom, it will have no charge. The copper forms the Cu^{2+} ion. This is the most common form of the ion (2+), so it appears first in the periodic table. The Cu^{2+} ion exists in combination with the chlorate ion, ClO_3^-, to give the ionic compound copper(II) chlorate.
- Write the skeleton equation:

Skeleton equation: $Cu_{(s)} + Au(ClO_3)_{3(aq)} \longrightarrow Cu(ClO_3)_{2(aq)} + Au_{(s)}$

e) zinc + sulfur $\longrightarrow$ (assume that there is enough heat to start the reaction)
- Classify the reaction: Both zinc and sulfur are elements. This must be a formation reaction, with only one product.
- Predict the names of the products: Zinc is a metallic element and is shown in the reactants simply by its symbol, Zn. It has no charge in this form because it is an atom. Sulfur exists at room temperature as the molecule S_8, which is how it appears in the reactants. The product is the compound formed from the zinc ion, Zn^{2+}, and the sulfide ion, S^{2-}, to give zinc sulfide.
- Write the skeleton equation:

Skeleton equation: $Zn_{(s)} + S_{8(s)} \longrightarrow ZnS_{(s)}$

Practice Problem

10. Classify each of the following reaction types. Predict the names of the product(s), and write the skeleton equation.
    a) $C_4H_{10(g)} + O_{2(g)} \longrightarrow$ (assume plenty of oxygen is available during the reaction)
    b) $Ca(NO_3)_{2(aq)} + Na_3PO_{4(aq)} \longrightarrow$
    c) calcium + silver nitrate $\longrightarrow$
    d) magnesium + oxygen $\longrightarrow$
    e) $AlCl_{3(s)} \longrightarrow$

Classifying Chemical Reactions

Purpose

To classify a variety of chemical reactions and write the chemical equations that represent them

Materials and Equipment

aluminium foil

copper(II) chloride solution

cobalt(II) chloride hexahydrate

silver nitrate solution

calcium chloride solution

sodium carbonate solution

10-cm length of copper wire

Bunsen burner or hot plate

4 test tubes

test tube rack

10-mL graduated cylinder

tongs

balance

Procedure

1. Roll up a 5 × 5 cm square of aluminium foil. Place 5 mL of copper(II) chloride solution in a test tube, and drop the aluminium foil into it. Record your observations.

2. Place 1 g of cobalt(II) chloride hexahydrate in a test tube. Use tongs to heat the test tube over a Bunsen burner. If you do not have a Bunsen burner, place the cobalt(II) chloride hexahydrate on aluminium foil and heat on a hot plate. Record your observations.

3. Place 5 drops of silver nitrate solution in a test tube and add the copper metal. Record your observations.

4. Place 5 drops of calcium chloride solution in a test tube. Add 5 drops of sodium carbonate solution. Record your observations.

5. These solutions contain toxic metal ions. They require special disposal procedures. Follow your teacher's instructions for disposing of all the substances you have used.

Questions

1. Write a word equation and a balanced formula equation for the reaction of copper(II) chloride solution with aluminium metal. Include state symbols.

2. Classify the reaction involving cobalt(II) chloride hexahydrate. Name one of the products of the reaction. What evidence was there that it was produced?

3. Classify the reaction of silver nitrate and copper metal. Only one of the products was a solid. What was it?

4. Classify the reaction involving calcium chloride and sodium carbonate. Write a word equation and a balanced formula equation for this reaction. Include state symbols. One of the products of the reaction is white. Indicate on the formula equation which one is white.

5. Which two reaction types that you studied did not occur in this experiment?

Example Problem A3.11

A solution of copper(II) nitrate is placed in an aluminium pot for storage. Almost immediately this proves to be a mistake. A sudden colour change and an increase in temperature indicate that a chemical reaction is taking place. Explain what is happening by using a word equation, a skeleton equation, and a balanced equation. Include state symbols in the balanced equation.

1. Identify the reactants and classify the reaction: An element and a compound are reacting together so this is a single replacement reaction. The element is a metal, so it will replace copper in the compound. Copper metal will be produced. The aluminium metal will form the Al^{3+} ion. This means the aluminium pot should look corroded.

2. Write the word equation:

   Word equation:
   aluminium + copper(II) nitrate $\longrightarrow$ copper + aluminium nitrate

3. Write the skeleton equation:

   Skeleton equation: $Al_{(s)} + Cu(NO_3)_{2(aq)} \longrightarrow Cu_{(s)} + Al(NO_3)_{3(aq)}$

   Both aluminium metal and copper metal are solids at or near room temperature. The copper(II) nitrate was in solution so it is aqueous. In the solubility table (Table C) in Student Reference 12, you can see that all nitrates are very soluble, so there will not be any precipitate from this new compound. It is aqueous.

4. Write the balanced equation:

   Balanced equation: $2\ Al_{(s)} + 3\ Cu(NO_3)_{2(aq)} \longrightarrow 3\ Cu_{(s)} + 2\ Al(NO_3)_{3(aq)}$

   We can conclude that the aluminium pot is corroding from the inside because of its reaction with the copper(II) nitrate solution. A pile of metallic copper powder should be sitting in the bottom of the pot. There is no pile of aluminium nitrate powder, because it is very soluble and remains in solution. Try plastic or glass next time!

*re*SEARCH

Most fertilizers contain ammonium (NH_4^+) salts and nitrate (NO_3^-) salts. These are synthesized from ammonia ($NH_{3(g)}$). Research the formation of ammonia from hydrogen and nitrogen using the Haber process. Begin your search at

 www.pearsoned.ca/school/science10

Practice Problems

11. A lead(IV) nitrate solution is placed in a zinc pot for storage. A sudden colour change and an increase in temperature indicate that a chemical reaction is taking place. Explain what is happening by using a word equation, a skeleton equation, and a balanced equation. Include state symbols in the balanced equation.

12. A reaction occurs when silver metal is placed in a solution of gold(III) nitrate. Write a balanced equation. Include the state symbols.

Knowledge

1. Classify each of the following reactions, and balance the equations.
   a) $CaCl_{2(s)} \longrightarrow Ca_{(s)} + Cl_{2(g)}$
   b) $Mg(ClO_4)_{2(s)} + Na_{(s)} \longrightarrow NaClO_{4(s)} + Mg_{(s)}$
   c) $NaN_{3(s)} \longrightarrow Na_{(s)} + N_{2(g)}$
   d) $Ca(NO_3)_{2(aq)} + Cu_2SO_{4(s)} \longrightarrow$
   $$CaSO_{4(aq)} + CuNO_{3(aq)}$$
   e) $C_5H_{10(l)} + O_{2(g)} \longrightarrow CO_{2(g)} + H_2O_{(g)}$
   f) $Li_4C_{(s)} + Ca_{(s)} \longrightarrow Li_{(s)} + Ca_2C_{(s)}$
   g) $PbO_{2(s)} \longrightarrow Pb_{(s)} + O_{2(g)}$
   h) $CH_{4(g)} + O_{2(g)} \longrightarrow CO_{2(g)} + H_2O_{(g)}$
   i) $Li_{(s)} + Cl_{2(g)} \longrightarrow LiCl_{(s)}$
   j) $NaI_{(aq)} + AlCl_{3(aq)} \longrightarrow NaCl_{(aq)} + AlI_{3(s)}$

2. Classify each of the following reactions, and write balanced formula equations for them.
   a) sodium sulfate + calcium chloride $\longrightarrow$
   sodium chloride + calcium sulfate
   b) magnesium + nitrogen $\longrightarrow$
   magnesium nitride
   c) strontium hydroxide + lead(II) bromide $\rightarrow$
   strontium bromide + lead(II) hydroxide
   d) nickel(III) nitrate + calcium $\longrightarrow$
   calcium nitrate + nickel
   e) methane + oxygen $\longrightarrow$
   carbon dioxide + water
   f) sodium + oxygen $\longrightarrow$ sodium oxide
   g) nitrogen + hydrogen $\longrightarrow$ ammonia
   h) hydrogen chloride $\longrightarrow$
   hydrogen + chlorine
   i) aluminium iodide + bromine $\longrightarrow$
   aluminium bromide + iodine
   j) water + sodium $\longrightarrow$
   sodium hydroxide + hydrogen

3. Classify each reaction, and write the formula of each product or products:
   a) $Li_{(s)} + O_{2(g)} \longrightarrow$
   b) $CuCl_{(s)} \longrightarrow$
   c) $CuSO_{4(aq)} + Al_{(s)} \longrightarrow$
   d) $CaBr_{2(aq)} + Pb(NO_3)_{2(aq)} \longrightarrow$
   e) $C_4H_{10(g)} + O_{2(g)} \longrightarrow$
   f) $AgNO_{3(aq)} + KCl_{(aq)} \longrightarrow$
   g) $NI_{3(s)} \longrightarrow$

   h) $Li_2S_{(aq)} + Cl_{2(g)} \longrightarrow$
   i) $Al_{(s)} + S_{8(s)} \longrightarrow$
   j) $C_{18}H_{38(s)} + O_{2(g)} \longrightarrow$

Applications

4. Write the balanced equation for the formation of solid zinc nitride from its elements.

5. Write the balanced formula equation for the decomposition of mercury(II) oxide into its elements.

6. Write the balanced formula equation for the combustion of benzene. Benzene is a liquid hydrocarbon with the formula $C_6H_{6(l)}$.

7. Liquid bromine is added to a solution of calcium iodide, and the mixture is stirred. A chemical reaction occurs that produces two products. Write the balanced equation.

8. When aqueous lead(II) nitrate is mixed with aqueous sodium iodide, a double replacement reaction occurs. Write the balanced formula equation for the reaction. Use the solubility table (Table C) in Student Reference 12 to determine the states of the products.

Extensions

9. An acid–base neutralization reaction is a specific example of one of the five reaction types that you have studied. Write the word and skeleton equations for the reaction of aqueous hydrochloric acid with sodium hydroxide. Then write the balanced formula equation. Decide which reaction type it resembles. Explain your reasoning.

10. Carbohydrates burn in oxygen to produce the same products as a hydrocarbon combustion reaction does. Write the formula equation for the combustion of table sugar, $C_{12}H_{22}O_{11(s)}$, and balance the equation.

A 3.4 The Mole

Chemists deal with atoms and molecules all the time, and they need to measure quantities of matter precisely. Balanced equations indicate the correct proportion of atoms and molecules to use in a reaction. Of course, chemists cannot measure materials by counting individual atoms or molecules. Instead, they place large numbers of them into groups of a convenient size and then count the number of groups.

We often group objects when counting them, both in chemistry and in everyday situations. The most common grouping quantity is the dozen. A dozen is a group of 12 objects. It makes no difference what the objects are. A dozen means 12 whether it is a dozen eggs, a dozen donuts, or a dozen pencils.

Since atoms and molecules are very small, the quantity used to measure them needs to be a very large number. Like the dozen, this quantity never changes, but unlike the dozen, its value is very, very large.

*info***BIT**

Mole day is celebrated on October 23 each year. It begins at 6:02 A.M. and ends at 6:02 P.M. The numbers associated with these dates and times are derived from Avogadro's number, a constant known to all chemists in the world. Its value is approximately 6.02×10^{23}.

Avogadro's Number and the Mole

The quantity that chemists use to measure elements and compounds is called the **mole** (symbol: mol). Like the dozen, the mole represents a number. The number of particles in 1 mol is called **Avogadro's number** (symbol: N_A).

To define the mole, chemists chose to work with an isotope of the element carbon: carbon-12. Carbon is a stable solid, so it is easy to work with, and it can be obtained in very pure form.

Here's how a chemist defines a mole:

1. Get a 12 g sample of carbon-12. The number of atoms in the sample is, by definition, exactly one mole (1 mol). Why use a 12-g sample? This way, the mass of one mole of any element will be the same or nearly the same as the mass number.
2. Find a way to count how many carbon atoms are in the sample. The total number of carbon atoms in the sample gives Avogadro's number (N_A). Avogadro's number is the number of atoms in 1 mol of carbon atoms. This number is approximately 6.02×10^{23}.

The mole can be used to measure any kind of particle—atoms, ions, molecules, and formula units. It is possible to have a mole of iron atoms, a mole of water molecules, and a mole of sodium chloride. They each contain the number of particles that is equal to Avogadro's number: 6.02×10^{23}.

Avogadro's number is to the mole what 12 is to the dozen. Sometimes, Avogadro's number is referred to as the "chemist's dozen." It is a very convenient amount of atoms to use in the lab, because 1 mol of most substances would just fill a small beaker. Figure A3.23 shows 1-mol amounts of five different elements.

This is how Avogadro's number looks when written out in common notation:

602 000 000 000 000 000 000 000

FIGURE A3.23 Each sample contains 1 mol: 6.02×10^{23} of atoms. Which element do you think has the heaviest atoms?

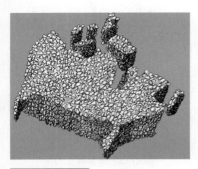

*info***BIT**

A sample of pure carbon contains a mixture of the isotopes carbon-12, carbon-13, and carbon-14. The atomic molar mass is an average of these masses. For carbon, the atomic molar mass is very close to 12.00 because 99% of carbon on Earth is composed of carbon-12.

Practice Problems

13. What is the molar mass of $CH_3OH_{(l)}$?

14. What is the molar mass of $Na_2SO_{4(s)}$?

15. What is the molar mass of $CO_{2(g)}$?

16. What is the molar mass of $(NH_4)_3PO_{4(s)}$?

Avogadro's number was named in honour of Amedeo Avogadro, an Italian scientist (1776–1856). Avogadro himself did not identify this number. It was named after him to honour his many contributions to chemistry. For example, he was the first to predict that oxygen was diatomic.

Molar Mass

The mass of one mole of a substance is called its **molar mass**. Experiments have been performed to find the mass of one mole of each of the elements. These have been recorded in the periodic table under the name **atomic molar mass**. The atomic molar mass of an element is the average mass in grams of one mole of atoms of that element. For example, in the periodic table in Figure A3.25, the molar mass of carbon is 12.01 g/mol.

You can use the atomic molar mass information from the periodic table to find the molar mass of any substance if you know its chemical formula. Recall that the molar mass of a substance is the mass of one mole of that substance. Example Problem A3.12 shows how to calculate molar mass of a compound.

Example Problem A3.12

What is the molar mass of methane?

The formula of methane is $CH_{4(g)}$, so one molecule contains one carbon atom and four hydrogen atoms.

$$
\begin{aligned}
\text{atomic molar mass of H} &= 1.01 \text{ g/mol} \times 4 = 4.04 \text{ g/mol} \\
+ \text{ atomic molar mass of C} &= 12.01 \text{ g/mol} \times 1 = \underline{12.01 \text{ g/mol}} \\
= \text{ molar mass of } CH_{4(g)} & \qquad\qquad\quad M = 16.05 \text{ g/mol}
\end{aligned}
$$

The molar mass of methane is 16.05 g/mol.

The number of moles of a substance is related to its molar mass by the following equation:

$m = n \times M$
where
m is the quantity of matter (mass) in grams,
n is the quantity of matter in moles, and
M is the molar mass.

Although this formula can be manipulated to convert between mass and moles, it is very common to use another method called the factor-label method.

The Factor-Label Method of Converting between Quantities

The factor-label method is a simple technique for converting between the number of moles of a substance and its mass. This method is based on the idea that different units can represent the same quantity of matter. For example, from the periodic table we know that 1 mol of carbon has a mass of 12.01 g. Both 1 mol of carbon and 12.01 g of carbon represent the same amount of carbon. From this equivalence we can write:

1 mol C = 12.01 g C

Because 1 mol C is equal to 12.01 g C, their ratio has a value of 1; that is,

$$\frac{1 \text{ mol C}}{12.01 \text{ g C}} = 1$$

This fraction is called a "factor" and the units are the "labels." It can also be written as:

$$\frac{12.01 \text{ g C}}{1 \text{ mol C}} = 1$$

Suppose we want to find the mass of 3.000 moles of carbon. This is a moles-to-mass conversion, so we choose the factor that has "mole" in the denominator so it will cancel out the "mol" in the 3.000 mol.

$$m_C = 3.000 \text{ mol} \times \frac{12.01 \text{ g}}{1 \text{ mol}}$$

$$= 36.03 \text{ g C}$$

Using the factor-label method, all the units will cancel except the one we want in the answer.

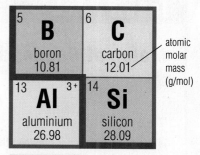

FIGURE A3.25 The periodic table shows the mass, in grams, of one mole of each of these elements.

Example Problem A3.13

How many moles of silicon are in a 56.18-g sample?

Using the atomic molar mass of Si   1 mol = 28.09 g

The factor is $\dfrac{1 \text{ mol}}{28.09 \text{ g}}$

Therefore $n_{Si} = 56.18 \text{ g} \times \dfrac{1 \text{ mol}}{28.09 \text{ g}}$

$$= 2.000 \text{ mol}$$

There are 2.000 mol of silicon in a 56.18-g sample.

Example Problem A3.14

What is the mass of 10.0 mol of water?

The molar mass of $H_2O_{(l)}$ is 18.02 g/mol

so   1 mol = 18.02 g

The factor is $\dfrac{18.02 \text{ g}}{1 \text{ mol}}$

Therefore $m_{H_2O} = 10.0 \text{ mol} \times \dfrac{18.02 \text{ g}}{1 \text{ mol}}$

$$= 180 \text{ g}$$

The mass of 10.0 mol of water is 180 g.

Practice Problems

17. What is the mass of 5.0 mol of $NaOH_{(s)}$?

18. How many moles are in 360 g of glucose, $C_6H_{12}O_{6(s)}$?

19. What is the mass of 5.00 mol of $NH_{3(g)}$?

20. How many moles are in a 20.0-g sample of magnesium nitrate?

Moles of Copper and Iron

The Question

Is there a relationship between the number of moles of iron that are consumed and the number of moles of copper that are produced when iron nails react with copper(II) chloride?

The Hypothesis

If copper(II) chloride and iron react, then they will do so according to a precise mole ratio.

Variables

Identify the manipulated, responding, and controlled variables in this inquiry.

Materials and Equipment

2 iron nails (not galvanized and not stainless)

copper(II) chloride

2 100-mL beakers

tongs

drying oven

paper towels

balance

Procedure

1. Measure and record the mass of a clean, dry 100-mL beaker. To get good results in this experiment, it is particularly important to measure all masses to as many decimal places as the balance will permit.

2. Add about 5 g of copper(II) chloride to the beaker. Record the mass of copper(II) chloride.

3. Add about 80 mL of water to the beaker. The actual amount added is not critical and need not be recorded.

4. Put both iron nails on the balance at the same time. Record their total mass.

5. Use one of the nails to stir the copper(II) chloride solution, then place both nails in the solution. The ends of the nails should stick out of the solution so you can pick the nails up again easily. After about 1 minute, lift one of the nails partly out of the solution and examine it. Record the colour. Place the nail back in the solution, and let it react for at least 30 minutes.

6. After waiting for at least 30 minutes, pick up the nails by the ends that are sticking out of solution. Clean them by scraping them together over the beaker. Make sure any copper falls into the beaker.

7. Dry the nails with paper towels. Measure and record their total mass.

8. Wait about 2 minutes. Then carefully decant (pour off) the liquid in the beaker. The purpose of this step is to leave the copper residue at the bottom of the first beaker.

9. Wash the copper by adding water to the beaker until the beaker is almost full. Then decant it, leaving the copper in the beaker. Repeat this several times.

10. Place the beaker containing the copper in a drying oven for at least 30 minutes or overnight.

11. Measure and record the mass of the copper and the beaker together.

12. Follow your teacher's instructions for disposing of all the substances you have used.

Analyzing and Interpreting

1. Subtract the mass of the nails after the reaction from the mass of the nails before the reaction. This gives the mass of the iron that reacted.

2. Subtract the mass of the beaker from the mass of the beaker and the dried copper. This gives the mass of the copper that was produced.

3. Calculate the number of moles of iron that reacted, based on the mass of iron that reacted.

4. Calculate the number of moles of copper that formed, based on the mass of copper that was produced.

5. Divide the number of moles of iron by the number of moles of copper, and round off to the nearest whole number. This number gives the ratio of moles of iron reacted to moles of copper produced.

6. Compare your result with the results of other students in the class.

Forming Conclusions

7. Using your result and the results of other students in the class, state your conclusion about whether there is a relationship between the number of moles of iron that are consumed and the number of moles of copper that are produced.

The Mole Concept and the Law of Conservation of Mass

Recall that the law of conservation of mass states that, in any reaction, the total mass of the reactants equals the total mass of the products. In balancing chemical equations, you applied this law. You made sure that the total number of atoms of each element in the reactants was equal to the total number of atoms of that same element in the products. You did this by placing coefficients in front of the element symbols and chemical formulas. When chemists read equations that have been balanced, they often read the coefficients as moles. One reason is that you can see a mole of something, while it is impossible to see an atom of something. Another reason is that chemists use the mole to measure out chemicals. For example, consider the reaction of sodium metal with oxygen gas in a formation reaction. The word equation for this reaction is:

sodium + oxygen $\longrightarrow$ sodium oxide

The balanced equation for this reaction is:

$$4\,Na_{(s)} + O_{2(g)} \longrightarrow 2\,Na_2O_{(s)}$$

You can read the balanced equation as:

4 atoms $Na_{(s)}$ + 1 molecule $O_{2(g)} \longrightarrow$ 2 molecules $Na_2O_{(s)}$

You can read this same equation as:

4 moles of $Na_{(s)}$ + 1 mole of $O_{2(g)} \longrightarrow$ 2 moles of $Na_2O_{(s)}$

A chemical equation is like a recipe where the quantities are measured in moles.

*re*SEARCH

Find out more about Amedeo Avogadro (1776–1856). What was his main contribution to chemistry? Find out how he came to distinguish between Dalton's idea of the atom and a new concept called a molecule. How did this lead Avogadro to predict that oxygen gas was diatomic? Begin your search at

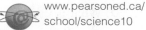
www.pearsoned.ca/ school/science10

Knowledge

1. How many particles are in one mole?

2. Which element was chosen as the standard for defining the mole? How many grams of this element are equal to one mole?

3. What is meant by the term "molar mass"?

4. What is the name given to the number of particles in one mole of substance? What is the symbol for this number?

Applications

5. How many atoms or molecules are present in each of the following?
   a) 1.0 mol of $Au_{(s)}$ atoms
   b) 2.5 mol of $He_{(g)}$ atoms
   c) 10.0 mol of $H_{2(g)}$ molecules
   d) 0.628 mol of $CO_{2(g)}$ molecules

6. How many moles are present in each of the following?
   a) 28 g of sodium
   b) 28 g of iron
   c) 150 g of zinc
   d) 100.0 g of $NaCl_{(s)}$
   e) 26.0 g of $N_{2(g)}$

7. What is the mass of each sample?
   a) 1.0 mol of nickel atoms
   b) 1.0 mol of carbon dioxide molecules
   c) 5.0 mol of water
   d) 36.8 mol of $MgCl_{2(s)}$
   e) 0.00127 mol of $Al_2S_{3(s)}$

8. In your notebook, complete equations a), b), and c). They are all related to the following formula equation:

$$3\ H_{2(g)} \quad + \quad N_{2(g)} \quad \longrightarrow \quad 2\ NH_{3(g)}$$

a) 3 mol + _____ $\longrightarrow$ 2 mol

b) _____ + 28 g $\longrightarrow$ 34 g

c) 1.83×10^{24} + 6.02×10^{23} $\longrightarrow$ _____
    molecules   molecules

Extensions

9. What is the mass of 3.01×10^{23} atoms of copper?

10. How many molecules of water are in 1000 g of water?

11. How many oxygen atoms are in 64 g of oxygen gas?

12. Which contains more atoms: a mole of iron or a mole of oxygen gas? Explain.

13. Write the balanced equation for the combustion reaction involving methane. Assume 15 mol of methane burned in the reaction. Predict how many moles of water would be produced.

Knowledge

1. Explain what is meant by the term "chemical reaction." List three characteristics common to all reactions.

2. List five different indications that a chemical reaction is taking place.

3. Many chemical reactions produce one or more gases. Give one example of a gas-producing reaction used in each of the following applications:
   a) household
   b) commercial

4. Use the following balanced chemical equation to answer the questions below:

$$4\,Na_{(s)} + O_{2(g)} \longrightarrow 2\,Na_2O_{(s)}$$

   a) What state symbols are present and what are their meanings?
   b) What coefficients are present and what are their meanings?
   c) Name the reactant(s) and the product(s).
   d) How do you know that this equation was properly balanced?

5. List five classes of chemical reactions. Write a general equation for each.

6. What is the value of Avogadro's number?

7. What is a mole?

8. What is meant by the term "atomic molar mass"?

9. How many moles are present in each of the following?
   a) 36.03 g of carbon
   b) 1000 g of $H_2O_{(l)}$
   c) 50.0 g of $CaCO_{3(s)}$
   d) 22.61 g of $NH_4NO_{3(s)}$
   e) 0.795 g of aluminium hydroxide

10. What is the mass of each sample below?
   a) 1.00 mol of gold atoms
   b) 5.6 mol of $Cu_{(s)}$ atoms
   c) 100 mol of $H_{2(g)}$ molecules
   d) 0.918 mol of $NaOH_{(s)}$
   e) 3.00 mol of magnesium acetate

Applications

11. Some single and double replacement reactions produce a precipitate. Weather forecasters also speak of the chance of precipitation occurring. Explain how the term "precipitation" actually has similar meaning in both cases.

12. Write the following sentences as balanced formula equations.
   a) Liquid bromine plus solid aluminium produces solid aluminium bromide.
   b) Solid ammonium carbonate plus aqueous calcium nitrate produces aqueous ammonium nitrate and solid calcium carbonate.
   c) Solid sodium hydroxide plus aqueous hydrochloric acid produces aqueous sodium chloride and liquid water.

13. Classify each of the following reactions, and balance the equations.
   a) $KBrO_{3(s)} \longrightarrow KBr_{(s)} + O_{2(g)}$
   b) $C_2H_{2(g)} + O_{2(g)} \longrightarrow CO_{2(g)} + H_2O_{(g)}$
   c) $AuCl_{3(aq)} + Pb_{(s)} \longrightarrow PbCl_{4(aq)} + Au_{(s)}$
   d) $K_{(s)} + N_{2(g)} \longrightarrow K_3N_{(s)}$
   e) $Sn(NO_3)_{4(aq)} + Ca(OH)_{2(s)} \longrightarrow$
      $\qquad\qquad Ca(NO_3)_{2(aq)} + Sn(OH)_{4(s)}$

14. Classify the following reactions. Then complete the equations and balance them.
   a) $F_{2(g)} + Ca_{(s)} \longrightarrow$
   b) $Cl_{2(g)} + NiBr_{3(aq)} \longrightarrow$
   c) $C_5H_{10(l)} + O_{2(g)} \longrightarrow$
   d) $KBr_{(s)} \longrightarrow$
   e) $AlF_{3(aq)} + Na_3PO_{4(aq)} \longrightarrow$

Extensions

15. Suppose that it was proposed that the law of conservation of mass be renamed the law of conservation of atoms. Explain why this new name would or would not correctly describe the processes that happen in a chemical reaction.

16. What is the mass of 1.204×10^{23} atoms of sodium?

17. How many molecules of carbon dioxide are there in 66.0 g of $CO_{2(g)}$?

Air Quality

The growth of industry and urbanization, combined with social and political events, has had many impacts on air quality. A number of pivotal events have resulted in legislation to prevent recurrences. Some of these events have happened over a long period. Others happened suddenly with dramatic and tragic consequences. Environmental legislation sometimes imposes standards that are technically impossible at the time that the legislation is introduced. To comply with the legislation, companies must develop new technologies. In this way, legislation can protect people's health and the environment and drive research and development.

Scenario

You are a member of a government committee responsible for advising on legislation for air quality. However, time is limited. Legislation can be written only in one area in the following year, so your committee can recommend only one area to focus on. To help decide on a priority area, your committee will examine events in transportation, industrial accidents, disaster response, and indoor air quality. Examples from each area are summarized below.

A) Transportation

Roughly one-half of the air pollution in Canada comes from transportation. Cars and other motor vehicles release the pollutants that include carbon monoxide, hydrocarbons, nitrogen oxides, lead, and particulate matter.

B) Industrial Accidents

Wherever chemicals are used or produced in large quantities, there is a potential for major industrial accidents. In Bhopal, India, a disaster occurred in December 1984 when a toxic chemical called methyl isocyanate gas was released from the Union Carbide plant located in the middle of the city. The massive leak resulted in the deaths of thousands of residents and in the permanent disability of tens of thousands of people.

C) Disaster Response

The twin towers of the World Trade Center in New York City were destroyed in a terrorist attack on September 11, 2001. Heroic efforts of emergency personnel were hampered by toxic fumes and dust from the burning and crumbling materials used to construct these buildings. Rescue workers were exposed to massive doses of particulates and chemicals, resulting in respiratory illness and exposure to cancer-causing chemicals. Existing protective devices either were not available or were ineffective.

D) Indoor Air Quality

Asthma rates and respiratory illness may have less to do with the air we breathe out of doors and more to do with indoor air quality. Secondhand smoke, poor ventilation, and materials used to build and furnish our living spaces affect indoor air quality. The poor quality of indoor air can affect our health because of the amount of time we spend inside buildings.

Research the Issue

Research the issue by referring to the following resources:

1. Look at the Web. Check the Internet for information on the occurrence you choose to investigate. Search for legislation that may have been written as a direct response to these occurrences.

2. Ask the experts. Contact community groups that have formed in response to any of these issues. Contact companies or agencies that have been directly involved with these events.

3. Look in magazines, newspapers, or books for information on the social impacts of, and responses to, these occurrences.

Analyze the Issue

4. Summarize the information you have found into a short report or electronic presentation. Include your recommendation to the committee on which area of air quality control requires new legislation. Briefly outline what the legislation should cover. Be sure to connect the need for the legislation to the importance of the issue in your particular community in the next several years. Also, consider whether the legislation should be enacted at the community, provincial, or federal level to have the greatest impact.

Address the Issue

5. Present your findings and conclusions to your classmates in a convincing presentation.

Project

Classifying Chemical Reactions Involving Magnesium

In this activity, you will perform and observe tests to distinguish between several types of chemical reactions. By carefully noting the reactants and observing the chemical changes, you will be able to classify them. You will also write balanced equations for these reactions.

Criteria for Success

- You must be able to distinguish between the types of chemical reactions.

- You must provide written observations and balanced formula equations showing states for each reaction.

Materials and Equipment

2 2-cm magnesium strips

1 mol/L hydrochloric acid

magnesium sulfate

sodium carbonate

magnesium carbonate

aluminium foil

4 test tubes

10-mL graduated cylinder

water

2 test tube stoppers

hot plate

CAUTION: Hydrochloric acid is corrosive.

Procedure

1. Pour 5 mL of 1 mol/L hydrochloric acid into a test tube. Drop in a piece of magnesium ribbon. Add a second piece so you can see the reaction again. Record your observations.

2. Place about 1 g of magnesium sulfate in a test tube and add about 5 mL of water. Stopper the test tube and shake it to dissolve the magnesium sulfate.

3. Place about 1 g of sodium carbonate in a test tube and add about 5 mL of water. Stopper the test tube and shake it in order to dissolve the sodium carbonate.

4. Mix the magnesium sulfate solution and sodium carbonate solution together. Record your observations.

5. Place magnesium carbonate on a sheet of aluminium foil and heat it on a hot plate. Record any observed changes in the magnesium carbonate.

Analysis

1. When magnesium reacts with hydrochloric acid, the hydrogen in the hydrochloric acid behaves chemically like a metal. What type of reaction is this? Write word and formula equations for this reaction.

2. When magnesium sulfate and sodium carbonate solutions mix, a white precipitate is observed. What is the identity of this precipitate? What type of reaction is this? Write word and formula equations for this reaction.

3. When the magnesium carbonate is heated on aluminium foil, the only reactant is magnesium carbonate. One of the products is carbon dioxide gas. The other product is also an oxide. What type of reaction is this? Write word and formula equations for this reaction.

Reporting

4. Write a summary report that contains your observations and the word and balanced chemical equations for each reaction.

Unit Summary

A 1.0 **The understanding that particles make up the underlying structure of matter has led to advancements in technology.**

Key Concepts

- WHMIS and safe practices
- evidence of chemical change
- how chemical substances meet human needs

Learnings

- Knowing how to interpret WHMIS symbols, other hazard symbols, and Material Safety Data Sheets is essential for lab safety.
- Chemical change occurs when a substance or substances react to create a different substance or substances in a chemical reaction. These products have completely different properties from the reactants.
- Human understanding of matter developed gradually as people learned to manipulate matter.
- The Greek philosopher Aristotle stated that matter was made up of earth, air, fire, and water.
- Aristotle's ideas were used for 2000 years, until John Dalton and other early scientists inferred the existence of atoms from experiments.
- Further investigation by scientists such as J. J. Thomson, Ernest Rutherford, and Neils Bohr gradually brought us to our current understanding of the atom.

A 2.0 **Elements combine to form many substances, each with its own set of properties.**

Key Concepts

- how chemical substances meet human needs
- International Union of Pure and Applied Chemistry (IUPAC) nomenclature, ionic and molecular compounds, acids and bases

Learnings

- Elements are substances made up of only one type of atom. There are 90 naturally occurring elements, and approximately 25 synthetic ones.
- Most elements are metals. Only 17 elements are non-metals. The remaining elements are called metalloids.
- The periodic table is an organized display of information about the elements. Rows are called periods, and columns are called groups or families. Elements in families tend to have similar properties.
- An atom is made up of a nucleus containing protons and neutrons and surrounded by electrons. Protons are positively charged; electrons are negatively charged; and neutrons have no charge.
- Electrons in the atom occupy specific energy levels around the nucleus, which can be empty, partly full, or full.

- Atoms of the same element containing different numbers of neutrons are called isotopes. Each isotope is assigned a mass number that equals the total number of neutrons and protons in its nucleus.
- An atom that loses or gains electrons has either a positive or a negative charge. It is called an ion.
- The International Union of Pure and Applied Chemistry (IUPAC) is responsible for the rules governing how chemical compounds are named.
- Ionic compounds form when electrons transfer from one atom to another to form an ionic bond. An ionic compound always contains a positive metal ion called a cation and a negative non-metal ion called an anion.
- Molecular compounds form when non-metallic atoms combine by sharing electrons to form a covalent bond.
- An acid is a compound that dissolves in water to form a solution with a pH lower than 7. A base is one with a pH higher than 7. The pH is a measure of the number of hydrogen ions in solution.
- Our society uses many potentially harmful chemicals. Their manufacture, use, and disposal must be carefully controlled and monitored.

A 3.0 **Chemical change is a process that involves recombining atoms and energy flows.**

Key Concepts

- how chemical substances meet human needs
- evidence of chemical change
- role and need for classification of chemical change
- writing and balancing equations
- law of conservation of mass
- the mole concept

Learnings

- Chemical changes are always accompanied by energy flows.
- Exothermic reactions release energy. Endothermic reactions absorb energy.
- The law of conservation of mass states that in a chemical reaction, the total mass of all the products equals the total mass of all the reactants.
- Five common types of chemical reactions are: formation, decomposition, hydrocarbon combustion, single replacement, and double replacement.
- Chemists use a quantity called the mole (symbol: mol) to measure elements and compounds. A mole contains the number of particles equivalent to Avogadro's number: 6.02×10^{23}. A mole is just a measure of quantity: it can be used to measure the number of atoms, molecules, ions, or any other item. The mass of 1 mol of any substance is called its molar mass.

Vocabulary

1. Create a concept map with the word "matter" at the centre that links all the terms in the list below.

acid
atomic number
base
compound
electron
element
energy level
endothermic
exothermic
group
ion
isotope
law of conservation of mass
molecule
neutron
nucleus
period
pH scale
proton
valence electron

Knowledge

A 1.0

2. Where are the fire extinguishers, the fire alarms, and the fire exits in your science class?

3. How does heating or freezing food each help to preserve it?

4. What are some of the practical advantages of copper over gold?

5. How did the Inuit obtain copper, and what did they use it for?

6. What is the difference between copper and bronze?

7. J. J. Thomson discovered a subatomic particle. What was it and how did he include it in his model of the atom?

8. State the law of conservation of mass.

9. What part of the atom did Rutherford discover? How did he include it in his model of the atom?

A 2.0

10. Name five groups in the periodic table and indicate where they appear in it. Which groups contain metals, and which ones contain non-metals?

11. Distinguish between the terms "period" and "family" as they apply to the periodic table.

12. How are mass number and atomic number of an element related?

13. Distinguish between cations and anions.

14. Complete the following table in your notebook. Use the periodic table (Table A) in Student Reference 12, as needed, to fill in the number of protons or the name of the element.

Element	Mass Number	Protons	Neutrons
carbon	13		
bromine	79		
bromine			46
	36		19
	57	26	
sodium			22

15. Use the periodic table (Table A) in Student Reference 12 to complete the following table in your notebook.

Atom or Ion	Overall Charge	Protons	Electrons	Symbol
sulfur atom				S
sulfide ion			18	S^{2-}
lithium ion		3		
		8	10	
				Cl^-
	2+	26		
	3−		10	

16. Using the solubility table (Table C) in Student Reference 12, state whether the following are slightly soluble or very soluble:
a) Na_2SO_4
b) NH_4Cl
c) PbI_2
d) $SrSO_4$
e) MgS
f) K_3PO_4

17. A pH measurement indicates whether a solution at 25°C is acidic, basic, or neutral. What values on the pH scale correspond to these types of solutions?

18. List three chemical properties that are unique to acidic solutions, and three properties that are unique to basic solutions.

19. Why is the IUPAC system of naming chemical compounds important?

20. List three high-risk activities associated with the misuse of alcohol.

A 3.0

21. Distinguish between a chemical reaction and a chemical equation.

22. Balance each of the following equations:
a) $Cl_{2(g)} + KBr_{(aq)} \longrightarrow KCl_{(aq)} + Br_{2(l)}$
b) $Li_{(s)} + O_{2(g)} \longrightarrow Li_2O_{(s)}$
c) $C_2H_{6(g)} + O_{2(g)} \longrightarrow H_2O_{(g)} + CO_{2(g)}$
d) $Na_{(s)} + N_{2(g)} \longrightarrow Na_3N_{(s)}$
e) $(NH_4)_3PO_{4(aq)} + Ca(NO_3)_{2(aq)} \longrightarrow$
$$NH_4NO_{3(aq)} + Ca_3(PO_4)_{2(s)}$$
f) $CaCO_{3(s)} \longrightarrow CaO_{(s)} + CO_{2(g)}$

23. For each of the following equations, identify which reaction type it represents: formation, decomposition, hydrocarbon combustion, single replacement, or double replacement.
a) methane + oxygen $\longrightarrow$
carbon dioxide + water
b) strontium + nitrogen $\longrightarrow$ strontium nitride
c) aluminium bromide + fluorine $\longrightarrow$
aluminium fluoride + bromine
d) calcium chloride $\longrightarrow$ calcium + chlorine

e) magnesium iodide + sodium carbonate $\longrightarrow$
magnesium carbonate + sodium iodide
f) silver nitrate + aluminium chloride $\longrightarrow$
aluminium nitrate + silver chloride

Applications

24. List five of the most important safety rules for your science class.

25. What safety hazard symbols would you expect to see on the following containers? What WHMIS symbols would you expect to see on each?
a) a bottle of bleach
b) a can of gasoline
c) a can of spray paint
d) a bottle of helium gas
e) a bottle of hydrochloric acid

26. Improvements in technology sometimes increase our ability to both wage war and to prosper in peace. Explain this idea using metallurgy advancements as an example.

27. What is the octet rule? How is it related to the filling of energy levels?

28. Draw diagrams to show the electron arrangements in:
a) a calcium atom
b) a calcium ion

29. Choose the correct words to complete the following statements:
a) When metals become ions, they (gain/lose) electrons in order to become (positively/negatively) charged.
b) When non-metals become ions, they gain (protons/electrons) in order to become (anions/cations).

30. Explain the meaning of the term "ion charge," using the iron(II) and iron(III) ions as examples.

31. Explain the term "electrolyte." Why do ionic compounds dissolve to form electrolytes but most molecular compounds do not?

32. Many molecular compounds melt below 200°C, while almost all ionic compounds melt above 200°C. Why?

33. Write formulas for the following ionic compounds:
    a) lithium chloride
    b) barium nitride
    c) zinc oxide
    d) silver carbonate
    e) calcium nitrite
    f) rubidium hydrogensulfate
    g) cadmium phosphate
    h) cobalt(III) hydroxide
    i) copper(II) permanganate
    j) chromium(III) oxide
    k) iron(III) chlorate

34. Write names for the following ionic compounds:
    a) $Na_3P_{(s)}$
    b) $MgS_{(s)}$
    c) $BeCl_{2(s)}$
    d) $(NH_4)_2S_{(s)}$
    e) $Cs_3N_{(s)}$
    f) $ZnI_{2(s)}$
    g) $FeF_{2(s)}$
    h) $Fe(HS)_{3(s)}$
    i) $AuNO_{3(s)}$
    j) $Pb(MnO_4)_{4(s)}$
    k) $NaCH_3COO_{(s)}$

35. Write formulas for the following molecular compounds:
    a) dinitrogen monosulfide
    b) sulfur dibromide
    c) chlorine monofluoride
    d) hydrogen sulfide
    e) methane
    f) phosphorus pentachloride

36. Write names for the following molecular compounds:
    a) $P_4O_{10(s)}$
    b) $NO_{2(g)}$
    c) $NCl_{3(g)}$
    d) $XeF_{6(s)}$
    e) $H_2O_{2(l)}$
    f) $NH_{3(g)}$

37. Explain how the polarity of water results in cations and anions surrounding it in special ways.

38. Use the solubility table (Table C) in Student Reference 12 to help you answer these questions. For each of the following solutions, state whether adding OH^- to it would result in the formation of no precipitate, one precipitate, or two precipitates. Identify any precipitates.
    a) a solution of $CsNO_{3(aq)}$ and $Fe(NO_3)_{2(aq)}$
    b) a solution of $CuNO_{3(aq)}$ and $Sr(NO_3)_{2(aq)}$
    c) a solution of $AgNO_{3(aq)}$ and $Cd(NO_3)_{2(aq)}$

39. A solution of hydrochloric acid has a pH of 1.0. It is mixed with a small amount of solid sodium hydroxide. After mixing, the pH of the solution is 3.0. Has the solution become more acidic or less acidic? Explain.

40. How can you recognize acids and bases by their formulas?

41. In what ways are alcohol and nicotine similar?

42. Give an example of a regulated substance used in industry. What kinds of regulations may be set in place governing its use?

43. Provide two examples where a chemical reaction and its reverse both occur: one in living systems and one in non-living systems.

44. A chemical reaction occurs inside a beaker. As the reaction progresses, the beaker becomes warmer. Is the reaction endothermic or exothermic? Explain your answer.

45. Explain the difference between a chemical change and a physical change.

46. Write balanced formula equations for the following reactions. Include state symbols:
    a) solid iodine reacts with liquid mercury to produce solid mercury(II) iodide
    b) aqueous potassium phosphate reacts with aqueous strontium hydroxide to produce aqueous potassium hydroxide and solid strontium phosphate
    c) solid magnesium reacts with aqueous hydrochloric acid to produce aqueous magnesium chloride and hydrogen gas

47. Classify each of the following reactions, and balance the equations:
    a) $CaI_{2(s)} + AgNO_{3(aq)} \longrightarrow Ca(NO_3)_{2(aq)} + AgI_{(s)}$
    b) $C_6H_{14(l)} + O_{2(g)} \longrightarrow CO_{2(g)} + H_2O_{(g)}$
    c) $MgCO_{3(s)} \longrightarrow MgO_{(s)} + CO_{2(g)}$
    d) $Li_2SO_{3(aq)} + Au(NO_3)_{3(aq)} \longrightarrow$ $LiNO_{3(aq)} + Au_2(SO_3)_{3(s)}$
    e) $Cs_{(s)} + S_{8(s)} \longrightarrow Cs_2S_{(s)}$
    f) $Al_{(s)} + CuSO_{4(aq)} \longrightarrow Al_2(SO_4)_{3(aq)} + Cu_{(s)}$

48. Classify each of the following reactions. Write the skeleton equation and balance it.
    a) $CaF_{2(aq)} + I_{2(s)} \longrightarrow$
    b) $RbI_{(s)} \longrightarrow$
    c) $C_3H_{8(g)} + O_{2(g)} \longrightarrow$
    d) $Cu(ClO_4)_{2(aq)} + Li_3PO_{4(aq)} \longrightarrow$
    e) $Zn_{(s)} + FeBr_{3(aq)} \longrightarrow$

49. How many moles are present in each of the following?
    a) 8.00 g of $He_{(g)}$
    b) 11.50 g of $Na_{(s)}$
    c) 72.08 g of $H_2O_{(l)}$
    d) 0.251 g of $Na_2SO_{4(s)}$
    e) 6.2 kg of $KCl_{(s)}$

50. What is the mass of each of the following samples?
    a) 2.00 mol of silver atoms
    b) 0.50 mol of $Pb_{(s)}$ atoms
    c) 10 mol of $O_{2(g)}$ molecules
    d) 9.67 mol of carbon disulfide
    e) 0.832 mol of calcium carbonate

Extensions

51. Describe how Antoine Lavoisier's experiments were an improvement over experiments conducted by earlier researchers.

52. The number of protons and electrons in a neutral atom are equal. Why is the atomic number defined as the number of protons rather than the number of electrons?

53. Distinguish between the terms "mass number" and "atomic molar mass."

54. Write the name or the formula for each of the following:
    a) $Na_2O_{(s)}$
    b) $Al_2(OOCCOO)_{3(s)}$
    c) $CH_3OH_{(l)}$
    d) ammonium hydrogenoxalate
    e) propane
    f) ruthenium(IV) dihydrogenphosphate
    g) $N_2O_{4(g)}$
    h) $W(Cr_2O_7)_{3(s)}$
    i) $OsO_{4(s)}$
    j) glucose
    k) platinum(IV) cyanide
    l) sodium thiosulfate

55. Commercial aircraft are equipped with oxygen masks in case of depressurization at high altitudes. A chemical reaction produces the oxygen supplied to the masks. The equation is:

$$KClO_{3(s)} \longrightarrow KCl_{(s)} + O_{2(g)}$$

Suggest at least three reasons why this method of delivering oxygen is better than supplying it from pressurized oxygen tanks.

56. How many atoms or molecules are present in each of the following?
    a) 2.0 mol of $Al_{(s)}$ atoms
    b) 36.0 mol of $SO_{3(g)}$ molecules
    c) 0.023 mol of $He_{(g)}$ atoms

57. How many moles are present in each of the following?
    a) 9.31×10^{22} molecules of $NH_{3(g)}$
    b) 1.63×10^{24} atoms of $Cu_{(s)}$
    c) 3.91×10^{23} molecules of $H_{2(g)}$

Skills Practice

58. A student wanted to verify the law of conservation of mass, so she reacted aqueous calcium chloride with aqueous sodium carbonate in a beaker. Although a precipitate formed, no change in the total mass of the reactants and products was observed. In a second experiment, the student reacted magnesium metal with hydrochloric acid in a beaker. A vigorous reaction occurred, and the mass of the products was several grams less than the mass of the reactants. Why did the law of conservation of mass seem to be obeyed in the first reaction and not in the second reaction?

59. Explain to a friend in a letter or e-mail how to determine whether an unknown liquid is an acid, a base, or neither. Specify several tests to perform, and explain how to interpret the results of the tests chemically. Include some safety precautions.

Self Assessment

60. What is one thing you learned in this unit that you would like to find out more about?

61. Why is it important to consider a variety of alternative perspectives when attempting to regulate the use of a potentially toxic industrial chemical?

62. Describe one aspect of your lifestyle that you could modify to reduce your use of environmentally hazardous materials.

Energy Flow in Technological Systems

A technician inspects a set of turbines.

In this unit, you will cover the following ideas:

B 1.0 **Investigating the energy flow in technological systems requires an understanding of motion, work, and energy.**

B1.1 Motion

B1.2 Velocity

B1.3 Acceleration

B1.4 Work and Energy

B 2.0 **Energy in mechanical systems can be described both numerically and graphically.**

B2.1 Forms of Energy

B2.2 Potential Energy

B2.3 Kinetic Energy and Motion

B2.4 Mechanical Energy

B2.5 Energy Conversions

B 3.0 **Principles of energy conservation and thermodynamics can be used to describe the efficiency of energy transformations.**

B3.1 Laws of Thermodynamics

B3.2 The Development of Engine Technology

B3.3 Useful Energy and Efficiency

B3.4 Energy Applications

Focus on Science and Technology

While studying this unit, you will be asked to organize your thoughts about how the science of energy and thermodynamics evolved and its corresponding effects on technology. As you work through this unit, think about the following questions:

1. Which came first: science or technology, and is it possible for technological development to take place without help from pure science?
2. How did efforts to improve the efficiency of heat engines result in the formulation of the first and second laws of thermodynamics?
3. How can the analysis of moving objects help in the understanding of changes in kinetic energy, force, and work?
4. Why are efficiency and sustainability important considerations in designing energy conversion technologies?

At the end of the unit, you may be asked to do these tasks:

Case Study Cost-Benefit Analysis of Energy Sources for Transportation
In this case study, you will analyze the costs and benefits of different energy sources for transportation. Based on your analysis, you will recommend which energy sources should be developed.

Project Build an Energy Conversion Device
For the project, you will design and build a Rube Goldberg device to demonstrate energy conversions. You will determine where energy is wasted in the design and suggest ways to reduce energy wastage.

Exploring

Hero's steam engine—the first mechanical device to use heat as a source of energy.

The Apollo spacecraft, which is located at the very top of the rocket, used fuel cells to produce electricity.

The two technological devices shown here were created almost two thousand years apart, but they have several things in common. For their times, they both were unique technological innovations and they both harnessed energy in new ways.

In the 1st century A.D., a Greek engineer named Hero of Alexandria designed the first heat engine. This engine, called a reaction turbine, was a primitive form of the modern steam engine. Hero's steam engine is a metal sphere connected by pipes to a container of water. Two narrow tubes bent at right angles extend from opposite sides of the sphere. The device is filled with water and placed over a fire. As the container is heated, the water boils, and steam is ejected from the nozzles. The sphere then rotates. His invention was the first mechanical device to use heat as a source of energy. However, this invention had no useful purpose; it was just a toy!

For the next 1500 years, people failed to realize the importance of this "hidden" source of energy. The secret of heat as a useful source of energy for machines was rediscovered only in the early 1600s. The start of the Industrial Revolution in the late 1700s brought the need for more sophisticated machines. Hero's steam engine was rediscovered and led to the development of more advanced technologies.

The Apollo spacecraft were among the most technologically advanced inventions of the 20th century and employed an innovative source of energy at the time, a hydrogen fuel cell. In actual fact, the science of the fuel cell was first described in the early 1850s. However, the science of the fuel cell was not applied successfully until the 1970s when it was first used in the Apollo space missions. The fuel cell is still used by NASA today to generate electricity in the space shuttle.

Fuel cell technology is no longer just being used for space flights. At the forefront of fuel cell research is a Canadian company called Ballard Power Systems, based in Vancouver. Although this company already has fuel-cell-powered buses operating in Canada and the U.S., it has unveiled four prototype fuel cell vehicles for DaimlerChrysler.

All Kinds of Energy

You probably use the word "energy" often in daily conversation. Did you ever stop to wonder how many different types of energy there are and where they are found?

Purpose

To identify different types of energy

Procedure

1. Go to each station, perform the procedures listed below, and record your observations. List the types of energy that come to mind at each station.

Station 1: Shine the light source on the radiometer.

Station 2: Turn on the flashlight.

Station 3: Bring a magnet close to a small piece of iron.

Station 4: Pull the pendulum ball back and release it.

Station 5: Use a spatula to place a small amount (approximately 5 g) of baking soda on an evaporating dish, and using the medicine dropper, place 1 or 2 drops of vinegar on the baking soda. Observe and then clean the evaporating dish.

Station 6: Place the hanging mass, which is attached to the block of wood, over a pulley at the edge of the ramp and allow the mass to fall to the table.

Station 7: Rub the ebonite rod with the fur and then bring the rod close to the bits of paper.

Station 8: Wind up the car and let it go.

Questions

1. How many different types of energy came to mind when you visited the stations?

2. Which stations demonstrated a type of energy that you did not know how to describe?

3. Which type of energy did you observe most commonly?

4. Did these demonstrations make you aware of some types of energy that you had never heard of?

Extending

5. Did you observe any transformations from one type of energy to another? Explain your answer.

Materials and Equipment

Station 1: a radiometer and a light source

Station 2: a battery-operated flashlight

Station 3: a magnet and small pieces of iron

Station 4: a pendulum attached by a string to a retort stand

Station 5: a beaker with vinegar, a dish of baking soda, and a medicine dropper

Station 6: a ramp, a pulley, a string, a mass, and a block of wood

Station 7: an ebonite rod, a piece of fur, and tiny bits of paper

Station 8: a wind-up car

Investigating the energy flow in technological systems requires an understanding of motion, work, and energy.

Key Concepts

In this section, you will learn about the following key concepts:

- one-dimensional motion
- work

Learning Outcomes

When you have completed this section, you will be able to:

- define, compare, and contrast scalar and vector quantities
- describe displacement and velocity quantitatively
- define acceleration quantitatively as a change in velocity during a time interval:

$$\vec{a} = \frac{\Delta \vec{v}}{\Delta t}$$

- explain that, in the absence of resistive forces, motion at constant speed requires no energy input
- recall from previous studies the operational definition for force as a push or a pull, and work as energy expended when the speed of an object is increased or when an object is moved against the influence of an opposing force
- investigate and analyze one-dimensional scalar motion and work done on an object or system using algebraic and graphical techniques

FIGURE B1.1 Competitors in the famous *Tour de France*

The *Tour de France* is considered to be the world's most prestigious bicycle race. Held in July, it winds its way through most of France. The course is divided into 20 stages. The overall winner each day gets to wear a prized yellow jersey. Perhaps the most gruelling stage of the tour occurs when the competitors reach the Pyrenees, where steep mountain roads test the endurance of the riders (Figure B1.1).

Pedalling a bike up a long steep hill can be extremely challenging and exhausting. When every muscle in your legs begins to feel like jelly, you might wish that someone could push you the rest of the way up the hill.

Humans always want to make life easier, and throughout history, we have invented technological devices and systems to help us perform heavy tasks. In designing new technological devices, people have discovered that many forms of energy can be harnessed to do work. Bicycles first used leg power, then motorbikes used energy from gasoline. Now, engineers have developed a prototype of a bicycle that uses energy from a hydrogen fuel cell. (Of course, this new fuel cell bike would never be used in the *Tour de France*, where "legwork" rules!)

The development of advances in technological systems depends on knowledge of the science involved and the link to technology. In this section, you will learn how studies of motion are related to the scientific concept of energy. By analyzing different types of motion, you will gain an understanding of the important relationships between forces and motion. After establishing these relationships, you will learn how they lead to a scientific concept of work. Finally, you will learn that only through a thorough understanding of work can the secret of the concept of energy be revealed.

B 1.1 Motion

Motion is all around us. It may be as simple as an object moving in a straight line at a constant speed, like the MAGLEV train in Figure B1.2, or as complicated as the circular motion of a Ferris wheel.

Motion is everywhere and easy to recognize, but it was not always easy to describe. The early Greek philosophers realized that motion involved an object travelling a certain distance in a time interval. However, they could not describe motion because they did not understand the idea of rate or how something changes in a certain amount of time.

Uniform Motion

We can analyze the motion of an object only if we compare the object's position to another point. This point is called a reference point, and all observations are made in relation to that point. For example, suppose you are floating on an air mattress on a swimming pool. You may not realize you are moving until you notice how far you are from the stairs where you entered the pool. The set of stairs is your reference point.

The **motion** of an object occurs when an imaginary line joining the object to the reference point changes in length or direction or both (Figure B1.3). In some cases, we may be interested only in the change in length of the line as an indication that motion has occurred. In other cases, we may be interested in both the change in length and the change in direction. Once we know that motion is present, we can then describe the type and the rate of motion.

In this section, we will concentrate on the simplest type of motion: uniform motion. **Uniform motion** is a term used to describe an object that is travelling at a constant rate of motion in a straight line. Many situations occur where an object appears to have uniform motion, but this type of motion is nearly impossible to maintain for long periods. For example, a car travels along a straight highway with the cruise control set at 100 km/h. The car appears to maintain a constant rate of motion, but various forces act to slow the car down, such as the friction of the tires on the road and wind resistance. Even with cruise control on, the car's rate of motion fluctuates around 100 km/h as its engine attempts to maintain the set rate. It is also almost impossible to maintain motion in a perfectly straight line in everyday situations.

FIGURE B1.2 This MAGLEV train displays uniform motion. It travels at a constant rate in a straight line, and it experiences almost no friction.

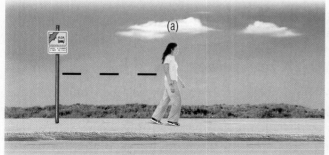
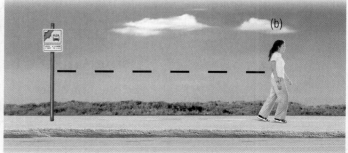

FIGURE B1.3 You can tell that the person has moved because the length of the imaginary line joining her to the bus stop changes between (a) and (b).

Average Speed

The car in the example above has a rate of motion or speed of 100 km/h. Because uniform motion is difficult to maintain, the term **average speed** is usually used. Average speed is uniform motion that involves travelling a distance in a specified time.

You might be able to estimate the average speed of an object based on your day-to-day experiences of motion. But to describe the speed of an object more accurately, you have to analyze it quantitatively with mathematical formulas or graphs.

Using Formulas to Analyze Average Speed

Use the following equation to determine the average speed of an object.

$$\text{average speed} = \frac{\text{distance travelled}}{\text{time elapsed}}$$

$$v = \frac{\Delta d}{\Delta t}$$

$$= \frac{d_{\text{final}} - d_{\text{initial}}}{t_{\text{final}} - t_{\text{initial}}}$$

Example Problem B1.1

A person walks 10.0 m away from a stop sign in 5.00 s. What is the average speed of the person?

Average speed:

$$v = \frac{\Delta d}{\Delta t}$$

$$= \frac{10.0 \text{ m} - 0.0 \text{ m}}{5.00 \text{ s} - 0.00 \text{ s}}$$

$$= \frac{10.0 \text{ m}}{5.00 \text{ s}}$$

$$= 2.00 \frac{\text{m}}{\text{s}}$$

The person walked at a speed of 2.00 m/s.

Practice Problems

1. A huge ocean wave, or tsunami, travels a distance of 4.0×10^6 m in 3.6×10^4 s. Calculate the average speed of the tsunami.

2. A Concorde airplane could fly at an average speed of 694 m/s. Calculate how long it would have taken the Concorde to fly around the world, which is approximately 4.00×10^7 m.

3. An electric train is travelling at an average speed of 6.9 m/s for 4.0 s. Calculate the distance travelled by the train.

Using Graphs to Analyze Average Speed

Creating a picture in your mind of an average speed can be difficult using formulas alone. A graph is an important tool for studying uniform motion because it not only shows the relationship between the two variables, but also provides a visual representation of the motion. For uniform motion, there are two types of graphs that can be used. They are a distance–time graph and a speed–time graph.

Plotting a Distance–Time Graph

Suppose a motorboat is travelling at a uniform speed. The boat passes marker buoys placed 5 m apart, which act as a measuring scale. As the boat passes the first marker, a person on shore starts to record the distance the boat travels away from the first marker every 2.0 s. Table B1.1 shows the measurements taken by the person on shore.

The graph in Figure B1.4 describes the motion of the motorboat. The line of best fit on the graph is a straight line with a positive slope. This indicates a direct linear relationship between the distance travelled and the time taken to travel the distance. This means that as time increases, the distance travelled also increases. Since the graph is a straight line, the change in distance travelled in relation to the time intervals is constant. This shows that the motorboat has uniform motion. As long as the line is a straight line, the object represented in the graph is displaying uniform motion. If the line of best fit were a curve of any type, this would mean the object was changing distance travelled in equal time intervals. In other words the object would be either speeding up or slowing down.

The slope of the line in Figure B1.4 also tells you something about the motion. The slope of the graph may be determined using the following formula:

$$\text{slope} = \frac{\text{rise}}{\text{run}}$$

$$= \frac{\text{change in distance}}{\text{change in time}} = \frac{\Delta d}{\Delta t}$$

$$= \text{speed} \qquad \text{Since } v = \frac{\Delta d}{\Delta t}$$

$$= \frac{\Delta d}{\Delta t}$$

$$= \frac{d_f - d_i}{t_f - t_i}$$

$$= \frac{30 \text{ m} - 10 \text{ m}}{6.0 \text{ s} - 2.0 \text{ s}}$$

$$= \frac{20 \text{ m}}{4.0 \text{ s}}$$

$$= 5.0 \frac{\text{m}}{\text{s}}$$

Therefore the average speed, v, is 5.0 m/s.

The slope of a distance–time graph is a visual representation of the speed of an object. A greater or steeper slope indicates a faster speed and a lesser slope indicates a slower speed.

TABLE B1.1 Progress of Boat Travelling past Marker Buoys

Time t (s)	Distance from First Marker d (m)
0.0	0
2.0	10
4.0	20
6.0	30
8.0	40
10.0	50

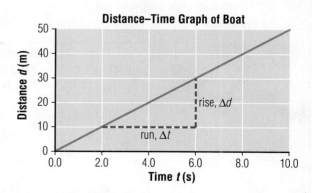

FIGURE B1.4 A distance–time graph produced from the data in Table B1.1

Distance–Time Graph of Three Objects

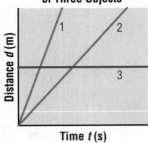

FIGURE B1.5
A distance–time graph showing three different motions

Figure B1.5 is a distance–time graph showing the motion of three objects. Line 1 shows an object with uniform motion. Line 2 shows an object with slower uniform motion than line 1. Line 3 shows a uniform motion of 0 m/s, meaning the object is at rest (not moving).

Example Problem B1.2

The data in Table B1.2 were collected for an object travelling at a uniform speed.
a) Draw a distance–time graph for the data in the table.
b) Determine the slope of the line.
c) What value does the slope of the graph represent?

TABLE B1.2 Time and Distance Data for Example Problem B1.2

Time t (s)	Distance from First Marker d (m)
0.0	0.0
1.0	3.9
2.0	8.0
3.0	12.2
4.0	15.9
5.0	20.1

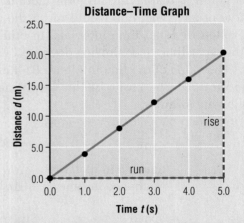

FIGURE B1.6 A distance–time graph for the data from Table B1.2

a) Figure B1.6 shows the graph drawn from the data in Table B1.2.

b) $\text{slope} = \dfrac{\text{rise}}{\text{run}}$

$= \dfrac{20.0 \text{ m} - 0.0 \text{ m}}{5.0 \text{ s} - 0.0 \text{ s}}$

$= \dfrac{20.0 \text{ m}}{5.0 \text{ s}}$

$= 4.0 \ \dfrac{\text{m}}{\text{s}}$

c) Since slope = speed, the average speed of the object was 4.0 m/s.

Practice Problem

4. The data in Table B1.3 were collected for a jet travelling at a uniform speed.
a) Draw a distance–time graph for the data in the table.
b) Determine the slope of the line.
c) What value does the slope of the graph represent?

TABLE B1.3
Time and Distance Data for a Jet Travelling at Uniform Speed

Time t (s)	Distance from First Marker d (m)
0.0	0
1.0	490
2.0	1020
3.0	1490
4.0	2010
5.0	2480

Plotting a Speed–Time Graph

Suppose the motorboat mentioned previously is travelling past the same marker buoys. This time, a person on shore uses a radar gun to record the speed of the motorboat every 2.0 s. The data are shown in Table B1.4.

The graph of the data (Figure B1.7) also describes the motion of the motorboat. The line of best fit is a straight line, indicating a linear relationship between the speed of the boat and the time elapsed. The line is horizontal, which means that as the time elapsed increases, the speed remains constant. This should be the case, since the boat has uniform motion.

You can confirm that the speed is uniform by calculating the slope of the graph. The slope of the line can be determined as follows:

$$\text{slope} = \frac{\text{rise}}{\text{run}} = \frac{\Delta v}{\Delta t}$$

$$= \frac{5.00\,\frac{\text{m}}{\text{s}} - 5.00\,\frac{\text{m}}{\text{s}}}{10.0\,\text{s} - 0.0\,\text{s}}$$

$$= \frac{0.00\,\frac{\text{m}}{\text{s}}}{10.0\,\text{s}}$$

$$= 0.0\,\frac{\text{m}}{\text{s}^2}$$

A slope of 0.0 m/s² confirms that the motion is uniform.

You can determine the distance the boat travelled by calculating the area under the line of the graph. The area under the line of best fit of the speed–time graph in Figure B1.7 is determined as follows:

$$\text{area under the line} = \text{area of a rectangle}$$

$$= \text{length} \times \text{width}$$

$$\text{area} = (v)(\Delta t)$$

$$= (5.00\,\text{m/s})(10.0\,\text{s} - 0.0\,\text{s})$$

$$= (5.00\,\tfrac{\text{m}}{\cancel{\text{s}}})(10.0\,\cancel{\text{s}})$$

$$= 50\,\text{m}$$

Since the speed formula, $v = \frac{\Delta d}{\Delta t}$, can be rearranged to $(v)(\Delta t) = \Delta d$, the area under the line is the same as Δd. Thus, the area under the line of a speed–time graph indicates the distance travelled in the time period.

If the line of best fit were a straight line with a slope $\frac{\Delta d}{\Delta t}$ other than zero, then the line would represent an object that is changing its speed as time passes. From the slant of the slope of the line of a speed–time graph, you can tell whether the speed of the object is increasing or decreasing (Figure B1.8). You will learn more about changes in speed in section B1.3.

TABLE B1.4 Speed of a Boat Passing Marker Buoys

Time when Boat Passes Marker t (s)	Speed of the Boat as It Passes Each Marker v (m/s)
0.0	5.00
2.0	5.00
4.0	5.00
6.0	5.00
8.0	5.00
10.0	5.00

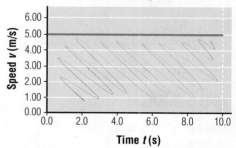

FIGURE B1.7 A graph of the speed of the motorboat as a function of time

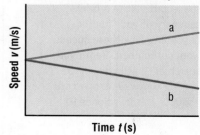

FIGURE B1.8 A line sloping upward (a) indicates that the speed is increasing. A line sloping downward (b) indicates that the speed is decreasing, so the object is slowing down.

Throughout this unit, you will be making calculations. It is important that you use the correct number of significant digits in your answers. Review the rules for determining significant digits and for operations involving significant digits in Student Reference 6: Math Skills, then answer the following questions and complete the calculations.

1. Indicate the number of significant digits each of the following measurements has.

   a) 3.1415 m

   b) 2001.10 g

   c) 34 000 g

   d) 0.0027 s

   e) 8.1 km

2. Solve the following problems. Give your answers to the correct number of significant digits.

   a) 3.20 cm + 2.1 cm

   b) 4.55 km − 1.6 km

   c) 3.20 km × 1.11 km

   d) 45.0 km ÷ 2.1 h

3. Solve the following problems. Give your answers to the correct number of significant digits.

   a) 0.00221 ÷ (1.006 + 2.23)

   b) 347 × 7.48 ÷ 21.2

   c) 6.4(9748 + 17.57)

   d) $\dfrac{0.56 - 0.05}{8.436 - 0.2}$

---

*re*SEARCH

Speed is an important physical quantity in describing motion. Use the Internet or your local library to research and answer the following questions. What is the fastest speed recorded for a human in a 100-m race and in a marathon? What are the fastest speeds recorded for an animal, a fish, an automobile, a boat, an airplane, and a spacecraft? Write a brief summary of your findings, describing how these speeds were determined. Begin your search at

www.pearsoned.ca/
school/science10

Example Problem B1.3

The data in Table B1.5 were collected for an object travelling at a uniform speed.

a) Draw a speed–time graph for the data in the table.

b) Determine the slope of the line. How does the slope indicate that the object is travelling with uniform speed?

c) Determine the area under the line for the time interval, $t = 0.0$ s to $t = 5.0$ s. What does this value represent?

TABLE B1.5   Time and Speed Data for Example Problem B1.3

Time t (s)	Speed v (m/s)
0.0	5.8
1.0	6.0
2.0	6.2
3.0	6.0
4.0	5.9
5.0	6.1

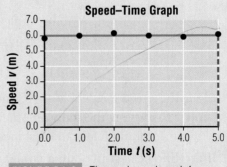

FIGURE B1.9   Time and speed graph for data from Table B1.5.

a) Figure B1.9 shows the graph drawn from the data in Table B1.5.

b) slope = $\dfrac{\text{rise}}{\text{run}}$

$= \dfrac{6.0\,\frac{m}{s} - 6.0\,\frac{m}{s}}{5.0\,s - 0.0\,s}$

$= \dfrac{0.0\,\frac{m}{s}}{5.0\,s}$

$= 0\,\dfrac{m}{s^2}$

A slope = 0 indicates that the speed was uniform.

c) area = length × width

$= (v)(\Delta t)$

$= (6.0\,\frac{m}{s})(5.0\,s)$

$= 30\,m$

The area represents the distance travelled.

Practice Problem

5. The data in Table B1.6 were collected for an object travelling at a uniform speed.
   a) Draw a speed–time graph for the data in the table.
   b) Determine the slope of the line. How does the slope indicate that the object is travelling with uniform speed?
   c) Determine the area under the line for the time interval, t = 0.0 s to t = 5.0 s. What does this value represent?

TABLE B1.6 Time and Speed Data for Practice Problem 5	Time t (s)	Speed v (m/s)
	0.0	9.8
	1.0	10.0
	2.0	10.2
	3.0	10.0
	4.0	9.9
	5.0	10.1

Skill Practice   Taking Measurements

In Activity B2, you will be taking measurements using two different measuring instruments. One of the most important skills in any science course is being able to use measuring instruments properly. For any type of instrument, your measurement must include a final digit that is an estimated digit. For example, when using a ruler that has the smallest grading in millimetres, the final digit of your measurement should be in tenths of a millimetre, as shown in Figure B1.10.

The correct measurement for the length of the line is not 2.3 cm or 2.4 cm but 2.35 cm.

1. Use your ruler to measure the width, length, and thickness of this textbook in centimetres. Record the data in your notebook. To how many decimal places can you measure with your ruler?

2. Use a stopwatch to measure the time taken in seconds for a ball to hit the floor if dropped from your desktop. Repeat this procedure several times. Record the data in your notebook. To how many decimal places were you able to measure the time?

0.0 cm   1.0 cm   2.0 cm   3.0 cm   4.0 cm   5.0 cm   6.0 cm   7.0 cm

FIGURE B1.10   A ruler with millimetre gradings

Inquiry Lab

Studying Uniform Motion

The Question

What kind of motion do falling dominoes exhibit?

The Hypothesis

State a hypothesis concerning the motion of the falling dominoes. Be sure to write an "if/then" statement.

Variables

Identify the type of data you will collect to support your hypothesis. State the manipulated, responding, and controlled variables in this investigation.

Materials and Equipment

65 dominoes (2.5 cm x 5.0 cm)

metre-stick or measuring tape   *& Type up*

5 stopwatches

masking tape

Procedure   *& type up*

1. Paste 3.00 m of masking tape on a flat table or countertop, making sure that the masking tape is perfectly straight.

2. At one end of the masking tape, make a pencil mark designating the starting position, 0.00 cm. From this starting position, make a mark every 50.00 cm on the masking tape, using the metre-stick or measuring tape.

3. Place the metre-stick or measuring tape parallel to the masking tape at the start position so that the 0.00 mark aligns with the 0.00 mark on the masking tape.

4. Place the first domino at the 0.00 cm mark on the masking tape (Figure B1.11). Place the next domino at 4.00 cm, and continue lining up the dominoes every 4.00 cm until you have at least 65 dominoes in a line.

5. One member of the group (each group has 6 students) positions him- or herself at the 0.00 cm, 50.00 cm, 100.00 cm, 150.00 cm, 200.00 cm, and 250.00 cm marks. Each student has a stopwatch except for the student at the 0.00-cm mark.

6. When the student at the 0.00-cm mark says "Start," he or she pushes over the first domino and the other students start their stopwatches.

7. Each student stops his or her stopwatch when the toppling dominoes reach his or her mark on the tape.

8. Record your results in a table like the one below.

9. Do at least three trials of the experiment, and calculate the average values of the times. Record the average values in your notebook.

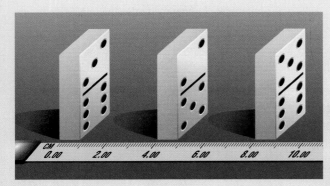

FIGURE B1.11   Step 4

Distance *d* (cm)	Time Elapsed *t* (s)
0.00	0.0
50.00	
100.00	

Analyzing and Interpreting

1. Identify the manipulated and the responding variables in this experiment.

2. Draw a distance–time graph. Remember that, although the manipulated variable should be on the *x*-axis of your graph, time (which is the responding variable in this experiment) is always plotted on the *x*-axis.

3. What type of line is your line of best fit?

4. What type of motion is depicted by your line of best fit?

5. Determine the slope of the line of best fit of the graph. What does this value represent?

6. From your data, calculate the speed during each time interval by determining the distance travelled during the interval and substituting the values in the formula

$$v = \frac{\Delta d}{\Delta t}$$

7. Using your calculated values for the speed of each time interval, create a table like the one below. Make sure your table has a title.

Time Interval Δt (s)	Speed v (m/s)

8. Draw a speed–time interval graph.

9. On the graph, determine the slope of the line of best fit.

10. Indicate on the graph what the value of this slope represents.

11. On the graph, determine the area under the line for the entire time.

12. Indicate on the graph what the value of this area represents.

Forming Conclusions

13. Study the distance travelled–time graph. Explain how this graph shows that the falling dominoes are displaying uniform motion.

14. Study the speed–time graph. Explain how this graph shows that the falling dominoes are displaying uniform motion.

B1.1 **Check and Reflect**

Knowledge

1. How can you determine if an object is in motion?

2. When is an object travelling in uniform motion?

3. What two quantitative methods can you use to analyze uniform motion?

4. What can you determine from the following calculations?
   a) the slope of a distance–time graph
   b) the slope of a speed–time graph
   c) the area under the line of a speed–time graph

5. Describe the motion of an object as shown in each segment of the graph in the right column. The graph represents the distance travelled as a function of time.

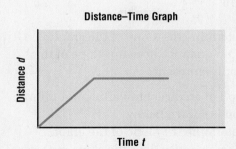

Distance–Time Graph

6. Describe the motion of an object as shown in each segment of the graph below. The graph represents the speed as a function of time.

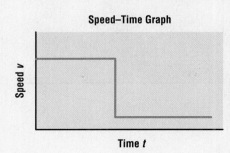

Speed–Time Graph

Applications

7. Which of the following situations most closely describes uniform motion? Explain your answer.
   a) a person sliding down a waterslide
   b) water falling down a waterfall
   c) electricity flowing through a wire

8. A skateboarder travels 50.0 m in 12.0 s. What is the average speed of the skateboarder?

9. A baseball player throws a ball a distance of 45.0 m at a speed of 30.0 m/s. How long is the ball in flight?

10. An airplane flies at a speed of 990 km/h for 4.10 h. How far does the airplane travel?

11. A bird is flying 6.00 km/h in a straight line at a constant rate. How long will it take the bird to travel 30.0 km?

12. A graph of an object travelling in uniform motion is shown below.

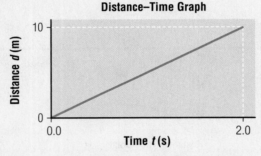

Distance–Time Graph

a) Determine the slope of the graph.
b) What quantity does the slope of this graph represent?

13. A graph of an object travelling in uniform motion is shown below.
   a) Determine the slope of the graph.
   b) What quantity does the slope represent?

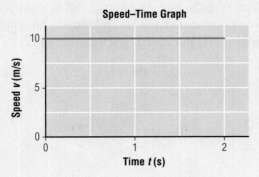

Speed–Time Graph

14. The ticker tape shown below shows a record of the motion of an object on a straight horizontal track. The marks were produced by a spark timer set at 10 sparks per second.

```
 •    •    •    •     •    •    •     •
0.00 s 0.10 s 0.20 s 0.30 s 0.40 s 0.50 s 0.60 s 0.70 s
```

a) In your notebook, create a data table that records the time and the distance travelled by the object from the starting point at 0.0 s.
b) Draw a distance–time graph of the data in your table.
c) Calculate the slope of the line of your graph.
d) What information does the slope of this graph give you?

15. Using the same ticker tape shown in question 14, answer the following questions.
   a) In your notebook, create a data table that records the average speed of the object at the end of each time interval.
   b) Draw a speed–time graph of the data in your table.
   c) Calculate the area under the line at the 0.70 s mark.
   d) What information does the area under the line give you?

16. A person walks 15.0 m in 5.00 s, and then walks 12.0 m in 10.00 s. What is the average speed of the person?

17. A person walks at a speed of 2.00 m/s for 10.00 s, and then walks at a speed of 1.50 m/s for 8.00 s. What is the average speed of the person?

Extensions

18. Sketch a distance–time graph with three lines on it: one that represents a slow-moving object; one for a fast-moving object; and one for an object that is not moving.

19. Why is it so difficult to find examples of objects travelling at uniform motion?

B 1.2 Velocity

You have probably heard people use the term "velocity" when they describe how fast a car is going. Most of the time, they are actually referring to "speed." As you learned in section B1.1, speed describes the rate of motion of an object. **Velocity** describes both the rate of motion and the direction of an object. You can determine the average speed of a car by looking at its speedometer. To determine its average velocity, you need both the speedometer and a compass, to show you its direction.

Scalar and Vector Quantities

The difference between speed and velocity is that speed is a **scalar quantity**, and velocity is a **vector quantity**. All quantities in science can be classified as either scalar or vector quantities. A scalar quantity is one that only indicates "how much" (the magnitude) of the quantity. A vector quantity indicates "how much" (the magnitude) *and* the direction of the quantity. A vector quantity is written with a vector arrow above the symbol for the measured quantity. For example, the symbol for speed is v, and the symbol for velocity is $\vec{v}$.

Distance Travelled and Displacement

Distance travelled and displacement are two other examples of related scalar and vector quantities. **Distance travelled** is a scalar quantity. It is a measurement of the change in distance of an object moving from a starting reference point. In Figure B1.12, the person moves from the bus stop to a point 10 m away from it. You would record the distance the person moved as $\Delta d = 10$ m. This indicates that the object (the person) moved 10 m from the reference point (the bus stop). The "Δ" shows that the number is a change in a quantity.

*info*BIT

The numbering of airport runways illustrates the importance of including direction when describing motion. Airport runways are numbered according to their angle from magnetic north at 0°. The runway number indicates the runway's angle from magnetic north in a clockwise direction, with the last "0" omitted. If the runway's heading is 40° from magnetic north, the runway is called runway 4.

0	1	2	3	4	5	6	7	8	9	10

FIGURE B1.12 The person has moved 10 m from the bus stop, so the distance travelled is written as $\Delta d = 10$ m.

Displacement is a vector quantity. It is a measurement of the change in distance *and* the direction or the change in position of an object from a reference point. To determine the displacement of the person relative to the bus stop in Figure B1.12, you need to know both the beginning and final positions of the person, and the direction that she moved in. You can record the displacement in this case as $\Delta \vec{d} = 10$ m [right]. This indicates that the object (the person) ends up 10 m from the reference point (the bus stop). It also indicates that the direction of travel was to the right of the reference point.

Figure B1.12 is a simple example of distance and displacement. In that example, the magnitudes of both the distance and the displacement are the same. The difference between the two is that displacement has a direction indicated. Figure B1.13 illustrates an important difference between distance and displacement. The distance (Δd) is the total distance travelled by the person on both sides of the bus stop. So Δd is 8 m. The displacement ($\Delta \vec{d}$) is the person's change in position relative to the bus stop. So $\Delta \vec{d}$ is only 2 m [left].

Note that you are describing motion when you record distance travelled and displacement. You must indicate this by using the "Δ" notation to indicate a change in the distance or the position of the object.

FIGURE B1.13 The difference between distance and displacement:
- The distance travelled by the person is $\Delta d = 3$ m + 5 m = 8 m.
- The displacement of the person relative to the bus stop is $\Delta \vec{d} = 3$ m [right] + −5 m [left] = −2 m [left].

Minds On... Classroom Scavenger Hunt

When you want to go somewhere, you need to know not only how far it is, but what direction it's in. For this activity, your teacher has hidden "treats" in four different locations in the classroom. You must use a written set of instructions to find the hidden treasure. Your group will need a set of instructions, a metre-stick, and a large blackboard protractor. Begin at the given starting point, and follow the instructions until you locate the treasure.

On a sheet of graph paper, use a student ruler and a student protractor to sketch a map showing how you found the treats. This map is a scale drawing showing the vector arrows of your hunt.

How to Identify Vector Directions

In the example shown in Figure B1.13, the vector directions given were [right] and [left]. These vector directions were determined using the *x*-axis method. You may also have seen vectors that refer to the compass directions: north, south, east, and west. For example, a plane flying from Calgary to Regina would have an "[E]" vector, which stands for "east." This vector direction is determined using the navigator method.

The X-Axis Method

The *x*-axis method for determining vector directions uses the mathematical method of setting up a coordinate system grid with an "*x*" axis and a "*y*" axis, similar to a graph. Figure B1.14 shows the grid for the *x*-axis method. Directions are stated from the *x*-axis, which is the starting reference point at 0°. From there, directions are determined in a counterclockwise direction.

Directions given along the *x*- and *y*-axis lines are given positive or negative values.

- [Up] and [right] are positive.

- [Down] and [left] are negative.

- Directions between the axis lines are given only in degrees and are not given a positive or negative value.

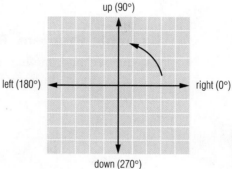

FIGURE B1.14 The *x*-axis grid for determining the directions of vectors

Example Problem B1.4

Use the *x*-axis method to determine the directions of the vectors A, B, C, and D shown in Figure B1.15. Give the magnitude and direction for each vector.

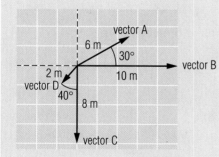

FIGURE B1.15 Vectors A, B, C, and D for Example Problem B1.4

The magnitude and directions of the vectors in Figure B1.15 are:

vector A = 6 m [30°]

vector B = 10 m [right]

vector C = –8 m [down]

vector D = 2 m [230°]

Practice Problem

6. A ball is rolling at a velocity of 2 m/s [135°]. Use the *x*-axis method to sketch this vector on a grid.

The Navigator Method

This method uses the directions of north [N], south [S], east [E], and west [W] on a grid to identify vector directions. North is the starting reference point of 0°. In this method, directions are stated *clockwise* from north. Figure B1.16 shows the grid to use for the navigator method.

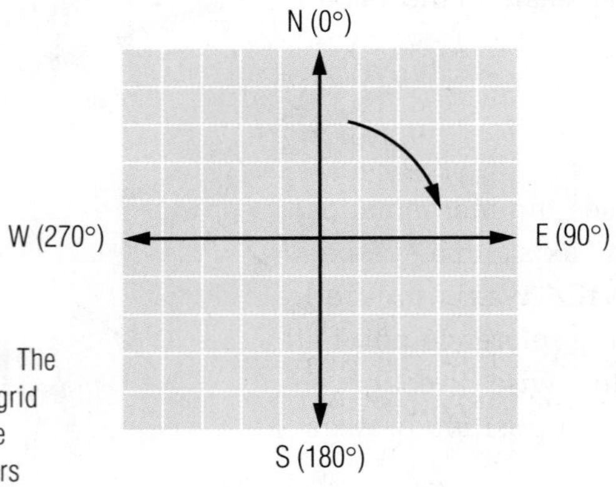

Directions given along the axis lines have positive or negative values.

- [N] and [E] are positive.
- [S] and [W] are negative.
- Directions between the axis lines are given only in degrees and are not given a positive or negative value.

FIGURE B1.16 The navigator method grid for determining the directions of vectors

Example Problem B1.5

Use the navigator method to determine the directions of the vectors A, B, C, and D shown in Figure B1.17. Give the magnitude and direction for each vector.

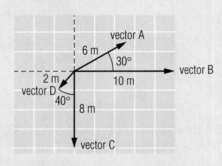

FIGURE B1.17 Vectors A, B, C, and D for Example Problem B1.5

The magnitude and directions of the vectors in Figure B1.17 are:
vector A = 6 m [60°]
vector B = 10 m [E]
vector C = −8 m [S]
vector D = 2 m [220°]

Practice Problem

7. A ball is rolling at a velocity of 2 m/s [135°]. Using a grid, sketch this vector using the navigator method.

In the two example problems B1.4 and B1.5, you probably noticed that you were identifying the same vectors. The magnitudes of the vectors were the same in both problems. The notation of their directions was different because two different methods were used to determine them. Remember to read vector problems carefully to see which method you are supposed to use to solve them.

Speed and Velocity

Now that you know the difference between scalar and vector quantities, let's look more closely at speed and velocity. In section B1.1, you used distance travelled in calculating average speed. Both distance travelled and speed are scalar quantities. Only the magnitude of each one is stated. For example, the average speed of a car may be stated as 100 km/h. To calculate average velocity, you use displacement. Both displacement and velocity are vector quantities, so you must state both the magnitude and the direction for them. For example, the average velocity of a car on the highway from Edmonton to Red Deer might be 100 km/h [S].

Using Formulas to Analyze Average Velocity

Average velocity is uniform motion that involves changing a position in a specified time. To determine the average velocity quantitatively, use the following equation:

$$\text{average velocity} = \frac{\text{displacement}}{\text{time elapsed}}$$

$$\vec{v} = \frac{\Delta \vec{d}}{\Delta t}$$

$$= \frac{\vec{d}_{\text{final}} - \vec{d}_{\text{initial}}}{t_{\text{final}} - t_{\text{initial}}}$$

Velocity is a vector quantity, so you must state its magnitude and direction.

Example Problem B1.6

A person walks 10.0 m [E] away from a bus stop in 5.00 s. What is the average velocity of the person?

Average velocity:

$$\vec{v} = \frac{\Delta \vec{d}}{\Delta t}$$

$$= \frac{10.0 \text{ m [E]} - 0.0 \text{ m}}{5.00 \text{ s} - 0.00 \text{ s}}$$

$$= \frac{10.0 \text{ m [E]}}{5.00 \text{ s}}$$

$$= 2.00 \frac{\text{m}}{\text{s}} \text{ [E]}$$

The person walked at an average velocity of 2.00 m/s [E].

Practice Problems

8. A student walks 10.0 m [E] in 7.00 s. Then he walks another 12.0 m [E] in 8.00 s. Determine:
   a) the displacement of the student in 15.00 s
   b) the average velocity of the student

9. A boat travels at a velocity of 8.00 m/s [N] for 14.0 s. What is the displacement of the boat?

10. An airplane flying at a velocity of 900 km/h [W] travels 400 km west. How long will the plane be in flight?

TABLE B1.7 Position of Boat Travelling past Marker Buoys

Marker	Time t (s)	Position of the Boat $\vec{d}$ (m) [E]
1	0.0	0.0
2	2.0	10.0
3	4.0	20.0
4	6.0	30.0
5	8.0	40.0
6	10.0	50.0

Using Graphs to Analyze Average Velocity

In section B1.1, you learned that graphs are an important tool for studying uniform motion. They show the relationship between two variables and provide a visual representation of the motion. You saw how distance–time graphs and speed–time graphs are visual representations of the speed of an object. You also learned how to use graphs to calculate the speed and distances travelled by objects. To analyze average velocity, you can use two types of graphs: a position–time graph and a velocity–time graph.

Plotting a Position–Time Graph

In section B1.1, you considered the speed and distance travelled by a motorboat. Now consider its velocity. Suppose a motorboat is travelling east past six marker buoys in the water placed 10.0 m apart. A person on the shore is recording the time it takes for the motorboat to pass each marker. Table B1.7 shows those measurements.

The graph in Figure B1.18 uses the data from Table B1.7 to describe the motion of the motorboat visually. The line of best fit indicates a linear or a straight-line relationship between the position and the time taken to travel. This means that as time increases, the position also increases. The straight line of the graph shows that the motorboat's displacement in relation to the time intervals is constant. Therefore, the motorboat is moving with uniform motion. Its velocity remains constant.

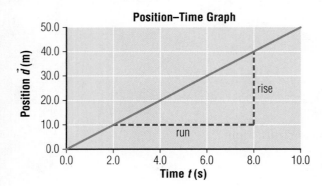

FIGURE B1.18 A position–time graph produced from the data in Table B1.7

You can use the slope of the line in Figure B1.18 to determine the average velocity of the motorboat.

Calculate the average velocity of the motorboat from Figure B1.18.

Average velocity:

$$\text{slope} = \frac{\text{rise}}{\text{run}} = \frac{\text{change in position}}{\text{change in time}}$$

$$= \text{velocity} \qquad \text{Since } \vec{v} = \frac{\Delta \vec{d}}{\Delta t}$$

$$= \frac{\Delta \vec{d}}{\Delta t}$$

$$= \frac{\vec{d}_f - \vec{d}_i}{t_f - t_i}$$

$$= \frac{40.0 \text{ m [E]} - 10.0 \text{ m [E]}}{8.0 \text{ s} - 2.0 \text{ s}}$$

$$= 5.0 \frac{\text{m}}{\text{s}} \text{ [E]}$$

The average velocity of the motorboat is 5.0 m/s [E].

Example Problem B1.7

Table B1.8 contains data collected for an object travelling at uniform velocity.
a) Draw a position–time graph for the data in the table.
b) Using the graph, identify the motion occurring between $t = 0.0$ s and $t = 5.0$ s, and justify your answer.
c) From the graph, determine the average velocity between $t = 0.0$ s and $t = 5.0$ s.

TABLE B1.8   Data for Example Problem B1.7

Time t (s)	Position of Object $\vec{d}$ (m) [N]
0.0	0.0
1.0	9.9
2.0	20.1
3.0	29.8
4.0	40.2
5.0	50.0

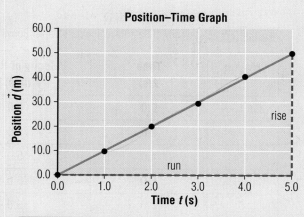

FIGURE B1.19   A position–time graph for the data from Table B1.8.

a) Figure B1.19 shows the graph drawn from the data in Table B1.8.
b) The graph is a straight line so it is showing uniform velocity between $t = 0.0$ s and $t = 5.0$ s.
c) average velocity = slope

$$\text{slope} = \frac{\text{rise}}{\text{run}}$$

$$= \frac{\vec{d}_f - \vec{d}_i}{t_f - t_i}$$

$$= \frac{50.0 \text{ m [N]} - 0.0 \text{ m [N]}}{5.0 \text{ s} - 0.0 \text{ s}}$$

$$= \frac{50.0 \text{ m [N]}}{5.0 \text{ s}}$$

$$= 10 \frac{\text{m}}{\text{s}} \text{ [N]}$$

Since slope = velocity, the average velocity of the object was 10 m/s [N].

Practice Problem

11. Table B1.9 contains data collected for an object travelling at uniform velocity.
    a) Draw a position–time graph for the data in the table.
    b) From the graph, determine the average velocity between $t = 0.0$ s and $t = 10.0$ s.

TABLE B1.9
Data for Practice Problem 11

Time t (s)	Position of Object $\vec{d}$ (m) [E]
0.0	0.0
2.0	49.8
4.0	100.0
6.0	150.1
8.0	199.9
10.0	250.2

Plotting a Velocity–Time Graph

A velocity–time graph is similar to the speed–time graph you studied in section B1.1. In the motorboat example, people studying the motorboat's motion would keep track of both the speed and direction to determine the velocity.

Suppose the motorboat is travelling east at uniform velocity past six marker buoys 10.0 m apart. On shore, one person is measuring the time using a stopwatch, and another is measuring the speed with a radar gun and using a compass to determine direction. Table B1.10 shows the measurements they took.

TABLE B1.10   Velocity of Boat Travelling past Marker Buoys

Marker	Time t (s)	Velocity of the Boat $\vec{v}$ (m/s) [E]
1	0.0	5.0
2	2.0	5.0
3	4.0	5.0
4	6.0	5.0
5	8.0	5.0
6	10.0	5.0

Figure B1.20 is the graph of the data from Table B1.10. The line of best fit is a straight line. This indicates a linear relationship between the velocity of the boat and the time it took to travel past the markers. The line is also horizontal. This means that the velocity remained constant during the time the motorboat was moving past the markers. The boat is travelling with uniform motion. In section B1.3, you will learn about motion that is not uniform, when objects increase and decrease velocity.

*re*SEARCH

The most common way to measure the magnitude of the velocity of vehicles is km/h. However, pilots and sea captains measure velocity in knots. Use the Internet or your local library to research the term "knot" as used to describe the velocity of an object. How did this term originate? What is a nautical mile? How do km/h and knots compare? Write a brief summary of your findings. Begin your search at

 www.pearsoned.ca/
school/science10

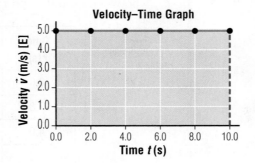

FIGURE B1.20   A graph of the velocity of the motorboat as a function of time

Knowledge

1. What is one difference between a scalar and a vector quantity?

2. Give two examples of scalar quantities and two examples of vector quantities.

3. Use the navigator method to determine the directions of vector 1 and vector 2 shown below.

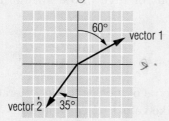

4. Use the x-axis method to determine the directions of vector 1 and vector 2 shown below.

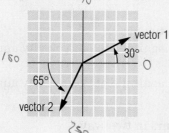

Applications

5. A ball rolls 10.0 m [S] in a time of 6.00 s, hits a wall, and rolls back a distance of 15.0 m [N] in a time of 10.00 s. Determine:
   a) the distance travelled by the ball
   b) the displacement of the ball
   c) the average speed of the ball
   d) the average velocity of the ball

6. An air puck is propelled from one side of an air table. It hits an elastic on the other side, and the elastic propels it back to the side where it started. Students recorded the motion of the air puck and analyzed the data. Their data are shown in the table at the top of the right column.
   a) Draw a position–time graph of the data in the table.
   b) Calculate the slope of the graph. What can you determine from the value of the slope?

Time t (s)	Position of the Air Puck $\vec{d}$ (cm)
0.00	0.00
0.10	5.25 [E]
0.20	10.51 [E]
0.30	15.74 [E]
0.40	10.52 [E]
0.50	5.26 [E]
0.60	0.00

7. Use the data table in question 6 to complete the following table in your notebook. Draw a velocity–time graph using the completed table. Then answer the questions below.
   a) How does the graph show that motion is uniform?
   b) How does the graph distinguish between uniform motion in one direction and uniform motion in the opposite direction?

Time Interval Δt (s)	Velocity of the Air Puck $\vec{v}$ (cm/s) (hint: Use $\vec{v} = \dfrac{\Delta \vec{d}}{\Delta t}$)
0.00 – 0.10	_____ [E]
0.10 – 0.20	_____ [E]
0.20 – 0.30	_____ [E]
0.30 – 0.40	_____ [W]
0.40 – 0.50	_____ [W]
0.50 – 0.60	_____ [W]

Extension

8. Draw a position–time graph and a velocity–time graph of each of the motions described below:
   a) A car travelling at a uniform velocity of 100 km/h, moves 200 km [S] in 2.0 h. It rests for 1.0 h and then returns 100 km [N] in 1.0 h.
   b) A hummingbird flying at a uniform velocity of 10 m/s travels 40 m [E] in 4.0 s. It stops at a feeder for 5.0 s, and then flies 20 m west for 2.0 s.

B1.3 Acceleration

On a long-distance flight, your plane may fly for long periods at 900 km/h. Unless you have a window seat, however, it may seem like the plane is not moving at all. Uniform motion can be relaxing—even at such a high speed. The excitement comes at the beginning of the trip as the plane takes off (Figure B1.21). Its speed changes rapidly from rest to take-off speed in several seconds. Because the airplane's speed is increasing, so is its velocity. This change in velocity during a specific time interval is called **acceleration**. You can experience acceleration in a vehicle or on your own. For example, when you start to run for the bus or dive into a swimming pool, you are accelerating.

FIGURE B1.21 An airplane accelerates rapidly when it takes off. Once it reaches cruising altitude, it travels in uniform motion for long periods.

Types of Acceleration

Uniform motion is the simplest type of motion, but accelerated motion is the most common type of motion. Like velocity, acceleration is a vector quantity, so you must determine both its magnitude and direction. Different types of acceleration are possible because both the magnitude and direction of velocity can change. When an object is speeding up, the magnitude of its velocity is increasing. When an object is slowing down, the magnitude of the velocity is decreasing.

Positive acceleration occurs in two ways:
1) when the change in both the magnitude of the velocity and the direction are positive (Figure B1.22(a)).
2) when the change in both the magnitude of the velocity and the direction are negative (Figure B1.22(b)).

Negative acceleration also occurs in two ways:
1) when the change in the magnitude of the velocity is negative while the direction is positive (Figure B1.22(c)).
2) when the change in the magnitude of the velocity is positive and the direction is negative (Figure B1.22(d)).

FIGURE B1.22 Examples of positive and negative acceleration

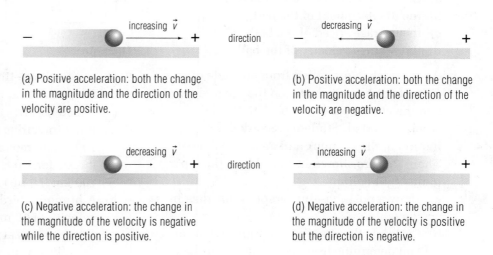

(a) Positive acceleration: both the change in the magnitude and the direction of the velocity are positive.

(b) Positive acceleration: both the change in the magnitude and the direction of the velocity are negative.

(c) Negative acceleration: the change in the magnitude of the velocity is negative while the direction is positive.

(d) Negative acceleration: the change in the magnitude of the velocity is positive but the direction is negative.

Your study of accelerated motion will concentrate on changes in magnitude of velocity in one direction. You will consider both accelerated motion that is speeding up and accelerated motion that is slowing down.

Using Formulas and Graphs to Analyze Accelerated Motion

As with uniform motion, you can study accelerated motion quantitatively by using formulas and graphs. To calculate acceleration, use the following formula:

$$\text{acceleration} = \frac{\text{change in velocity}}{\text{time interval}}$$

$$\vec{a} = \frac{\Delta \vec{v}}{\Delta t}$$

where $\Delta \vec{v} = \vec{v}_{final} - \vec{v}_{initial}$

and $\vec{v}_f$ is the final velocity and $\vec{v}_i$ is the starting velocity

so, $\vec{a} = \dfrac{\vec{v}_f - \vec{v}_i}{\Delta t}$

Remember that acceleration is a vector quantity so you must determine the magnitude and the direction of the acceleration.

Example Problem B1.8

A racing car accelerates from rest to a speed of 200 km/h (55.6 m/s) [E] in 6.00 s. What is the acceleration of the car?

$$\vec{a} = \frac{\vec{v}_f - \vec{v}_i}{\Delta t}$$

$$= \frac{55.6 \frac{m}{s} \,[E] - 0.00 \frac{m}{s}}{6.00 \text{ s}}$$

$$= 9.27 \frac{\frac{m}{s}}{s} \,[E] \text{ or } 9.27 \frac{m}{s^2} \,[E]$$

The car's velocity is increasing at the rate of 9.27 m/s² [E]. (This is positive acceleration.)

Note that the units for velocity were converted from km/h to m/s, and the units for acceleration are stated as m/s².

In some situations, only the magnitude of the acceleration is required, and the direction is ignored. For these situations, the formula can be adjusted so that the vectors are not included:

$$a = \frac{v_f - v_i}{\Delta t}$$

Practice Problems

12. A shuttle craft accelerates from rest to a velocity of 50 m/s [upward] in 4.00 s. What is its acceleration?

13. A baseball thrown at 25.0 m/s strikes a catcher's mitt and slows down to rest in 0.500 s. What is the magnitude of the ball's acceleration?

14. A hockey puck travelling at 10.0 m/s strikes the boards, coming to rest in 0.0300 s. What is the magnitude of the puck's acceleration?

15. A car driver applies the brakes and slows down from 15.0 m/s [E] to 5.00 m/s [E] in 4.00 s. Determine the car's acceleration.

Plotting a Position–Time Graph

In section B1.2, you learned that you could determine the velocity of an object from the slope of a position–time graph. The line of best fit for an object travelling with uniform motion was shown to be a straight line because the velocity was uniform. For accelerated motion, the line of best fit is a smooth curve. Here's an example.

Suppose that a motorboat is travelling with accelerated motion in an easterly direction. It passes marker buoys placed 5 m apart. As the boat passes the first marker buoy, a person on shore starts to estimate and record the position of the motorboat every 2 s relative to the first marker buoy. Table B1.11 shows the data collected by the person on shore.

TABLE B1.11 Change in the Position of the Motorboat

Time t (s)	Position of the Boat $\vec{d}$ (m) [E]
0	0
2	1
4	4
6	9
8	16
10	25

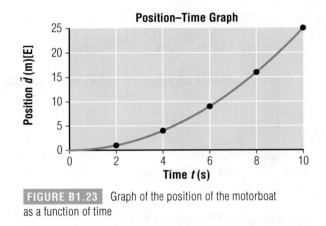

FIGURE B1.23 Graph of the position of the motorboat as a function of time

The graph in Figure B1.23 describes the accelerated motion of the motorboat. The slope of the line is gradually increasing, which indicates that the velocity of the boat is gradually increasing or accelerating. The shape of the curve of a graph of accelerated motion indicates whether the object has a positive or a negative acceleration.

Figure B1.24 shows two position–time graphs of accelerated motion. Graph (a) has an increasing slope, which indicates positive acceleration. Graph (b) has a decreasing slope, which indicates negative acceleration.

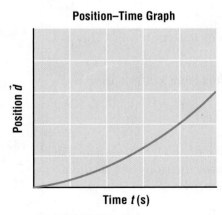

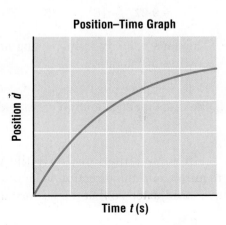

FIGURE B1.24 (a) This graph represents positive acceleration because the slope is increasing.

(b) This graph represents negative acceleration because the slope is decreasing.

Example Problem B1.9

Table B1.12 shows data for an object travelling with accelerated motion.
a) Draw a position–time graph for the data shown in the table.
b) Using the graph, identify the motion occurring in the time intervals given below. Justify your answer for each one.
    i) between $t = 0.0$ s and $t = 3.0$ s
    ii) between $t = 3.0$ s and $t = 6.0$ s
    iii) between $t = 6.0$ s and $t = 8.0$ s

TABLE B1.12   Time and Position Data for Example Problem B1.9

Time t (s)	Position $\vec{d}$ (m) [E]
0.0	0.0
1.0	10.0
2.0	40.0
3.0	90.0
4.0	140.0
5.0	190.0
6.0	240.0
7.0	270.0
8.0	290.0

a) Figure B1.25 shows the graph drawn from the data in Table B1.12.

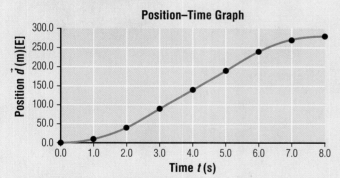

FIGURE B1.25   Graph of the data in Table B1.12

b) i) The curve has an increasing slope so it shows positive acceleration [E].
   ii) The straight line shows uniform motion [E].
   iii) The curve has a decreasing slope so it shows negative acceleration [E].

Practice Problem

16. Table B1.13 shows data for a rollercoaster travelling with accelerated motion.
    a) Draw a position–time graph for the data shown in the table.
    b) Using the graph, identify the motion occurring in the time intervals given below. Justify your answer for each one.
       i) between $t = 0.0$ s and $t = 3.0$ s
       ii) between $t = 3.0$ s and $t = 6.0$ s
       iii) between $t = 6.0$ s and $t = 8.0$ s

TABLE B1.13   Time and Position Data for Practice Problem 16

Time t (s)	Position $\vec{d}$ (m) [E]
0.0	0.0
1.0	2.0
2.0	8.0
3.0	18.0
4.0	28.0
5.0	38.0
6.0	48.0
7.0	54.0
8.0	56.0

Get in Motion!

Before You Start...

Accurately describing the motion of an object is sometimes difficult. You must know where the object is relative to a point of reference. You need to have an idea of what direction the object is moving in and how fast it is going. You must also be aware of any changes in speed (acceleration). One excellent way to describe the motion of an object is with the help of a motion sensor.

Motion sensors use pulses of sound that reflect off an object to determine its position. In this activity, you will use a motion sensor connected to a computer to track the motion of an object. By producing a graph of the motion, you will be able to describe when the object is moving, and whether it is moving at a constant speed or is changing speed. In this activity, you will be the moving object!

The Question

What does the movement of an object look like on a position–time graph?

The Hypothesis

Look at step 2 of the procedure and form a hypothesis for this investigation based on the question above.

Variables

Identify the type of data you will collect to support your hypothesis. State the manipulated, responding, and controlled variables in this investigation.

Materials and Equipment

computer and data-collection software

motion sensor

printer

alternative materials if no motion sensor is available

metre-sticks

adding machine tape

marker

tape

stopwatch

grid paper

Procedure

Method 1: Using a Motion Sensor

1. Connect the motion sensor (Figure B1.26) to the computer and activate the data-collection software. Configure the software to display a position–time graph.

2. Have a partner activate the motion sensor. Stand in front of the sensor, as shown in Figure B1.27. Perform the following sequence.
   - Stand still for 5 s.
   - Move slowly away from the sensor at a steady rate.
   - When you are about 2–3 m away from the sensor, gradually come to a stop.
   - Stand still for a few seconds.

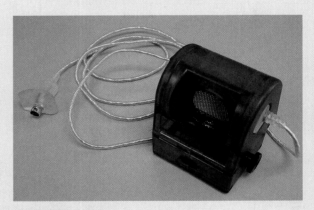

FIGURE B1.26   A motion sensor

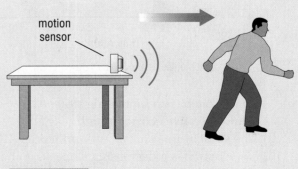

FIGURE B1.27   Step 2

③ When you have completed the sequence, your partner should stop recording.

④ Once you have your graph scaled correctly on screen, print it out.

⑤ Repeat the sequence in step 2, but move more quickly.

Method 2: Using Metre-Sticks and Paper

⑥ Lay out the metre-sticks end-to-end and tape down a long strip of paper (adding machine tape) next to the sticks.

⑦ Stand at the beginning of the path, and start the stopwatch. Begin the motions described in step 2, but while you are moving, call out "Now!" every second. (If you find this difficult, have someone else control the stopwatch.)

⑧ Have a partner follow you and mark your position on the paper or at each time interval indicated by "Now."

⑨ Repeat steps 7 and 8 as many times as necessary to obtain a good result. (It may take practice!)

⑩ Measure the positions of consecutive marks on the paper, and record the position–time data in a table. Use the data to construct a position–time graph.

⑪ Repeat the procedure, but do the movements more quickly.

Analyzing and Interpreting

1. Label the following on the position–time graph you have printed or created:
   • areas of no movement
   • areas of constant speed
   • areas of acceleration

2. Explain why you labelled the areas as you did in step 1 of Analyzing and Interpreting. For example, what characteristic of the line on the graph indicates no motion? Constant speed? Acceleration?

3. How are different speeds indicated on your graphs? Explain.

Forming Conclusions

4. Write a few summary sentences that answer the question: "What does the movement of an object look like on a position–time graph?"

5. Did your results match your hypothesis?

Applying and Connecting

6. Imagine a car leaving the school parking lot. It slowly accelerates in a straight line away from the school, and then travels at a constant slow speed for a period of time. The car then slows down as it approaches a stop sign, and remains motionless for a period of time. The car then continues in the same straight line, accelerating rapidly to a high speed. It continues at that high speed for a period of time before coming to an abrupt halt. Sketch a position–time graph of the car's position.

Extending

7. Refer back to the motion graphs you created in this activity. For the areas of the graph that indicate constant speed, calculate the actual speed you were travelling. Speed is calculated by dividing distance by time. In the case of the graph, this can be done for the line indicating constant speed, by calculating the *slope* of the line (how much the line *rises* or *falls*, divided by how much it *runs*).

Plotting a Velocity–Time Graph

Again, suppose that the motorboat is accelerating in an easterly direction. A person on the shore uses a radar gun and records the velocity of the motorboat every 1.0 s, as soon as it passes the first marker buoy. Table B1.14 shows the measurements taken by the person on shore.

TABLE B1.14 Change in the Velocity of the Motorboat

Time t (s)	Velocity of Boat $\vec{v}$ (m/s) [E]
0.0	0.0
1.0	2.0
2.0	4.0
3.0	6.0
4.0	8.0
5.0	10.0

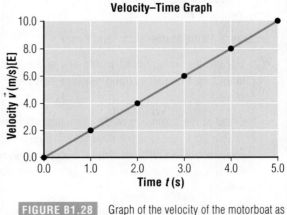

FIGURE B1.28 Graph of the velocity of the motorboat as a function of time

reSEARCH

Which would accelerate the fastest and win a 50-m race between a racehorse, a race car, and a human? Use the Internet or your local library to research the acceleration of a racehorse, a race car, and the fastest human. Using the data from your research, determine who would win the race. Write a brief summary of your findings. Begin your search at

 www.pearsoned.ca/ school/science10

The graph in Figure B1.28 uses the data from Table B1.14 to describe the accelerated motion of the motorboat. The graph shows the line of best fit for this data. This is a straight line with an increasing slope. This indicates that the velocity of the motorboat is increasing with time. The slope of the line of best fit can be calculated as follows:

$$\text{slope} = \frac{\text{rise}}{\text{run}}$$

$$= \frac{\Delta \vec{v}}{\Delta t} \qquad \text{Since acceleration} = \frac{\Delta \vec{v}}{\Delta t}$$

$$= \text{acceleration}$$

$$= \frac{10.0 \frac{m}{s} [E] - 0.0 \frac{m}{s} [E]}{5.0 \text{ s} - 0.0 \text{ s}}$$

$$= \frac{10.0 \frac{m}{s} [E]}{5.0 \text{ s}}$$

$$= 2.0 \frac{m}{s^2} [E]$$

The acceleration of the boat is 2.0 m/s² [E]. If the slope had a negative value, this would indicate that the boat had a negative acceleration. In other words, it was slowing down.

Figure B1.29 shows two velocity–time graphs of accelerated motion. Graph (a) has an increasing slope, which indicates positive acceleration. Graph (b) has a decreasing slope, which indicates negative acceleration.

Velocity–Time Graph

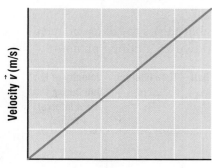

Velocity–Time Graph

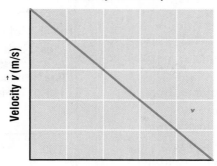

FIGURE B1.29 (a) This graph represents positive acceleration because the slope is increasing.

(b) This graph represents negative acceleration because the slope is decreasing.

Example Problem B1.10

Table B1.15 shows data for an object travelling with accelerated motion.

a) Draw a velocity–time graph for the data shown in the table.
b) Using the graph, identify the motion occurring in the time intervals given below. Justify your answer for each one.
   i) between $t = 0.0$ s and $t = 3.0$ s
   ii) between $t = 3.0$ s and $t = 5.0$ s
   iii) between $t = 5.0$ s and $t = 8.0$ s

TABLE B1.15 Time and Velocity Data for Example Problem B1.10

Time t (s)	Velocity $\vec{v}$ (m/s) [E]
0.0	0.0
1.0	2.0
2.0	4.0
3.0	6.0
4.0	6.0
5.0	6.0
6.0	4.0
7.0	2.0
8.0	0.0

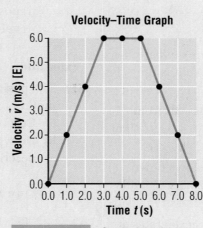

FIGURE B1.30 Graph of the data in Table B1.15

a) Figure B1.30 shows the graph drawn from the data in Table B1.15.
b)   i) The straight line with a positive slope shows that the object was travelling with positive acceleration [E].
   ii) The straight horizontal line shows uniform motion [E].
   iii) The straight line with a negative slope shows negative acceleration [E].

Practice Problem

17. Table B1.16 shows data for an object travelling with accelerated motion.
    a) Draw a velocity–time graph for the data shown in the table.
    b) Using the graph, identify the motion occurring in the time intervals given below. Justify your answer for each one.
       i) between $t = 0.0$ s and $t = 3.0$ s
       ii) between $t = 3.0$ s and $t = 5.0$ s
       iii) between $t = 5.0$ s and $t = 8.0$ s

TABLE B1.16 Time and Velocity Data for Practice Problem 17

Time t (s)	Velocity $\vec{v}$ (m/s) [E]
0.0	0.0
1.0	5.0
2.0	10.0
3.0	15.0
4.0	15.0
5.0	15.0
6.0	10.0
7.0	5.0
8.0	0.0

Knowledge

1. Identify the following motions as positive or negative accelerations:
   a) An object changes its velocity from 10 m/s [E] to 20 m/s [E] in 4.0 s.
   b) An object changes its velocity from 20 m/s [E] to 10 m/s [E] in 4.0 s.
   c) An object changes its velocity from 10 m/s [W] to 20 m/s [W] in 4.0 s.
   d) An object changes its velocity from 20 m/s [W] to 10 m/s [W] in 4.0 s.

2. Explain how an object can be speeding up and have a negative acceleration.

3. A train is travelling along a straight stretch of track.
   a) Identify one situation when the train could be exhibiting positive acceleration.
   b) Identify one situation when it could be exhibiting negative acceleration.

Applications

4. Rearrange the acceleration equation,

$$\vec{a} = \frac{\vec{v}_f - \vec{v}_i}{\Delta t}, \text{ to solve for:}$$

   a) Δt
   b) $\vec{v}_f$

5. A transit bus travelling at 15 m/s [N] applies its brakes and stops in 3.0 s. What is the acceleration of the bus?

6. A race car driver accelerates his car from 25.0 m/s [W] to 40.0 m/s [W] in 4.00 s. What is the acceleration of the car?

7. A golf ball rolling on a green slows down from 2.00 m/s to 1.50 m/s in 2.00 s. What is the magnitude of the acceleration of the ball?

8. An object starts from rest and accelerates at 1.30 m/s² [N] for 6.00 s. What is the final velocity of the object?

9. An object, initially at rest, is dropped off a building and accelerates to Earth at −9.81 m/s² [downward]. How long will it take for the object to reach a final velocity of −49.1 m/s [downward]?

10. The following table shows the data collected as a ball rolled down an inclined plane.

Time t (s)	Position of the Ball Down the Incline $\vec{d}$ (cm)	Time Interval Δt (s)	Velocity of the Ball During the Time Interval $\vec{v}$ (cm/s)
0.00	0.00	—	—
2.00	4.00	0.00 – 2.00	
4.00	16.00	2.00 – 4.00	
6.00	36.00	4.00 – 6.00	
8.00	64.00	6.00 – 8.00	
10.00	100.00	8.00 – 10.00	

   a) Draw a position–time graph of the motion. Explain how the graph proves either uniform or accelerated motion.
   b) Complete the above table of values in your notebook, and draw a velocity–time graph of the motion.
   c) Using the velocity–time graph, calculate the acceleration of the ball.
   d) Explain how you would determine the displacement of the ball using the:
      i) position–time graph
      ii) velocity–time graph

Extensions

11. The position–time graph below depicts the motion of an object:
    a) Describe the motion in each segment.
    b) Draw a velocity–time graph to match your description in part (a).

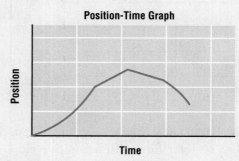

Position-Time Graph

12. You are observing an airplane taking off from a runway. Describe the measurements you could take to determine the acceleration of the airplane.

B1.4 Work and Energy

The question of why objects exhibit uniform or accelerated motion puzzled philosophers and scientists for centuries. It wasn't until the 1600s that Isaac Newton described the important relationships between forces and motion.

Activity B4
QuickLab

Forces

Purpose

To distinguish between observed forces

Materials and Equipment

Station 1:
a spring scale (20 N)
2 10-N weights
2 pulleys and clamps
string
sheet of paper
tape

Station 2:
a retort stand with a ring clamp
1 10-N weight with hooks on both ends
string

Procedure

Station 1:

1. Clamp the pulleys on opposite ends of a table. Tape the paper on the face of the scale to hide the reading.

2. Attach a 10-N weight to each end of the scale. Use enough string so that each weight hangs over a pulley with the scale centred between the two pulleys (Figure B1.31).

3. Without looking at the reading on the scale, write down what you think it will be. Remove the paper and record the reading on the scale.

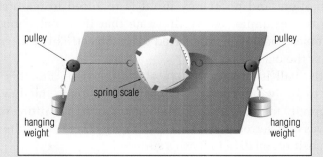

FIGURE B1.31 Pulleys and weights for procedure step 2

Station 2:

4. Tie a string to both ends of the weight. Attach one string to the ring on the retort stand, and let the other string hang down freely (Figure B1.32).

5. Predict which string will break when you pull on the lower string. Slowly and gently pull on the lower string. Gradually increase the "pull" until a string breaks.

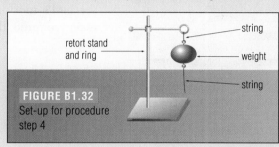

FIGURE B1.32
Set-up for procedure step 4

6. Reattach the weight to the ring on the retort stand. Predict which string will break when you give the lower string a quick jerk. Give the lower string a quick jerk.

Questions

Station 1:

1. Are there forces acting on the scale? Justify your answer.

2. Are these forces a "push" or a "pull" on the scale?

3. What is the cause of the forces?

4. What reading did you predict for the scale? What was the actual reading? Was it the same as your prediction?

5. Explain why the reading on the scale must be the same as one of the hanging weights (10 N).

Station 2:

6. Before you pulled gently on the bottom string, which string did you predict would break? Which string broke?

7. Before you jerked sharply on the bottom string, which string did you predict would break? Which string broke?

8. Explain why a different string broke in each procedure.

   (Hint: Consider the action of the hanging weight in each procedure.)

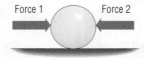

FIGURE B1.33 (a) Balanced forces are equal in magnitude (force 1 equals force 2) but opposite in direction. They cancel each other out.

(b) Unbalanced forces are forces that are not equal in magnitude (force 2 is greater than force 1) or are not opposite in direction.

FIGURE B1.35 Lifting a ball from the floor requires the application of a force to overcome the force of gravity.

Force

A ball at rest on a billiard table will remain at rest. It does not move because all forces acting on it are balanced (Figure B1.33(a)). Recall that a **force** is defined as a push or a pull on an object. Force is measured in newtons. The resting ball will only move when an unbalanced force is applied to it through a distance. With an unbalanced force, the force acting in one direction is greater than the force acting in the opposite direction (Figure B1.33(b)). If a person hits a stationary ball with a cue, he or she used energy to apply the force. The energy was transferred from the person to the ball through the cue. The ball then gained energy and, as a result, acquired a change in motion.

Once an object is in motion, it tends to remain in motion, moving at a constant speed in a straight line. However, if an unbalanced force is applied to the moving ball, it will either speed up or slow down (accelerate). If the unbalanced force is applied in the same direction as the ball's motion, the ball will speed up (Figure B1.34(a)). The person applying the force to the ball transfers energy to the ball. If the unbalanced force, such as friction between the table and the ball, is applied in the direction opposite to the direction of the ball's motion, the ball will slow down (Figure 1.34(b)). Without such a resistive force, the ball would tend to keep moving.

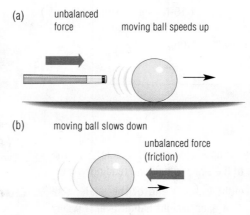

FIGURE B1.34 An unbalanced force acting on a moving ball will speed up (a) or slow down (b) the ball, depending on the direction of the force.

In the absence of any external unbalanced forces, such as resistive forces, all objects tend to maintain uniform motion or stay at rest. An object in motion will stay in motion, and no energy input is required to maintain uniform motion. The two examples above illustrate that if an unbalanced force is applied to an object, energy is transferred to the object. This causes a change in the motion of the object.

In Figure B1.35, the ball is lifted and held above the floor. For this to occur, the person had to apply a force in the opposite direction to the downward force of Earth's gravity to raise the ball. The person doing the lifting did work and the energy was transferred to the ball. This energy transfer results in a change in the ball's position relative to Earth's surface.

This situation describes how one force (supplied by the person) applied against another force (due to Earth's gravitational field) can result in a transfer of energy, resulting in a change in position of the object.

Figure B1.36 illustrates a person boring a hole with a cork borer. The person must apply a force to turn the cork borer and, in the process, the person uses up energy. This energy is transferred to the cork and the cork borer and results in a change in temperature. Both the cork and the cork borer will now feel warm to the touch.

All these examples have something in common: all involve using energy to apply a force to an object over a distance, and the object then changes in some way. They are all the result of an energy transfer, and an application of a force applied through a distance was required to achieve the change. Somehow, force and energy are related.

FIGURE B1.36 A person applies a force to turn the cork borer. Energy transfers to the cork borer.

Work

Whenever a force moves an object through a distance that is in the direction of the force, then **work** is done on the object. The work done is calculated by multiplying the force by the distance travelled in the direction of the force.

$$\text{work} = \text{force} \times \text{distance the object travels}$$
$$W = Fd$$
$$\text{joule} = \text{newton} \times \text{metre} \qquad \text{Note: } N = \frac{\text{kg} \cdot \text{m}}{\text{s}^2}$$
$$1\,\text{J} = 1\,\text{N} \cdot \text{m}$$
$$= \frac{1\,\text{kg} \cdot \text{m}}{\text{s}^2} \cdot \text{m}$$
$$= 1\,\frac{\text{kg} \cdot \text{m}^2}{\text{s}^2}$$

In physics, work is a very specific term and has a more specific meaning than its everyday meaning. For example, you may think that studying for a test, or sitting at a desk and doing your homework is doing work. After all, it can be quite exhausting. However, in terms of the physical definition for work, you are not doing work because nothing is moving or changing position.

There are three conditions for work to be done on an object:

1. There must be movement.
   Someone pushing against a wall with 100 N of force is not doing any work on the wall because the wall does not move.

2. There must be a force.
   A person riding a bicycle that is coasting (Figure B1.37) is not doing any work on the bike because even though there is movement, the person is not applying a horizontal force to the bike.

3. The force and the distance the object travels must be in the same direction.
   A person is not doing any work on a pack (Figure B1.38) when she's carrying it parallel to the ground because the force of her hand on the pack is vertical and the distance the pack travels is horizontal.

direction

FIGURE B1.37 When coasting on a bicycle, the rider is travelling over a distance, but no force is being applied.

direction

force

FIGURE B1.38 Carrying a pack can be strenuous, but are you doing work?

Inquiry Lab

Doing Work

Before You Start...

The energy that is supplied to do work on an object is called "work input." When work is done on an object, it gains energy. The work equivalent of this energy is called "work output."

The Question

How much work must be done to move an object a given distance up an inclined plane?

Variables

Read over the procedure and identify the manipulated, responding, and controlled variables in the investigation.

Materials and Equipment

inclined plane

block of wood, with or without wheels, and a hook to attach the spring scale

metre-stick

spring scale (measuring in newtons of force)

string

protractor

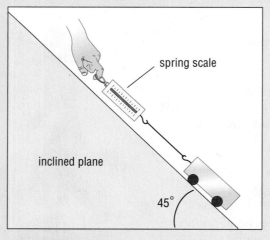

FIGURE B1.39 Step 8

Procedure

1. Set up an inclined plane, at least 60.0 cm long, at an angle of about 45°, or place one end of a long board on a stack of books and the other end on a table so that the angle of the board is about 45°.

2. At the 0.50-m mark, measure the vertical height of the inclined plane from the tabletop. Record this value in your notebook.

3. Measure the weight of the block of wood by suspending it from the spring scale. Record this value in your notebook.

4. Attach one end of a string to the hook on the block of wood and the other end to the spring scale.

5. Place the block of wood near the bottom of the inclined plane so that the spring scale is holding the block of wood at rest on the inclined plane. Use the marker to mark the position of the front end of the block on the board. This will indicate the starting position.

6. From this starting position, use a metre-stick to measure and mark the distance in 10.0-cm increments up the inclined plane. There should be at least five increments.

7. Create a data table in your notebook like the one below. Make sure your data table has a title.

Distance *d* (m)	Force *F* (N)
0.00	
0.10	

8. Using the spring scale attached to the block, slowly pull the block up the inclined plane (Figure B1.39). Be sure to pull at a steady rate so that the block maintains the same speed the entire way up the inclined plane.

9. Have your partner note the reading on the spring scale at the initial mark and at each of the 10.0-cm marks as you pull the block of wood up the inclined plane.

10. Record your readings on the scale at each increment.

Analyzing and Interpreting

1. Draw a graph of force as a function of the distance travelled by the block. Make sure that distance (the manipulated variable) is on the horizontal axis of the graph and force (the responding variable) is on the vertical axis of the graph.

2. Plot the points on the graph and then draw a line of best fit through the points.

3. At the 0.50-m point on the x-axis, draw a vertical line from the x-axis to the line of best fit. Do the same at the 0.0 point. The figure that you have created should resemble a rectangle.

4. Shade in this rectangle with a colored pencil.

5. Determine the area of the rectangle using:

   area = (length of y-axis)(width of x-axis)

6. What does the value of the area under the line represent? Look at the units of measurement of the length and width to help you answer this question.

   Hint: If $W = Fd$

   and if area = (length of y-axis or F) (length of x-axis or d)

   then what does the area represent?

7. Is the value you calculated from the area a work input or a work output?

8. Determine the work done in lifting the block of wood a vertical distance by using the height of the inclined plane at 0.50 m, the weight of the block, and the formula

   $W = Fd$ where F is the weight and d is the vertical distance.

9. Is this value a work input or work output?

Forming Conclusions

10. Are the values of work input and work output equal?

11. Which value would you suggest is the "useful" work done?

12. If the values are not the same, suggest reasons why they are not the same.

Extending

13. Conduct the experiment again after changing the height of the inclined plane. Predict how the experimental results will change.

The Relationship between Work Output and Work Input

When a force is applied to move an object through a distance, work is done on the object. This is called the work input or energy input. The work input can be calculated using the formula $W = Fd$. Suppose the force applied to the object is constant throughout the distance that it acts on the object. In that case, a force–distance graph should be a straight horizontal line. The area under the line of best fit can be used to determine the work input. The object gains energy as a result of this work done on the object. This energy is called energy output or work output.

In the absence of any outside forces, such as friction, the total work input should equal the total work output.

re**SEARCH**

The unit for specifying the amount of work done is given in joules. Use the Internet or the local library to research the origin of the name for this unit. Write a brief summary of your findings. Begin your search at

www.pearsoned.ca/
school/science10

Example Problem B1.11

A weightlifter lifts a barbell a vertical distance of 2.40 m. If the average force required to lift the barbell is 2.00×10^3 N, how much work is done by the weightlifter on the barbell?

$$W = Fd$$
$$= (2.00 \times 10^3 \text{ N})(2.40 \text{ m})$$
$$= 4.80 \times 10^3 \text{ J}$$

The work done by the weightlifter is 4.80×10^3 J or 4.80 kJ.

Practice Problems

18. A tugboat is towing a tanker through a canal using a towrope. Calculate the work done by the tugboat if it applies an average horizontal force of 6.50×10^3 N on the towrope while towing the tanker through a horizontal distance of 150 m.

19. A large crane did 2.2×10^4 J of work in lifting a demolition ball a vertical distance of 9.5 m. Calculate the average force exerted by the chain of the crane on the demolition ball.

Energy

If a body has energy, then the body can do work by transferring the energy to another object. This leads to the definition of energy. **Energy** is the ability to do work. Work and energy are actually the same thing. If a body does work on an object, then the body doing the work loses energy, and the object that has work done to it gains energy. For example, a pool cue loses energy as it hits a ball, and the ball, once hit, gains the energy the cue loses. An energy transfer has occurred.

Since work and a change in energy are the same, then they must have the same units. If work is given in joules (J), then energy is also given in joules.

change in energy = work

$$\Delta E = W$$
$$J = J$$

Example Problem B1.12

A weightlifter does 4.80×10^3 J of work in lifting a barbell. How much energy is gained by the barbell?

Since $\Delta E = W$

and $W = 4.80 \times 10^3$ J

then $\Delta E = 4.80 \times 10^3$ J

Practice Problem

20. A large crane does 2.2×10^4 J of work in lifting an object. How much energy is gained by the object?

Knowledge

1. What is force? Use an example in your explanation.

2. What happens to an object when work is done on it?

3. Explain how force, energy, and work are related.

4. Force is measured in newtons, which is a derived unit. What is one newton (N) in terms of the fundamental units of measurement, which are m, kg, and s?

Applications

5. Explain why there is no work being done by the student in the following situations:
   a) studying two hours for a test
   b) carrying a book across the room
   c) dropping a ball

6. Calculate the work done in each of the following situations.
   a) A 98.0-N rock is lifted a vertical distance of 1.50 m.
   b) A boy applies a horizontal force of 25.0 N on a sleigh and pushes it 2.00 m horizontally.
   c) A mother cat picks up a 2.00-N kitten in her mouth and lifts it vertically 0.100 m. With the kitten in her mouth, the mother cat then carries the kitten 10.0 m across the room.

7. A worker does 43.0 J of work in moving an object 3.20 m horizontally across a floor. How much force did the worker exert in doing the work on the object?

8. A machine does 2.00×10^4 J of work in lifting an object. If the force exerted by the machine was 1.20×10^3 N, how high did the machine lift the object?

9. A person applies a force of 30.0 N in sliding an object 1.30 m up a ramp. What is the work done by the person along the ramp? Is this work a work input or a work output?

10. The graph below shows the relationship between the constant force applied as a function of the distance that the object is moved.

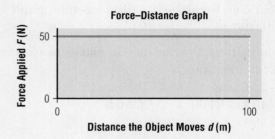

a) Calculate the area under the line for the distance from 0 m to 100 m.
b) What does the area under the line represent?

Extensions

11. Does your heart do work? Explain.

12. A weightlifter strains to lift a 1000-N barbell a vertical distance of 2.30 m from the ground to a position above his head. He then holds the barbell above his head for a time period. Is he doing more, less, or the same work holding the barbell above his head as compared to the work done in lifting the barbell to that position? Justify your answer.

13. Is the force of gravity a push or a pull? Explain your answer.

14. A spacecraft has left Earth's atmosphere and is travelling through space to the Moon. Explain why the engines in the spacecraft can be shut off at this point and the spacecraft will still reach the Moon.

Knowledge

1. What is the difference between uniform motion and accelerated motion?

2. What is the difference between average speed and average velocity for an object?

3. Does a car's speedometer measure the speed or the velocity of an object?

4. What does the slope of a distance–time graph indicate?

5. Identify the following measurements as scalar or vector quantities.
   a) 2.30 km
   b) 40 km/h [W]
   c) 50°C
   d) 25 cm [S]
   e) 2.0 h

6. Describe the type of motion that an object will have if:
   a) balanced forces act on the object
   b) an unbalanced force acts on the object

7. Why do work and energy have the same units?

8. If 15.0 J of work is done on an object, how much energy must the object gain?

Applications

9. A dog walks a total distance of 23.0 m in 14.2 s. What is the average speed of the dog?

10. A motorboat moving at an average speed of 5.30 m/s travels in a straight line for 55.0 s. What is the distance travelled by the boat?

11. An airplane flying at an average speed of 800 km/h travels from City A to City B, a distance of 4200 km. How long will it take the plane to complete its journey?

12. The table at the top of the next column shows data obtained when a police radar gun measured the speed of a car at 1.00 s intervals.
   a) Draw a speed–time graph with time on the horizontal axis.
   b) Calculate the slope of the graph and state what this slope represents.
   c) Calculate the area under the line of the graph and state what this area represents.

Time t (s)	Speed v (m/s)
0.00	20.0
1.00	20.0
2.00	20.1
3.00	19.9
4.00	20.0
5.00	20.2

13. A student walks 2.0 m [E], then 5.0 m [W].
   a) What is the total distance travelled by the student?
   b) What is the total displacement of the student?

14. The motion of objects A and B are represented by vector arrows shown in the diagram below. State the direction of vectors A and B using:
   a) the navigator method
   b) the x-axis method

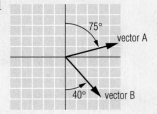

15. A jogger runs 500 m [N] in 150 s, then turns around and runs 300 m [S] in 100 s. Determine the jogger's
   a) distance travelled   c) average speed
   b) displacement   d) average velocity

16. The table below shows data for an object travelling at a uniform velocity.

Time t (s)	Position $\vec{d}$ (m) [N]
0.00	0.00
2.00	6.00
4.00	12.00
6.00	18.00
8.00	24.00
10.00	30.00

a) Draw a position–time graph of the object.

b) Calculate the slope of the graph and describe what this value represents.

17. A ball, initially at rest, rolls down an incline and speeds up to 4.50 m/s in 8.00 s. What is the magnitude of the ball's acceleration?

18. A car accelerates from rest at the rate of 3.00 m/s² [W] for 4.00 s. What is the velocity of the car at the end of the 4.00 s?

19. How long will it take for a girl running at a velocity of 2.50 m/s [N] to reach a velocity of 4.00 m/s [N], if she is accelerating at the rate of 0.500 m/s² [N]?

20. The velocity of an object was recorded each second for 5.00 s, as shown in the table below.

a) Plot a velocity–time graph.

b) What does the shape of the graph indicate about the object's motion?

Time t (s)	Velocity v (m/s) [E]
0.00	0.00
1.00	3.00
2.00	6.00
3.00	9.00
4.00	12.00
5.00	15.00

21. What is the unbalanced force acting on the following object?

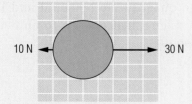

10 N ← → 30 N

22. A force of 15.0 N moves an object through a displacement of 40.0 m. What is the work done on the object?

23. A force of 35 N acts on an object through a vertical displacement of 3.0 m. How much energy does the object gain?

24. Moving a crate through a horizontal displacement of 10.0 m causes 350 J of work to be done. How much force must be applied to the crate to do this work?

Extensions

25. a) Can the displacement of an object from its starting position ever be greater than the total distance travelled?

b) Can the total distance travelled of an object ever be greater than the displacement of the object from its starting position?

26. Is it possible for an object to have an average speed of 2.0 m/s and at the same time have an average velocity of 0 m/s? Justify your answer.

27. A car travels at a velocity of 100 km/h [E] for 3.00 h and then at a velocity of 110 km/h [E] for 1.00 h. What is the average velocity of the car?

28. The motion of a vehicle is shown in the position–time graph shown here.

a) Describe the motion of the vehicle in each of the segments shown in the graph.

b) Draw a velocity–time graph of the motion of the vehicle.

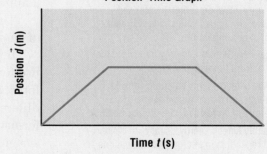

Position–Time Graph

Position $\vec{d}$ (m)

Time t (s)

29. a) A car on a journey from Edmonton to Red Deer is travelling at a speed of 100 km/h. Does the engine of the car have to be operating to provide the necessary energy to maintain this constant speed? Explain your answer.

b) A spacecraft is travelling at a speed of 28 000 km/h on its way to Mars. Do the engines of the spacecraft have to be operating to provide the necessary energy to maintain this constant speed? Explain your answer.

Energy in mechanical systems can be described both numerically and graphically.

Key Concepts

In this section, you will learn about the following key concepts:

- forms and interconversions of energy
- mechanical energy conversions and work
- design and function of technological systems and devices involving potential and kinetic energy, and thermal energy conversions

Learning Outcomes

When you have completed this section, you will be able to:

- illustrate, by use of examples from natural and technological systems, that energy exists in a variety of forms
- describe, qualitatively, current and past technologies used to transform energy from one form to another, and that energy transfer technologies produce measurable changes in motion, shape, or temperature
- analyze and illustrate how the concept of energy developed from observation of heat and mechanical devices
- describe the evidence for the presence of energy (i.e., observable physical and chemical changes, and changes in motion, shape, or temperature)
- derive the SI unit of energy and work, the joule, from fundamental units
- define kinetic energy as energy due to motion, and define potential energy as energy due to relative condition or position
- quantify kinetic energy using $E_k = \frac{1}{2}mv^2$ and relate this to energy transformations
- relate gravitational potential energy to work done using $E_p = m\vec{g}h$ and $W = Fd$ and show that a change in energy is equal to work done on a system or $\Delta E = W$
- describe chemical energy as a form of potential energy
- define gravitational potential energy as the work done against gravity

FIGURE B2.1 Inuit doing a blanket toss

A visit to Canada's Far North can be especially exciting if you happen to visit an Inuit settlement that is hosting the Arctic Summer Games. The games include traditional challenges like the blanket toss shown in Figure B2.1. In this activity, a group of Inuit men and women all hold on to a large circular blanket (originally, it used to be a large animal hide). By setting up a rhythm, they can toss a person on the blanket high into the air. Today, the blanket toss is only for recreation, but it used to serve an important purpose. In the flat barren lands of the northern tundra, there are few high hills or ridges to climb to survey the landscape. By being tossed into the air, a hunter could see over the horizon and locate herds of caribou.

The blanket toss is similar to a trampoline and is a good example of an energy transformation.

In the previous section, you studied motion and learned how to use formulas and graphs to describe it. You also studied how work, force, and energy are related. In this section, you will learn about the different forms that energy can take. You will also learn how transformations from one form to another are put to use in technological systems. You will learn how to quantify the potential and kinetic energy of an object and how mechanical energy combines both kinetic energy and potential energy.

B 2.1 Forms of Energy

The idea of energy eluded early scientists because energy is a very difficult concept to define. Ask what the definition of energy is, and what comes to mind are visions of what energy can do. For example, the Sun's energy causes snow to melt in the spring. We know that a person who has just run a marathon has used up a lot of energy. We only see the evidence of energy when something is done. So it is not surprising that the development of the concept of energy went hand in hand with the development of technologies that used energy. It was only through observing the changes in these technologies that scientists started to get a clear picture of the concept of energy.

By the 1850s, scientists were convinced of the existence of a scientific concept called energy. However, energy was still difficult to describe because it involves only an abstract idea, not a material object. Experimental evidence had supported the theory that heat was just another form of energy and that it could be converted into other forms following certain principles. With these scientific breakthroughs, scientists realized that other physical phenomena in science might be explained in terms of energy, and that other forms of energy might exist.

Chemical Energy

From the experiments of the early alchemists, it was known that there were "hidden secrets" in chemical reactions. While they tried to make gold by mixing the four known elements (earth, air, fire, and water), the alchemists began to discover that mixing certain chemicals could produce surprising results. Thus the science of chemistry began. However, it was not until the early 1800s that French chemist Antoine Lavoisier realized that when equal amounts of different substances burned, the chemical reactions could produce different amounts of heat. With this discovery, chemists and physicists shared a common interest in heat.

When wood burns, the energy in the cellulose molecules is released, turning to heat. This is evidence that there is energy in a chemical reaction, and that this energy can be converted to heat. **Chemical energy** is the potential energy stored in the chemical bonds of compounds. The food you eat contains chemical energy that the body uses to do work in the cells.

Electrical Energy and Magnetism

Electricity, or **electrical energy**, is the work done by moving charges. The Volta Pile (Figure B2.2) is made of stacked layers of two different metals such as copper and silver, with moistened paper sandwiched between each layer. If a wire is connected from either end of the stack to an external circuit, the Volta Pile can produce a constant electric current. Invented by Italian physicist Alessandro Volta in the early 1800s, this device constituted the first battery. It provides evidence of a connection between chemical energy and electrical energy. The study of current electricity and electrical energy thus began.

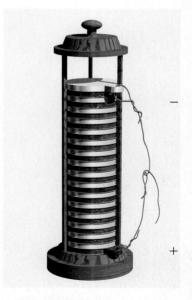

FIGURE B2.2 The Volta Pile—the first battery—was invented by Italian physicist Alessandro Volta.

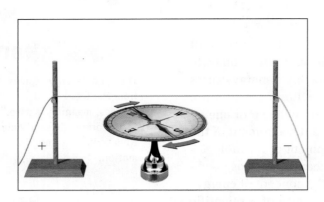

FIGURE B2.3 Oersted's experiment. As a metal wire with a current passing through it passes over the compass, the compass needle moves.

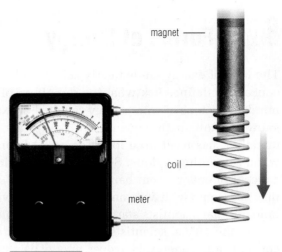

magnet

coil

meter

FIGURE B2.4 By moving a magnet through a coil of wire, Faraday developed the first electric generator.

If you hold a magnet above iron filings, the filings move toward the magnet, indicating that magnetism is a form of energy.

In 1820, Danish physicist and philosopher Hans Oersted discovered that an electric current in a wire could produce magnetic effects. By accident, he passed a metal wire that had a current passing through it over a compass. As he did this, he noticed that the compass needle moved (Figure B2.3). This change in the needle's position showed that electricity can produce magnetism. This discovery led to the invention of the electromagnet.

While Oersted showed that electricity can produce magnetism, Michael Faraday in London, England, in 1831 showed that the reverse can happen. He moved a magnet through a coil of wire and observed that this caused an electric current to flow through the wire (Figure B2.4).

In 1821, Estonian-German physicist Thomas Seebeck took a strip of one type of metal and joined its ends to a strip of another type of metal to form a loop (Figure B2.5). He heated one of the junctions of the two metals and kept

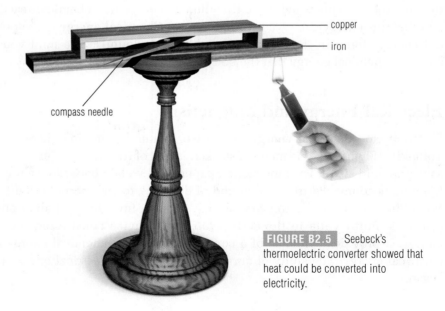

copper

iron

compass needle

FIGURE B2.5 Seebeck's thermoelectric converter showed that heat could be converted into electricity.

the other cold. The difference in temperature between the junctions caused the electrons inside the metal to move, producing an electric current. The magnetic field created by the current caused a compass needle to move. This experiment was evidence that heat could be converted into electricity.

The invention of the light bulb by American Thomas Edison in the late 1800s showed that heat and light are two forms of energy that could be produced from electricity.

Nuclear and Solar Energy

In France, in 1896, Henri Becquerel observed that certain atoms spontaneously disintegrate, and in the process, emit radiation or radiant energy. This led to the development of a new source of energy, nuclear energy. **Nuclear energy** is the potential energy stored in the nucleus of an atom. When the nucleus of an atom is split (nuclear fission) or when the nuclei of two atoms combine (nuclear fusion), this energy is released.

Originally, scientists thought that the source of energy in the Sun was chemical energy from burning. However, they soon realized that it would take only about five thousand years before all the mass of the Sun was burned up completely. Once the secrets of nuclear fission and fusion reactions were discovered, scientists then understood that these reactions must be the source of energy in the Sun. **Solar energy** results from a hydrogen–hydrogen nuclear fusion reaction with the release of nuclear energy. This radiant energy travels to Earth as electromagnetic radiation. It is converted to other forms of energy such as heat.

Motion and Energy

When a group of English scientists watched a demonstration of a Newton's cradle (Figure B2.6) in 1666, it caused great concern. They had no idea why the ball on the opposite side rises to nearly the same height as the first ball. At that time, there were no theories to explain the ball's motion.

About 20 years after this demonstration, German philosopher and mathematician Gottfried Leibniz reasoned that whatever caused the ball to move resembled a force that seemed to be transmitted through the balls. He called this physical quantity *vis viva*, a Latin word meaning "living force." (The term "energy" wasn't used until the 1850s, but for simplicity, "energy" is used here instead of *vis viva*.) He also reasoned that two types of energy could be observed in nature.

1. Flowing water, wind, or any object in motion could be made to do work because of its motion, and thus has **kinetic energy**.

2. An object raised above Earth's surface has the potential to do work because of its position, and thus has **gravitational potential energy**.

Although Leibniz had mistaken energy for a force, his definitions of kinetic and potential energy were accurate. The sum of the energy of motion and position is known as **mechanical energy**.

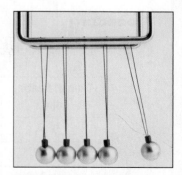

FIGURE B2.6 When a metal ball on one side is pulled away a certain distance and released, it swings back and collides with the other balls in a line. After the collision, the first ball remains nearly motionless, while a ball at the opposite end rises to almost the same height.

Mechanical Energy and Heat

The Question

What is the relationship between mechanical energy and heat?

The Hypothesis

In this activity, you will be applying mechanical energy to a system. State a hypothesis about the relationship between the amount of mechanical energy you apply and the heat gained by the system.

Variables

Read through the procedure for this experiment. Identify the manipulated, responding, and controlled variables.

Materials and Equipment

300 mL of water at room temperature

500-mL beaker

thermometer

egg beater

Procedure

1 Construct a table like the one below to record your data:

Time of Beating (min)	Temperature of Water (°C)
0	
2	
4	
6	
8	
10	

2 Pour the water into the beaker. Use the thermometer to measure the temperature of the water. Make sure that it is at room temperature (about 25°C). Record this value in the temperature column in your table at time 0 min.

3 Place the egg beater in the water and beat the water at a steady rate for 2 minutes. Quickly record the final temperature of the water.

4 Repeat procedure step 3 four more times. Make sure that you begin the next 2-minute period of beating quickly, to prevent the water from cooling off.

Analyzing and Interpreting

1. Using your data, draw a graph of temperature as a function of the time you used the egg beater.

2. What is the shape of the line of best fit of your graph? What does this shape indicate about the relationship between the time of beating and the temperature of the water?

3. Which of the variables on the graph corresponds to the mechanical energy applied to the system?

4. Which of the variables on the graph corresponds to the heat gained by the system?

Forming Conclusions

5. Based on your graph, explain the relationship between the mechanical energy applied to the system and the heat gained by the system.

6. Does the experiment prove your original hypothesis? If not, modify your hypothesis to fit the results of your experiment.

Heat and Energy

At about the same period, other scientists were puzzling over what caused heat. The ancient Greeks had no knowledge of the concept of energy, but they speculated about what the heat from fire actually was. One group of Greek philosophers, called Atomists, thought that heat was somehow related to the motion of "atoms," or tiny particles, within a substance. However, this idea seemed ridiculous to another group of Greek scientists who believed that the existence of atoms was impossible. Thus, the relation of heat to atomic motion was largely forgotten until the 1700s.

In 1750, Scottish physician Joseph Black observed that when a cold object is placed in a cup of hot water, and then removed, the object becomes much warmer. He explained this by suggesting heat was an invisible fluid, called a caloric fluid, which flows naturally from hot to cold things. Black mistakenly thought that a substance was being transferred from the water to the spoon. However, his observation on the flow of heat became one of the principles of **thermodynamics**, a science dealing with the study of the interrelationships of heat, work, and energy.

While Black was trying to perfect his caloric theory for heat, other scientists were reviving the theory that atomic motion explained heat. They suggested that the movement of atoms within a substance determines the thermal energy of the substance. Atoms move or vibrate more quickly in hot than in cold substances. The transfer of this thermal energy from a hot object to a cold object is defined as **heat**.

Heat and Mechanical Energy

In 1800, American-born Benjamin Thompson, who later became Count Rumford, became the minister of war in Bavaria. While supervising workers boring brass cylinders to make cannons, he noticed that a huge amount of heat was being generated in the bored metal. In fact, he could boil a kettle of water on the cannon. He also noticed that this supply of heat was endless, so long as the workers continued boring the hole. The experiments of Count Rumford produced strong evidence that heat was not a fluid as Black had thought. According to the caloric theory, the cannons would have run out of fluid at some point, but they never did. Rumford suggested that heat could be manufactured by the motion of the workers. He was the first to realize that heat and mechanical energy were related.

Scientists then started to realize that heat and mechanical energy were different types of energy that could be converted from one to the other. Around 1807, English physicist Thomas Young linked mechanical energy to Leibniz's theory of kinetic and potential energy in moving objects. While Leibniz thought an object had *either* kinetic *or* potential energy, Young correctly suggested that mechanical energy combined *both* kinetic and potential energy. He also thought that mechanical energy was related to the work a system can do. This led to the current definition of energy, which is the capacity to do work.

*info***BIT**

The term "calorie," which we commonly use to describe the energy content in foods, was called "caloric" by the Calorists in the 1700s. They literally burned food and measured the amount of heat it produced.

*info***BIT**

Traditionally, First Nations peoples used a wooden drill to start fires for cooking, warmth, or drying food. The drill consisted of a stick with a string (made of tree root or sinew) wound around it, a hand rest, and a wooden base. Pulling the string turned the stick rapidly in the wooden base. This drilling motion generated enough heat to start a fire.

reSEARCH

Though Benjamin Thompson spent most of his life in England and became Count Rumford in Bavaria, he was actually born in America. Use the Internet and other sources to research the life of Thompson. Write a brief summary of his achievements. Why did he not live in America? Begin your search at

www.pearsoned.ca/
school/science10

Joule's Experiments

Later, Sadi Carnot, a French engineer, performed experiments in an attempt to transform heat into mechanical energy. He discovered that the transformation of heat into mechanical energy could only occur when thermal energy flows from a hot object to a cool object. He also discovered that in this process some heat is always lost. From these experiments, he was able to determine the laws of heat efficiency of heat engines.

By 1840, it was widely accepted that heat was not a physical substance. Scientists now realized that heat could be exchanged for mechanical energy. This led to the birth of a new concept. In England, James Prescott Joule properly substituted the term "energy" for *vis viva*. He argued that heat is just another form of energy.

Figure B2.7 illustrates Joule's experiment that supports a connection between potential energy and heat. As the masses fall, the wheel rotates, heating up the water. If the masses are increased, there is a proportional increase in the amount of heat produced, and thus a proportional increase in the water temperature. Joule explained these findings. As the masses fall, they lose gravitational potential energy. The paddle has work done to it so it gains the energy the masses lose, in the form of kinetic energy, which is then transformed into heat.

Figure B2.8 illustrates Joule's experiment that supports a connection between kinetic energy and heat. In this experiment, a block of wood is in motion and so has kinetic energy as it falls. However, it loses kinetic energy when it collides with the other block. During the collision, the temperature of the other block increases. When the speed of the falling block is increased, its kinetic energy is also increased, and a corresponding temperature increase happens in the other block. Again, Joule explained these observations. As one block collides with the other, the first loses kinetic energy and the second one gains this energy in the form of heat.

Early scientists and engineers wanted to use energy to do useful work. They created technologies and they refined them. Scientists' concepts of energy, work, and heat were also refined, ultimately leading to the principles of thermodynamics, which you will study in section B3.0.

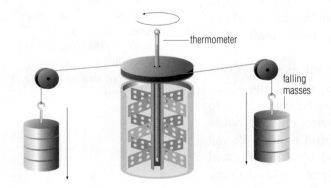

FIGURE B2.7 Joule's experiment that supported a connection between potential energy and heat

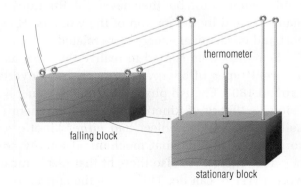

FIGURE B2.8 Joule's experiment that supported a connection between kinetic energy and heat

Perry Ambrose has worked for 13 years as a Power Engineer at EPCOR's Rossdale Generation Station in Edmonton. EPCOR is an Edmonton-based utility company that focusses on power generation, distribution, and transmission.

Power Engineer

Describe your job.

Generally speaking, I am responsible for ensuring that the power plant is operating safely, reliably, and efficiently. My duties include monitoring and evaluating all equipment and systems that keep the plant running, and ensuring that we are adhering to environmental standards. I am also required to respond to "load changes," which means starting and stopping the power generators when necessary.

At the start of my 12-hour shift, I check on the equipment. I start at the top of the boiler and walk down it, looking and listening for leaks or other problems.

After that, I check the turbine-generator for problems with the oil pressure and temperature, and look for abnormal conditions. I then check the pumps, feedwater heaters, and compressors for abnormal conditions. Then, I take water samples from the boiler and check them to ensure we have the right chemicals in the boiler water. The rest of my shift is spent checking equipment, isolating equipment for maintenance work, and re-doing the troubleshooting rounds.

What education is required to do your job?

I went through the power-engineering program at the Northern Alberta Institute of Technology (NAIT). Anyone interested in this line of work should have strong math and physics skills and a mechanical aptitude.

What are the possibilities for a career in this field?

You can use these job skills in other areas besides power generation. For example, you can be a process operator in the pulp, paper, and petrochemical industries, or work in any area related to pressure vessels and inspections. The settings can also vary. You can even decide to pursue a career with the government's boilers branch. The majority of these jobs entail shift work.

What is the most interesting part of your job?

Personally, I like the troubleshooting aspect of the job. This gives me the greatest sense of accomplishment. A lot of the work is predictable, but when alarms go off, you have to be ready to identify and correct the problem right away. This could mean determining why a piece of equipment isn't working, or whether a valve is malfunctioning. In the end, if the plant's process isn't running as smoothly as it should, then it's your job to find out why.

1. What education is required to pursue a career as a power engineer?

2. What aspect of a career in power technology would you find most interesting?

Knowledge

1. Oersted showed experimentally that electricity can produce magnetism. Who demonstrated that magnetism can produce electricity, which is the reverse?

2. For each of the following scientists, describe his invention, the type of energy the inventor was able to produce, and how it was produced.
   a) Oersted
   b) Faraday
   c) Seebeck
   d) Edison
   e) Volta

3. For each of the inventions identified in question 2, state a practical use of the invention today.

4. What is the difference between nuclear fusion and nuclear fission? How are they similar?

5. What did early scientists think was the source of energy from the Sun? Why was their theory not accepted?

6. What is the modern theory of the source of energy from the Sun?

7. Why was it difficult for ancient Greek scientists to define energy?

8. In the Newton's cradle demonstration, how did the scientists of the 1600s explain the fact that the ball at the opposite end of the row would rise to the same height?

9. Describe the contributions the following people made to the nature of heat:
   a) Sadi Carnot
   b) James Young
   c) Joseph Black
   d) Count Rumford

10. Using Figure B2.7, explain how Joule proved that heat could be produced from potential energy. In your description, state the manipulated variable and the responding variable, and describe how a change in the manipulated variable affected the responding variable.

Applications

11. In your science classroom, list all the different forms of energy you can see.

12. Given the following situations, identify the major form of energy involved.
    a) An antacid tablet is placed in a glass of water and the tablet starts to bubble.
    b) A fluorescent dial on a wristwatch glows at night.
    c) A downhill skier begins to ski down the slope with increasing speed.
    d) A tingling sensation is felt on the tongue when it is touched to the terminals of a 9-V battery.
    e) The inside of a car gets extremely warm if the car is left in the sunshine.
    f) A seagull lifts a clam high above the beach.
    g) A compass needle held over the surface of Earth points north.

13. Describe an appliance or machine that, for its operation, requires the following forms of energy:
    a) chemical
    b) light
    c) heat
    d) electrical
    e) magnetic

14. Describe an appliance or machine that produces the following forms of energy, as it operates:
    a) chemical
    b) light
    c) thermal
    d) electrical
    e) magnetic

Extension

15. How would you design an experiment to investigate whether sound is a form of energy?

B 2.2 Potential Energy

Sometimes, the force applied to an object is being used not to change the motion of the object, but to oppose another force acting on the object. In Figure B2.9, a force is applied to lift the car on the midway ride against the downward force of Earth's gravity. Application of an upward force to lift the car through a vertical distance results in work being done on the car. Recall that if work is being done, the person or object doing work must lose energy. This energy is transferred to the car, and the car gains kinetic energy. However, when the car reaches the top, it stops gaining kinetic energy because it is no longer moving. What has happened to the energy?

The car has gained potential energy. In some cases, an object may store energy because of its position relative to some other object. It is called **potential energy** because it has the potential to do work. Potential energy is energy that is stored or held in readiness. There are several types of potential energy. The type of potential energy depends on how the energy is stored.

Gravitational Potential Energy

In the case of the midway ride, a force is applied against the force of gravity (or the weight of the object), resulting in energy being stored. The energy stored in the car at any position above Earth is called gravitational potential energy, $E_{p(grav)}$.

Note that there is an important difference between the mass of an object and its weight. Mass (m) is a scalar quantity and is measured in kilograms (kg). The weight of the object ($\vec{W}$) is a vector quantity. It is a measure of the force of gravitational attraction on an object in newtons (N). The mass of an object does not change because the amount of matter the object possesses is constant. However, the weight of an object depends on the acceleration due to gravity ($\vec{g}$), and this value changes, so the weight of an object can change. For example, on the Moon, you would weigh less than you do on Earth because gravity is weaker on the Moon. But your mass would be the same because the size and shape of your body hasn't changed.

The equation that determines the weight of an object from its mass is:

$$\vec{W} = m\vec{g}$$

Suppose a person has a mass of 50.0 kg on the surface of Earth where the value of the acceleration due to gravity is 9.81 m/s². The person's weight would be:

$$\vec{W} = m\vec{g}$$
$$= (50.0 \text{ kg})(9.81 \text{ m/s}^2)$$
$$= 491 \text{ N}$$

The acceleration due to gravity ($\vec{g}$) represents the strength of Earth's gravitational field. Its value near the surface is 9.81 m/s². You will learn more about $\vec{g}$ in future science studies.

FIGURE B2.9 As the car on the ride slowly rises, it gains energy from the work being done to lift it. Once at the top, it still has energy even though it is not moving. As the ride's car falls, it starts to lose the gravitational potential energy it gained.

infoBIT

Isaac Newton was the first to realize that the natural state of all objects was to maintain uniform motion or stay at rest. He also noted that all objects tend to resist a change in this state. This tendency to resist a change in motion is called "inertia." It is a property of all matter. The more massive an object is, the harder it is to change its motion; thus the more inertia it has. This led to a definition of mass as "the amount of inertia an object possesses."

To calculate the gravitational potential energy, use the following formula:

gravitational potential energy = work done to lift object through a vertical height

$$E_{p(grav)} = W$$

$$E_{p(grav)} = Fd$$

$$J = N \cdot m$$

$$J = J$$

OR

gravitational potential energy = (mass of object)(acceleration due to gravity)(height above the ground)

$$E_{p(grav)} = mgh$$

$$J = (kg)(m/s^2)(m)$$

$$J = J$$

Note: g = acceleration due to gravity

$= 9.81$ m/s^2

(Use the scalar value of the acceleration due to gravity in all calculations involving gravitational potential energy.)

Example Problem B2.1

A 3.00-kg box is lifted by an upward force 1.50 m above the surface of Earth to the top of a table. What is the potential energy stored in the box at this new position?

$$
\begin{aligned}
E_{p(grav)} &= mgh \\
&= (3.00 \text{ kg})(9.81 \text{ m/s}^2)(1.50 \text{ m}) \\
&= 44.1 \text{ J}
\end{aligned}
$$

The gravitational potential energy of the box is now 44.1 J.

Practice Problem

1. A child with a mass of 25.0 kg is at the top of a slide in an amusement park. If the vertical height of the slide is 4.00 m, calculate the gravitational potential energy of the child relative to the ground.

Example Problem B2.2

A 55.0-kg diver standing on a diving platform has a gravitational potential energy of 5.40×10^3 J. What is the vertical height of the diving platform?

$$E_p = mgh$$

$$h = \frac{E_p}{mg}$$

$$= \frac{5.40 \times 10^3 \text{ J}}{(55.0 \text{ kg})(9.81 \frac{m}{s^2})}$$

$$= \frac{5.40 \times 10^3 \frac{kg \cdot m^2}{s^2}}{(55.0 \text{ kg})(9.81 \frac{m}{s^2})}$$

$$= 10.0 \text{ m}$$

The vertical height of the diving board is 10.0 m.

Practice Problems

2. An 800-g bird has 47.0 J of gravitational potential energy when it is perched high up in a tree. Calculate the bird's vertical height from the ground.

3. A hanging sign is 3.00 m above the ground and has 1.47×10^3 J of gravitational potential energy. Calculate the mass of the sign.

Elastic Potential Energy

There are other situations in which a force can be applied against an opposing force, resulting in a change in potential energy. If a force is used to stretch an elastic, the force acts against the elastic force of the material. This results in a change in the shape of the elastic and in energy being stored. This energy is called **elastic potential energy**, $E_{p(elas)}$. This is also the type of energy stored in a stretched or compressed spring, a trampoline (Figure B2.10), or a spring diving board.

These are all examples of work being done by applying a force through a distance against an opposing force, which results in an energy transfer to the object. This energy is then stored in the object as potential energy.

FIGURE B2.10 The person exerts a stretching force on the trampoline.

Catapults

The Question

What is the relationship between the gravitational potential energy of a ball on a catapult and the elastic potential energy of the catapult's elastic band?

The Hypothesis

State a hypothesis concerning the relationship between the gravitational potential energy of a small object propelled upward by a catapult and the elastic potential energy of the catapult's elastic band.

Variables

Read over the procedure and identify the type of data you will collect to support your hypothesis. State the manipulated, responding, and controlled variables in this investigation.

Materials and Equipment

10-N spring scale (measuring in newtons (N))

balance (measuring in grams (g))

empty paper towel tube or plastic tube

rubber elastic band about 5 mm thick

metre-stick

retort stand

small cork

string

masking tape

scissors

Procedure

1. Follow the instructions to make a catapult launcher.
   a) Cut the elastic band.
   b) Tape the elastic to the paper towel tube so that the elastic is fairly taut over one end of the tube.
   c) Tie a piece of string to the centre of the elastic and let the string hang down through the tube.
   d) Make a loop at the other end of the string. Attach a spring scale to this loop (Figure B2.11).

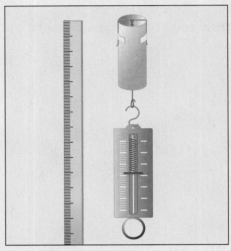

FIGURE B2.11 Step 1d)

2. Create a data table like the one below in your notebook. Make sure your data table has a title.

3. Use the balance to measure the mass of the cork in kilograms. Record this value in the appropriate column in your data table.

Trial	Force on the Spring Scale $F_{(max)}$ (N)	Initial Distance of Spring Scale d_1 (m)	Final Distance of Spring Scale d_2 (m)	Distance the Spring Scale Moves d (m)	Elastic Potential Energy of the Elastic (work done on the elastic) $E_{p(elas)} = F_{(ave)}d$ (J)	Mass of Cork m (g)	Initial Height of Cork h_1 (m)	Final Height of Cork h_2 (m)	Height the Cork Rises h (m)	Gravitational Potential Energy of Cork $E_{p(grav)} = mgh$ (J)
1										

4. Tape the metre-stick to a retort stand in a vertical position. Place the stick and the stand close to the edge of a table.

5. Hold the tube vertically with the elastic end up. Place it near the bottom of the metre-stick.

6. Note the position of the elastic on the metre-stick. Record this value as the initial distance of the spring scale in your data table.

7. Place the cork on the elastic band.

8. Slowly pull down on the spring scale and note how far you pulled it down. Record this value as the final distance of the spring scale in your data table. Remember to convert the distance to metres.

9. Note the reading on the spring scale. This is the maximum force on the elastic. Find the average force, F_{ave}, by dividing the maximum force, F_{max}, by 2. Record the average force in your data table.

> CAUTION: Be careful not to aim the launcher toward any of your classmates.

10. Make sure the tube is vertical and then quickly cut the string.

11. Note the distance the cork rises vertically in the air. Record this value in the table of values.

12. Attach a new piece of string to your catapult and repeat steps 5 to 11, pulling the spring scale a different distance in each trial. Do four or five trials.

Analyzing and Interpreting

1. What was the manipulated variable in this experiment?

2. What was the responding variable in the experiment?

3. How does the elastic potential energy at the beginning of each trial correspond to the gravitational potential energy at the end of each trial?

4. Can you account for any loss in energy?

Forming Conclusions

5. Was your hypothesis correct? Support your conclusion with data from the lab.

Extending

6. Besides the amount of stretch of the elastic, can you suggest any other variables that might affect the height to which the cork rises? How could the experiment be changed to determine the effect of these variables?

Elastic and Gravitational Potential Energy and Catapults

Activity B7 demonstrates the two main types of potential energy studied in this section. If work is done on an elastic, the elastic gains elastic potential energy. When the elastic is released, the cork is propelled vertically into the air. The elastic potential energy is converted into kinetic energy of the cork. As the cork rises, the kinetic energy is converted into gravitational potential energy. If no energy is lost, then the initial work done should equal the elastic potential energy. The elastic potential energy should, in turn, equal the gravitational potential energy.

This activity shows an important point about potential energy. As you know, potential energy is energy that is stored and has the potential to do work. So, potential energy is only useful when it is converted into some other form of energy. In the activity, the elastic potential energy only becomes useful when it is converted into the kinetic energy of the moving cork. This is true of all types of potential energy. The potential energy of a battery only becomes useful when it is converted into electrical energy. The gravitational potential energy of a diver on a diving tower only becomes useful once the diver starts to dive.

reSEARCH

One of the factors that determines the gravitational potential energy of an object is the strength of Earth's gravitational field. The value of the acceleration due to gravity, $\vec{g}$, is 9.81 m/s^2 near the surface. However, this value changes depending on the location. Using the library or the Internet, research how the location determines the value of the acceleration due to gravity, $\vec{g}$. Write a brief summary of your findings. Begin your search at

www.pearsoned.ca/school/science10

Chemical Potential Energy

The energy found in chemicals is a form of potential energy. This energy is stored in the bonds of chemical compounds. When a chemical change takes place, the positions of electric charges are altered and energy is released. Any substance that can be used to do work through a chemical reaction has potential energy. For example, the potential energy of fossil fuels such as gasoline is only released when the gasoline undergoes a chemical combustion reaction.

B2.2 Check and Reflect

Knowledge

1. Why is potential energy not as obvious as kinetic energy?

2. Identify the type of potential energy in the following situations:
   a) A rubber ball striking a wall is compressed and deformed at the exact moment it strikes the wall.
   b) An elevator in an office building slowly rises to the 20th floor and then stops.
   c) A bow string is slowly drawn back, bending a fibreglass bow.
   d) An arrow rises vertically into the air after the bow string is released.
   e) Natural gas burns in a fireplace.

3. State two differences between kinetic energy and gravitational potential energy.

Applications

4. A force of 32.0 N is required to lift a box 3.00 m vertically against the force of Earth's gravity.
   a) Calculate the work done against Earth's gravitational field.
   b) Calculate the gravitational potential energy stored in the box.

5. An object gains 155 J of gravitational potential energy when it is lifted 1.20 m above the surface of Earth. Calculate the force exerted on the object.

6. Standing on level ground, a person with a mass of 55.0 kg jumps straight up into the air to a position where the person has gained 800 J of gravitational potential energy. How high did the person leap?

7. A person jumping on a trampoline exerts an average force of 500 N in stretching the trampoline a distance of 0.750 m. Calculate the elastic potential energy stored in the trampoline.

8. An elastic that is stretched 10.0 cm has 320 J of stored elastic potential energy. Calculate the force required to stretch the elastic.

9. A 60.0-kg person climbs up a ladder to the roof of a building that is 3.50 m above the surface of Earth. Calculate the gravitational potential energy stored in the person.

Extensions

10. Suggest two ways you could increase the elastic potential energy of a spring.

11. Can an object have two values of gravitational potential energy at the same instant? Explain your answer.

B 2.3 Kinetic Energy and Motion

Motion was the first physical quantity to be associated with the concept of energy. The type of energy associated with the motion of an object is called **kinetic energy**, from the Greek word *kinema*, which means "motion." Kinetic energy can be quantified. To calculate the kinetic energy of an object, use the following formula:

$$\text{kinetic energy} = \tfrac{1}{2}\,(\text{mass of the object})\,(\text{speed})^2$$

$$E_k = \tfrac{1}{2}\,mv^2$$

$$J = (kg)(\tfrac{m}{s})^2$$

$$= (kg)(\tfrac{m}{s})(\tfrac{m}{s})$$

$$= \frac{kg \cdot m^2}{s^2}$$

This shows how the joule is derived from fundamental units of measurement (kilograms, metres, and seconds).

*info***BIT**

A snowball, with a mass m and speed v, will have a certain amount of kinetic energy. Another snowball with twice the mass $2m$ and the same speed v, should have twice the kinetic energy. However, a third snowball with the same mass m but twice the speed $2v$, will have four times as much kinetic energy.

Example Problem B2.3

A 0.300-kg ball is pushed horizontally at a speed of 20.0 m/s. Calculate the kinetic energy of the ball at the moment it starts to move.

$$E_k = \tfrac{1}{2}\,mv^2$$

$$= \tfrac{1}{2}\,(0.300 \text{ kg})(20.0\,\tfrac{m}{s})^2$$

$$= 60.0 \text{ J}$$

The ball has a kinetic energy of 60.0 J.

The ball in example problem B2.3 has gained kinetic energy because of an energy transfer from the work done on it. The work done came from the person applying a force on the ball to move it through a distance. The kinetic energy gained by the ball is equal to the work done.

Example Problem B2.4

The kinetic energy of an object moving at a speed of 14.2 m/s was determined to be 950 J. What is the mass of the object?

$$E_k = \tfrac{1}{2}\,mv^2$$

$$m = \frac{2E_k}{v^2}$$

$$= \frac{2(950 \text{ J})}{(14.2\,\tfrac{m}{s})^2}$$

$$= 9.42 \text{ kg}$$

The mass of the object is 9.42 kg.

Practice Problems

4. Calculate the kinetic energy of an electron with a mass of 9.11×10^{-31} kg moving at a uniform speed of 2.00×10^5 m/s.

5. A small toy moving horizontally at a uniform speed of 2.2 m/s has a kinetic energy of 18 J. Calculate the mass of the toy.

Kinetic Energy and Motion

Before You Start...

In this activity, you will use an elastic to launch an object on a horizontal frictionless surface. When the elastic launches the object, the elastic potential energy of the elastic will be converted to the kinetic energy of the object. This is evident in the speed of the object as it travels across the surface.

The Question

What is the relationship between an object's speed and its kinetic energy?

The Hypothesis

State a hypothesis concerning the speed of an object and its kinetic energy.

Variables

Read over the procedure and identify the type of data you will collect to support your hypothesis. State the manipulated, responding, and controlled variables in your investigation.

Materials and Equipment

air table and accessories

elastic launcher

spark paper

air puck

balance

marking pen

ruler

Procedure

1. Follow the instructions to set up the air table and launcher.
   a) Connect the air source and the spark generator to the air table. Set the spark generator to 10 sparks per second.
   b) Place the carbon paper on the air table. Place the recording paper on top of the carbon paper.
   c) Set up the puck launcher on one edge of the air table so it will launch the puck straight across the table.
   d) On the top of the puck launcher, mark five equal distances for the five different lengths that you will stretch the elastic to launch the puck at different speeds.
   e) Practise launching the puck at these different lengths so that the air puck is launched at ever greater speeds.

2. Create a data table like the one below. Make sure to give your table a title.

3. Using a balance, measure the mass of the air puck. Record this value in kilograms in the data table.

4. Turn on the spark generator and the air source.

5. Pull the air puck against the elastic, stretching the elastic to the first mark. Sharply release the air puck, and observe the spark marks generated on the recording paper. Turn off all the equipment.

6. Slide the recording paper sideways on the air table so that you can take another reading on the same paper.

7. Repeat steps 4 through 6 four more times, stretching the elastic different lengths.

Trial	Mass of the Air Puck m (kg)	Time Interval of the Generated Sparks Δt (s)	Average Distance Travelled During Each Time Interval Δd (m)	Average Speed of the Air Puck v (m/s) Use: $v = \frac{\Delta d}{\Delta t}$	Kinetic Energy of the Air Puck E_k (J) Use: $E_k = \frac{1}{2} mv^2$

8 Remove the recording paper. Label each trail of spark marks as Trial 1, Trial 2, etc.

Analyzing and Interpreting

1. On the recording paper, locate the spark marks generated for Trial 1. Choose four consecutive spark marks near the beginning of the trail. Label these marks as 0, 1, 2, and 3.

2. Carefully measure the distances in metres between marks 0 and 1, 1 and 2, and 2 and 3. Find the average value of the distance travelled, and record this value in the data table.

3. Repeat steps 1 and 2 for the other four trials.

4. Plot a graph of kinetic energy as a function of speed. What does the shape of the graph suggest about the relationship between the speed of an object and its kinetic energy?

Forming Conclusions

5. Was your hypothesis correct? Support your conclusion with results from your graph.

Example Problem B2.5

What is the speed of an 800-kg automobile if it has a kinetic energy of 9.00×10^4 J?

$$E_k = \frac{1}{2}mv^2$$

$$mv^2 = 2E_k$$

$$v^2 = \frac{2E_k}{m}$$

$$v = \sqrt{\frac{2E_k}{m}}$$

$$= \sqrt{\frac{2(9.00 \times 10^4 \text{ J})}{800 \text{ kg}}}$$

$$= \sqrt{\frac{18.0 \times 10^4 \frac{\text{kg} \cdot \text{m}^2}{\text{s}^2}}{800 \text{ kg}}}$$

$$= \sqrt{\frac{1.80 \times 10^5 \frac{\text{kg} \cdot \text{m}^2}{\text{s}^2}}{800 \text{ kg}}}$$

$$= \sqrt{225 \frac{\text{m}^2}{\text{s}^2}}$$

$$= 15.0 \frac{\text{m}}{\text{s}}$$

The automobile has a speed of 15.0 m/s.

reSEARCH

People have used the kinetic energy of the wind for centuries. Some of these uses include transporting people and goods, grinding grain, pumping water, and drying clothes. Find out how the wind's kinetic energy has been used in various ways. Why is the wind still being used in many places in the world? Begin your search at

 www.pearsoned.ca/school/science10

Practice Problems

6. A baseball with a mass of 300 g has a kinetic energy of 304 J. Calculate the speed of the baseball.

7. A moving toy with a mass of 7.4 kg has a kinetic energy of 18 J. Calculate the speed of the toy.

Knowledge

1. What type of energy is associated with the motion of an object?

2. What two factors determine the kinetic energy of an object?

3. Energy is measured in joules, which is a derived unit. State what 1 J is in terms of the fundamental units of measurement. (These units are kilograms (kg), metres (m), and seconds (s).)

4. A mass is attached to a vertical spring and released. It moves through one complete vibration (down and back up).
   a) Discuss the changes in the kinetic energy of the mass from the time that it is released, at the top, to the time that it returns to its starting position.
   b) If energy cannot be created or destroyed, how is it possible for the mass to
      i) gain kinetic energy during part of its vibration?
      ii) lose kinetic energy during part of its vibration?

Applications

5. Determine the kinetic energy of each of the following.
   a) A 0.500-kg ball is thrown horizontally at 12.0 m/s.
   b) A 75.0-kg person is in free-fall and reaches a terminal velocity of 40 m/s.
   c) A 4.00-g bullet is travelling at 140 m/s.

✳ 6. A curling rock, sliding down the ice at a speed of 2.40 m/s, is determined to have a kinetic energy of 57.6 J. What is the mass of the curling rock?

7. A 40.0-kg object has an initial kinetic energy of 320 J.
   a) What is the initial speed of the object?
   b) An unbalanced force is applied to accelerate the object to a final kinetic energy of 400 J. What is the change in speed of the object?

8. The kinetic energy of an object was determined while the object's speed was increasing. The data collected were recorded in the table below.
   a) Draw a graph of kinetic energy as a function of the speed.
   b) What does the shape of the graph tell you about the relationship between the speed and the kinetic energy of an object?

Speed v (m/s)	Kinetic Energy E_k (J)
0.0	0.0
1.2	1.4
2.4	5.8
3.6	13.0
4.8	23.0
6.0	36.0

9. The kinetic energy of an object was determined for an object with increasing mass, travelling at a constant speed. The data collected were recorded in the table below.
   a) Draw a graph of kinetic energy as a function of the mass.
   b) What does the shape of the graph tell you about the relationship between the mass and the kinetic energy of an object?

Mass m (kg)	Kinetic Energy E_k (J)
0.00	0.00
1.10	0.55
2.20	1.10
3.30	1.65
4.40	2.20
5.50	2.75

Extension

10. A ball with a mass m travelling at a speed v has a kinetic energy of 40.0 J. Calculate the kinetic energy of the ball if:
   a) the mass is doubled
   b) the speed is doubled

B 2.4 Mechanical Energy

When energy is transferred to an object, it can cause a change in both kinetic and potential energy simultaneously. A ball thrown upward has kinetic energy because of its motion, and also has potential energy because of its position above the surface of Earth. Since kinetic and potential energy are so closely related in many situations involving energy transfers, they are combined as a general type of energy called **mechanical energy**, E_m, which is defined as the energy due to the motion and the position of an object.

Since an object can have both kinetic and potential energy at the same instant, mechanical energy can be calculated using the following formula:

mechanical energy = kinetic energy + potential energy

$$E_m = E_k + E_p$$

*info*BIT

A roller coaster has no engine. It runs on mechanical energy. The conversion of potential energy to kinetic energy and back again drives it as it clatters down and then around the hilly track.

Example Problem B2.6

A 0.300-kg baseball is thrown in a straight line through the air. At a height of 2.50 m above the surface of Earth, it has a speed of 20.0 m/s. What is the total mechanical energy of the baseball?

$$E_m = E_k + E_p$$

$$= \frac{1}{2}mv^2 + mgh$$

$$= (\frac{1}{2})(0.300 \text{ kg})(20.0 \text{ m/s})^2 + (0.300 \text{ kg})(9.81 \text{ m/s}^2)(2.50 \text{ m})$$

$$= 60.0 \text{ J} + 7.36 \text{ J}$$

$$= 67.4 \text{ J}$$

The kinetic energy of the ball is 60.0 J, the potential energy of the ball is 7.36 J, thus the mechanical energy of the ball is 67.4 J.

FIGURE B2.12 An archer draws back on the string of the bow to shoot an arrow into the air.

The illustration shown in Figure B2.12 can be used to describe an important concept in physics that involves mechanical energy. When the person pulls the bow string, an average force is being exerted through a distance, and work is being done. This work is stored in the bow as $E_{p(elas)}$. When the string is released, elastic energy is converted into kinetic energy, E_k, as the arrow is released. As the arrow rises into the air, it slows down and loses kinetic energy, but it is rising higher above the surface of Earth, and so gains gravitational potential energy, $E_{p(grav)}$. This illustrates that potential energy can be converted into kinetic energy and kinetic energy into potential energy.

Practice Problems

8. A seagull flying horizontally at 8.00 m/s carries a clam with a mass of 300 g in its beak. Calculate the total mechanical energy of the clam when the seagull is 30.0 m above the ground.

9. A 55.0-kg high-jump athlete leaps into the air in an attempt to clear the bar. At the top of the leap, the athlete has a total mechanical energy of 3.00×10^3 J and is moving at 8.33 m/s. Calculate the gravitational potential energy of the athlete.

10. A construction worker drops a 2.00-kg hammer from a roof. When the hammer is 50.0 m above the ground, it has a total mechanical energy of 1.88×10^3 J. Calculate the kinetic energy of the hammer.

Law of Conservation of Energy

The law of conservation of energy states that the total amount of energy in a given situation remains constant. Energy can be converted from one form to another but the total amount of energy never changes. Thus, the total amount of mechanical energy remains constant. In the absence of outside forces, kinetic energy may be converted to potential energy and vice-versa, without loss, so that the total amount of mechanical energy always remains constant.

$$\text{potential energy} \rightleftharpoons \text{kinetic energy}$$

$$E_p \rightleftharpoons E_k$$

This law is fundamental in situations involving mechanical energy.

Example Problem B2.7

A 1.50-kg rock is dropped over the edge of a cliff, 30.0 m above the surface of a lake. What is the speed of the rock just before it strikes the surface of the lake?

$$E_{p(top)} = E_{k(bottom)}$$

$$mgh = \frac{1}{2}mv^2$$

$$mv^2 = 2\,mgh$$

$$v^2 = 2\,gh$$

$$v = \sqrt{2\,gh}$$

$$= \sqrt{2(9.81\,\tfrac{m}{s^2})(30\,m)}$$

$$= 24.3\,\tfrac{m}{s}$$

The speed of the rock is 24.3 m/s, just before it strikes the surface of the lake.

Practice Problems

11. A 10.0-kg water balloon is dropped from a height of 12.0 m. Calculate the speed of the balloon just before it hits the ground.

12. A 30.0-kg child on a trampoline jumps vertically into the air at an initial speed of 1.60 m/s. Calculate how high the child will rise.

Figure B2.13 shows an example of the conversion and the conservation of mechanical energy. If the masses are released, then the difference in masses causes the larger mass to fall with increasing speed. Because the two masses are attached by a string, the smaller mass will rise with increasing speed. The 2.00-kg mass loses potential energy because it loses height, and it gains kinetic energy because it speeds up during its fall toward Earth's surface. At the same instant, the 1.00-kg mass gains potential energy because it rises above Earth's surface. It also gains kinetic energy because it is speeding up as it rises. The two masses are connected by a string and so they must move at the same speed. Thus, there are three increases in energy and only one decrease in energy. Is this a contradiction of the law of conservation of mechanical energy? The answer is no. The mechanical energy lost by the 2-kg mass would equal the mechanical energy gained by the 1-kg mass. Energy is always conserved!

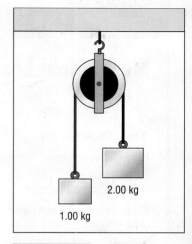

Example Problem B2.8

An average force of 100.0 N is required to pull back a bow string a distance of 0.500 m. The bow is aimed vertically.

a) What is the work done on the bow?

b) How much potential energy is stored in the bow?

c) How much kinetic energy does the arrow have at the instant it is released from the bow?

d) What will be the potential energy of the arrow at its highest position in its flight in the air?

a) $W = Fd$

$= (100.0 \text{ N})(0.500 \text{ m})$

$= 50.0 \text{ J}$

The work done on the bow is 50.0 J.

b) $\Delta E_{p(elas)} = W$

$E_{p(elas)} = 50.0 \text{ J}$

The amount of elastic potential energy in the bow is 50.0 J.

c) $\Delta E_k = E_{p(elas)}$

$E_k = 50.0 \text{ J}$

When the arrow is released, it has 50.0 J of kinetic energy.

d) $\Delta E_{p(grav)} = E_k$

$E_{p(grav)} = 50.0 \text{ J}$

As it reaches its highest point, the arrow has its maximum potential energy, 50.0 J.

Practice Problems

13. A 20.0-g dart is fired from a dart gun with a horizontal speed of 4.10 m/s. The total mechanical energy of the dart is 0.481 J. Calculate the gravitational potential energy of the dart.

14. A pendulum consists of a 500-g metal ball suspended on a 50.0-cm string. The ball is pulled horizontally and up a total vertical distance of 10.0 cm. It is then released. At the bottom of the arc, the mechanical energy of the ball was determined to be 0.491 J. What was the speed of the ball at the bottom of its arc?

This example describes the relationship between work and energy and the transformations of kinetic and potential energy. It also illustrates the law of conservation of energy.

Inquiry Lab

Student Reference **5, 6, 7**

Mechanical Energy and the Pendulum

The Question

Is mechanical energy conserved as a pendulum swings?

The Hypothesis

When a pendulum is pulled back to form a 45° angle with the vertical, work is done on the pendulum. This work is stored as potential energy in the pendulum and, when the pendulum is released, the potential energy is converted into kinetic energy. State a hypothesis concerning the law of conservation of mechanical energy in this situation.

Variables

Read over the procedure and identify the type of data you will collect to support your hypothesis. State the manipulated, responding, and controlled variables in this investigation.

Materials and Equipment

string, 1 m long

object

retort stand and clamp

large blackboard protractor

metre-stick

stopwatch

balance (measuring in grams (g))

masking tape

Procedure

1. Attach the string to the object.

2. Measure the mass of the object using the balance. Record this value in your notebook.

3. Tie the other end of the string to the clamp on the retort stand.

4. Tape the metre-stick vertically to the retort stand, so that one end of the metre-stick touches the tabletop. Rest the object on the tabletop and adjust the clamp on the retort stand so that the string is taut.

5. Secure the protractor on the clamp at the top of the string so that the string hangs vertically down at the 90° mark on the protractor. Make sure that the string is not touching the surface of the protractor.

6. Slide the base of the retort stand slowly toward the edge of the table so that the pendulum hangs over the side of the table and can swing freely. Secure the base so that the retort stand does not topple over.

7. Pull the pendulum back to the 45° on the protractor.

8. Use the metre-stick to measure the height of the pendulum from the tabletop and record this value in your notebook.

9. Calculate the maximum potential energy of the pendulum using the formula $E_p = mgh$.

Note: Data may be collected using either of the two methods described below. Choose the most appropriate method based on the type of equipment available in your laboratory. Proceed to step 10 or step 14 depending on your equipment.

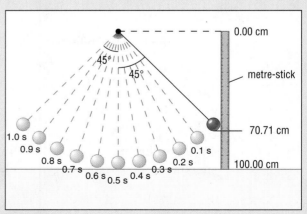

FIGURE B2.14 The positions of the pendulum as it swings through half an arc

Method 1: Using a Motion Sensor and a Computer Interface or a Graphing Calculator

10. Connect the motion sensor to a computer or a graphing calculator. Set the time intervals at 0.10 s and set the distance travelled by the pendulum in metres. Record the data in a table, with time interval as the *x* variable and distance travelled as the *y* variable.

11. Release the pendulum, and allow it to swing to its maximum height on the other side. This is half an arc (Figure B2.14).

12. Stop the pendulum on the other side.

13. Proceed to step 1 of Analyzing and Interpreting.

Method 2: Using Simulated Data

14. If you do not have access to a motion sensor and a computer interface, the measurements have been done for you and are displayed in the table below. Proceed to step 11 of Analyzing and Interpreting.

Time Elapsed as the Pendulum Makes $\frac{1}{2}$ Arc t (s)	Distance Travelled by the Pendulum d (m)	Speed of the Pendulum at Each Time v (m/s)
0.00	0.00	0.00
0.10	0.02	0.48
0.20	0.10	0.96
0.30	0.22	1.44
0.40	0.38	1.92
0.50	0.60	2.40
0.60	0.82	1.92
0.70	0.98	1.44
0.80	1.10	0.96
0.90	1.17	0.48
1.00	1.20	0.00

Analyzing and Interpreting

Method 1. Using a Motion Sensor and a Computer Interface or a Graphing Calculator

1. Complete your data table.

2. Analyze the results of the motion of the pendulum in the data table on your computer. The results should be displayed in a table similar to the one shown here. Make sure your data table has a title.

Time Elapsed as the Pendulum Makes $\frac{1}{2}$ Arc t (s)	Distance Travelled by the Pendulum d (m)

3. Program the computer to display these results on a distance–time graph.

4. What is the shape of your graph?

5. What does the shape of the graph indicate about the motion of the pendulum?

6. Program the computer to display the results as a speed–time graph.

7. What is the maximum speed attained by the pendulum?

8. At what point in the pendulum's swing does it reach this speed?

9. Using the formula $E_k = \frac{1}{2} mv^2$, calculate the maximum kinetic energy of the pendulum when it reaches the bottom of its swing.

10. Compare this value with the maximum potential energy of the pendulum at the top of its arc that you calculated previously.

Method 2: Using Simulated Data

11. Using the simulated results in procedure step 14, draw a distance–time graph.

12. What is the shape of your graph?

13. What does the shape of the graph indicate about the motion of the pendulum?

14. Using the simulated results, draw a speed–time graph.

15. What is the maximum speed reached by the pendulum?

16. At what point in the motion of the pendulum does it reach this speed?

17. Using the formula $E_k = \frac{1}{2} mv^2$, calculate the maximum kinetic energy of the pendulum at the bottom of its swing.

18. Compare this value with the maximum potential energy of the pendulum at the top of its arc that you calculated previously.

Forming Conclusions

19. Based on your calculations, is mechanical energy conserved in the motion of the pendulum? Justify your answer.

reSEARCH

Watch a pendulum for an extended period of time and you will notice that the back and forth motion changes slowly to a circular motion. Using the library or the Internet, research this phenomenon. Why does the pendulum have this circular motion? Is the circular motion clockwise or counterclockwise? How is this motion similar to the circular motion of water going down a drain? Begin your search at

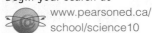 www.pearsoned.ca/ school/science10

Conversion and Conservation of Energy in a Pendulum

The pendulum is an excellent example of the law of conservation of energy. When the pendulum is initially lifted a certain height above the table, work is done against the opposing force of gravity. The energy expended to do the work is stored in the pendulum as gravitational potential energy. When the pendulum is released and begins its swing, gravitational potential energy is converted into kinetic energy, and the pendulum speeds up. At the midpoint of the arc, the pendulum is moving at its maximum speed, and all the potential energy has been converted into kinetic energy. At this point, the kinetic energy of the pendulum is exactly equal to the initial amount of potential energy. As the pendulum begins to rise toward its maximum position on the other side of its arc, the pendulum slows down, and kinetic energy is converted back to potential energy. At the highest position on the other side, the pendulum stops and has no more kinetic energy. Its potential energy equals the amount of potential energy it had at the beginning because it rises to exactly the same height. Energy is conserved!

B2.4 Check and Reflect

Knowledge

1. What is mechanical energy?

2. A kicker on a football team kicks a football that travels in a trajectory, shown in the diagram: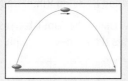

   a) What types of energy does the football have at the moment the ball leaves the kicker's foot?

   b) What types of energy does the football have at a point halfway up to its highest point?

   c) What types of energy does the football have at the highest point of its path?

   d) At what part of its motion are the kinetic and the gravitational potential energy equal?

   e) At what part of its motion is the kinetic energy the least?

   f) At what part of its motion is the gravitational potential energy the least?

   g) Where is the total mechanical energy the greatest? Explain your answer.

3. What is the law of conservation of energy?

4. A ball is thrown vertically upward from the ground. It rises to a certain height and then falls back to the ground.

   a) Analyze the graph below. What is happening to the potential energy of the ball as a function of its height above the ground?

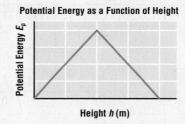

Potential Energy as a Function of Height

   b) Analyze the graph below. What is happening to the kinetic energy of the ball as a function of its height above the ground?

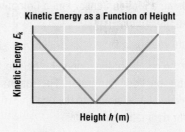

Kinetic Energy as a Function of Height

c) Analyze the graph below. What is happening to the mechanical energy of the ball as a function of its height above the ground?

Mechanical Energy as a Function of Height

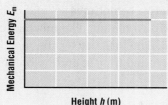

Applications

5. An average force of 40.0 N is needed to compress a spring 0.100 m. A 1.00×10^{-2} kg ball is placed on the spring.
   a) Calculate the work done in compressing the spring.
   b) What happens to the work done on the spring?
   c) If the spring is released, what happens to the energy of the spring?
   d) Calculate the energy the ball has at the instant that the ball leaves the spring.
   e) What will be the speed of the ball as it leaves the spring?
   f) If the ball is fired up into the air by the spring, how much gravitational potential energy will the ball gain?
   g) What will be the maximum height that the ball will rise into the air?

6. A 60.0-kg athlete jumps vertically upward from the ground to a height of 0.910 m above the ground. What was the athlete's initial vertical speed?

7. A 0.300-kg billiard ball is propelled from a table at a horizontal speed of 1.50 m/s. If the table is 1.30 m above the floor, what is the mechanical energy of the ball at the instant it leaves the table?

8. A ball is thrown vertically upward from the ground. It rises and then falls back to the ground in a measured time.
   a) Sketch a graph showing gravitational potential energy as a function of time.
   b) Sketch a graph showing kinetic energy as a function of time.

c) Sketch a graph showing mechanical energy as a function of time.

9. A 2.00-kg ball is suspended from a ceiling by a rope 1.50 m long. The ball is pulled sideways and up until the rope is horizontal.
   a) How much gravitational potential energy will be acquired by the ball?
   b) If the ball is then released, what is the maximum speed it acquires?
   c) If the ball swings through its arc to the opposite side, as shown in the diagram, at what position or positions will it have:
      i) maximum gravitational potential energy?
      ii) maximum kinetic energy?
      iii) maximum mechanical energy?

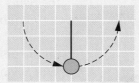

Extensions

10. If a ball at a certain position above the surface of Earth has gravitational potential energy, explain why the ball will not necessarily have the same amount of kinetic energy when it is dropped back down to Earth's surface.

11. Three identical objects are projected horizontally from the same height at the same speeds. The graph below depicts the mechanical energy of each object as a function of time.
    a) Describe what is happening for each object. (Each object is represented by a different line on the graph.)
    b) Which line depicts an impossible situation?

Mechanical Energy as a Function of Time

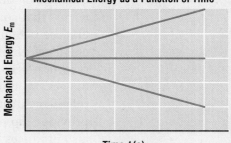

B 2.5 Energy Conversions

In your daily life, you constantly encounter energy conversions. When you turn on a light, electricity is converted to light energy. Your body converts the chemical energy in food into the electrical impulses your brain uses to transmit signals. To get the desired type of energy, sometimes several conversions have to happen. Take the example of striking a match. The mechanical energy that moves the match is converted to heat. The heat causes the match to release its stored chemical energy, which is converted to heat and light energy.

Evidence of Energy Conversions

In general, one of several things might happen as a consequence of energy being converted from one form to another.

Motion is the most obvious evidence that an energy conversion has happened. When a pitcher throws a ball, her arm does work, which becomes the ball's kinetic energy.

Climbing stairs is a less obvious evidence of energy. A diver gains gravitational potential energy by climbing the stairs of a diving tower. When he's on the platform, he has raised his position relative to the surface of the water. Whenever something is raised above the surface of Earth, this *change in position* is evidence of gravitational potential energy.

A *change in shape* is also evidence that an object has undergone a change in energy. The drawn bow in Figure B2.15 has gained elastic potential energy as the archer pulls the bow string back, changing its shape. When she releases the bow, it will change its shape again as the elastic potential energy changes to kinetic energy of the released arrow. A stretched elastic band or a pole vaulter's pole mid jump has gained elastic potential energy.

For a pot of water on the stove, a *change in temperature* is evidence of energy transfer. Energy is being transferred from the hot stove to the cooler pot and water. The pot and water are gaining heat. Heat is the transfer of kinetic energy of the particles in one substance to another; in this case from the element to the pot and water.

Energy Conversions in Natural Systems

The hydrogen–hydrogen nuclear fusion reaction that occurs at the centre of the Sun releases tremendous amounts of solar energy that travels to Earth as electromagnetic waves. When this radiation strikes Earth, it is either absorbed by Earth or reflected back into space. When light energy from the Sun strikes the chlorophyll in plants, a chemical reaction, photosynthesis, occurs that converts carbon dioxide and water into glucose and oxygen. The glucose contains chemical potential energy. When animals eat plants, this chemical potential energy in the glucose is released through the process of respiration in the animals' bodies. Glucose (sugar) from food reacts with oxygen in animal cells to produce carbon dioxide and water. The energy released during respiration, in the form of adenosine triphosphate (ATP), provides the energy necessary for the animal to carry out life functions. It also produces heat.

info **BIT**

Before metal pots were available, First Nations people used hot stones and non-metal containers to heat water for cooking. They would fill leather bags or pits in the ground with water and then add stones that had been heated in the fire. The heat transferred from the hot stones to the water, raising its temperature.

FIGURE B2.15 When the archer has drawn the bow to its maximum position, the bow has gained elastic potential energy through changing its shape.

Millions of years ago, as plants and animals died, they became buried under sediment. As time passed, the layers of dead plants and animals sank deeper into Earth's crust. Through pressure, heat, and other processes, they were transformed into huge deposits of coal, oil, and gas. When these fossil fuels are burned in chemical combustion reactions, they are releasing energy that was trapped millions of years ago.

Minds On... Identifying Energy Conversions in Nature

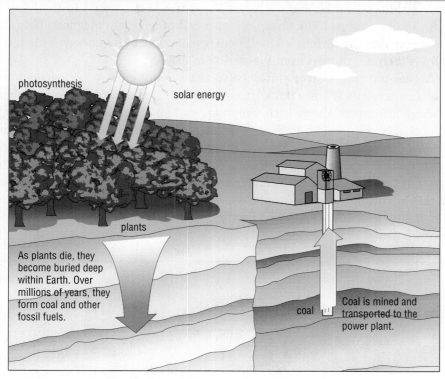

photosynthesis

solar energy

plants

As plants die, they become buried deep within Earth. Over millions of years, they form coal and other fossil fuels.

coal

Coal is mined and transported to the power plant.

FIGURE B2.16 Energy conversions from the Sun to fossil fuels

In Figures B2.17 and B2.18 on the next page, you will see the energy conversions in hydro-electric and coal-burning power stations. These conversions seem to begin with the dam reservoir and the stockpile of coal, respectively. But the trail of energy conversions really starts at the initial source, the Sun.

Analyze Figure B2.16, depicting the flow of energy from the initial stage of the production of solar energy on the Sun, through to the production of fossil fuels such as coal, oil, and gas. Then answer the following questions.

Questions

1. List all the energy conversions, in order, starting from solar energy being emitted from the Sun to the final use of fossil fuels.

2. Is all the solar energy that strikes plants stored as chemical potential energy in fossil fuels? Can you identify places where solar energy is wasted in this energy conversion system?

3. What is the main difference between photosynthesis and respiration or combustion?

Energy Conversions in Technological Systems

Hydro-electric dams convert the energy of moving water into electricity. This conversion takes many steps. Figure B2.17 shows a cross-section of a hydro-electric power station. The water reservoir behind the dam, A, stores water at a higher level than the generator below the dam, so the water has gravitational potential energy due to its higher position. The water behind the dam is released into the penstock, B. As it flows down the penstock, it loses gravitational potential energy but gains kinetic energy as it increases speed. When the water reaches the turbines, C, its kinetic energy pushes the blades of the turbines. The kinetic energy of the water is converted to the kinetic energy of the turbines. The turbines turn a coil of wire in a magnetic field, D, which converts the turbine's kinetic energy into electrical energy. This electricity is then distributed from the station to users.

A coal-burning power station also uses many energy conversions to generate electricity (Figure B2.18). Coal is placed in the combustion chamber, A, where it burns at a very high temperature. The chemical potential energy in the coal is converted into heat. This heat is then used to change the water in the boiler, B, into steam. The steam is under pressure and is injected into the turbines, C, causing the turbines to rotate. The thermal energy and kinetic energy of the moving steam is converted into kinetic energy as the turbines rotate. The turbines use the kinetic energy to turn a coil of wire in a magnetic field in the generator, D. The kinetic energy is converted into electrical energy.

FIGURE B2.17 A hydro-electric power station converts the gravitational potential energy of water into electrical energy through a series of energy conversions.

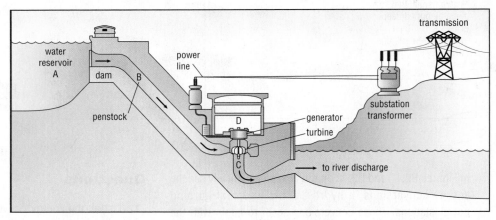

FIGURE B2.18 A coal-burning power station converts the chemical potential energy stored in coal into electrical energy through a series of energy conversions.

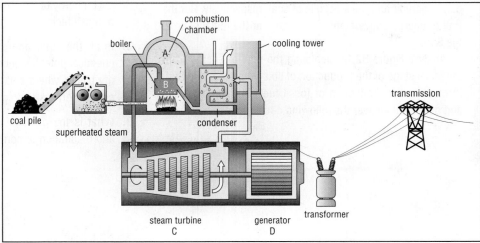

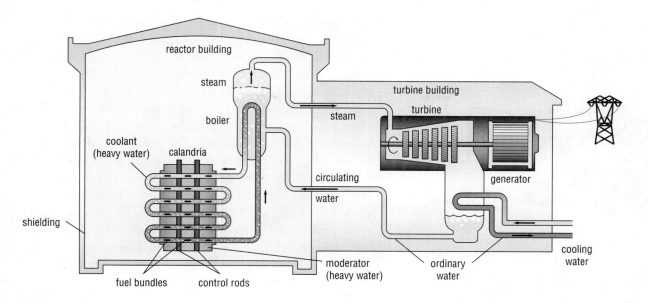

FIGURE B2.19 A schematic diagram of a CANDU nuclear reactor that is used to generate electricity. To rotate the turbines, which generate electricity, steam is heated by nuclear reactions. Instead of a water reservoir or a coal deposit, they require a source of uranium.

Nuclear Energy Conversions

After the Second World War, engineers used the technology of splitting the atom to create a new method of generating electricity. Nuclear power is now used to generate electricity in Canada and around the world.

One of the most widely used nuclear reactors is the Canadian CANDU (CANadian Deuterium Uranium) reactor (Figure B2.19). In the reactor, uranium disintegrates during nuclear fission, releasing nuclear energy as radiation. This radiation is converted to thermal energy, which is used to heat water to steam. Under pressure, the steam is then piped into the turbines and causes them to move. The steam's kinetic energy is converted into the turbines' kinetic energy. The turbines turn a coil of wire in a magnetic field. This converts the turbines' kinetic energy into electrical energy. This sequence of energy conversions is very similar to the conversions in a coal-burning power station. In fact, nuclear power stations and coal-burning power stations are both **thermal power stations**. They create heat to produce steam, which drives the turbines. Power stations powered by natural gas are also thermal power stations.

Solar Energy Conversions

Although the Sun is not really a new source of energy, it is considered new because engineers have only recently developed technologies that efficiently convert sunlight to other forms of energy. One of the most recent and common solar energy conversion technologies is the solar cell.

Solar cells are unlike other technological systems that you've studied so far. They have no moving parts and they convert solar energy directly to electricity. A solar cell is usually composed of two layers of silicon, one with

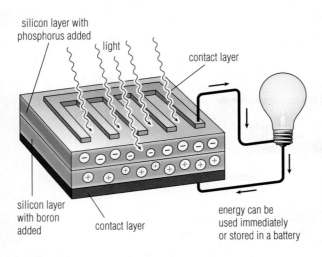

silicon layer with phosphorus added

light

contact layer

silicon layer with boron added

contact layer

energy can be used immediately or stored in a battery

FIGURE B2.20 A cross section of a solar cell illustrates the build-up of charges on the silicon layers.

phosphorus added and one with boron added (Figure B2.20). Normally, electrons are bound up in the silicon crystals in these layers. However, when sunlight hits the silicon layers, it provides energy for some of the electrons to break free of the crystals and move freely. The silicon layer with added phosphorus becomes negatively charged. The second silicon layer with added boron becomes positively charged. The positive and negative layers act in the same way as the positive and negative terminals of a battery, and an electric current flows. The current is then collected by the electrical contact layers shown in Figure B2.20. The electricity can be used directly or stored in a conventional battery for later use.

This energy conversion system can be applied to systems as large as the International Space Station or as small as a solar-powered calculator.

Activity B10

Design a Lab

Student Reference **2, 5, 7, 11**

Required Skills
- Initiating and Planning
- Performing and Recording
- Analyzing and Interpreting
- Communication and Teamwork

Kinetic Energy or Potential Energy?

There are many situations where energy is converted from one form to another. However, the most common type involves mechanical energy, where kinetic and potential energy are interconverted.

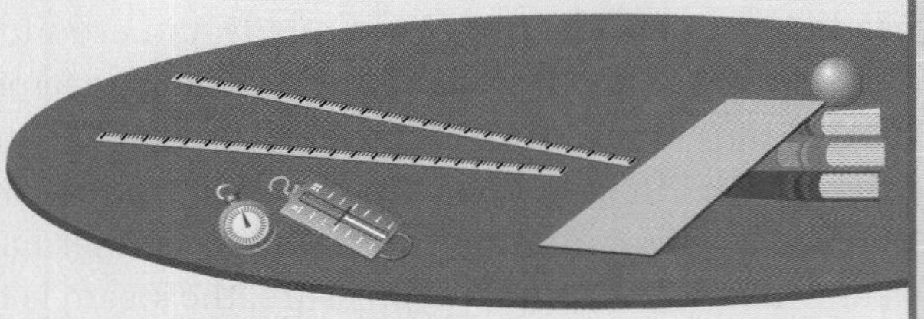

FIGURE B2.21 Possible materials for the investigation

The Question

In a situation where potential and kinetic energy are inter-converted, will mechanical energy be conserved?

Design and Conduct Your Investigation

1 After considering the above question, write a hypothesis.

2 Decide on the materials and the equipment you will need to test your hypothesis (Figure B2.21).

3 Plan your procedure. For example:
- What variables are you working with? Identify the manipulated, responding, and controlled variables. Predict what results will occur in the responding variable when a change is made in the manipulated variable and give a reason why.
- How will you vary the manipulated variable to obtain the results you need?

- What steps do you have to go through to collect the data you need to test your hypothesis?
- How will you collect the data?
- How will you record the data?
- What type of quantitative analysis of your data must be performed to verify your hypothesis?

4 Write up your procedure and show it to your teacher.

5 Carry out the experiment.

6 Compare your results with your hypothesis. Did your results support your hypothesis? If not, what possible reasons might there be for any discrepancy?

7 Compare your experimental design and findings with those of your classmates. How do your results compare with theirs?

Fuel Cells

Like a solar cell, a hydrogen fuel cell operates like a battery. In fact, it's known as the new, improved battery. It converts the chemical energy in a fuel, such as hydrogen, into electrical energy. However, unlike a battery, it does not require recharging. It will produce electrical energy as long as it has fuel. The byproducts of the hydrogen fuel cell are water and heat.

This is why the hydrogen fuel cell is so popular in spacecraft. Not only can the fuel cell supply the necessary electricity to maintain all the electrical instruments on board the spacecraft, but it can also supply all the heat and water necessary for the trip, from the "waste" products of the cell's reaction.

*re*SEARCH

Fuel cells are now being used to power vehicles. Use the Internet and other resources to find out how fuel cells work. Draw and label a diagram of a fuel cell to show how it operates. Begin your search at
 www.pearsoned.ca/ school/science10

B2.5 Check and Reflect

Knowledge

1. List all the energy conversions that occur in a hydro-electric power station.

2. List all the energy conversions that occur in a coal-burning power station.

3. a) What single energy conversion in a hydro-electric station produces the most waste heat?
   b) What single energy conversion in a thermal coal-burning power station produces the most waste heat?

4. Explain why more energy is wasted in a coal-burning power station than in a hydro-electric power station.

5. One method to show energy conversions is to use concept maps. Map the conversion of energy in a nuclear reactor, from the initial form of nuclear energy to the final form of electrical energy.

6. Explain how solar cells are similar to batteries.

Applications

7. List all the energy conversions you can see in your classroom. State the initial form of energy and the resulting form of energy.

8. Trace the chain of energy transformations from the Sun to the final form of energy, in each of the following:
   a) A heating pad is plugged into an electrical outlet.
   b) A lawn mower is idling.
   c) A horse is pulling a cart.

9. Give an example to justify each of the following statements:
   a) Energy comes in many forms.
   b) Energy can be stored for a long time.
   c) Energy can be changed from one form to another.

10. A weightlifter holds a barbell above his head and drops it. What evidence is there that an energy conversion has taken place?

Extension

11. In what ways could heat be regarded as mechanical energy?

Knowledge

1. List seven different types of energy.

2. What is the current definition of energy?

3. Define the term "thermodynamics."

4. What was one principle of thermodynamics that was developed during the study of the nature of heat?

5. What is the difference between nuclear fusion and nuclear fission?

6. What type of nuclear reaction is occurring in the Sun?

7. What is the difference between kinetic energy and potential energy?

8. Describe an example where an object has:
   a) only kinetic energy
   b) only gravitational potential energy
   c) kinetic and potential energy

9. When does potential energy become "useful" energy?

10. What term is common to kinetic and potential energy?

11. Explain the difference between the mass and the weight of an object.

12. Why is chemical energy considered a form of potential energy?

13. A person leaps high up into the air. At what point in the upward motion does the person have:
    a) maximum kinetic energy?
    b) minimum kinetic energy?
    c) maximum gravitational potential energy?
    d) minimum gravitational potential energy?
    e) kinetic energy equal to gravitational potential energy?

14. Give an example of mechanical energy being converted to:
    a) thermal energy
    b) sound
    c) light
    d) electricity

15. What are the byproducts of a hydrogen fuel cell?

Applications

16. Scientists who observed a demonstration of Newton's cradle in 1666 could not explain one of their observations. What was this observation? How did scientists later in the 1600s try to explain it?

17. How did Young unite the terms "work" and "mechanical energy"?

18. Describe an example where each of the following forms of energy can be found in a technology:
    a) chemical
    b) light
    c) thermal
    d) radiant
    e) electric
    f) kinetic
    g) sound

19. Describe a natural system in which the following forms of energy can be found:
    a) chemical
    b) light
    c) thermal
    d) radiant
    e) electric
    f) kinetic
    g) sound

20. The inclined plane shown below has a vertical distance of 1.00 m and the length along the incline is 1.50 m. A force of 30.0 N, applied to the string parallel to the incline, slides a 1.00-kg block of wood a distance of 1.50 m up the incline.

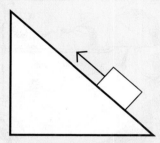

Calculate the work done by the force in moving the block of wood up the incline to the top.

21. Determine the gravitational potential energy of the block of wood at the top of the incline.

22. Explain why the work done in question 20 is not equal to the energy gained by the object in question 21.

23. A 50-kg gymnast leaps on a springboard and rises vertically to a height where the gravitational potential energy of the gymnast is 800 J. Calculate the elastic potential energy stored in the springboard when the gymnast first leaped on the springboard.

24. State the assumption you had to make to answer question 23.

25. Calculate the initial vertical speed of the gymnast at the moment the feet of the gymnast left the springboard in question 23.

26. State the assumption you had to make to answer question 25.

27. Describe a process involving your body in which there is a transformation of at least three different types of energy.

28. Describe a process where there is a transformation of the following forms of energy:
a) chemical to light
b) light to chemical
c) kinetic to heat
d) heat to kinetic
e) electric to magnetic
f) magnetic to electric

29. Why are solar cells used in providing the electrical energy for space stations?

30. An ice cube is placed at the top of an inclined plane. Eventually, a coating of water begins to appear between the ice cube and the inclined plane. Slowly, the ice cube begins to slide down the inclined plane. Identify the evidence that energy is involved in each of these observations.

Extensions

31. Design an experiment to investigate the conversion of kinetic energy into potential energy. In your design, state a problem, identify the manipulated and the responding variables, make a hypothesis that describes the relationship between the two variables, and suggest a procedure that could be used to take the desired measurements.

32. Discuss all the ways that the energy of a drop of water in a cloud is different from the energy of a drop of water in the surface of a calm lake.

33. Does Earth have mechanical energy as it travels in its orbit around the Sun? Explain your answer.

34. Discuss the different approaches of a scientist and an environmentalist in arguing the importance of the development of a hydrogen fuel cell automobile for the future.

35. Which source of energy do you think should be further developed for the future? Justify your answer.

Principles of energy conservation and thermodynamics can be used to describe the efficiency of energy transformations.

Key Concepts

In this section, you will learn about the following key concepts:

- technological innovations of engines that led to the development of the concept of energy
- design and function of technological systems and devices involving potential and kinetic energy, and thermal energy conversions
- efficient use of energy, and environmental impact of inefficient use of energy

Learning Outcomes

When you have completed this section, you will be able to:

- describe how the first and second laws of thermodynamics have changed our understanding of energy conversions
- describe qualitatively, and in terms of thermodynamic laws, energy transformations in devices and systems
- define, operationally, "useful" energy from a technological perspective, and analyze the stages of "useful" energy transformations in technological systems
- recognize that there are limits to the amount of "useful" energy that can be derived from the conversion of potential energy to other forms in a technological device
- identify the processes of trial and error that led to the invention of the engine, and relate the principles of thermodynamics to the development of more efficient engine designs
- explain, quantitatively, efficiency as a measure of the "useful" work compared to the total energy put into an energy conversion process or device
- apply concepts related to efficiency of thermal energy conversion to analyze the design of a thermal device
- compare the energy content of fuels used in thermal power plants in Alberta (costs, benefits, efficiency, sustainability)
- explain the need for efficient energy conversions to protect our environment and to make judicious use of natural resources

FIGURE B3.1 This drawing shows a humorous attempt at designing the perfect machine.

Rube Goldberg, a cartoonist during the 1920s, poked fun at the gadgets that were being designed to supposedly make people's lives easier. His "inventions" were drawn only for amusement, but surprisingly, they could actually work. One of his inventions, an automatic napkin, is shown in Figure B3.1. It uses a complicated set of machines to accomplish a very simple task: wiping the diner's moustache.

Rube Goldberg's drawing is humorous because we know intuitively that the machine is extremely inefficient. One swipe of the diner's hand could eliminate the nine or so automatic steps. In fact, Rube Goldberg machines have come to symbolize inefficient machines: they exert a lot of effort to produce small results. In the real world, engineers do the opposite of Rube Goldberg. They design efficient machines that exert the minimum possible effort to produce largest possible results.

At the start of the Industrial Revolution, engineers developed machines to do work, and as time passed, they tried to make these machines do work more efficiently. As scientists looked at these attempts to increase efficiency, they developed some principles about how heat behaves.

In this section, you will learn about the laws that govern heat. You will also learn how the development of technologies during the Industrial Revolution led to advances in the scientific concept of energy and how these technologies were improved and refined over time. You will study the efficiency of energy conversions in machines. Finally, you will investigate how thermal energy conversions affect our environment.

B 3.1 Laws of Thermodynamics

*info*BIT

Although the automobile engine is one of the most popular heat engines used, up to 33% of the energy supplied to the automobile is lost as heat.

All machines in daily life are governed by physical laws. These laws describe the relationships between work and energy transformations. However, they focus on one type of energy transfer: heat. The previous sections showed how energy transformations or transfers resulted in changes in motion or position of an object. This section will deal with changes in temperature that are also a result of work and energy transformations or transfers.

Systems

For investigations into work done and energy transfers, it is necessary to set boundaries for the objects involved. These boundaries define the system. A **system** is a set of interconnected parts. In studies of work and energy transfers, the system is the object or objects involved in the transfers. Everything else is considered the surroundings or the environment. For example, in a gasoline-powered lawn mower, the system could be the engine. The surroundings could be the other parts of the mower, the ground, and the air around the mower. The set boundaries are arbitrary, and you can change them. In the lawn mower example, the system could have been the entire lawn mower. The surroundings would then be the ground and the air.

After you define a system and its surroundings, you should state the type of system you are studying.

- An **open system** is one that exchanges both matter and energy with its surroundings. For example, suppose Earth is a system and the universe is its surroundings. Earth is an open system, since it can exchange both energy and matter with its surroundings.
- A **closed system** is one that cannot exchange matter but can exchange energy with its surroundings. For example, a closed can of soup is a closed system because matter cannot move into or out of it, but energy can move into the can.
- An **isolated system** is one that cannot exchange either matter or energy with its surroundings.

FIGURE B3.2 (a) Heat flows from the fire to the metal rod.

✓ The First Law of Thermodynamics and the Law of Conservation of Energy

It is important to distinguish heat from work. Work involves the movement of matter from one location to another, whereas heat is a transfer of thermal energy from one location to another. Both heat and work can affect systems.

The energy of a system can be increased in two ways. Either heat can be added to a system from the surroundings (Figure B3.2(a)), or work can be done on a system by its surroundings (Figure B3.2(b)). Work done on the system by the surroundings is considered positive work because the energy of the system increases.

Similarly, the energy of a system can decrease in two ways. Either heat

(b) The person does work on the spring of the pogo stick.

(a) Heat flows from the hot metal rod to the water.

(b) The spring of the pogo stick does work on the person.

can flow out of a system to its surroundings (Figure B3.3(a)), or work can be done by a system on its surroundings (Figure B3.3(b)). Work done by a system on its surroundings is considered negative work because the energy of the system will decrease.

In the previous section, you were introduced to the law of conservation of energy as it relates to mechanical systems. The law of conservation of energy can be stated in more general terms: Energy cannot be created or destroyed. It can only be transformed from one form to another, and the total amount of energy never changes. The **first law of thermodynamics** is really just a restatement of the law of conservation of energy, except one of the forms of energy involved is heat. This law states that the total energy, including heat, in a system and its surroundings remains constant. Whenever heat is added to a system, it transforms into an equal amount of some other form of energy. This law is supported by Joule's experiments, outlined in section B2.1.

When heat is added to a system, some of the energy goes into increasing the internal energy of the system. This increases the temperature. Some of the energy is used to move parts or to do work on the system. This increases the mechanical energy.

heat added to the system = mechanical energy + heat

This is what happens in most real-world situations. Most machines involve many moving parts that are in contact with one another. These parts rub together and this friction produces heat. Even though some energy is lost as heat, the law of conservation of energy or the first law of thermodynamics still applies: The amount of heat put into a system must equal the amount of mechanical energy plus heat lost by the system. Theoretically, the system could gain the same amount of mechanical energy as the heat input energy. But in reality, the mechanical energy gained never comes close to the theoretical maximum because most of the input energy is lost from the system as heat.

Inquiry Lab

Bouncing Balls

The Question

Which type of ball most closely resembles a perfect machine?

The Hypothesis

A perfect machine transfers all of its energy into the same or another form of energy completely, with no energy lost to the surroundings as heat or other forms of energy. Study the balls in the materials, and state a hypothesis about which of the given balls would do the best job of converting one form of energy into another. In your hypothesis, state how you would determine if the bouncing ball resembles a perfect machine.

Variables

Identify the manipulated, responding, and controlled variables in the experiment.

Materials and Equipment

3 different types of balls (basketball, golf ball, lacrosse ball, super ball, etc.)

metre-stick

balance (measuring in grams(g))

Procedure

1. Create a data table in your notebook like the one below. Make sure your table has a title.

2. Put the ball on the balance. Record its mass in the appropriate column of your table.

3. Set the metre-stick in a vertical position with the "0" reading at the bottom.

4. Drop a ball from the top of the metre-stick to the floor, and carefully note the height to which the ball bounces. Repeat this procedure three or four times and record each value in your notebook. Use these values to calculate the average value for the return height. Record the value in the appropriate column in the table.

5. Repeat steps 2 to 4 for the other balls.

Analyzing and Interpreting

1. List the energy conversions from the moment you lift the ball to the top of the metre-stick, to the time that the ball reaches its highest point on its bounce.

2. Explain how the conversion of energy for each ball illustrates the first law of thermodynamics.

3. What happened to the lost energy? Is the lost energy a violation of the law of conservation of energy?

Forming Conclusions

4. According to your data, which ball best resembles a perfect machine? Justify your answer.

5. Which ball least resembles a perfect machine? Justify your answer.

6. Do the results of the experiment agree with your hypothesis?

Type of Ball	Mass of the Ball m (kg)	Starting Height h (m)	Starting Potential Energy $E_p = mgh$ (J)	Average Return Height h (m)	Ending Potential Energy $E_p = mgh$ (J)	Loss of Potential Energy ΔE_p (J)
		1.00				

The Perfect Machine Cannot Be Achieved

Ideally, once energy is added to start a machine, the machine should convert all this input energy directly into mechanical energy output, without any energy loss. Since all the input energy is converted completely into mechanical energy, the amount of mechanical energy produced by the machine should equal the amount of energy put into the machine. If no energy is converted to other forms of energy, then the machine should continue to operate indefinitely. These types of machines are called **perfect machines** or **perpetual motion machines**. Although they come close, those shown in Figure B3.4 are not perfect or perpetual motion machines. It is impossible to create a truly perfect machine.

In order for a machine to be classified as a perfect or perpetual motion machine, all the mechanical energy in the system must be completely conserved as mechanical energy during any transformations. In the activity with the bouncing balls, when a ball is lifted into the air, it has mechanical energy in the form of gravitational potential energy. When the ball is dropped, the potential energy is converted into kinetic energy. When the ball hits the floor, the ball bounces upward converting kinetic energy into gravitational potential energy. If no energy is lost to the surroundings, then the ball should rise to exactly the same height. The ball that bounces highest most resembles a perpetual motion machine. In the experiment, no balls will rebound to the same height as the previous bounce because some of the energy is converted to heat, sound, and deformation in each collision with the floor.

✓The Second Law of Thermodynamics

If you place a hot-water bottle in your bed, the bed will warm up and the hot-water bottle will slowly cool down. Eventually, the bottle and the bed will reach the same temperature. The heat transfers from the bottle to the bed, so the total amount of energy in the bottle and bed remains constant. This is consistent with the first law of thermodynamics, but it also illustrates the **second law of thermodynamics**, which describes the direction of energy flow in natural processes. The second law states that heat always flows naturally from a hot object to a cold object, but never naturally from a cold object to a hot object.

FIGURE B3.4 Attempts at perpetual motion machines

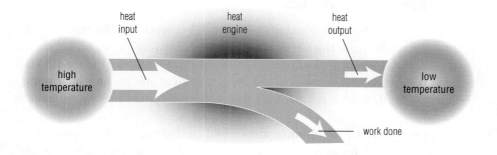

heat
input

heat
engine

heat
output

high
temperature

low
temperature

work done

When the heat in a **heat engine** flows from a high-temperature area to a low-temperature area, this heat can be converted into mechanical energy, which can do work. A heat engine is a device that converts heat into mechanical energy. However, only some of the input heat can be converted to mechanical energy output. The remaining heat is expelled as exhaust heat (Figure B3.5).

For example, in an internal combustion engine, the fuel in the combustion chamber burns at a high temperature, causing the piston to move and gain mechanical energy. The remaining energy is expelled as heat through the exhaust. The exhaust heat has a lower temperature than the input heat.

The hypothetical temperature-difference boat shown in Figure B3.6 is an application of the second law. One pipe leads to the surface of the ocean, which is warmer. The other pipe leads to the deep ocean, which is cooler. Heat flows from hot to cold, so as the heat from the warm-water tank flows to the cool-water tank, it turns a turbine, which turns the propeller. The cold water flows out through the pipe deep in the ocean. Hypothetically, the boat should move because the water is flowing from hot to cold and does work in the process.

According to the second law of thermodynamics, heat never flows naturally from cold to hot. However, heat can be made to move from cold to hot. You have to do work to make this happen.

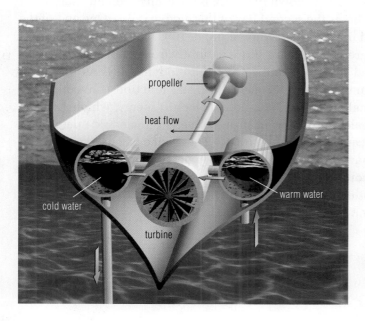

propeller

heat flow

cold water

warm water

turbine

FIGURE B3.6 A hypothetical temperature-difference boat

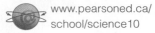
Heat Engines and Heat Pumps

The study of the interrelationships between heat, work, and energy is called thermodynamics, from the Greek word *therme,* meaning "heat." It began less than 200 years ago out of efforts to produce heat engines (Figure B3.7(a)), which are devices that convert heat into mechanical energy, and **heat pumps** (Figure B3.7(b)), which are devices that use mechanical energy to transfer heat.

Heat engines and heat pumps are similar in that they both operate on the principle that heat flows naturally from a hot substance to a colder one and, in the process, can be made to do work. However, there is an important difference between them.

(a) The jet engine is an example of a heat engine.

(b) The air conditioner is an example of a heat pump.

FIGURE B3.7 Examples of a heat engine and a heat pump

√ *Heat Engines*

A thermo-electric converter, shown in Figure B3.8, is an excellent example of a heat engine that follows the second law of thermodynamics. One end of the converter is inserted in water at a temperature of 10°C and the other end is in water at a temperature of 90°C. Heat flows naturally from a hot substance to a cooler one, as stated in the second law of thermodynamics. As this heat, which is thermal energy, flows through the metal junction connecting the two sides, the thermal energy is converted to electric energy, which runs the electric motor. The electric motor, in turn, converts the electric energy into mechanical energy causing the fan to rotate. The device has used a temperature difference to convert heat into mechanical energy. Friction in the electric motor limits the amount of heat that is converted to mechanical energy. The steam engine is another example of a heat engine. You will learn more about steam engines in section B3.2.

electric motor

fan

90°C

10°C

FIGURE B3.8 A thermo-electric converter is an example of a heat engine.

Heat Pumps

A refrigerator pumps heat from inside the cooler interior space to warmer air outside the refrigerator. This process is not natural, and so work must be done by the refrigerator (Figure B3.9). To accomplish this, the refrigerator uses electric energy to pump a refrigerant through copper piping, which is an excellent heat conductor. The refrigerant has a very low boiling point and changes from a liquid to a gas at about −40°C. The process begins at the compressor. Here, the refrigerant emerges as a cool liquid under low pressure. As it is pumped through the copper piping, it absorbs heat from the interior and so the interior cools. As the refrigerant absorbs heat, its temperature rises above −40°C. It then vaporizes into a gas and flows into a compressor, where the gas is compressed causing its temperature and pressure to rise. When this happens, the gas gives off thermal energy. This thermal energy is transferred to the air surrounding the refrigerator. The refrigerant is then pumped into a condenser, where it is cooled and liquefied. The cycle then repeats.

FIGURE B3.9 A refrigerator is a heat pump. Heat has to be pumped from inside the refrigerator to outside the refrigerator.

B3.1 Check and Reflect

Knowledge

1. Define the term "thermodynamics."

2. State the first law of thermodynamics.

3. What is the distinction between work and heat?

4. Identify whether each of the following is best explained by the first or second law of thermodynamics.
   a) A bouncing ball eventually comes to rest on the floor.
   b) A metal spoon eventually becomes hot when placed in a pot of boiling water.
   c) Energy cannot be created or destroyed.

5. What is the difference between a heat engine and a heat pump? Give an example of each.

6. What is a perpetual motion machine?

7. State the second law of thermodynamics.

Applications

8. If two sticks are rubbed together and ignite, is the work being done on the sticks positive or negative work?

9. Water is observed to condense on the outside of a cold glass. Which way is heat flowing?

10. Which law of thermodynamics best describes the following statements? Explain your answer.
    a) You can't get something for nothing.
    b) You can't even get close.
    c) A rock will never suddenly jump into the air.

Extensions

11. Is it possible to cool a room down on a hot day by leaving the refrigerator door open? Justify your answer using the laws of thermodynamics.

12. What is the difference between a perpetual motion machine and a Rube Goldberg machine?

B 3.2 The Development of Engine Technology

Early scientists and engineers realized the importance of inventing machines for making heavy tasks easier to do. However, their machines were limited to simple mechanisms, such as the lever, pulley, wheel and axle, and the screw. Initially, the sources of energy to operate these machines were humans or animals. Later, wind and flowing water were also used. All early machines used sources of energy that people could see or touch. People had not yet discovered that there were "hidden" sources of energy, so the concept of energy was unknown.

The first machine to use a "hidden" source of energy was Hero's steam engine, shown on page 124. But his machine was only a novelty device and did nothing useful, so no one studied it seriously at the time. People did not recognize heat as a useful source of energy for machines.

For most of recorded history there were humans and animals to do all the necessary tasks, and humans used wood to fuel their fires. There was no need to invent sophisticated machines. But things changed in the 1600s. By then, practically all the trees in England had been cut down. So people switched to using coal. Because the demand for coal grew and grew, deeper mines were dug to extract it.

One of the major problems in coal mining was pumping water from deep mines. At first, miners used existing pump systems to pump out the water. These systems (Figure B3.10) had limitations. The Archimedes screw and the Persian wheel, which are turbines, could not lift the water very far because of the downward force of the water. The water held in a large Archimedes screw or Persian wheel was simply too heavy to lift. In a reciprocating pump (Figure B3.11),

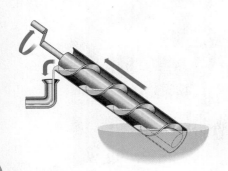

(a) The Archimedes screw

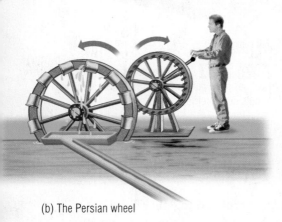

(b) The Persian wheel

FIGURE B3.10 These simple turbines were used to pump water. They could be turned by animals, moving water, or wind.

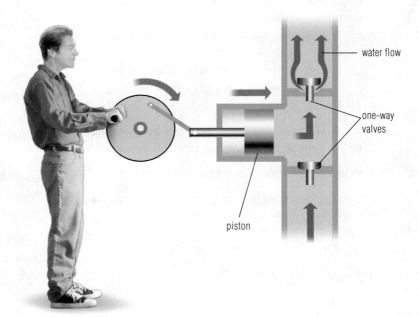

water flow

one-way valves

piston

FIGURE B3.11 A simplified version of a reciprocating pump, which uses a piston moving back and forth in a pipe to drive water upward. As the piston is pulled outward, it creates a vacuum, and atmospheric pressure pushes water into the cylinder through the one-way intake valve. When the piston is pushed inward, water is pushed upward through the one-way outtake valve.

atmospheric pressure can only push water up to a height of 9 m. So the reciprocating pump was also limited in the height it could raise water. Miners needed a more powerful machine that could be operated continuously, with an engine that used some other, more powerful source of energy to drive the pump.

Developing a Technology

Technology does not suddenly appear out of nowhere. Developing a technology involves a step-by-step process. The process usually starts with some understanding of scientific concepts. Inventors and engineers use these concepts to create a technology. This new technology usually has flaws or drawbacks, and others try to improve it. As they try to improve it, their knowledge of the science grows. They use this increased knowledge and new scientific discoveries to improve the technology. Today's internal combustion engine followed this process. It began with the gunpowder engine, as described in detail below. Figure B3.15 summarizes the process in a time line.

The Gunpowder Engine

THE SCIENCE In 1680, Christian Huygens, a Dutch mathematician and physicist, recognized that a successful reciprocating pump needs a force to drive the piston forward and a force to pull it back. Could a piston be driven forward using an internal source of energy?

THE TECHNOLOGY Huygens experimented with a gunpowder engine, in which gases generated by an explosion inside the engine drove a piston forward into a cylinder.

THE DRAWBACKS This engine was not developed because of the obvious hazards of explosions and because there was no powerful internal mechanism to pull the piston back so that the engine could operate continuously.

The Heat Engine

THE SCIENCE Breakthroughs in the development of an engine came with two scientific discoveries. In 1654, Otto von Guericke, a German physicist, demonstrated the tremendous forces of vacuums. He fitted two hollow hemispheres together and created a vacuum inside by extracting the air through a valve. Two teams of eight horses pulling in opposite directions could not pull the hemispheres apart. The other discovery was that water increases its volume by 1300 times when heated to form steam.

THE TECHNOLOGY Using these discoveries, French scientist Denis Papin designed the first heat engine in 1690 (Figure B3.12). This device would use heat to create steam to do work.

THE DRAWBACKS Papin did not pursue the development of his engine because he had difficulty making the large drum in which the water was to be heated.

The first powered road vehicle was built in France in 1769 and had a steam-powered engine. It was called the Cugnot road locomotive.

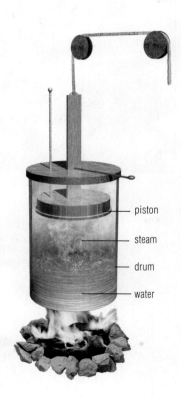

- piston
- steam
- drum
- water

FIGURE B3.12 Illustration of the first steam-powered engine, developed by Papin

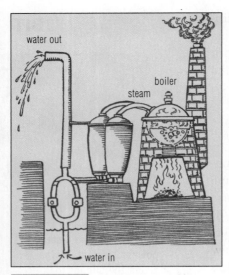

An illustration of the Savery engine in a mine

The Savery Engine

THE TECHNOLOGY In England, in 1698, Thomas Savery invented the first successful steam-powered pump (Figure B3.13), which was used to pump water out of mines.

THE DRAWBACKS This pump could lift water to a height of only 6 m and so it wasn't much of an improvement over animal-powered pumps. To lift to higher distances, the steam would have to be under higher pressure. But the boiler could not produce that amount of pressure without exploding.

The Newcomen Engine

THE TECHNOLOGY Patented in 1712 by Thomas Newcomen, the next heat engine also used steam as the driving force (Figure B3.14). A boiler produced steam that forced the piston up a cylinder. When cold water was sprayed on the outside of the cylinder, the steam would condense and the piston would move back down the cylinder. The piston rod was connected to a pivoting beam, which in turn was connected to the mine pump. The up-and-down motion of the piston drove the pump.

THE DRAWBACKS This steam engine was easy to build and maintain and could pump water to higher distances. However, the cycle of heating and cooling the cylinder was very inefficient, and the engine required tremendous amounts of heat to function.

FIGURE B3.14 The Newcomen engine was also called the beam engine. A pivoting beam connected the piston on the left to the mine pump on the right.

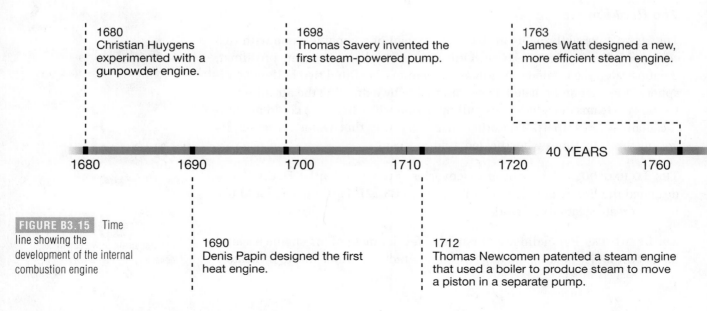

1680
Christian Huygens experimented with a gunpowder engine.

1698
Thomas Savery invented the first steam-powered pump.

1763
James Watt designed a new, more efficient steam engine.

40 YEARS

1680   1690   1700   1710   1720   1760

FIGURE B3.15 Time line showing the development of the internal combustion engine

1690
Denis Papin designed the first heat engine.

1712
Thomas Newcomen patented a steam engine that used a boiler to produce steam to move a piston in a separate pump.

The Watt Engine

THE TECHNOLOGY In 1763, a Scottish instrument maker named James Watt was asked to repair a Newcomen engine. He was shocked by its poor performance. He realized that there was a tremendous waste of heat when water was heated and cooled in the same cylinder. Watt designed a new, more efficient steam engine that had a separate condenser to cool the steam so that the boiler cylinder always remained hot. This reduced the amount of heat required to operate the steam engine, making it over three times more efficient than Newcomen's engine. For over 100 years, the Watt steam engine dominated the market. During this period, there were many improvements in the design of the steam engine (Figure B3.16). Steam engines weren't just used to drive water pumps. They also drove the huge machinery in mills, as well as in trains and ships.

THE DRAWBACKS Although steam engines were relatively easy to build and maintain, they were very large. They needed big boilers to create the steam that was piped to parts of the machine that did the work. Because of this, steam engines could not be made small enough to replace horse-drawn carriages. They were also hot, dirty, and very inefficient at converting heat to useful energy. Most of the heat they created was lost to the surroundings. The time was right for a change in engine technology.

FIGURE B3.16 In this later model of a Watt engine, piston rods were connected to a flywheel, which allowed the engine to be used to drive different types of machinery.

info**BIT**

To help finance his work on the steam engine, James Watt surveyed canals and designed bridges.

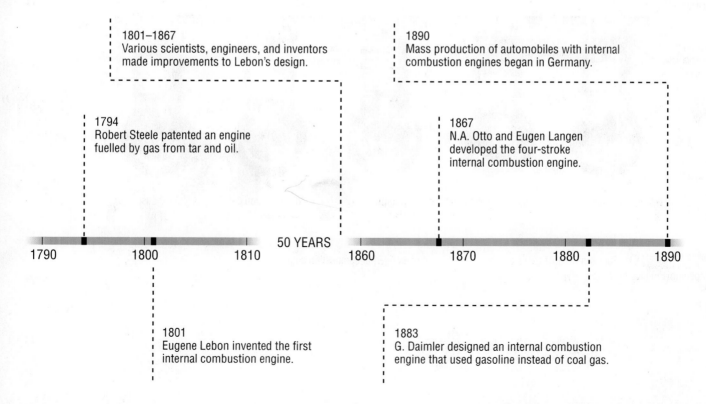

1801–1867
Various scientists, engineers, and inventors made improvements to Lebon's design.

1890
Mass production of automobiles with internal combustion engines began in Germany.

1794
Robert Steele patented an engine fuelled by gas from tar and oil.

1867
N.A. Otto and Eugen Langen developed the four-stroke internal combustion engine.

50 YEARS

1790 1800 1810   1860 1870 1880 1890

1801
Eugene Lebon invented the first internal combustion engine.

1883
G. Daimler designed an internal combustion engine that used gasoline instead of coal gas.

The Internal Combustion Engine

THE SCIENCE In 1794, Robert Steele looked for another source of energy to replace steam. He revived Huygen's idea of using the gas produced from explosions and lodged a patent for a piston engine fuelled by gas from tar and oil, ignited by a flame.

THE TECHNOLOGY Seven years later, in 1801, Philippe Lebon invented an engine that improved on Steele's design. It used coal gas ignited by an electrical spark. This was an **internal combustion engine**, meaning energy was released by burning fuel, ignited by an electrical spark, inside the engine. (This ignition method is used in modern vehicle engines through spark plugs.)

THE DRAWBACKS This engine was still very inefficient and could not produce sufficient force necessary to operate a machine.

THE TECHNOLOGY In 1867, in Germany, N.A. Otto and Eugen Langen improved the efficiency of the engine by compressing the coal gas–air mixture before ignition. Under pressure, the explosion of the mixture produces more force. They developed the four-stroke internal combustion engine, which is still used in many modern automobile engines (Figure B3.17). The four-stroke internal combustion engine works by moving a piston up a cylinder, compressing the gas–air mixture. The firing of the spark plug ignites the gas–air mixture, creating high temperature and pressure in the cylinder. The high pressure moves the piston down the cylinder. The movement of the piston turns the crankshaft, which turns the wheels.

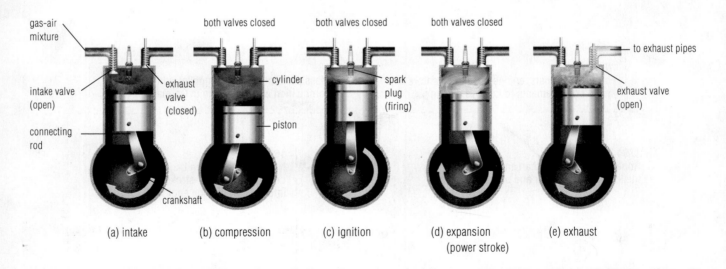

FIGURE B3.17 Fuel and exhaust gases are moved in and out of an internal combustion engine by opening and closing valves.

Almost every engine in the early 1900s was an Otto engine and it could produce the same amount of power as a horse, or 1 hp (horsepower).

THE DRAWBACKS The Otto engine used coal gas as a fuel, which doesn't burn very hot, and so the engine was not very powerful.

THE TECHNOLOGY The most important innovation in the internal combustion engine came in the 1880s, again in Germany, after Gottlieb Daimler designed a petroleum-fuelled internal combustion engine that used gasoline instead of coal gas. Petroleum burns much hotter than coal gas. This engine was small enough to power road vehicles. The technology of the engine had evolved to become practical, and mass production of these engines for use in automobiles began (Figure B3.18).

*info*BIT

One horsepower (hp) was a measure of the amount of power generated by a horse that could lift a 4500-kg mass a distance of 1 m in 60 s. This historical measure for the power of an engine was determined by James Watt as he watched horses working in the coal mines. 1 hp (horsepower) = 746 W (watts)

FIGURE B3.18 Mass production of cars with internal combustion engines

Minds On ...   Motors and Engines Today

Motors and engines are devices that convert energy into some form of motion. For example, the motor in an electric fan causes the fan blades to turn. Engines and motors have become so much a part of our lives that it is difficult to imagine life without some of them.

Part A

• Identify up to 10 different types of devices that use engines to operate. These devices may be in machines, appliances, games, or gadgets in and around your home.

• For each device, identify its energy source (electrical outlets, batteries, gasoline, solar cells, etc.). For each device, decide if you could not possibly, could possibly, or could definitely live without it.

• Summarize your results in a table.

1. What type of engine or motor was the most commonly found in devices at home?

2. What was the most common source of energy?

3. Were you surprised at the devices you could not live without? or those that you could live without?

Part B

• In groups of two or three, brainstorm the uses of effective engines in industrialized societies such as Canada. Research examples from your list or additional examples and explain how these engines have a central role in our society. Write a summary report relating the importance of effective engines to modern industrialized societies.

Problem-Solving Investigation

Using Steam to Power Boats

Recognize a Need

Early engineers harnessed the power of steam to drive mining equipment. But steam can also be used to propel vehicles, including boats. In this investigation, you will create a model boat that is powered by a chemical combustion reaction. A burning candle boils water, causing steam to be produced, which propels the boat.

The Problem

How do you build a boat that uses a burning candle as its energy source?

Materials and Equipment

1 piece of Styrofoam, 10 cm × 15 cm, 2 cm thick

1 piece of Styrofoam, 10 cm × 10 cm, 2 cm thick

1 piece of Styrofoam, 10 cm × 8 cm, 2 cm thick

aluminium foil

water

rubber or cork stopper with hole to fit medicine dropper or glass tubing

medicine dropper or glass tubing

test tube

2 laboratory candles, 2 cm in length

box cutter

matches

glue

metre-stick

stopwatch

lab sink or small aquarium

modelling clay

Criteria for Success

- Build a steamboat. Use the materials and the basic design listed below.

- Test your boat. It must travel in a straight line on the water for approximately 15 cm.

- Alter the basic design to improve the performance of the boat.

- Analyze the alterations you made and communicate how they affected the boat's performance.

Build a Prototype

CAUTION: Be careful when handling the box cutter.

1. Use the 10 cm × 15 cm piece of Styrofoam as the bottom of your boat. Glue the 10 cm × 10 cm piece of Styrofoam to one end of the bottom of the boat, as shown in Figure B3.19. This is the back of your boat.

2. Glue the 10 cm × 8 cm piece of Styrofoam near the front of the boat to act as a support for the test tube, as shown.

3. Cover the top of the boat's bottom with the aluminium foil.

4. Carefully insert the medicine dropper or glass tubing through the hole in the rubber or cork stopper.

5. Fill the test tube about half-full of water. Insert the stopper with tubing into the test tube.

6. Using the box cutter, make a hole in the back of the boat for the medicine dropper or glass tubing, as shown. With the dropper or tubing through the hole, position the test tube so it is resting at a slight angle on the front support.

7. Glue the two candles to the foil on the bottom of the boat near the bottom of the test tube, as shown.

8. Place the metre-stick along the length of a sink or a tank in your lab.

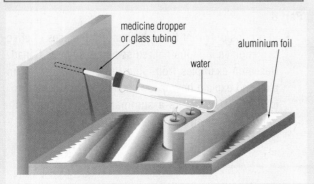

medicine dropper or glass tubing

water

aluminium foil

FIGURE B3.19 Steam-powered boat

Test and Evaluate

9. Place the boat in water and mark the starting position of the boat.

10. Light the candles with matches.

11. Measure the time it takes to travel 15 cm or to come to a stop, whichever comes first.

12. Record your boat's initial time in your notebook.

13. Note whether your boat moves at all or whether it moves in circles.

14. Consider aspects of the engine design that could affect the propulsion of the steamboat and make a list of these aspects.

15. Modify one aspect of the design and do two trials of this modification.

16. Create a table in your notebook like the one shown and record data from your design alterations. Make sure your data table has a title.

17. Decide how you will evaluate whether a modification improved the boat's performance.

Modification Made to the Steamboat	Trial #	Time Taken for the Steamboat to Travel 15 cm (s)
	1	
	2	

Communicate

1. Study your results and list the modifications that affected the propulsion of the steamboat.

2. State how each modification affected the propulsion of the steamboat.

3. How successful was your design in producing the necessary energy to propel the steamboat?

Developing Future Technologies

You have learned how, in the development of engine technology, the concept of energy and the laws of thermodynamics were discovered. Thus, developing a technology can lead to new scientific concepts.

Likewise, new technologies can be developed based on existing scientific laws and concepts. Spacecraft engineers have already predicted that using solar winds (discovered in the early 1950s) will be more efficient than using rocket fuel in propelling a human-operated space vessel across the vast expanse of space to Mars. They have designed spacecraft with wind sails, based on the concepts of wind energy and interplanetary magnetic field theory.

Science-fiction writers often dream up amazing futuristic systems and machines. When these are brought to "life," through special effects, on a television or movie screen, the possibilities do not seem far-fetched at all. Could a machine ever be able to replicate food and beverages out of "thin air," simply from a voice command to do so? Would it really be possible for living objects to be "beamed" or transported from one point in space to another, reappearing intact and fully functional on the other side? What type of energy would be required for such technological systems?

For now, many of these imaginative machines remain just that—part of the imagination—either because the pure science behind such technologies is not known to us yet, or because the science is simply not possible at all. But there is no doubt that in the research to develop a new technology, new aspects of the science behind the technology are being unravelled all the time.

reSEARCH

Using the Internet or the library, research the manufacture of some of the largest steam engines.
- Which ship had the larger steam engine: the *Titanic* or the *Queen Mary*?
- What locomotive had the largest steam engine and what railway company used it?

Begin your search at

 www.pearsoned.ca/school/science10

Recently, scientists have been able to "transport" a photon of light from one point of space to another. This is still very far off from the transportation of an atom, let alone a living cell! But, in using concepts developed in the theoretically-based science of quantum physics, the researchers have revealed yet again that *anything* is possible. Indeed, the development of future technologies is limited only by the limits of our existing scientific and technological knowledge.

B3.2 Check and Reflect

Knowledge

1. Explain why Hero's steam engine was used only for entertainment purposes.

2. What events in the 1600s led to the invention of technologies that used steam energy?

3. What two scientific discoveries in the 1600s led inventors to use steam to drive an engine?

4. Why was the steam engine developed before internal combustion engines that used coal gas or gasoline?

5. Why did Watt consider the Newcomen steam engine highly inefficient?

6. What was one change that Watt made to the design of the steam engine to make it more efficient?

7. List two advantages and two disadvantages of the steam engine.

8. What innovation did Daimler introduce to the internal combustion engine and why was it an improvement?

9. In the internal combustion four-stroke engine, what is the purpose of the intake valve and the exhaust valve?

Applications

10. Identify the major innovation in the design of the steam engine introduced by the following inventors. Describe how each innovation improved on the design.
    a) Papin
    b) Newcomen
    c) Watt

11. Draw a simplified diagram of a reciprocating piston. Describe the process that draws water into the cylinder through the intake valve and the process that forces water through the outtake valve.

12. Why was the internal combustion engine rather than the steam engine chosen to propel road vehicles?

Extensions

13. Research each of the following vehicles or machines and state whether the engine, in most cases, employs a reciprocating piston or a turbine.
    a) a minivan
    b) a 747 airplane
    c) a small propeller airplane
    d) a small propeller boat
    e) a lawn mower
    f) a motorcycle

14. Identify three appliances or machines in your home that use:
    a) a piston engine
    b) a turbine

B 3.3 Useful Energy and Efficiency

After machines had been developed to harness energy transformations to do work, the focus shifted to how efficiently these machines could do the work. When James Watt was asked to repair a Newcomen engine, he saw how poorly the engine performed. He was the first engineer to examine the efficiency of machines.

If machines or engines are to produce mechanical energy, then they must have moving parts. These moving parts rub against each other and produce friction, which in turn produces heat. For example, when two sticks are rubbed together, the heat generated can ignite them. While the person wants to produce heat with the sticks, heat from friction is unwanted in most machines.

Engineers try to reduce the amount of friction between moving parts to reduce waste heat. Magnetic technology is allowing for some near-zero-friction situations. It does this by minimizing contact between the moving parts. The infoBIT at the beginning of section B1.1 describes how MAGLEV trains in Japan are designed to overcome friction by eliminating wheels and tracks. High-powered magnets force the train to rise (levitate) above a guideway and move forward. This technology allows the trains to achieve higher speeds than conventional trains.

Useful Energy

The purpose of a machine is to convert the initial energy added to it into the type of energy needed to do the work that you want done. All other types of energy produced and work done are considered wasted energy or work. The initial energy source is called **energy input**. The desired energy needed to do the work is called **useful energy output**, and the work the machine is supposed to do is the **useful work output**.

For example, the purpose of a light bulb is to provide light by converting electric input energy to light output energy. However, a light bulb also produces heat in the process. The light is the useful energy output and the heat is the wasted energy (Figure B3.20).

Systems with moving parts always lose some energy as heat, which is consistent with the first and second laws of thermodynamics. In the first law, the energy that is supplied to a system must equal all the energy that is gained by the system. For example, the energy supplied to your body (the system) by food energy must equal the energy of all the useful work done, plus all the wasted energy, which includes heat and the mechanical energy of the moving parts of your body. According to the second law, heat flows from hot to cold and, in the process, it can be made to do work. However, during the thermal energy transfer, some energy is always lost to the surroundings. Thus the efficiency of a system can never be 100%. This means that you can never come close to getting the energy out of a system that you put into it.

FIGURE B3.20 A light bulb produces more heat than useful light energy.

Efficiency

Efficiency is a measurement of how effectively a machine converts energy input into useful energy output. It is expressed as a ratio:

$$\text{efficiency} = \frac{\text{useful work output}}{\text{total work input}}$$

If efficiency is expressed as a percent, then the term is called the percent efficiency of a machine. Since there are different types of energy conversion devices, there are several formulas to calculate their percent efficiencies. Table B3.1 shows the efficiencies of some common engines.

TABLE B3.1 Efficiencies of Some Common Engines

Type of Machine or Engine	Efficiency (%)
automobile internal combustion engine	12–15
electric engine	Up to 95
steam reciprocal engine	50–75
steam turbine engine	Up to 40

1. Conversion of Total Mechanical Energy to Useful Mechanical Energy

Some machines or systems involve the conversion of mechanical energy to another form of mechanical energy. For example, a crane uses mechanical energy to do the work of lifting a load vertically to the top of a building (Figure B3.21). The load gains mechanical energy in the form of gravitational potential energy. The mechanical energy efficiency can be calculated as shown below.

$$\text{percent efficiency} = \frac{\text{useful mechanical energy or work output}}{\text{total mechanical energy or work input}} \times 100\%$$

$$= \frac{E_{m(\text{useful output})}}{E_{m(\text{total input})}} \times 100\% \quad \text{OR} \quad = \frac{W_{\text{useful output}}}{W_{\text{total input}}} \times 100\%$$

FIGURE B3.21 The mechanical efficiency of a crane is much less than 100%.

Practice Problem

1. In lifting a car, the total mechanical energy input of a hydraulic hoist is 5.61×10^4 J, while the useful mechanical energy output is 1.96×10^4 J. Calculate the percent efficiency of the hoist.

Example Problem B3.1

A crane lifts a load of construction materials from the ground to the second floor of a building. In the process, the crane does 2.30×10^4 J of work or mechanical energy input, while doing 8.00×10^3 J of useful work or mechanical energy output in lifting the load. What is the mechanical percent efficiency of the crane?

$$\text{percent efficiency} = \frac{E_{m(\text{useful output})}}{E_{m(\text{total input})}} \times 100\%$$

$$= \frac{8.00 \times 10^3 \text{ J}}{2.30 \times 10^4 \text{ J}} \times 100\%$$

$$= 34.8\%$$

The crane is 34.8% efficient.

Example Problem B3.2

An internal combustion engine with an efficiency of 15.0% is used to do 3.20×10^4 J of useful work, or mechanical energy output. Calculate the mechanical energy input that had to be supplied by the combustion of fuel in the engine.

$$\text{percent efficiency} = \frac{E_{m(\text{useful output})}}{E_{m(\text{total input})}} \times 100\%$$

$$15.0 = \frac{3.20 \times 10^4 \text{ J}}{E_{m(\text{total input})}} \times 100\%$$

$$15.0 = \frac{(3.20 \times 10^4 \text{ J})(100\%)}{E_{m(\text{total input})}}$$

$$E_{m(\text{total input})} = \frac{(3.20 \times 10^4 \text{ J})(100\%)}{15.0}$$

$$= 2.13 \times 10^5 \text{ J}$$

The mechanical energy input was 2.13×10^5 J or 213 kJ.

Practice Problem

2. A small electric motor has an efficiency of 85%. In lifting a small load, it produces 15 J of mechanical energy input. Calculate the useful mechanical energy output of the motor.

---

2. Transfer of Total Thermal Energy to Useful Thermal Energy

If a pot of water is sitting on a hot stove element, the heat from the element will be transferred to the pot and the water. The efficiency of heat transfer in a system may be determined using the following formula.

$$\text{percent efficiency} = \frac{\text{heat}_{\text{useful output}}}{\text{heat}_{\text{total input}}} \times 100\%$$

Example Problem B3.3

In heating a pot of water, 2.00×10^3 J of heat was supplied by the stove element. If only 5.00×10^2 J of heat was actually gained by the water (heat output), what was the percent efficiency of the stove element?

$$\text{percent efficiency} = \frac{\text{heat}_{\text{useful output}}}{\text{heat}_{\text{total input}}} \times 100\%$$

$$= \frac{5.00 \times 10^2 \text{ J}}{2.00 \times 10^3 \text{ J}} \times 100\%$$

$$= 25.0\%$$

The stove element has an efficiency of 25.0%.

Practice Problem

3. A Bunsen burner supplies 4.00×10^3 J of heat to a small beaker of water. Only 125 J of heat is actually gained by the beaker and water. Calculate the percent efficiency of the burner.

Efficiency of a Thermal Device
(Teacher Demonstration)

Before You Start...

Your teacher will do all the steps in this activity that involve handling the lead shot. Make sure to record the data carefully.

The Question

What is the relationship between the mechanical energy and heat in an energy conversion device?

The Hypothesis

Read over the procedure and state a hypothesis concerning the relationship between changes in the device's mechanical energy and its heat output.

Materials and Equipment

clear plastic tube with a 2.5-cm diameter, 1 m long

2 cork or rubber stoppers

1500 g of lead shot or pellets

thermometer or temperature probe

5 medium-sized Styrofoam cups

electronic balance or triple beam balance

metre-stick

Procedure

1 Create a data table like the one below. Be sure to give it a title.

CAUTION: Lead is poisonous. Use gloves when handling lead shot, and wash your hands thoroughly when you have finished.

2 Label the five cups as 1, 2, 3, 4, and 5, respectively.

3 Place the first Styrofoam cup on the balance. Measure the mass of the empty cup in grams.

4 Slowly add about 300 g of lead shot into the Styrofoam cup.

5 Carefully measure the mass of lead shot and the cup and then calculate the mass of the lead shot. Record this value in the appropriate column of your data table.

6 Using a thermometer or a temperature probe, determine the initial temperature of the lead shot to the nearest 0.1°C.

7 Place a stopper into one end of the hollow tube and carefully pour the lead shot into the tube. Place the other stopper into the open end.

8 Hold the tube upright and use the metre-stick to measure the distance, to the nearest 0.01 m, between the top of the lead shot in the tube and the stopper at the top. This distance is the average height the lead shot will fall in the next step. Record this value in your data table.

9 Hold the tube in a vertical position, keeping the stoppers firmly in place with both hands. Quickly flip the tube 180° and stop the tube in a vertical position, allowing all the lead shot to drop the entire length of the tube to the bottom. Continue flipping the tube in this manner 7 more times for a total of 8 flips.

Styrofoam Cup	Mass of Lead Shot m (g)	Initial Temperature $t_{initial}$ (°C)	Final Temperature t_{final} (°C)	Average Height the Lead Shot Falls h (m)	Number of Times the Tube Was Flipped
1					8
2					16

10 Remove the bottom stopper and let out the lead shot into the Styrofoam cup and measure the final temperature of the shot. Record this value in the appropriate column in your data table.

11 Repeat steps 3 to 10 using Styrofoam cups 2, 3, 4, and 5 and fresh lead shot at room temperature, but flipping the tube 16, 24, 32, and 40 times, respectively.

Analyzing and Interpreting

1. Complete a table in your notebook similar to the one below. Determine the change in gravitational potential energy of the lead shot in each trial. Note that the masses of lead shot should be converted to kilograms in this table.

Styrofoam Cup	Mass of the Lead Shot m (kg)	Acceleration Due to Gravity g (m/s²)	Total Height the Lead Shot Falls h (m) (h = distance of one fall × the number of flips)	Change in Gravitational Potential Energy of the Lead Shot E_m (J) ($E_m = E_p = mgh$)
1		9.81		
2		9.81		

2. Complete a table in your notebook similar to the one below, determining the heat gained by the lead shot in each trial.

Styrofoam Cup	Mass of the Lead Shot m (g)	Temperature Change Δt (°C)	Specific Heat Capacity of Lead c (J/g°C)	Heat Gained by Lead Shot H (J) $H = mc\Delta t$
1			0.159	
2			0.159	

3. Construct a data table that includes the changes in gravitational potential energy of the lead shot and the heat gained by the lead shot for each trial. Using the data, draw a graph of heat gained by the lead shot as a function of the changes in the gravitational potential energy of the device. Draw the line of best fit through the data points.

4. Determine the slope of the line of best fit. What does this represent?

5. For each trial, determine the percent efficiency of the conversion of gravitational potential energy to heat. What is the average value of the percent efficiency of this device?

Forming Conclusions

6. Do your results support your hypothesis concerning the relationship between changes in mechanical energy and heat?

Applying and Connecting

7. Compare the percent efficiency of this device with the percent efficiency of other devices you have studied in this section. Is this device a good energy conversion device? Justify your answer.

Extending

8. The air in the tube is also heated as the tube is flipped. If this did not happen, would the percent efficiency be higher or lower? Explain.

9. Compare your results with those of other groups in your class. Determine what factors could have caused any difference in the percent efficiency values.

10. Suggest alterations to the design of the device that could improve the efficiency of the energy conversion.

3. Conversion of Total Thermal Energy to Useful Mechanical Energy or Vice Versa

In many systems, the energy conversions involve thermal energy and mechanical energy. For example, the thermo-electric converter, or thermo-couple, in Figure B3.8, page 204, converts thermal energy to mechanical energy to turn a fan. Not all the heat input is converted to mechanical energy in the process. Some of the heat is lost to the surroundings. To calculate the percent efficiency of this type of device that converts heat to mechanical energy, use the following equation:

$$\text{percent efficiency} = \frac{E_{\text{m (useful output)}}}{\text{heat}_{\text{total input}}} \times 100\%$$

For devices that convert mechanical energy to heat, use

$$\text{percent efficiency} = \frac{\text{heat}_{\text{useful output}}}{E_{\text{m (total input)}}} \times 100\%$$

In general, when you find the percent efficiency of any device, you are determining the percent of useful energy compared with the total energy input.

B3.3 Check and Reflect

Knowledge

1. In most machines, what type of energy is usually found as wasted energy?

2. Which component in the operation of a car consumes the most energy?

3. Explain what is meant by the term "efficiency," when applied to a machine.

4. What type of engine is the most efficient?

Applications

5. A machine consumes 1000 J of energy in doing 800 J of work in lifting a load.
   a) What is the energy input?
   b) What is the energy output?
   c) What value is classified as useful work?
   d) What value is classified as wasted energy?
   e) Calculate the percent efficiency of the machine.

6. Describe one situation where you would consider thermal energy as useful energy and one situation where you would consider thermal energy as wasted energy.

7. Calculate the percent efficiency of an engine that consumes 3.50×10^3 J of energy in doing 2.30×10^3 J of work.

8. The percent efficiency of a machine is 35.0%. What is the useful work done if the machine consumes 1.20×10^4 J of energy?

9. The percent efficiency of a machine is 35.0%. What is the input energy required if a 2.00×10^3-kg object is to be lifted 5.00 m?

Extensions

10. Suppose you wanted to determine the percent efficiency of your skateboard. What would you measure as the work input and what would you measure as the work output?

11. Compare a perpetual motion machine and an internal combustion engine in terms of percent efficiency.

12. Compare a perpetual motion machine and a Rube Goldberg machine in terms of percent efficiency.

B 3.4 Energy Applications

Two things about energy are certain: we cannot live without it and we cannot create it. We use it to heat homes, run machines, cook food, and power appliances, tools, and gadgets. Through all the centuries of discoveries by brilliant and inventive scientists and engineers, we have not found a way to create energy. The best we can do is control it or transform one form of energy into another. Where does all this energy come from?

Energy Supply

Since the beginning of time, the most important and reliable source of energy on Earth has been the Sun (Figure B3.22). All primary energy sources are classified into two main categories: solar and non-solar energy sources.

Solar Energy Sources

Solar energy sources are those that are derived either directly or indirectly from the energy of the Sun. *Solar radiation* is the radiant energy from the Sun emitted by the hydrogen–hydrogen nuclear fusion reaction that occurs in the Sun's core. This radiant energy travels through space as electromagnetic radiation. It is captured directly by plants (through photosynthesis) or by Earth's surface, or by devices such as solar panels, solar cells, photovoltaic cells, and so on.

Wind energy is the result of heating of the surface of Earth by the Sun. This heating causes convection currents of air, or wind. The energy in the movement of air may be used to turn wind turbines. The kinetic energy of the turbine is converted into other forms of energy such as electrical energy.

Water energy results when surface water is heated by the Sun. It drives a hydrologic cycle. Heating causes evaporation of water into the atmosphere where it then condenses, creating rain. The falling rain creates flowing water in streams and rivers. This moving water can be converted into other forms of energy through hydro-electric dams.

Biomass is any form of organic matter, such as wood, wood residues, crop residues, seaweed, algae, and animal wastes. These substances are indirect solar energy sources, since they store energy from the Sun through the process of photosynthesis. All of these can be combusted to release chemical potential energy.

Fossil fuels such as oil, natural gas, and coal are also considered indirect solar energy sources because all fossil fuels were formed from plants and animals that lived millions of years ago.

Non-Solar Energy Sources

Non-solar energy sources have no relationship to the Sun. They include nuclear energy, which is the energy obtained from a conversion of mass to energy in a nuclear reaction. This reaction can be either *fission* (uranium or plutonium fission) or *fusion* (hydrogen–hydrogen fusion). Fission reactions can be controlled in a nuclear reactor, such as the CANDU reactor.

Geothermal energy is thermal energy from Earth's interior. Superheated

FIGURE B3.22 The Sun is the primary energy source for life on Earth.

water is evidence of the tremendous heat deep inside Earth. This water gushes to Earth's surface via geysers and hot springs, and it can be used to generate electricity. Geothermal power plants use the superheated water to create steam to power turbines. Geothermal energy can only be exploited in those areas with volcanic activity, where geysers and hot springs are found.

Tidal energy involves the movement of ocean water, creating tides. Tides are caused by the gravitational pull by the Moon and, to a lesser extent, by the Sun. The kinetic energy in this movement of water can be converted to other forms of energy, such as electricity. The tides in the Bay of Fundy are the highest in the world, reaching up to 17 m.

Renewable and Non-Renewable Energy Sources

Energy sources can also be further classified as **renewable energy sources** and **non-renewable energy sources**. Renewable energy sources are ones that are continually and infinitely available (solar, wind, water, geothermal, tidal, and biomass). Biomass is considered a renewable source of energy because forest reserves can be replaced in a reasonable length of time. Non-renewable energy sources are ones that are limited and irreplaceable (nuclear and fossil fuels).

Energy Sources and Electricity Generation

Although energy sources can be used directly, most of these energy sources are used to produce electrical energy, which is then used for a multitude of purposes. Electrical energy is one of the most important forms of energy in industrial societies. Before the 1900s, electricity was not widely used, but today it provides over 40% of all the energy consumed. Power-generating stations most commonly use fossil fuels, flowing water, wind, or nuclear energy as the initial energy sources, which are then converted into the mechanical energy used to rotate the turbines. Deciding which energy source to use when a power station is built depends on which source is the most readily available and practical in that area. For example, Pincher Creek in southern Alberta is very windy, which makes it an ideal location for wind turbines (Figure B3.23).

FIGURE B3.23 There are 60 wind turbines at the Castle River Wind Farm west of Pincher Creek in southern Alberta. Each turbine produces enough energy to power 300 homes a year.

Energy Demand

Historically, our ancestors used renewable sources of energy, such as solar energy and wood or biomass. Today, these sources make up only a small fraction of our energy supply. Our current consumption of energy from different sources is shown in Table B3.2.

TABLE B3.2 Global Yearly Energy Consumption from Different Sources (2001)

Energy Source	Global Yearly Energy Consumption ($\times 10^{18}$ J)
conventional oil	150*
coal	96
natural gas	92
hydro	25
nuclear	26

*includes shale oil and oil sands

Adapted from *BP Statistical Review of World Energy 2002*

Several factors have placed dangerous demands on our energy supplies. First, the amount of energy consumed per person has been increasing exponentially. Our ancestors consumed about 10 000 000 J or 10 MJ of energy per person per day. Today, the global average for energy consumption per person per day is 180 MJ. This figure rises for people in industrialized countries, who consume, on average, 1000 MJ per person per day!

Second, the world population is also growing exponentially. Up until the 1950s, the growth of the world's population was steady but slow. In the 1950s, there were huge innovations in medicine, such as the development of vaccines and antibiotics. Better public health increased the average life span. There were also technological innovations which improved people's lifestyles. As a result of all these developments, the world population has been increasing at an exponential rate (Figure B3.24). Currently, there are over 6 billion people on the planet. So, there are more people consuming more energy.

Third, many societies now use non-renewable energy sources rather than renewable sources as the primary source of energy. Until the 1950s in Alberta, most power stations produced electrical energy from hydro power, or flowing water. When large coal reserves were discovered near Edmonton, it then became cheaper to build coal-fired generating stations than hydro-electric dams. Today, only 5% of electricity generation in Alberta is from hydro power and 85% is from coal. The other 10% is from natural gas.

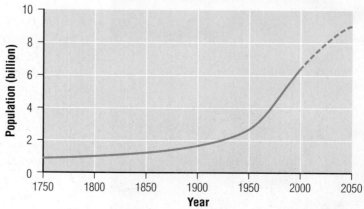

Adapted from United Nations *World Population Prospects, The 2002 Revision* and estimates by the Population Reference Bureau

FIGURE B3.24 The global population is predicted to reach 9.3 billion by 2050.

Comparing the Energy Content of Fossil Fuels Used in Alberta

Begin your search at
www.pearsoned.ca/
school/science10

The Issue

Which type of fossil fuels should be used in thermal energy plants in Alberta?

Background Information

Modern technological demands for readily available and relatively inexpensive energy sources have made fossil fuels the most widely used source of energy. Power stations use technologies that rely on fossil fuels as an initial source of energy. Alberta has reserves of all three fossil fuels, and they can be transported to all parts of the province. Coal is the most readily available, followed by oil, and then natural gas.

Suppose the Alberta government has proposed the construction of a power station in your area, and the station must use a fossil fuel as the initial source of energy. Your group has been asked to research which fossil fuel to use: oil, gas, or coal. The government will use the results of your research to make the most appropriate decision.

Analyze and Evaluate

1. Use the library or the Internet to do your research.
   a) Research the energy content of each type of fossil fuel in joules per kilogram of fuel (J/kg).
   b) Research the environmental effects of using each fossil fuel in your area.
   c) Research which source of energy will supply the most energy over the long term.

2. Analyze your research and decide which fossil fuel should be used.

3. Once your group has completed a written report recommending a particular fossil fuel, present the report to the rest of the class who will act as representatives of the government and the community. After the presentation, each member of your group must be able to justify and defend your recommendation.

FIGURE B3.25 (a) Oil is often transported in tankers. When tankers leak, spills can have lasting effects on ecosystems.

(b) Burning fossil fuels contributes to thermal pollution.

The Effects of Energy Use

Our dependence on fossil fuels has placed a strain on existing supplies. It has also had significant effects on the environment (Figure B3.25). The search for and extraction of fossil fuels have resulted in damage to ecosystems. For example, drilling for oil in the muskeg of northern Alberta has left scars on the landscape. There is also the danger of oil leaking from wells, polluting the surrounding area.

Even though fossil fuels are relatively cheap and convenient sources of energy, burning them may damage our environment permanently. Emissions from the combustion of fossil fuels contain greenhouse gases and oxides. Greenhouse gases contribute to climate change and oxides contribute to acid rain.

The overall effect of an increasing population, an increasing demand for energy, and the shift toward the exploitation of non-renewable energy sources is having far-reaching consequences.

Every time there is an energy conversion, some energy is wasted in the form of heat, as stated in the second law of thermodynamics. It has been determined that hydro-electric generating stations are 70% efficient and coal-burning stations are only 35% efficient. This means that twice as much energy is lost as heat in coal-burning power stations as in hydro-electric stations.

Study the diagrams of a hydro-electric power station and a coal-burning power station on page 192 and answer the following questions.

Questions

1. How many energy conversions take place in each type of generating station?

2. Identify all the locations where energy could be lost as heat.

3. Using your answers to the previous questions, explain why hydro-electric power stations are more efficient than coal-burning power stations.

4. Can you suggest how efficiency could be improved in each type of power station?

Energy Consumption and Conservation

Before the 1970s, the reserves of fossil fuels seemed inexhaustible. Because they were relatively simple to extract, fossil fuels were the most inexpensive and desirable sources of energy. In the 1970s, the major oil-producing nations severely cut back on oil production, which caused an oil shortage (Figure B3.26). The shortage, in turn, caused oil prices to skyrocket. The sudden shortage was called an energy crisis. This forced experts in industrialized nations to examine their consumption of oil and other fossil fuels. Experts realized that at the current rates of consumption, the reserves of the fossil fuels would soon be depleted. Because industrialized countries were greatly dependent on fossil fuels, efforts were made to research and develop alternative energy sources and technologies that could harness them.

At the current rate of consumption, our known fossil-fuel reserves are fast becoming depleted. Table B3.3 projects the number of years remaining for each fossil fuel as an energy source. Proven reserves are those that geological and engineering information indicates can be recovered in the future from known deposits under current economic and operating conditions.

FIGURE B3.26 The oil shortage in the 1970s resulted in long line-ups at gas stations.

TABLE B3.3 Comparison of Three Fossil Fuels

Fossil Fuel	Global Yearly Consumption of the Fossil Fuel as of 2001 ($\times 10^{18}$ J)	Proven Reserves of the Fossil Fuel as of 2001 ($\times 10^{18}$ J)	Projected Number of Years Left (assuming 2001 demands)
conventional oil	150*	6 088[†]	40[†]
coal	96	21 362	216
natural gas	92	5 893	62

*includes shale oil and oil sands   [†] does not include shale oil and oil sands

Adapted from *BP Statistical Review of World Energy 2002*

If everyone reduced their consumption of fossil fuels by 25%, this would extend reserves for several more years. An alternative is to search for new fossil fuel reserves around the world. However, these two approaches are only short-term solutions because they are merely prolonging the inevitable.

Any initial energy source may be used to generate electricity. Power stations tend to be located close to their energy supply. For each of the generating stations listed below, determine why each station is located where it is. Copy the table and fill in the third column.

Initial Energy Source	Location of Electrical Generating Station	Why is the Generating Station Located There?
nuclear	Pickering, Ontario	
biomass	Clover Bar Landfill, Edmonton, Alberta	
fossil fuel (coal)	Keephills, Alberta	
hydro or water	Bighorn Dam, Alberta	

Begin your search at

www.pearsoned.ca/ school/science10

Yet another approach is to search for alternative energy sources. However, the search for new sources of energy is extremely expensive and it will be difficult to incorporate new energy sources into society and develop technologies that use the new sources. Imagine every machine that we possess having to be changed to adapt to a new energy source.

Until we develop a new energy source, the most practical solution to dwindling fossil fuel supplies is to conserve as much energy as possible by reducing our energy use. To do this, we must consume our current energy supplies efficiently. This has to be done across all fronts—personal, commercial, industrial, and transportation—until a new practical energy source is developed.

The largest consumers of energy in industrialized countries are business and industry, so it is important that they use energy efficiently. Most companies could conserve large amounts of energy by doing such things as turning out unused lights, turning off equipment or placing it in standby mode, and buying energy-efficient products. Many companies have already installed more energy-efficient lighting, heating, and cooling equipment to conserve energy.

Another less obvious method is to encourage industries to use **cogeneration**. This is the process of using waste energy from one process to power a second process. For example, in a thermal power station, the steam that is used to turn the turbines could then be used to heat local buildings before returning to the combustion chamber to be reheated. Currently in some power stations, the heat from the steam, once it has passed through the turbine, is wasted because it is vented to the outside surroundings.

TransAlta, a Calgary-based energy company, operates plants that use cogeneration. Its Cancarb Thermal Carbon Black Plant in Medicine Hat is a conventional thermal power plant that burns natural gas to create heat and electricity. Beside this plant is its Cancarb Waste Heat Recovery Power Plant, a cogeneration plant. This cogeneration plant generates steam from the waste heat created by the thermal plant to drive a turbine to generate electricity for the city of Medicine Hat. This cogeneration reduces the overall CO_2 emissions in southern Alberta by 160 000 tonnes per year.

Individuals also have to use energy efficiently. The tables below suggest some methods individuals can use to conserve energy and give statistics that can help consumers make energy-efficient choices.

Methods to Conserve Energy
Turn off all unnecessary lights.
Turn down the thermostat a few degrees at night.
Take a bus or car pool to work or school.
Avoid using energy-wasting appliances and gadgets.
Take shorter showers.

Be Aware of Efficiency Statistics
Major electric appliances must meet a minimum standard of energy efficiency. New appliances must show an EnerGuide label, which shows the appliance's yearly energy consumption in kWh. The lower the number, the more efficient the appliance.
A frost-free refrigerator uses twice as much energy as a conventional refrigerator.
An electric stove uses twice as much energy as a gas stove.
An incandescent light bulb uses three times as much energy as a fluorescent bulb.
A large sport utility vehicle uses more than three times as much energy as a smaller compact vehicle.

Achieving energy efficiency and conservation are, at present, the best solutions to preventing an energy crisis, but it can also be argued that even these are merely postponing the inevitable. Sooner or later, we will deplete all the non-renewable sources of energy.

All sectors of society must become conscious of the problem and search for a solution. The solution or solutions can't benefit just a few places for a short while; they must benefit all societies over the long term. The solution must be **sustainable**. A sustainable process will not compromise the survival of living things or future generations while still providing for our current needs.

Sustainable Development and Planning for the Future

Sustainable development is economic development that meets current needs without compromising the ability of future generations to meet their needs. If we want to achieve sustainable development, continuing our current energy practices that emphasize depletion of non-renewable resources will not help. When we, as a society, develop large-scale energy policies for the future, we have to keep sustainability in mind. If energy policies place more emphasis on reducing current energy demands and improving efficiency of current and future power plants, they will improve the sustainability of our fossil fuel reserves. However, a more proactive approach that emphasizes research into cost-efficient ways to obtain energy from renewable resources may help society reach the goal of true sustainability. Some people believe that governments should lead the way.

B3.4 Check and Reflect

Knowledge

1. Give three examples of solar energy sources and three examples of non-solar energy sources.

2. What is the ultimate source of energy in the Sun?

3. What is biomass?

4. What is cogeneration?

5. What is meant by the term "sustainable"?

Applications

6. Why are fossil fuels regarded as indirect solar energy sources?

7. Explain why photosynthesis is considered a direct use of solar energy while a windmill is an indirect use of solar energy.

8. Why is biomass considered a renewable energy source?

9. What three factors are chiefly responsible for the modern strain on our supply of non-renewable energy sources?

10. Discuss the term "energy crisis."

11. Identify two short-term solutions to the energy crisis.

12. What is the most practical solution to the energy crisis?

Extensions

13. List five costs and five benefits of developing thermal power stations.

14. It has been suggested that in order to conserve energy, governments should impose a "user-pay" tax for users of fossil fuels. Give three advantages and three disadvantages of this tax.

Knowledge

1. What is the energy conversion in a heat engine?

2. What are the two statements that describe the second law of thermodynamics?

3. Under what conditions will a machine be classified as a perpetual motion machine?

4. If you are forming a snowball with your bare hands, what is the direction of heat flow?

5. Explain the operation of a thermo-electric converter.

6. Name three sources of energy that pre-industrial societies used to operate their simple machines.

7. What are three benefits and three costs of non-renewable energy sources?

8. Why is southern Alberta a prime area for the development of windmills for the generation of electricity?

Applications

9. Describe one example in your classroom that can be explained using the first law of thermodynamics.

10. A soft rubber ball and a steel ball bearing are both dropped from the same height onto a concrete floor. Which ball do you predict will rise higher? Justify your answer and state the law of thermodynamics that is best applied to this situation.

11. Can the heat output of a heat engine be greater than the heat input? Does this violate the first law of thermodynamics?

12. Compare a hydro-electric power station and a thermal power station. Which of the two methods is the most efficient at generating electricity? Explain your answer in terms of useful and wasteful energy.

13. Explain what is meant when it is stated that the efficiency of an engine is 25%.

14. A heat engine with an efficiency of 35% has a heat input of 1000 J.
    a) What is the heat output?
    b) What happens to the rest of the energy?

15. What is the energy crisis?

16. What is the current method of solving the energy crisis?

17. To lengthen the life span of non-renewable energy sources, energy conservation can be practised by all parts of society. Describe one method of energy conservation that can be applied in the following areas:
    a) residential   c) industrial
    b) commercial   d) transportation

18. Explain why energy conservation and efficiency are merely postponing the energy crisis.

19. What is a better solution to the energy crisis?

20. In terms of energy content of fuels, suggest why thermal power plants in Alberta use non-renewable sources of energy such as coal and natural gas, instead of renewable sources such as wood.

Extensions

21. Explain why the freezer compartment in the older model refrigerators was always at the top.

22. How is efficiency related to the conservation of energy?

23. The hot-water heater is one of the largest consumers of energy in the home. Explain at least three ways the hot-water heater can be made more efficient.

24. If the internal combustion engine is so much less efficient than an electric motor, why do automobiles still use the internal combustion engine as a source of power?

25. How does the phrase "sustainable development" differ from the perspective of an environmentalist or an oil industry employee?

Cost-Benefit Analysis of Energy Sources for Transportation

Begin your search at
www.pearsoned.ca/
school/science10

Background Information

Whenever a controversial change in a technology is proposed, experts in the field are usually consulted to do a cost-benefit analysis of the technology before any further steps are taken to develop the technology. "Costs" refers to all the factors that weigh against the technology, such as negative impacts on society and the environment. "Benefits" refers to all the factors that favour the development of the technology.

Cost-benefit analyses are done often by industry and governments because they help these organizations make decisions on difficult issues.

Scenario

Imagine that you are given the task of presenting a proposal to the government concerning the advantages and disadvantages of different energy sources used for transportation. The results of your proposal will determine which type of electrical generating station is to be developed in your area.

Research the Issue

1. To enable you to present your proposal, you will need to complete cost-benefit charts like the ones shown below.

2. Identify at least three energy sources that can be used in transportation.

3. Research five costs and benefits for each energy source.

Analyze the Issue

4. In the chart, list the benefits and the costs of each type of energy source. Rate each benefit and cost using a scale of 1 to 10, 10 being the greatest benefit or cost.

5. Once you have rated all the costs and benefits, total your ratings for costs and benefits.

6. According to your results, which energy source has the greatest benefit?

7. According to your results, which energy source has the greatest cost?

Address the Issue

8. Using the information that you have researched and your analysis, prepare a cost-benefit analysis that clearly outlines how you reached your decision as to which energy source should be used.

Energy Source	Benefits	Rating (1–10)	Costs	Rating (1–10)
Gasoline	1.		1.	
	2.		2.	

Energy Source	Benefits	Rating (1–10)	Costs	Rating (1–10)
Electricity	1.		1.	
	2.		2.	

Build an Energy Conversion Device

In this activity, you will design and build your own device to demonstrate the principles of energy conversion and transformation. At the beginning of section B3.0, in Figure B3.1, you saw an example of a Rube Goldberg machine. This is an opportunity for you to design and build your own such machine.

Criteria for Success

- Your device must perform at least three energy transformations.

- You must be able to explain what happens at each transformation.

- You must be able to describe how your working model functions and identify all places where energy is wasted.

Procedure

1. Working in a small group, brainstorm possible designs.

2. Choose one design. Draw and label the design. Identify the energy transformations and where they will take place. Identify where you think energy will be wasted.

3. Make a list of materials you will need to construct your device. Choose materials that you can bring from home or find in the science lab.

4. Have your design approved by your teacher.

5. Once you have finalized your design and chosen your materials, construct a working model of your device.

6. Test your device to see if it works and make modifications if necessary. Keep notes on any modifications you make.

7. Demonstrate your model to the class.

Analysis

1. Demonstrate and describe the energy conversions and transformations in your device.

2. Identify all the places where energy is wasted.

3. What type of energy is released as wasted energy?

4. Describe any modifications you could still make to improve your device.

Reporting

5. Create a summary report that describes how the design, construction, modification, and demonstration of your device met the criteria listed above.

Unit Summary

B 1.0 **Investigating the energy flow in technological systems requires an understanding of motion, work, and energy.**

Key Concepts

- one-dimensional motion
- work

Learnings

- Uniform motion is represented as a straight line on a distance–time graph and as a straight line with a slope of zero on a speed–time graph.
- All physical quantities in physics can be classified as scalar or vector quantities, depending on whether direction must be included in their measurement.
- Velocity is a vector quantity describing the displacement of an object during a time interval.
- Acceleration is a vector quantity describing the rate of change of the velocity of an object.
- If a force is applied to an object, there is a transfer of energy to the object, which causes a change in the motion of the object. For work to be done, there must be movement and a force; the force and the distance travelled must be in the same direction.
- Work being done by applying a force through a distance against an opposing force results in a transfer of energy.

B 2.0 **Energy in mechanical systems can be described both numerically and graphically.**

Key Concepts

- forms and interconversions of energy
- mechanical energy conversions and work
- design and function of technological systems and devices involving potential and kinetic energy, and thermal energy conversions

Learnings

- Heat and kinetic energy or potential energy can be converted into each other. This finding led to the definition of energy as the capacity to do work.
- Other forms of energy are: chemical energy, stored in chemical bonds; electrical energy, produced by moving electrons; magnetism; light energy; nuclear energy; and solar energy.
- Potential energy may be gravitational, elastic, or chemical.
- Potential energy can be converted to kinetic energy and kinetic energy can be converted to potential energy.

- According to the law of conservation of energy, the total amount of energy in a given situation remains constant.
- Evidence of energy transformations comes from observed changes, such as changes in motion, shape, or temperature.

B 3.0 **Principles of energy conservation and thermodynamics can be used to describe the efficiency of energy transformations.**

Key Concepts

- technological innovations of engines that led to the development of the concept of energy
- design and function of technological systems and devices involving potential and kinetic energy, and thermal energy conversions
- efficient use of energy, and environmental impact of inefficient use of energy

Learnings

- Thermodynamics is the study of the interrelationships between heat, work, and energy. The total energy, including heat, in a system and its surroundings remains constant.
- Perpetual motion or perfect machines are not possible because some of the input energy is converted to heat and lost to the surroundings.
- Heat flows from warmer objects to cooler ones and, in the process, some heat can be converted to mechanical energy to do work. The efficiency of a system is always less than 100%. You can never get as much useful energy out of a system as you put in.
- Throughout history, devices have been invented to harness different forms of energy to do work. Innovations in the technology used in different types of engines led to the development of the concept of energy.
- Over time, different people made improvements to the design of the steam engine, making it more efficient.
- The internal combustion engine depends on energy produced by burning fuel inside the engine.
- Solar energy sources include radiant energy, wind energy, water energy, biomass, and fossil fuels. Non-solar energy sources include nuclear energy, geothermal energy, and tidal energy.
- The change from the use of renewable sources of energy to non-renewable sources, the exponential growth in world population, and the increase in energy consumed per person have created a crisis in energy.

Unit Review

Vocabulary

1. Using your own words, define the following terms:

   acceleration
   cogeneration
   efficiency
   energy
   first law of thermodynamics
   force
   heat
   kinetic energy
   law of conservation of energy
   potential energy
   second law of thermodynamics
   sustainable
   system
   uniform motion
   velocity
   work

Knowledge

B 1.0

2. Classify the following terms as either scalar or vector quantities and give an example of a measurement of each (include the units and a direction if necessary):
   a) distance travelled
   b) displacement
   c) speed
   d) velocity
   e) acceleration
   f) work
   g) energy
   h) force

3. What two measurements would you take to determine the speed of an object?

4. In your own words, describe how acceleration differs from uniform motion.

5. What happens to the motion of an object when an unbalanced force is applied:
   a) in the same direction as the initial motion of the object

   b) in the opposite direction as the initial motion of the object

6. When is work done on an object?

7. Describe one situation where a force is being applied to an object and the object moves through a distance, yet no work is done on the object.

8. A force of 20.0 N is required to lift an object 1.30 m from the floor to the top of a table. How much work was done on the object?

B 2.0

9. Show how the unit for kinetic energy, which is the joule, J, is derived from the fundamental units (kg, m, and s).

10. Define kinetic energy.

11. Name two types of potential energy.

12. Describe the relationship between the weight of an object and the work done on it.

13. When a rock is projected into the air by the elastic of a slingshot, explain why the rock will go faster if the elastic is stretched an extra distance.

14. A rock is shot vertically into the air with a catapult. At what point is the kinetic energy of the rock the greatest? At what point is the gravitational potential energy the greatest?

15. Give an example of an energy transfer in:
    a) a technological system
    b) a biological system
    c) a chemical system

16. What is the energy conversion in a solar cell?

17. Explain why hydro-electric generating stations are so much more efficient than thermal generating stations.

18. Identify all the energy conversions that take place when you turn a page in this book.

B 3.0

19. What is the difference between a heat engine and a heat pump? Give an example of each.

20. How are the first law of thermodynamics and the law of conservation of energy related?

21. Describe a situation in your home that illustrates the first law of thermodynamics.

22. If heat is added to a perpetual motion machine, ideally what should happen?

23. How are the first and second laws of thermodynamics related?

24. Describe an example in your home that illustrates the second law of thermodynamics.

25. Draw a simplified diagram of a Newcomen steam engine and describe its operation.

26. What are two differences between the Watt steam engine and the internal combustion engine?

27. Why is coal considered as actually being energy from the Sun?

28. Describe three energy sources in your home that could be converted from non-renewable to renewable sources of energy.

29. Define cogeneration and describe an example of how cogeneration could be applied in your school.

Applications

30. Sketch a distance–time graph showing the motion of objects travelling at 10 km/h, 20 km/h, and an object at rest.

31. A car travelling at 90.0 km/h travels 180 km. How long will the journey take?

32. A bird flies straight down from its perch on the branch of a tree to the ground, a distance of 10.0 m. The bird then returns straight up to the perch. The total time of flight is 4.0 s. What is the bird's
    a) distance travelled?
    b) displacement?
    c) average speed?
    d) average velocity?

33. A car accelerates from rest to 50.0 m/s [N] in 6.00 s. What is the acceleration of the car?

34. A student applies a force of 6.0 N to slide a book a distance of 0.33 m across a tabletop. Calculate the work done by the student.

35. A chain and boom mechanism is frequently used to hang advertising signs on a storefront, as shown below.

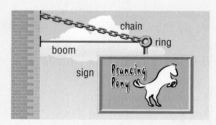

State whether each of the three forces acting on the ring (caused by the chain, boom, and sign) is a push or a pull on the ring.

36. A force of 100 N is required to push an object a distance of 5.00 m. Calculate the work done.

37. Why are water reservoirs in smaller communities placed high up on a hill or in high water towers?

38. A crate is pushed horizontally along the floor. Describe the changes in kinetic energy and in potential energy.

39. A 2.30-g bumblebee is flying at a speed of 2.50 m/s. What is the kinetic energy of the bumblebee?

40. A 2.00×10^3-kg car has a kinetic energy of 4.00×10^5 J due to its motion. What is the speed of the car?

41. A 0.400-kg rock is balancing on the edge of a cliff 500 m above a valley. What is the gravitational potential energy of the rock with respect to the valley below?

42. A construction worker with a weight of 800 N is walking on a steel beam high up in an office tower under construction. If the construction worker has 7.90×10^5 J of gravitational potential energy at this point, how high is the worker above the surface of Earth?

43. A cannon in a circus stunt fires a 750-N performer vertically to a height of 15.0 m. What was the speed of the performer just as the cannon was fired?

44. Each of the following describes a situation involving potential energy:
  i) Water is stored in a reservoir high up on a hill.
  ii) A model rocket is attached to its launching apparatus.
  iii) A spring-loaded toy gun is set to fire a "nerf" dart.
  For each of the above situations:
  a) Identify the type of potential energy stored.
  b) Explain how the stored potential energy in each case can be made to do "useful work."
  c) Describe the type of energy into which this potential energy can be transformed.

45. After finding an AA battery in a drawer and installing it in a CD player, a student was surprised when the CD player operated, even though the student knew that the battery was at least a year old.
  a) What is the initial source of energy in a battery and why is it called potential energy?
  b) Why was the battery still functional, even after a long period of time?
  c) Where does this initial potential energy go when the battery is used to operate a CD player?

46. A 0.300-kg bullet is fired from a gun at a speed of 747 km/h. If the bullet rises straight up into the air, what is the maximum height that the bullet can reach?

47. A 2.00-N ball is lifted 1.00 m above the ground and dropped. Explain how you would determine the speed of the ball just before it hits the ground.

48. A 2.00-kg object is rolling on the floor and begins to climb an incline. Explain how you would determine the height to which the object will rise up the incline. What factor must you ignore?

49. Give an example in your home where waste heat could be reused.

50. A matchstick is rubbed on a surface and ignites. Explain all the energy conversions that take place.

51. The energy that we require for our existence comes from the chemically stored energy in food. What happens to the person whose work output is less than the energy consumed?

52. For centuries, inventors have been trying to design a perfect machine or a perpetual motion machine. Theoretically, there are different types of perpetual motion machines.
  i) Machines with an efficiency of over 100%.
  ii) Machines that can extract heat energy from a source and convert it completely to other forms of energy.
  iii) Machines that convert mechanical energy into mechanical energy, with no loss.
  a) Using the first law of thermodynamics, explain why the first situation is impossible.
  b) Describe a technology that could be explained by the statements in ii) and iii).

53. A steam engine has a heat input of 1000 J and does 350 J of useful work. What is the percent efficiency of the engine?

54. An internal combustion engine has a percent efficiency of 15%. How much is the work input if the engine lifts a 400-N object through a vertical distance of 3.50 m?

55. A hot-water bottle is filled with hot water and then sealed. Consider the hot-water bottle as a system.
   a) What would be classified as its surroundings?
   b) What type of system is it: open, closed, or isolated? Explain your answer.
   c) What type of system would it be if it began leaking?

56. How did scientists realize that the energy from the Sun could not be chemical energy from the combustion of matter?

57. A coal-burning power station has three major components where energy transformations occur.
   a) Name each component.
   b) In each component, identify a "useful" energy produced in a transfer or transformation, and a "wasteful" energy produced.

58. Consider the power plant in the previous question. Describe how cogeneration may be used to increase the efficiency of each energy transfer or transformation, and so reduce "waste" energy produced in each component.

59. Homeowners can help heat their homes by installing a fireplace that can burn wood, coal, or gas. Your neighbours have asked you to help them decide which fuel type to use. For each fuel source, identify the following:
   a) its major benefit
   b) its major drawback or risk
   c) how sustainable it is

60. In section B3.1, a hypothetical temperature-difference boat was shown as an application of the second law of thermodynamics. Theoretically, this method should be able to propel a boat. Identify and discuss two limitations of this boat. Discuss how the second law of thermodynamics prevents the boat from being 100% efficient.

Extensions

61. Describe an example where trial and error resulted in the development of a technology.

62. Why do the terms "science" and "technology" seem to go hand in hand?

63. What do you think was the most important technology developed in the 1900s? Justify your answer by stating how this technology has affected your life.

64. Whenever a transfer of energy occurs, an object may undergo a change in motion, position, or temperature. Using thermal energy as one of the energy, describe a situation depicting a change in:
   a) motion
   b) position
   c) temperature

65. What single energy conversion in your home contributes the most to the loss of energy? Can you suggest any methods to improve the efficiency of this energy conversion?

66. When an object is thrown up into the air, there is a constant change in the kinetic and potential energy of the object. Describe the changes in the mechanical energy of the object and justify your answer.

67. A 10.0-g marble is dropped from a tabletop 1.30 m above the floor. Using calculations, determine at what height above the floor the kinetic and the potential energy are equal.

68. A dog lifts a 30.0-g bone from the bottom of a hole that was 20.0 cm deep. If the dog lifts the bone to the surface of Earth, does the bone gain any gravitational potential energy? Explain your answer.

69. A pendulum is lifted to the same height on Earth and on the Moon. Explain the differences in the kinetic and potential energy.

70. Hydro, thermal, and nuclear generating stations are located in various regions in Canada.
a) Where would each station be ideally located?
b) Describe two similarities between all these types of generating stations.
c) Describe two differences between a thermal and a nuclear generating station.
d) Rate each type of generating station in terms of efficiency.

71. A superconductor is a device that can transport a current without any loss of energy. Can it be classified as a perpetual motion machine? Use the first and second laws of thermodynamics to explain your answer.

72. Describe an example where the principle of cogeneration of heat could be applied in the home.

73. The following topics were listed in the agenda of a meeting of energy specialists:
a) energy conservation
b) energy efficiency
c) alternative sources of energy
d) environmental concerns

Which topic should be the most important goal for governments to consider when discussions regarding energy and the future are being held? Explain your answer.

74. How would the discovery of a new energy source to replace fossil fuels affect your home and some technologies in your home?

Skills Practice

75. The ticker tape below depicts the motion of an object:

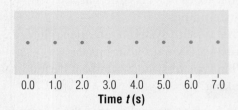

0.0   1.0   2.0   3.0   4.0   5.0   6.0   7.0
Time *t* (s)

a) Using a ruler to measure distances, complete a table of values, similar to the one shown below, depicting the distance from the starting point at various times.

Time *t* (s)	Distance *d* (cm)
0.0	

b) Draw a distance–time graph.
c) From the graph, what type of motion is the object undergoing?
d) Calculate the slope of the line of best fit.
e) What does this value represent?
f) What type of graph would depict the motion of an object that is accelerating?

76. Use the ticker tape from the previous question.
a) Complete a table of values by calculating the speed of the object during the time intervals indicated.

Time Interval *t* (s)	Speed *v* (cm/s)
0.0 – 1.0	
1.0 – 2.0	
2.0 – 3.0	
3.0 – 4.0	
4.0 – 5.0	
5.0 – 6.0	
6.0 – 7.0	

b) Draw a speed–time graph.
c) What type of motion is displayed by the shape of the graph?

d) What would the shape of the graph be if the object was travelling with accelerated motion?

e) Calculate the slope of the line of best fit of the graph.

f) What does this value represent?

g) Extrapolate the line of the graph to 7.0 s and calculate the area under the line at 7.0 s.

h) What does this value represent?

77. The following graph represents a force being applied to move an object through a horizontal distance. Calculate the work done on the object to move it 5.0 m.

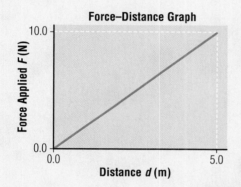

Force–Distance Graph

78. The position–time graph in the next column displays the motion of an object in accelerated motion. Study the graph and answer the following questions.

a) In your notebook, draw the four different segments displaying accelerated motion in the graph.

b) For each segment, identify whether the object is speeding up or slowing down. State whether the motion is in a positive or negative direction.

c) Sketch a velocity–time graph of the four accelerated motions displayed in the position–time graph.

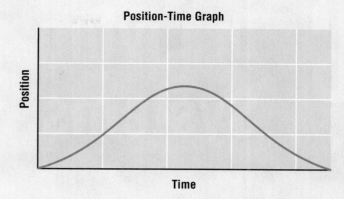

Position-Time Graph

79. Imagine that you are stranded on a small, uninhabited tropical island. After combing the entire island, you discover that the only vegetation are coconut palms, hollow bamboo plants, fruit trees, and various grasses. For protection, you decide to build a hut on a cliff overlooking the ocean and directly above a fresh water stream. Using concepts that you learned from this unit, describe a method you could devise to transport water up to the hut. Identify at least two problems that might have to be overcome in the design of your technology and discuss how your design solves each problem.

Self Assessment

80. Throughout the unit, when doing investigations and research projects, you have had to draw conclusions. In science, how important is the process of drawing conclusions? What affects how good those conclusions are?

81. Describe what you found most interesting in studying energy and technological systems in this unit.

82. Identify one issue that you would like to explore in more detail.

83. Think back to the first section of the unit. Why do you think the concept of energy was so difficult to develop and what role did technology play in helping develop the concept?

84. What changes in your own life would you undertake to conserve energy?

UNIT C

Cycling of Matter in Living Systems

A reflected light image of the jellyfish species in which the gene for the luminescent green fluorescent protein (GFP) was discovered. **Inset:** Genetically engineered mice, carrying the gene for GFP, luminesce under ultraviolet light.

In this unit, you will cover the following ideas:

Focus on the Nature of Science

In this unit, you will learn how cell structures and organelles function to carry out the life processes in living organisms. You will discover how technological advancements have improved our understanding of cell structure and function.

Useful questions to guide you in your study include:

1. How did the cell theory replace the concept of "spontaneous generation" and revolutionize the study of life sciences?

2. How do single-celled organisms carry out life functions?

3. How do plants use specialized cells and processes to accomplish the same functions as a single cell, but on a larger scale?

4. How does imaging technology further our understanding of the structure and function of cells?

At the end of the unit, you may be asked to do these tasks:

Case Study Help Wanted

In this case study, you will research engineering applications of transport systems in cells. You will prepare a presentation on a specific area of research to make the case for its application in industry or medicine.

Project The Impact of Environmental Factors on Plant Function

In this project, you will develop a proposal to investigate the question: Are plant cells able to respond to changing levels of carbon dioxide? You will state a question and hypothesis, identify relevant variables, and design an experimental procedure.

Exploring

■ Municipalities are responsible for maintaining the quality of drinking water provided through water treatment facilities.

In May 2000, the residents of Walkerton, Ontario, suffered Canada's worst case of water contamination. Most types of the bacterium, *Escherichia coli*, are harmless; several types are even found in the intestines of humans and animals. However, *E. coli* strain O157:H7, the strain that entered the water supply of this small town, produces a powerful toxin that can cause serious illness. Seven people in Walkerton died as result of ingesting *E. coli* strain O157:H7 bacteria. These deaths brought renewed national attention to the importance of clean, safe drinking water. Victims of the Walkerton contamination were offered an experimental drug developed at the University of Alberta by Dr. Glen Armstrong, called "Synsorb," which is able to absorb *E. coli* toxins in the human digestive tract.

How do we protect against water contamination like that experienced in Walkerton? Environment Canada identifies good drinking water as being free of disease-causing organisms, harmful chemical substances, and radioactive matter. The water should have a good taste and be odourless and clear. Maintaining clean drinking water is an important task and not an easy one. Bacteria, viruses, and other physical, chemical, and biological contaminants may be washed into lakes, rivers, streams, reservoirs, and groundwater, which are all common sources of drinking water for cities and towns. Municipalities are responsible for maintaining the quality of drinking water provided to their residents. In order to accomplish this task, water treatment facilities usually have a pre-filtering process to eliminate large contaminants, and then a full-scale water purification process to ensure that the water is potable (fit for drinking). This process includes treatment to solidify impurities, filtration through several layers of sand or charcoal, and the addition of chlorine disinfectant.

There are other, more expensive, methods of purifying water that use little or no chemical disinfectant and depend on what have become known as "membrane technologies." The membrane is a synthetic fibre barrier that contains microscopic holes or pores through which pure water can pass, but physical and biological contaminants cannot. You may have heard of "reverse osmosis" water purification systems, in which water is passed through a series of membranes at very high pressure. This is one of many types of membrane technologies that are being developed.

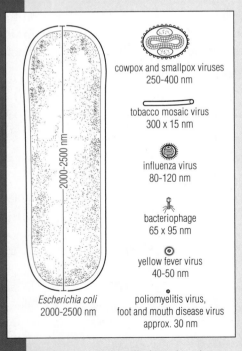

cowpox and smallpox viruses
250–400 nm

tobacco mosaic virus
300 x 15 nm

influenza virus
80–120 nm

bacteriophage
65 x 95 nm

yellow fever virus
40–50 nm

poliomyelitis virus,
foot and mouth disease virus
approx. 30 nm

Escherichia coli
2000–2500 nm

2000–2500 nm

■ Micro-organisms like bacteria and viruses can range in size from 10 μm to just a few nanometres.

Membrane technologies are used not only in water purification, but also in chemical, petrochemical, pharmaceutical, food, agricultural, environmental, and biotechnology industries. What you may not know is that the use of membranes, to select which substances can pass through, is modelled on the way in which plant and animal cells transport materials. Technology enables the study of natural systems, but the reverse is true, as the study of natural systems can help us to identify and develop synthetic systems to perform similar functions at high efficiency. Some of these systems and their applications in industry will be explored in this unit.

Pore Size in Various Materials

The pore size of a material will determine what can pass through it. This concept is important in water filtration systems. If a product cannot eliminate bacteria and viruses, additional purification methods may be needed.

Purpose

To examine the relative pore size of different materials and to relate pore size to the ability to exclude micro-organisms

Materials and Equipment

cloth samples (e.g., linen, cheesecloth, unbleached muslin, polyester, or other materials such as waterproofed fabric)

paper samples (e.g., filter paper, paper towel)

scissors

water

dropper

microscope slides

dissecting microscope (optional) or magnifying glasses

small, flat, transparent metric ruler

CAUTION: Use proper technique when handling microscopes and magnifying glasses. Handle glass slides carefully.

Procedure

1. Cut a small square (of side about 1.0 cm) of each of the cloth and paper samples provided by your teacher.

2. Using a dropper, place several drops of water on a microscope slide. Add one square of cloth to the water to make a flattened wet mount.

3. Examine the square of cloth through the dissecting microscope or by using the magnifying glass. Place a ruler on the wet mount and, using the magnifying glass, count or estimate the number of pores present in the cloth along a line 0.5 cm as shown on the ruler.

4. Draw a diagram of the weave of the cloth or the surface of the paper.

5. Repeat your observations for two other samples. Compare your results with those of another student who has used different materials.

Questions

1. Compare the weave and pore size of the different materials you observed. Which material would be most efficient as a filtration membrane? Explain your choice.

2. What is the relation between pore size and filtration ability? Rank the materials supplied to the class in order of their ability to filter out particles.

3. Consider the pore size of each type of filter system listed across the top of the table shown below. Complete the table to indicate which of the micro-organisms listed in the left hand column can be excluded by which filter. Use + to indicate that a filter can prevent an organism from passing through it and − to indicate that it cannot.

Filters	Granulated Activated Carbon (20 μm)	Carbon Block (0.5 μm)	Micro Filtration (0.1–1.0 μm)	Ultra Filtration (0.001–0.01 μm)
Paramecium caudatum (180–300 μm)				
Giardia lamblia (8–12 μm)				
Escherichia coli (2.0–2.5 μm)				
smallpox virus (0.25 μm)				
poliomyelitis virus (0.03 μm)				

4. Explain why simple filtration alone may not be sufficient to maintain a safe water supply.

Our current understanding of the cell is due in part to developments in imaging technology.

Key Concepts

In this section, you will learn about the following key concepts:

• microscopy and the emergence of cell theory

Learning Outcomes

When you have completed this section, you will be able to:

• trace the development of the cell theory: all living things are made up of one or more cells and the materials produced by these, cells are functional units of life, and all cells come from pre-existing cells

• describe how advancements in knowledge of cell structure and function have been enhanced and are increasing as a direct result of developments in microscope technology and staining techniques

• identify areas of cell research at the molecular level

FIGURE C1.1 Compare the detail seen in these three images of table salt.

Look at the images of grains of salt seen through the naked eye, under 400× magnification, and using an electron microscope (Figure C1.1). Describe "salt" as seen through each image.

Microscopes are used in many areas of our lives. Forensic scientists solve crimes through the microscopic analysis of hair, fluids including blood, body tissues, fibres, soil, and DNA. Crop diseases and pathogens in food, water, and air can all be detected through the study of microorganisms under the microscope. Tiny defects in the metal of bridges and airplanes are found with the use of microscope technology. Diseases like malaria and tuberculosis can be prevented and treated because of information obtained through the use of microscopes.

Microscope technology even affects surgery. Today, many operations are performed using new instruments and a technology known as laparoscopic or keyhole surgery. In this procedure, the surgeon makes one to three tiny incisions, and then inserts a fibre-optic light, scalpel, and other surgical tools through a thin tube. A baton-like instrument fitted with a magnifying eyepiece with a tiny video camera provides a highly magnified view of the surgical area on a television screen. There are many benefits to laparoscopic surgery; the patient generally loses less blood, experiences less pain, has a faster recovery time, and the tiny incisions produce less scarring. This technique is used in performing knee surgery, removing gallstones, hernia operations, and a ground-breaking procedure called "closed-heart bypass surgery," in which a blocked cardiac artery is repaired using robotic and computer-assisted tools, without the need to open the chest cavity.

In this section, you will learn how our understanding of the cell and its structure and function has developed over time, and has depended on advancements in imaging technology. You will also be introduced to areas of cell research that have an impact on the daily lives of many people, whether they know it or not.

C1.1 A Window on a New World

Throughout history, people have been intrigued by the structure of living things. Our current understanding of life processes is the result of developments that date from the time of Aristotle, a Greek philosopher of the 4th century B.C. As you know from earlier studies, the inquiry process for science involves a cause-and-effect question that leads to a hypothesis, and an experiment to test the hypothesis. To know what questions to ask, a scientist must first carefully observe the system being studied. The early Greeks were primarily philosophers, preferring to think out possible answers to questions rather than testing their ideas, but Aristotle followed a pathway of accurate observation and record making, followed by reasoning and interpretation. Aristotle made careful observations and descriptions of more than 500 animal species and set up a classification system based on his observations. His approach was a fore-runner of methods used by modern scientists. It was not until the invention of the microscope, however, that scientists were able to see and begin to understand the building blocks of living things.

Early Microscopes and Microscopists

A window was opened on the microscopic world when the development of the theory of optics and the discovery of the magnifying properties of lenses allowed scientists to study objects smaller than could be seen with the human eye. It is believed that Hans and Zacharias Janssen, Dutch lens-makers, invented the microscope in about 1595, using a two-lens system of an eyepiece, or ocular lens, and an objective lens (Figure C1.2(a)). This would have been the first "compound" microscope, meaning that it made use of more than one lens to magnify objects. The Janssens' microscope had a magnifying power of approximately 20×.

By 1665, Robert Hooke in England was using a hand-made microscope (Figure C1.3) that had a three-lens system (Figure C1.2(b)). The illumination was a beam of light concentrated on the specimen by passing the light through a water-filled glass flask. In that year, Hooke published his *Micrographia* containing 38 illustrations of plant, animal, and non-living objects viewed through the microscope. Hooke was interested in gaining information about the structure of cork. It was not understood at the time why cork had its unusual properties: it was lightweight; could float on water; was firm, yet compressible under force. He examined thin slices and saw many empty chambers which he called "cells," as shown in Figure C1.4.

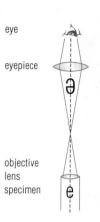

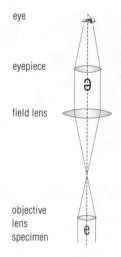

(a) A two-lens system with a single eyepiece (ocular) lens

(b) Hooke's three-lens system has two lenses in the ocular. The field lens passes light rays in a straight line to the eyepiece. This allows better conservation of light from the object.

FIGURE C1.2 Lens systems in the light microscope

FIGURE C1.3 The elegant compound microscope made for Robert Hooke in 1660

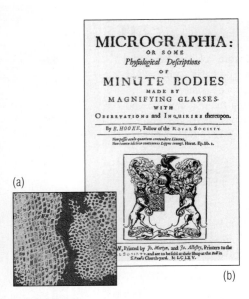

(a)

(b)

FIGURE C1.4 Hooke's drawings of cork cells (a) appeared in his *Micrographia* of 1665 (b).

re**SEARCH**

Sometimes, "scientists" are thought of as stereotyped old, eccentric brains in white lab coats. In reality, the people responsible for major scientific discoveries often have interesting and even colourful stories to their lives. Find out about the people who were involved in the development of the microscope. Write a biographical paragraph about one of these personalities. Try to capture their interests and pursuits, including but not limited to contributions to science. Begin your search at

www.pearsoned.ca/
school/science10

The cork therefore consisted primarily of air pockets surrounded by a thin mesh of fibre. He did not know then that these tiny chambers were the remnants of living cells, the simplest functional units of life.

At about the same time, a Dutch businessman, Antoni van Leeuwenhoek, using only a simple single-lens microscope rather like a magnifying glass, was the first to see the movement of different types of single cells that we now know as bacteria, sperm, and unicellular protozoa. These were the first observations of individual free-living cells surviving as independent systems. Van Leeuwenhoek made careful drawings of his discoveries and named them "animalcules." His microscopes were small, probably about the size of his palm, and the lens was held directly at the eye. This system was difficult to use. However, because of van Leeuwenhoek's skill in making the tiny lenses for his microscopes, he was able to produce higher magnifications than those of the compound microscopes of the day (up to 250×). In bright light, this allowed for clear observation of cell structure and movement. Light microscopes continue to be important instruments to the cell biologist because they allow the scientist to see the movement of living cells. Hooke and van Leeuwenhoek both recorded their observations in detail and made them available to others by publishing through the Royal Society of London.

Improvements in Lens Technology

Van Leeuwenhoek's success was mainly due to the quality of his lenses. Early compound microscopes were less efficient than van Leeuwenhoek's single lenses because the images produced by the compound microscopes were often blurry, with a halo of light around the object. These image problems were the result of the light being scattered as it passed through the different lenses. During the 18th century, a combination of lenses called an achromatic lens was developed to control the halo and improve the amount of detail that could be seen.

Skill Practice   Calculating Magnification

In Activity C2 Estimating an Object's Size with the Microscope, you will use the compound microscope to estimate the size of objects. This Skill Practice will give you the chance to review how magnification is calculated. In a modern compound microscope, the power of the objective lens and the power of the eyepiece are multiplied to give the magnifying power or **magnification** of the system. What is the magnification of a system that has a 4× objective lens and a 10× eyepiece ?

magnification = (power of objective lens) (power of eyepiece)

= (4)(10)×

= 40×

What is the magnification if the following combinations of lenses are used?

a) a 2.5× low-power objective lens and a 10× eyepiece

b) a 100× high-power objective lens and a 10× eyepiece

Inquiry Lab

Required Skills
- Initiating and Planning
- Performing and Recording
- Analyzing and Interpreting
- Communication and Teamwork

Estimating an Object's Size with the Microscope

A compound light microscope magnifies specimens. The magnification depends on the combination of lenses used. It is interesting and informative to view objects under a microscope, but it is often difficult to know the actual size of the object being observed. Magnification causes us to lose our perspective on size. In this lab, you will learn how to estimate the size of an object by comparing it with something you already know—the diameter of the **field of view**.

The Question

How can the compound microscope be used to estimate the size of microscopic specimens?

The Hypothesis

If the diameter of the field of view is known, then the size of an object can be estimated.

Materials and Equipment

compound light microscope

flat transparent metric ruler small enough to be positioned on the microscope stage

prepared slides: animal cells, plant cells, unicellular organisms

unlined paper

pencil

mathematical compass

FIGURE C1.5 Set-up for measuring the diameter of the field of view

CAUTION: Observe proper technique with the microscope and slides to ensure safe handling of equipment.

Procedure

1. Review the proper handling and use of the microscope in Student Reference 8: The Compound Light Microscope.

2. Set up your microscope and place a transparent metric ruler on the stage so that it covers about half of the stage as shown in Figure C1.5.

3. Observe the ruler under low power. The **field of view** is the entire area that you see when you look through the microscope. Move the ruler so that you are measuring the diameter (width) of the low-power field of view from left to right and set one of the millimetre divisions at the edge of the field of view as shown in Figure C1.6.

FIGURE C1.6 Move the ruler so that you can measure the diameter of the field of view. Line up a millimetre mark at the edge of the circle.

4. Create a data table in your notebook like the one below. Remember to give your table a title. Record the magnification for each power.

Field	Magnification	Field Diameter (mm)	Field Diameter (µm)
low power			
high power			

Measure the diameter of the low-power field to the nearest tenth of a millimetre. Record this measurement in the table in your notebook. Convert the diameter from millimetres to micrometres. Record in the table. Remember, 1 mm = 1000 µm.

5. You cannot measure the diameter of the high-power field of view using the procedure outlined above because it is less than one millimetre, but you can use the following ratio to calculate the field diameter under high power. This relationship between the field of view and the degree of magnification is represented in the following formula:

$$\frac{\text{high-power field diameter}}{\text{low-power field diameter}} = \frac{\text{low-power magnification}}{\text{high-power magnification}}$$

Show your work. Record the high-power field diameter in millimetres and micrometres.

6. Examine a prepared slide of an animal or plant specimen through the low- and high-power objective lenses. Draw what you see in the field of view on low power. Calculate the **scale** of your drawing by comparing the diameter of the circle in your drawing with the field diameter that you obtained in step 5. For example, if the field diameter of the low-power objective was 3 mm and the diameter of the circle on the drawing was 3 cm (30 mm), the scale of the drawing would be 10:1. Refer to Student Reference 8 for a discussion of scale drawings.

7. Estimate the size of objects you view under the microscope by comparing them with the diameter of the field of view. An organism that takes up one-half of a field of view that is 500 µm in diameter, has a size of about one-half of 500 µm, or 250 µm.

8. Obtain prepared slides of various organisms and practise estimating their lengths and/or widths. Record the information in a data table.

9. Return your microscope and slides to their proper storage locations once you have finished this activity.

Analyzing and Interpreting

1. How many times is the magnification increased when you change from the low-power to the high-power lens?

2. How many times is the field diameter decreased when you change from the low-power to the high-power lens?

Forming Conclusions

3. State how you would estimate the size of an object viewed under the high-power (40×) objective lens, if you were given the size of the field diameter, when using the low-power (4×) objective lens.

C1.1   Check and Reflect

Knowledge

1. Contrast the methods and results of Hooke and van Leeuwenhoek.

2. List ways that the investigations of Aristotle, Hooke, and van Leeuwenhoek were similar to modern scientific investigations.

3. What is the difference between a simple and a compound microscope?

4. What is the field of view when making observations through the light microscope?

5. Explain how to calculate total magnification when using a compound light microscope. Give an example.

Applications

6. Using the medium-power (10×) objective lens, a student measured the diameter of the field of view as 1.5 mm. Convert this diameter to micrometres.

7. Use the value you found in question 6 to calculate the field diameter when the student used the high-power (40×) objective lens.

8. A structure on a diagram measures 2.5 cm. The actual size of this structure is 0.5 mm. What is the scale of the diagram?

Extension

9. Using what you have learned about optics in previous science courses, research and explain the use of convex lenses in a compound light microscope.

C1.2 Development of the Cell Theory

Sometimes, scientists find that even with solid evidence to support new ideas, it is difficult to change traditional thought. Social pressure has an effect on the acceptance of scientific ideas and technological advancements. The attitudes and skills of scientific inquiry, including questioning, predicting, observing, and recording, are required to provide unbiased and factual information. Investigations must follow ethical guidelines, and results must be reproducible under controlled conditions. An example of the way that science, technology, and society are linked is found in the development of our current understanding of the way living cells function. The microscope provided the technology to explore the world of microscopic particles and organisms. It was then possible to obtain evidence for or against generally accepted opinions or theories about living things.

Spontaneous Generation

The idea that life could emerge spontaneously from non-living matter was widely accepted from the time of the Romans through to the 19th century. Even during the time of Robert Hooke and Antoni van Leeuwenhoek, it was generally accepted that to produce mice, one simply had to put sweaty underwear and husks of wheat in an open jar. After about 21 days, the sweat and husks would combine and change the husks into mice. You may find this theory amusing, but how would you explain the presence of the mice in the jar?

In 1668, Francesco Redi, an Italian physician and poet, questioned the belief that maggots appeared spontaneously from raw meat. Instead, he believed that flies laid their eggs in the meat. Redi set up an experiment to test his hypothesis. He set out flasks containing raw meat, but some were sealed, some were covered in gauze, and some were open to the air. In this way, he controlled the access of flies to the meat. Maggots were found only in the flasks that were open and accessible to flies to lay their eggs (Figure C1.7). Despite the evidence, the idea of **spontaneous generation** continued to thrive.

In an effort to prove that living things could be produced from non-living matter, in 1745, English clergyman John Needham boiled chicken broth and put it in a flask and sealed it. Everyone accepted that boiling killed micro-organisms, since boiling was a common method of removing substances that would make one ill; however, in Needham's experiment, micro-organisms still appeared. Victorious, Needham suggested there was a **life force** that produced spontaneous generation. Lazzaro Spallanzani, an Italian priest and scientist, refuted Needham's claim and instead proposed that there were micro-organisms in the air that were responsible for the new growth. He repeated Needham's experiment but drew off the air in the flask. Nothing grew in the remaining broth. Critics suggested that all Spallanzani had shown was that air was required for spontaneous generation to occur. The theory of spontaneous generation continued to be accepted.

In 1859, the French Academy of Sciences announced a contest for the best experiment to prove or disprove spontaneous generation. The French

FIGURE C1.7 In Redi's experiment, the manipulated variable was access of flies to the meat.

chemist <u>Louis Pasteur</u> submitted the following experiment in 1864. He used the work of Needham and Spallanzani with an important change. Before boiling meat broth in a flask, Pasteur heated the neck of the flask and bent it into an "S" shape, as shown in Figure C1.8. Air could reach the broth, but micro-organisms and other particles would get caught in the S-bend. Nothing grew in this broth, but if the flask were tipped so that the broth reached the S-bend in the neck, moulds would later appear. The text on page 249 is taken from a translation of hand-written notes of a speech in French given by Louis Pasteur at the *Sorbonne Scientific Soiree* on April 7, 1864.

This text allows us to review the characteristics of a scientific experiment. Pasteur controlled his experiment in that he used the same broth, the same type of flasks, and the same light and temperature conditions. All of these—broth type, flask type, light, and temperature—are the **controlled variables**. Pasteur's **manipulated variable** was the access of dust to the flask; his **responding variable** was the ability to grow mould in the broth. In the experimental series in which he manipulated the access of dust to the flask, Pasteur had an experimental **control**, a part of the experiment in which the manipulated variable is not changed in any way from its normal condition. His experimental control was the flask in which dust had normal access to the broth after boiling, with the result that mould growth occurred.

His experimental treatments were:

a) to prevent the access of dust to the broth, resulting in evidence of no growth of mould;

b) to allow access of dust to the broth very briefly, resulting in evidence of mould growth.

Pasteur (Figure C1.9) provided strong evidence that spontaneous generation did not occur, but also that micro-organisms are found in the air. His work opened new doors to microbiology, immunology, and biochemistry, and gave credibility and new importance to the processes of conducting controlled experiments, maintaining detailed records of observations, and connecting results to conclusions. On the discipline of strict experimental tests, he commented: *"Imagination should give wings to our thoughts but we always need decisive experimental proof, and when the moment comes to draw conclusions and to interpret the gathered observations, imagination must be checked and documented by the factual results of the experiment."*

FIGURE C1.9 Louis Pasteur, a French scientist who disproved the concept of spontaneous generation

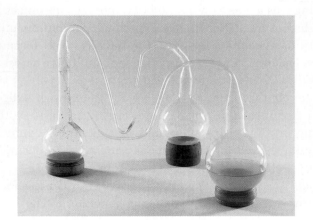

FIGURE C1.8

Examples of Pasteur's flasks that did not become contaminated. The one in the middle is sealed; the others open but with an S-bend.

Pasteur Tackles Spontaneous Generation Theory

"Now suppose I decant a portion of this infusion of organic material into a long-necked flask, such as this one. If I boil it and allow it to cool, then in a few days, it will contain fully-developed moulds or infusoria. By boiling the infusion, I destroyed any germs there might have been in the liquid, or on the walls of the flask. But as this infusion remains in contact with the air, it undergoes alteration, like all such infusions.

But now suppose I repeat this experiment, but before boiling the liquid, I place the neck of the flask over a glazier's torch, allowing it to bend and stretch, while remaining open. I then boil the liquid, and allow it to cool. Now, the liquid in this second flask will remain completely unaltered, not just for two days, or three, or four, or even a month, a year, three years, or four! For the experiment just described has already been underway that long. The liquid remains completely pure, as clear as distilled water. What, then, is the difference between the two flasks? They both contain the same liquid, they both contain air, and they are both open. Why does one undergo alteration, while the other remains unchanged? Gentlemen, the only difference is this: In the case of the first flask, the germs contained in air-borne dust can fall down the neck of the flask, reaching the liquid, where they find appropriate nourishment, and proceed to develop. In the case of the second flask, however, it is impossible, or at least very difficult for air-borne dust to enter the flask, unless the air is extremely turbulent. Where does it go instead? It falls on the curved neck of the flask. When air enters the flask in accordance with the laws of diffusion, or as a result of relatively minor changes in temperature, it enters slowly, slowly enough that all of the dust and other solid particles it carries fall before they reach the opening, or along the early portions of the curved neck.

Gentlemen, this experiment is generous in its lessons. For notice that everything in the air, with the exception of dust, may enter the flask with extreme ease, thus coming into contact with the liquid. Whatever you imagine air to contain—electricity, magnetism, ozone, and perhaps even substances as yet unknown to us—it all passes through, reaching the infusion. The one thing which can't enter easily is dust, as demonstrated by the fact that, if I shake the flask violently two or three times, the infusion will, two or three days later, be seen to contain animalcules and mould. Why? Because the rapid entry of air brought the infusion into contact with dust."

This excerpt is from a translation of notes for a speech given by Pasteur at the *Sorbonne Scientific Soirée* on April 7, 1864. This work was published in the journal *Revue des cours scientifiques de la France et de l'ètranger*, **1**(21), 23 avril 1864, 257–265. (Review of scientific studies in France and abroad, 23 April, 1864.)

Examining Pond Water

Until the late 19th century, there was a common belief that it was possible for life to spring from non-living matter. This belief in spontaneous generation arose in part because humans were unable to see the micro-organisms present in air and water. Pasteur's experiments provided strong evidence against spontaneous generation.

The Question

How many different organisms can be found in a sample of pond or aquarium water?

The Hypothesis

Write a statement predicting the variety of microscopic organisms present in samples taken at the surface, from the middle, and from the bottom of the container of pond or aquarium water provided by your teacher.

Materials and Equipment

pond or aquarium water

compound light microscope

3 glass slides and coverslips

tweezers or toothpicks

dropper

unlined paper

pencil

mathematical compass

unlined index cards

grease pencil or marker

glycerine or protoslo®

paper towel

chart paper

CAUTION: If any student in the class is taking immuno-suppressive drugs, micro-organisms should not be cultured in the classroom. Wash your hands at the beginning and end of this lab activity. Disinfect droppers, slides, and tweezers with a 10% bleach solution at the end of the activity. Dispose of equipment and clean your work area as directed by your teacher.

Procedure

1. Review Student Reference 8: The Compound Light Microscope, for the technique of making a wet mount slide.

2. Make 3 wet mount slides from the pond or aquarium water provided by your teacher. Take one sample from near the surface of the water, one from the middle, and one from the bottom of the container. Try to incorporate a small amount of debris in each wet mount. Label each slide with the part of the container from which it came.

3. Set up your microscope, and using the low-power objective, carefully examine each slide for signs of living organisms. Examine the organisms using the low-power objective lens.

4. Use the medium- and high-power objectives to study the organisms in more detail. Use the fine adjustment knob to bring the organisms into focus. Organisms may be swimming in and out of your field of view.

5. Add a drop of glycerine or protoslo® to the slide at the edge of the coverslip and draw it under the coverslip to slow down the movement of the organisms.

6. Draw a diagram of each of the organisms that you see. Place one diagram on each index card. Label any structures you recognize and record which part of the container the organism came from.

Analyzing and Interpreting

1. Did you detect differences between the 3 slides of samples taken from different parts of the container of water? What might this tell you about the presence of life at different levels in the container?

2. How many different types of organisms did you find? Do you think the variety of organisms may change over time if the water were to stay untouched for several days? Explain your answer.

Forming Conclusions

3. Write a statement to explain the diversity and quantity of microbes found in the pond or aquarium water.

Extending

4. How might an examination of pond water contribute to a consideration of the idea of spontaneous generation? Provide a reasonable argument that life cannot arise from non-living matter.

5. Using the diagrams on your index cards, sort the organisms by common characteristics. Determine your own criteria for classification. Compare your criteria and groupings with those of other lab groups. What similarities and differences were there in the classification systems? What similarities and differences were there in the organisms observed?

The Cell Theory

It was not until the 1830s, with the improvements in lens technology and the increased number of observations made by scientists in several countries, that the importance of the cell as the functional unit of life was recognized. In 1833, Scottish microscopist Robert Brown identified an important cell structure, the **nucleus**, in his study of orchids. Brown saw an opaque granular spot within the cell. Others before Brown had seen these spots, but he was the first to recognize that this cell structure must have some importance for cell function. Examine Figure C1.10 to see a picture of what Brown saw.

In 1838, a German professor of botany, M. J. Schleiden (Figure C1.11 (a)), observed that all plants were composed of cells and he proposed that the nucleus was in fact the structure responsible for the development of the remainder of the cell. Schleiden discussed his work with a friend, Theodor Schwann (Figure C1.11(b)), who was studying animal physiology. Schwann believed that there must be similarities between plant and animal tissue. When Schwann searched for the opaque spots in animal tissue, he found structures that resembled the cells that botanists were studying in plant tissue, and the nucleus structure that Brown and Schleiden had identified. He used his new-found information to put forward what has since been called the cell theory. Schwann and Schleiden proposed that all plants and animals were composed of cells and that the cell was the basic unit of all organisms. In 1859, the cell theory was further extended by Rudolf Virchow's statement that all cells arise only from pre-existing cells.

info BIT

Many of the organisms you observed in pond water are called "Protozoans." They are neither animals nor plants but belong to a separate kingdom, the Kingdom Protista. Some protozoans move by using a whip-like structure called a flagellum. Others move by using cilia, small hair-like projections along the sides of the cell that beat like tiny oars projecting them through the water. The amoeba, a jelly-like protozoan, moves by projecting a "false foot" or pseudopodium. Other protozoans are spore-like and have no method of locomotion.

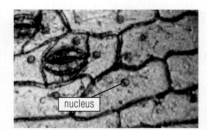

FIGURE C1.10 The nucleus is clearly shown in each cell in this photograph taken through Robert Brown's microscope. This preparation was made in a repeat of Brown's experiment and shows the view that he would have seen through his rather primitive instrument. (approx. ×200)

(a) Matthias Schleiden

(b) Theodor Schwann

FIGURE C1.11 Schleiden and Schwann proposed the cell theory in 1839 as a result of observations of plant and animal specimens through the microscope.

re**SEARCH**

Research other scientific contributions made by Louis Pasteur beyond his experiment to refute spontaneous generation. Begin your search at www.pearsoned.ca/school/science10

The cell theory states:

> - All living things are made up of one or more cells and the materials produced by these cells.
> - All life functions take place in cells, making them the smallest unit of life.
> - All cells are produced from pre-existing cells through the process of cell division.

We now know that the cell theory applies to all living things regardless of their size, shape, or the number of cells involved. Subcellular particles like viruses and prions fall into a category that is neither living nor non-living although they may exhibit certain characteristics of living cells. Evidence in support of the cell theory also came from Louis Pasteur's 1864 experiment to investigate the concept of spontaneous generation in micro-organisms, which was discussed earlier in this section. The cell theory has since become the cornerstone of the study of biology.

C1.2   Check and Reflect

Knowledge

1. Explain how the use of microscopes led to the development of the cell theory.

2. What is meant by spontaneous generation? Provide examples.

3. State the three components of the cell theory.

4. Describe the work of Louis Pasteur in refuting the theory of spontaneous generation.

5. The development of the cell theory from Hooke to Schleiden and Schwann was based on the very careful work of the scientists involved. What are the key components of scientific inquiry that are required for work to receive acknowledgement by the scientific community and society in general?

Applications

6. Create a visual representation to compare spontaneous generation and the cell theory.

7. Make a timeline of the experiments concerning spontaneous generation from Redi to Pasteur. Choose an appropriate format to present or display your work.

8. If straw is added to water, in a few days micro-organisms can be observed. Write one short paragraph in support of and another against the concept of spontaneous generation under these conditions.

9. Assume you are a scientist with the Canadian Space Agency analyzing data received from a distant space probe. There is a question about whether a certain material found on a new planet is living or not. List the characteristics that you will look for in your analysis to determine whether to classify the new substance as living.

Extension

10. Consider your findings from the examination of pond water. Design an experiment to test whether water temperature has an effect on the movement of the organisms.

C1.3 Developments in Imaging Technology and Staining Techniques

Light microscopes magnify cells through the use of one or more curved lenses and a light source. The compound light microscope is an important magnifying tool; research light microscopes have a maximum magnification of 1000–2000×. However, magnification is not the only factor that affects what can be seen through the microscope. Two other important aspects are contrast and resolution. You may have noticed when you examined organisms in your pond water preparation that it can be difficult to observe all of the cell structures because the organisms themselves are pale or transparent, and their background is equally pale. Any cell structures that you were able to distinguish were visible to you because more light was absorbed by that structure and it therefore appeared darker than its surroundings. The slight shading difference between components of the cell may be enough to distinguish them from one another, but not enough to observe subtle variations. As in art or photography, contrast is essential in order to see detail. Artists use lines, shading, and colour to create the illusion of three-dimensional images as seen in Figure C1.12.

The variation created by shading and colour allows the eye to focus on different aspects of the picture and to see depth. In the same way, scientists have perfected techniques to provide greater ability to see magnified objects in more detail. These technological advances allowed science to move ahead. Processes of innovation continue to meet the new challenges of inquiring minds and of new problems to be solved.

Contrast

When light passes directly through cells in what is called **brightfield** microscopy, most of the cells seen are colourless. Scientists quickly discovered that manipulating the light source could alter the contrast between structures in the cell and improve the image. Experiments with stains or

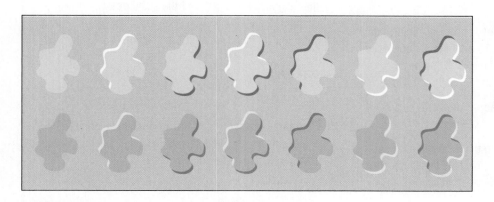

FIGURE C1.12 These images demonstrate the effect of different levels of contrast.

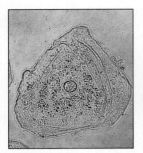 

(a) Unstained (approx. ×1500) (b) Stained (approx. ×1500)

FIGURE C1.13 A comparison of human cheek cells as seen through the light microscope

colouring agents showed that particular stains attached to particular parts of the cell, improving the contrast between internal structures and producing better images. Staining techniques can be as simple as adding methylene blue or iodine stain to a specimen. Chemical preservatives "fix" the cells and allow more complex staining procedures. We now know that the staining properties depend on the chemical composition of the structures in the cell. One disadvantage of these techniques is that fixation and staining kill the cells, so it is not possible to view living tissue. Figures C1.13 and C1.14 (on page 255) show the detail to be seen when different stains are used.

Activity C4
QuickLab

Student Reference 8

Staining Cells

Purpose

To use a staining technique to provide contrast in order to observe plant cells

> CAUTION: Handle glass slides and coverslips carefully. Remember that biological stains also stain clothing. Wear disposable gloves during the activity. Wash your hands at the end of the lab activity.

Materials and Equipment

compound light microscope

4 glass slides

4 coverslips

flat wooden toothpicks

stains: iodine, and methylene blue

droppers

paper towel or tissues

yellow or white onion

Procedure

1. Review Student Reference 8 and follow the directions when making a wet mount preparation, drawing a scientific diagram, and calculating the scale of a scientific diagram.

2. Remove the dry, outermost layers from an onion and use a thin, transparent layer of the onion to get one layer of cells. You may stain the onion with iodine or with methylene blue. Prepare a wet mount slide.

3. Under low magnification, observe the cells you have stained. Draw and label what you see in the field of view.

4. Examine your slide further using the medium- and high-power objectives. What are you now able to see that you could not see with the low-power magnification?

5. Estimate the size of the onion cells by comparing them with the diameter of the field of view that you determined in Activity C2. Draw and label the cells. Indicate the magnification used and the scale on each drawing. Compare your preparation of onion cells with that of a student who has used a different stain.

Questions

1. Describe the cells present in your preparations.

2. Compare what you saw in the unstained pond water organisms to what you saw in these stained cells. What advantages are gained by using stains?

3. What differences are observed at the different magnifications? Describe them.

4. What was the effect of using a different stain on the onion cells?

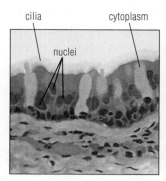
cilia   cytoplasm
nuclei

(a) The epithelial cells have cilia on the surface. Their nuclei (plural for nucleus) stain more deeply purple than their cytoplasm. (approx. ×120)

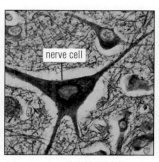
nerve cell

(b) The nerve cell stains dark brown. (approx. ×120)

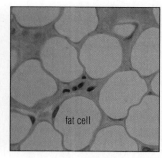
cytoplasmic banding

(c) Cells in one type of muscle tissue show a clear pattern of banding in the cytoplasm. (approx. ×250)

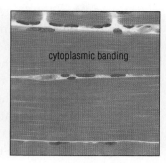
fat cell

(d) Cells that contain fat droplets in living tissue appear colourless in stained preparations because the fixation process dissolves the lipids. (approx. ×120)

FIGURE C1.14 Staining techniques have been developed to highlight certain parts of cells seen through the light microscope.

Resolution

Magnification is an important component of the microscope but it is not enough simply to magnify an object. There are other aspects that are important to image formation. Hold two pencils or pens close together upright directly in front of you. Make a mental note of the detail that you observe. Now move the pencils to one side. If you kept looking straight ahead, you could probably still see the pencils from the corner of your eyes. However, you probably could not see the images of two pencils distinctly. **Resolution**, or **resolving power**, is the ability to distinguish between two structures that are very close together. You get better resolution when you look at something directly in front of you than when you look from the corner of your eyes. Resolution is an important aspect of any image—an image should have high resolution if it is to show its details.

Look at the images in Figure C1.15. The images are of the same object but the clarity is very different. The first one is fuzzy and difficult to decipher. You may even be able to see individual dots or squares of colour, called pixels. Pixels are used in creating the images you see on your computer monitor or from a digital camera. The second one provides a more clearly defined view. In this image, the pixels are smaller and there are more of them per unit area than in the first one. The second image has a higher resolution and you can see the details more clearly.

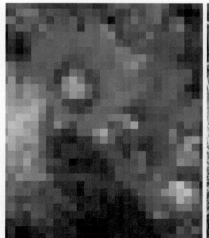

FIGURE C1.15 The resolution of the image can make a great difference in the amount of detail seen.

The human eye can distinguish images of objects that are 0.1 mm (1×10^{-4} m) or larger. A microscope must provide the capability to see anything smaller than this, or to see individual objects that might be closer together than 0.1 mm. Regardless of the level of magnification, the clarity of images depends on the resolving power of the microscope. The efficiency of the light microscope is limited because as light is focussed into smaller and smaller diameters, the image becomes blurred. Because light microscopes depend on white light illumination, and even with the improvements in lens making made during the 19th century, the resolving power of the light microscope is limited by the wavelength of light. Points closer together than one-half the wavelength of light will not be seen as separate. The limit of resolution of a standard light microscope is 0.2 μm (2×10^{-7} m).

Contrast Enhancing Techniques and Fluorescence Microscopy

As science progresses, it tends to reach the limits of what can be accomplished with available technology and so pushes the limits of that technology. If innovations in technology are not available, progress may be limited. Some structures in cells can change the speed and direction of light passing through them more than others can. In the first half of the 20th century, techniques were developed to improve images by altering the light path through the specimen. These included darkfield, phase contrast, and differential interference contrast illumination. Figures C1.16(a)–(d) show images of *Paramecium* under different systems of illumination. Fluorescence microscopy was developed and gave information about molecules on the cell surface. With this technique, fluorescent substances that

FIGURE C1.16 Images of *Paramecium* seen through the light microscope under different systems of illumination

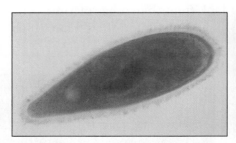

(a) Brightfield illumination (approx. ×400)

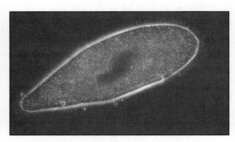

(b) Darkfield illumination (approx. ×400)

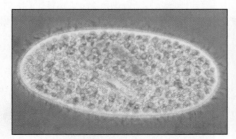

(c) Phase contrast illumination (approx. ×250)

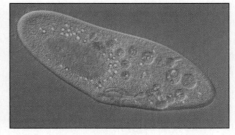

(d) Differential interference contrast illumination (approx. ×250)

were attached to molecules in tissues could be located. When the specimen was subjected to ultraviolet light, the fluorescent molecule emitted light of a different wavelength, causing it to glow. Depending on the fluorescent substance being used, the glow could be yellow, orange, or green. In 1941, J. H. Coons used antibody molecules labelled with a fluorescent substance to show that antigens were on the surface of cells. The molecules that determine blood groups in humans are examples of cell surface antigens.

Confocal Technology

Since the 1980s, the use of laser beams and computers has made it possible to view living, transparent cells in three dimensions through the compound light microscope. In the **confocal microscope**, a laser concentrates light onto a specimen. The reflection is passed through a tiny opening called the confocal pinhole and reaches an electronic detector that converts the light into an image. Only the light returning from an exact plane of focus can pass through the pinhole to the detector because, as Figure C1.17 shows, out of focus light is blocked by the edges of the pinhole. Therefore, every image formed is of a very thin section through the specimen. Each image is stored in a computer and images of many sections are combined to produce a three-dimensional image that can be viewed on a computer monitor. Figure C1.18 shows a worm that is used in research under confocal laser scanning microscopy.

*re*SEARCH

Find out more about the various types of contrast enhancing techniques used to improve the detail of microscopic images. Begin your search at

www.pearsoned.ca/ school/science10

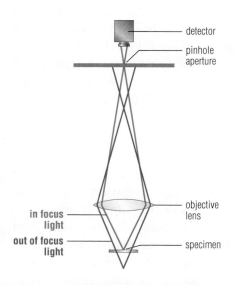

FIGURE C1.17 In a confocal system for the light microscope, only light from any part of the specimen that is in focus will pass through the pinhole to the electronic detector. Out of focus light will be blocked by the sides of the pinhole and not reach the detector. This produces the effect of a thin section with high resolution. Many sections can be combined to produce a three-dimensional image.

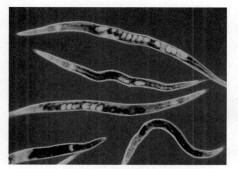

FIGURE C1.18

A nematode worm viewed under confocal laser scanning microscopy. The round internal structures are eggs. (approx. ×80)

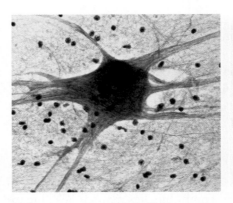

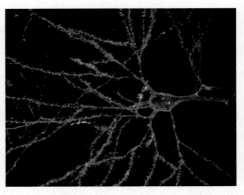

FIGURE C1.19 Nerve cells under different forms of illumination

(a) A motor neuron under brightfield illumination (approx. ×250)

(b) A brain neuron fluorescing under ultraviolet light, seen through confocal laser scanning microscopy

Figures C1.19(a) and C1.19(b) compare images of nerve cells obtained using brightfield illumination and confocal technology. Under brightfield illumination the processes called dendrites that bring information to the cell body of the motor neuron merely appear fibrous, but, using confocal technology, the finely branched three-dimensional structure of the brain neuron dendrites can be seen.

The confocal microscope gives opportunities for the use of other techniques to study the cell. Among these is the use of the green fluorescent protein (GFP), first found in a luminescent jellyfish called *Aequorea victoria*, shown on the opening pages of this unit. This protein glows a bright green when exposed to ultraviolet light, in the same way that fluorescent paint glows in the presence of black light. Scientists have been able to attach GFP to certain parts of cells that they wish to study, almost like a tiny lamp! While staining methods kill the cell, the use of fluorescence microscopy with GFP allows the study of living cells in a way that was not possible prior to current technology.

Electron Microscopy

In the first half of the 20th century, as scientists struggled to improve light microscopes, researchers were also looking for ways to improve the resolution of imaging systems. They turned to forms of illumination other than light. In the 1930s at the University of Toronto, James Hillier and Albert Prebus developed the first functional **electron microscope**. An electron microscope uses a beam of electrons instead of a light wave and is able to produce images that provide fine detail. The image is formed by the absorption or scattering of the electron beam because **electron-dense** materials do not let the electrons pass through. Focussing is done by adjustment of electromagnets instead of by movement of glass lenses.

The **Transmission Electron Microscope (TEM)** depends on a beam of electrons passed through a very thin section of fixed and stained tissue embedded in plastic. The electrons that pass through the specimen fall on a fluorescent screen (see Figure C1.20) or on photographic film and black-and-white photographs are produced.

The TEM may operate at magnifications of up to 1 500 000× and has a resolution for biological specimens of about 2.5 nm. This is an improvement of one-hundred-times over the detail shown in the light microscope. Some aspects of image formation in the light and electron microscopes are compared in Table C1.1.

TABLE C1.1 Comparison of Light and Transmission Electron Microscopes

Feature	Light Microscope	Electron Microscope
source	lamp or laser	electron gun
radiation	UV or visible light	electron beam
lenses	curved glass surfaces	electromagnets
receiver	eye or digital image	fluorescent screen or digital image
focus	up and down movement of lenses	adjustment of magnetic field

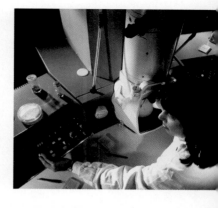

FIGURE C1.20 Electrons travelling down the microscope column pass through the specimen and an image forms on a fluorescent screen at the bottom of the column. The scientist views the image on the screen.

The **Scanning Electron Microscope (SEM)** was developed in the 1940s. This technology gives information about the surface features of a specimen. Specimens are fixed and covered with an electron-dense material like gold, which reflects electrons. While the investigator scans the surface of the specimen, the electrons bouncing off the surface are picked up by a sensor and a three-dimensional image is formed. Figure C1.21 shows an SEM view of *Paramecium*. The SEM operates up to a magnification of 300 000× and has a resolution of 20 nm. The image may be viewed on a screen or captured on computer and viewed on a monitor. The investigator can move the specimen in three dimensions with coarse and fine adjustments or the sample stage may be computer controlled (Figure C1.22).

Photographs taken through either scanning or transmission electron microscopes are called electron micrographs. They provide a detailed view of the cell's surface texture, the shape and size of the particles in the cell, and how the materials are arranged. Electron microscopes provided more detailed images of cell structures that were already known, such as the nuclear envelope and Golgi apparatus. Electron micrographs also showed

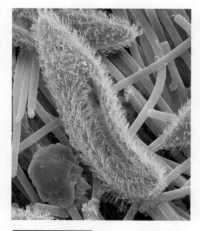

FIGURE C1.21 The surface of *Paramecium* is covered by cilia, short hair-like structures, used for swimming and wafting food into the groove-like mouth. (approx. ×300)

FIGURE C1.22 The electron beam coming down the microscope column sweeps over the gold-coated specimen and a three-dimensional image is formed.

reSEARCH

Investigate recent developments in microscopy. Begin your search at

www.pearsoned.ca/ school/science10

structural arrangements, such as the two layers making up the cell membrane, that may have been suggested by experiment but had never been seen before. Scientists were able to view cells at magnifications of 500 000 times and more. Figure C1.23 shows some of the detail available in electron micrographs.

One of the drawbacks of the TEM is the difficulty of building up a three-dimensional picture of the cell from very thin sections. The detail is impressive but the area covered by each image is very small. Also, the specimens are fixed, and therefore no longer living, and the microscope must be operated in a vacuum. Recently, a form of the SEM has been developed that allows the use of live material.

Each type of microscopy has its important place in cell research. Depending on the investigation, biologists may use different types of microscopes, staining technologies, and contrast enhancing technologies to explore cell structure and function.

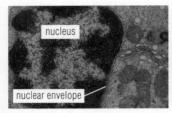
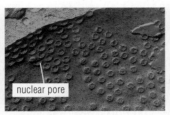
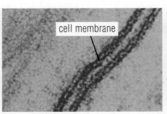

(a) A transmission electron micrograph of a white blood cell shows detail of the nucleus and nuclear envelope, and mitochondria in the cytoplasm. (approx. ×49 000)

(b) A transmission electron micrograph prepared by freeze fracture which splits the structure into two parts, shows detail of the pores in the nuclear envelope. (approx. ×90 000)

(c) In a transmission electron micrograph, the cell membrane can be seen as two thin dark lines separated by a clear layer in two adjacent cells. (approx. ×25 000)

(d) In a scanning electron micrograph, the surface features of cells can be seen, as in the cilia shown here. (approx. ×11 000)

FIGURE C1.23 Transmission and scanning electron micrographs show different detail of cells.

C1.3 Check and Reflect

Knowledge

1. What are the advantages and disadvantages of using a light microscope?

2. Explain why investigators need to stain cells.

3. When would there be a need for using an electron microscope?

4. Describe ways in which a confocal microscope works differently from the light microscope you use in your science lab.

5. What is fluorescence microscopy? Give an example of a study using fluorescence microscopy.

6. Describe similarities in the ways in which a light microscope and a TEM work.

Applications

7. Choose two advances in imaging technology and explain how they have led directly to a new understanding of cell structure and function.

8. Create a poster or PowerPoint presentation showing a variety of microscopes and/or techniques. Explain why each would be useful for a particular study.

C1.4 Cell Research at the Molecular Level

As a result of new technology, research on cells has led to major break-throughs in medicine and industry. There are many areas in which research is now at the molecular level. The recently developed Scanning Tunnelling Microscope (STM) and Atomic Force Microscope (AFM) are able to reveal even smaller structures than the transmission or scanning electron microscopes can. Scanning tunnelling microscopes and atomic force microscopes allow scientists to produce images of molecules, and, therefore, to improve their understanding of the structure and function of molecules within the cell. New interpretations are possible when observations made by earlier scientists are combined with modern chemical and computer methods. Figure C1.24 contrasts (a) a model of DNA superimposed on an actual cell with (b) an STM image of DNA in which the yellow peaks represent the ridges of the DNA helix.

Gene Mapping

In less than 200 years since Brown observed the nucleus in the orchid, scientists have made great progress in understanding the cell. Microscopists in the 19th century saw chromosomes in the nuclei of cells. Geneticists showed that material in the chromosomes was associated with patterns of inheritance. Chemists, biochemists, and microbiologists showed that the genetic material in the chromosomes was DNA and that DNA has a structure that enables it to direct all other activities in the cell. Improvements in techniques of molecular biology allowed mapping of the human genome to begin. In 2001, a draft of the complete genetic map of humans was published in the results of the Human Genome Project.

Gene mapping of many plant and animal species is progressing. The mapping of DNA sequences in genes involves many techniques, including breaking cells down to release their DNA, using chemical techniques to make many copies of the DNA, and finding the sequence of chemical subunits through computer analysis. DNA analysis and gene mapping open up our understanding of the way different parts of the genetic material work together. This knowledge may one day allow scientists to manage disease-causing abnormalities; for example, cancer research is benefiting from a deeper understanding of the molecular functioning of the cell.

Gene mapping of crop plants may result in new varieties that are resistant to pests or can thrive in drought conditions. However, concerns have been raised about resistance being incorporated into weed species as well. Ethical issues have also been raised about ways in which knowledge and procedures related to DNA and gene mapping may be used in the future. The technology available sets limits to the science that can be done, and in a similar way, the needs and issues in society must provide guidelines for how science is conducted.

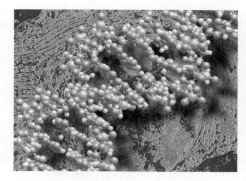

(a) Computer artwork of a DNA molecule superimposed on a TEM of a human cell

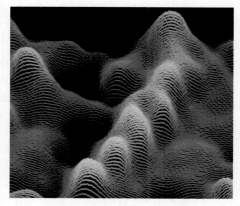

(b) An STM image of a double-stranded DNA molecule (approx. ×2 000 000)

FIGURE C1.24 The genetic material can be represented in several different ways.

Extracting DNA from Pea Soup

> **CAUTION: Wash your hands at the end of the lab activity.**

In animal and plant cells, the genetic material, DNA, is found in the nuclei. The DNA is arranged into structures called chromosomes in which it is bound to protein molecules. The first step in gene mapping is to extract the DNA from cells. This is a simpler process than you might expect.

Purpose

To extract DNA, the genetic material of life, from pea soup

Materials and Equipment

50 mL dried green split peas

250 mL water

250 mL 90% rubbing alcohol chilled in a freezer and kept on ice

salt

meat tenderizer

liquid dishwashing detergent

250-mL beaker

blender

strainer

tablespoon or 25-mL measuring spoon

25 × 200 mm test tube

dissecting probe, crochet hook, or bamboo skewer

Procedure

1. Place approximately 50 mL of dried green split peas, a pinch of salt, and about 100 mL of water in a blender. Blend for about 20 s. Blending helps to separate the pea cells.

2. Pour the mixture through a strainer into a beaker. Discard the material left in the strainer. Measure the amount in the beaker and add about one-sixth of that amount of water to the beaker.

3. Add about 1 tablespoon of liquid dishwashing detergent to the beaker and mix. Allow the mixture to sit for 10 min.

4. Pour the mixture into the 25 × 200 mm test tube until about one-third full and add a pinch of meat tenderizer to the test tube.

5. Slowly and carefully, pour chilled rubbing alcohol down the side of the test tube to form a clear layer on the top of the mixture. Use about the same volume of alcohol as the volume of pea mixture in the test tube.

6. With a dissecting probe, crochet hook, or bamboo skewer, gently pull out the stringy material that forms in the alcohol layer. Spool this material onto the holder with a twirling motion. This is DNA from the green split peas!

Questions

1. Why do you think you added detergent in step 3?

2. The meat tenderizer is a protein called an enzyme that cuts other proteins away from the DNA. What does a meat tenderizer do when you use it on steak?

3. Write the recipe for extracting DNA from liver or onion cells.

infoBIT

A group of diseases appear to be linked not to bacteria or viruses but to specific proteins called "prions" that act as infectious agents. These proteins spread spongiform encephalopathies, which produce large vacuoles or empty pockets in the brain. Bovine spongiform encephalopathy (BSE) results from prion infection and is commonly known as "mad cow disease."

Cell Communication

An **open system** is one that must interact with its environment to maintain its existence. Cells are efficient open systems able to carry on all of the life processes. To function efficiently, cells must interact with their environment and with each other. For cell-to-cell communication, messenger molecules from other cells travel through the bloodstream and attach to specialized molecules on the surface of the target cell. These molecules, known as receptors, may change in shape and trigger a chain reaction to carry the message to the proper location inside the cell. You might think of how the structure of your front door key, fitting into the shape of the door lock, allows you to pass the barrier of your front door and bring in information about your day to your family inside the house. Techniques that show binding of substances to cell membranes, such as the fluorescent antibody technique, allow diagnosis of diseases carried by viruses, bacteria, and protozoans, as well as diseases of the immune system.

Decision-Making Investigation

Gene Mapping: Opportunity or Risk?

The Issue

How would you weigh the risks and benefits associated with one type of cell research at the molecular level?

Background Information

In April 2002, a Swiss agrochemical company announced that, in collaboration with Chinese researchers, they had determined the gene sequences of two commonly grown rice species. Canadian physicist Gane Ka-Shu Wong, working at the University of Washington, was involved in this ground-breaking discovery. The importance of mapping the genes of crop plants should not be underestimated. There are major agricultural and societal implications. For instance, with approximately 50 000 genes in rice (as compared to 30 000–40 000 in humans), plant breeders may be able to create "designer" strains. They may be able to produce plants that are drought or pest resistant. Since rice is very vulnerable to environmental factors, especially drought, resistant strains would ensure better crops even in poor conditions. Farmers would be able to plant crops that produce higher yields on less land. We may be able to develop grains that are of higher nutritional value than those that are currently grown. When you consider the numbers of people worldwide who consume and depend on rice as a main staple food, the possibilities for plant breeding and agriculture are enormous. Rice is closely related to other cereal grains including wheat, barley, and corn. Cracking the genetic code for these plants cannot be far off.

Some scientists are concerned about using information on the genetic make-up of crop plants to selectively modify or change species. They argue that concentrating on only a few varieties of rice, for instance, will reduce diversity and impact ecosystems. New diseases or environmental conditions could wipe out all of the monoculture crops. Examples of this risk have been seen in monocultures produced by older forms of plant breeding; for example, much of the corn crop in the United States was wiped out by a blight-causing fungus in 1970. They also suggest that farmers may be forced to pay inflated prices to obtain the genetically modified seed in order to remain competitive. Some argue that we still do not know if there are significant health concerns to be considered when dealing with genetically modified crops. The possibility that the attractive qualities of disease resistance or environmental tolerance could be transferred into weed species remains a concern.

Analyze and Evaluate

1. State a definition of a "risk" and a "benefit" as it pertains to the issue of cell research at the molecular level. Share your definitions with your classmates. Modify your definitions based on the discussion.

2. In chart form, identify the risks and benefits of gene mapping of crop plants. Be sure that the ideas you list fit with your definitions of "risk" and "benefit."

3. Susan R. McCouch, an associate professor of plant breeding at Cornell University, stated in a press release in 1996 that "Land mass is actually shrinking in Asia, and as a society, we've increased rice yields per acre about as much as we could. We can't increase the land, so we have to do something. Fertilization is no longer an effective way to boost yield—it's plateaued. So, instead of boosting land mass—which we can't do—we're manipulating the plant's genetics." (Reference: www.news.cornell.edu/releases/Nov96/Rice.Nature.bpf.html) Use electronic and print resources to research the current applications of gene mapping of crop plants in Canada and around the world. Begin your search at www.pearsoned.ca/school/science10.

4. There are many different perspectives surrounding the issue of gene mapping. Assume that you are chosen to represent one of these perspectives at an international conference on genome mapping. Identify the risks and benefits from the point of view of one of the following conference delegates, and present your views.
   - President of an agrochemical company
   - Traditional farmer
   - Organic farmer
   - United Nations Food and Agriculture Organization (FAO) representative
   - President of the Canadian Medical Association
   - Consumer of commercial and agricultural goods
   - Federal Agriculture Minister
   - Canadian International Development Agency (CIDA) representative

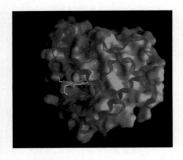

FIGURE C1.25 Computer-generated model of the protein myoglobin, the oxygen-storage compound in muscles, showing the binding site for oxygen

Three-Dimensional Structure of Molecules

Molecules inside the cell or on its surface often act as switches to control cell activity. The structure of a molecule, such as whether it is coiled or straight or whether it is made of repeated units, may determine how the molecule will function. **X-ray crystallography** uses X-rays, special sensors that analyze patterns of X-ray scattering, and computer technology to allow scientists to learn the details of molecular structure to help them understand how the molecules work. This technique was essential to studies that led to the model of the DNA molecule, and our understanding of how DNA functions in the cell. Researchers are now studying the three-dimensional shape of normally functioning and defective proteins to find the parts of the molecules that control the activity of the proteins. One of the first molecules to be studied this way was myoglobin, the protein that stores oxygen in muscles. Figure C1.25 shows a three-dimensional model of myoglobin.

Green Fluorescent Protein (GFP) Technology and Genetic Studies

re SEARCH

Investigate the types of technology used in studies of the three-dimensional structure of molecules. Begin your search at

www.pearsoned.ca/school/science10

Huntington's, Alzheimer's, and Parkinson's diseases are degenerative diseases of the nervous system. GFP technology, which was discussed on page 258, is being used in the study of these diseases at the molecular level. It is known that in affected individuals, abnormal proteins clump together and inhibit the normal functioning of cells. The use of GFP technology is allowing scientists to compare proteins in living cells of healthy tissue and in tissue that is affected by one of these diseases. In time, this information may lead to effective methods of treatment and change the lives of people living with these conditions.

C1.4 Check and Reflect

Knowledge

1. Describe one example of cell research in industry or medicine.

2. List three of the technologies used in X-ray crystallography.

3. What is one advantage of using GFP technology in cell studies?

Application

4. Draw a chart like the one below in your notebook or journal and list the risks and benefits of DNA and gene mapping. Share your responses with a partner.

Risks	Benefits

Extensions

5. Take a stand for or against further research into the genome and indicate your reasoning, based on your list from question 4. Write a paragraph defending your position.

6. What additional information would you like to have on the issue of gene mapping that would help to make the issue clearer?

7. Using the Internet, report on new knowledge or treatments in an area of medicine or industry that have resulted from cell research.

8. Molecular research has enhanced an area of science called biochemistry. Find out about the types of job opportunities in this field.

Knowledge

1. Describe the method of inquiry used by Aristotle and compare it with the methods used by other philosophers of his time.

2. The microscope invented by Hans and Zacharias Janssen is considered to be a "compound microscope." Why?

3. State what you consider to be Robert Hooke's contribution to microscopy and the understanding of the cell.

4. Briefly describe the advantages of laparoscopic surgery and how it depends on microscopy.

5. Explain what is meant by a "control" in an experiment.

6. Sketch the parts of Pasteur's experiment on spontaneous generation. Explain how this experiment provides evidence against spontaneous generation.

7. What similarities and differences did you see among pond water organisms?

8. Describe how to make a wet mount slide.

9. State the three main points of the cell theory and attribute each one to the scientist(s) responsible.

10. Outline two methods for improving the contrast in a specimen viewed under the microscope.

11. What are the advantages of confocal laser technology applied to microscopy?

12. What is X-ray crystallography? How is this technique used to advance cell research?

13. What is GFP and how is it used in genetic studies?

Applications

14. A microscope has a low-power magnification of 100×, a high-power magnification of 450×, and a low-power field diameter of 1800 μm. What is the high-power field diameter in micrometres?

15. If the minimum image size the human eye can detect is 0.1 mm, what is the minimum magnification needed to make an object measuring 1 μm visible? Explain how you determine your answer.

16. You have determined the field size of the low- and high-power objective lenses. How could you calculate the field diameter of the medium-power lens? Include an equation in your answer.

17. What important lesson about canning foods can be drawn from the experiments to disprove spontaneous generation?

18. You have just isolated a new microbe from your aquarium. Which type of microscopy would be used to determine:
    a) its movement?
    b) if this specific strain is present in other aquariums?
    c) if there are internal sub-structures?
    d) if there are special surface structures on the cell?

19. How might your life be different if the microscope had never been invented?

20. Identify the most significant thing you learned from this section, and one area that you would like to know more about.

Extensions

21. Using your diagrams of the organisms observed in the pond water, and electronic and print resources, try to identify each microbe.

22. Although the design of the compound light microscope in use today is essentially the same as that developed 350 years ago, Hooke would be surprised at the detail that we can now see. List advances in technology and techniques that have improved the images seen through the light microscope. Explain how each advance has led to an increase in our understanding of the cell.

23. Find a current newspaper or magazine article on an area of cellular research. Paste it in your notebook and describe the risks and benefits associated with this area of research.

Living systems are dependent upon the functioning of cell structures and organelles.

Key Concepts

In this section, you will learn about the following key concepts:

- cellular structures and functions and technological applications
- active and passive transport of matter
- relationship between cell size and shape, and surface area to volume ratio
- use of explanatory and visual models in science

Learning Outcomes

When you have completed this section, you will be able to:

- compare passive transport of matter by diffusion and osmosis with active transport in terms of the particle model of matter, concentration gradients, equilibrium, and protein carrier molecules
- use models to explain and visualize complex processes like diffusion and osmosis, endo- and exocytosis, and the role of cell membrane in these processes
- describe the cell as a functioning open system that acquires nutrients, excretes waste, and exchanges matter and energy
- identify the structure and describe, in general terms, the function of the cell membrane, nucleus, lysosome, vacuole, mitochondrion, endoplasmic reticulum, Golgi apparatus, ribosomes, chloroplast, and cell wall, where present, of plant and animal cells
- compare the structure, chemical composition, and function of plant and animal cells, and describe the complementary nature of the structure and function of plant and animal cells
- describe the role of the cell membrane in maintaining equilibrium while exchanging matter
- describe how knowledge about semi-permeable membranes, diffusion, and osmosis is applied
- describe cell size and shape as they relate to surface area to volume ratio, and explain how that ratio limits cell size

FIGURE C2.1 Medieval cities were enclosed by walls to limit entry and exit of people and materials.

In an open system such as the cell in which matter and energy are exchanged with the environment, interaction with the surroundings is crucial to provide needed materials, produce what is required, and ship out any excess. Consider the analogy of a medieval town or Old West fort that had enclosures for protection. Here, the enclosures were built so that threats would be kept out, but needed supplies and materials could get in. In addition, anything produced inside the enclosure could be transported outside the walls. Contrast this with a closed system or with an isolated system in which there is no interaction with the outside.

Today's towns and cities do not have elaborate enclosures, but they continue to operate as open systems in much the same way. City Hall is the hub of a town's activities where decisions are made that will affect the growth, economy, and living conditions of the town. Factories and processing plants depend on raw materials brought in from mining, drilling, or agriculture. The products may be in the form of food or materials to support the growth and operation of the community. Some products may be in greater supply than the town needs and these are shipped to other places. Other products may be brought in from other communities. The movement of substances into, around, and out of the town is accomplished using trucks, trains, airplanes, or other means. Services like hospitals, grocery stores, schools, police and fire departments, and sanitary dumps are all necessary parts of the town. Sometimes, it may be necessary to bring in specialists from the outside. The success of the town is based on its ability to maintain a positive environment to sustain itself. The cell is an open system much like the town described here. The components of the cell are called **organelles**, meaning little organs, and the functioning of these structures maintains the life processes of the cell.

This section considers the cell organelles and how they carry out the functions necessary for the cell to survive. Models will be used to represent and explain these processes and some of their applications in medicine and industry.

C 2.1 The Cell as an Efficient, Open System

Any efficient open **system** has many parts that work together for a particular goal. Each part has its own function. Cells, the basic units of life, maintain the life processes within specialized structures called organelles, each with its own function to perform. Cells are highly efficient, open systems that are able to exchange matter and energy with their surroundings. Cells carry on all of the life processes including:

- intake of nutrients
- movement
- growth
- response to stimuli
- exchange of gases
- waste removal
- reproduction

A cell must work constantly to maintain a fine balance among the different life processes in order to be efficient and to conserve energy. A good starting point for understanding the functions of the cell is to identify the major structures involved in each of the cell's activities. Turn to page 270, Figure C2.10, to see diagrams that show the components of a typical animal cell and a typical plant cell. Table C2.1, below, provides photomicrographs of cell structures, as seen through the light and electron microscopes, and briefly describes their functions.

Turn to page 270, Figure C2.10

TABLE C2.1   Cell Structures and Their Functions

Cell Structure and Function	Photomicrograph
The **cell membrane** is a protective barrier for the cell: allows the transport of needed materials into the cell and waste materials out; is important for cell interaction and communication, and for recognition of molecules.	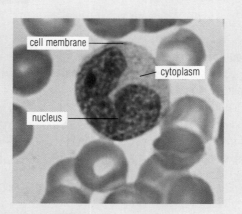
The **nucleus** is the organelle that contains DNA, the genetic material of the cell, and directs all cellular activities. The nucleus is surrounded by the nuclear envelope, which has pores to allow the transport of materials.	**FIGURE C2.2** The cell membrane, nucleus, and cytoplasm in a human white blood cell seen through the light microscope. (approx. ×300)
The **cytoplasm** is a gel-like substance inside the cell membrane: contains the nutrients required by the cell to carry on the life processes. The organelles are suspended in the cytoplasm. The physical nature of the cytoplasm allows for the movement of organelles and molecules within the cell, referred to as **cytoplasmic streaming**.	

The cell wall is found in plants, bacteria, some **protists**, and fungi: the cell wall is a rigid frame around the cell that provides strength and support.

Chloroplasts are found only in plants and some protists. They contain chlorophyll that produces a green colour; are the sites of photosynthesis, the process which uses energy from the Sun to convert carbon dioxide and water into sugars for the plant's use and storage. The equation for photosynthesis is:

$$6H_2O_{(l)} + 6CO_{2(g)} \xrightarrow{\text{chlorophyll + light}} C_6H_{12}O_{6(aq)} + 6O_{2(g)}$$

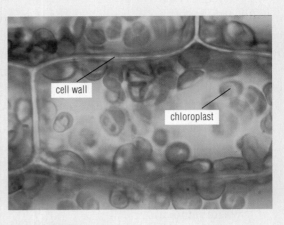

FIGURE C2.3   The cell wall and chloroplasts in a plant cell seen through the light microscope. (approx. $\times 2000$)

Vacuoles and **vesicles** are membrane-bound structures that serve to store nutrients, products of secretion, and fats, depending on the tissue type. In plants, the central vacuole stores water for the cell. In plant cells, when fluids enter, the central vacuole swells, increasing the **turgor pressure** and causing the cell to become firm or **turgid**. Vesicles transport substances throughout the cell.

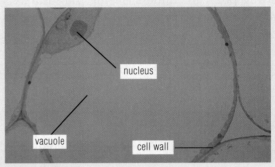

FIGURE C2.4   Vacuoles may store materials or fluids. Transmission electron micrograph (approx. $\times 24\,000$)

The **endoplasmic reticulum** is a series of interconnected small tubes that branch from the nuclear envelope. Materials can be transported through these tubes. **Rough endoplasmic reticulum** has ribosomes attached to it and is associated with protein synthesis; **smooth endoplasmic reticulum** is associated with fat and oil production.

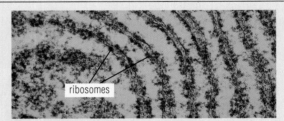

FIGURE C2.5   (a) Rough endoplasmic reticulum has ribosomes attached to it. Transmission electron micrograph (approx. $\times 95\,000$)

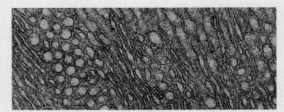

(b) Smooth endoplasmic reticulum does not have ribosomes. Transmission electron micrograph (approx. $\times 130\,000$)

All of the cell organelles, except the ribosomes, are enclosed by a membrane.

Cell Structure and Function	Photomicrograph

Ribosomes are dense-looking granules formed of two parts. They may be attached to the endoplasmic reticulum or free in the cytoplasm. Ribosomes are the sites where amino acids are assembled into proteins in the process of **protein synthesis.**

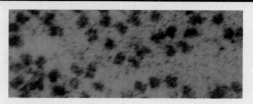

FIGURE C2.6 Whether free or attached, ribosomes are the sites of protein synthesis. Transmission electron micrograph (approx. ×340 000)

Lysosomes are membrane-bound sacs in the cell in which digestion can go on. The various roles of lysosomes include defence against invading bacteria, destruction of damaged cell organelles, and controlled digestion of certain tissues during development.

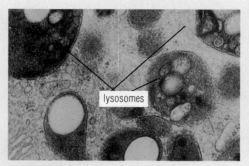

lysosomes

FIGURE C2.7 Lysosomes contain strong chemicals that digest molecules within cells. Transmission electron micrograph (approx. ×29 000)

The **Golgi apparatus** is composed of flat, disc-shaped sacs involved in secretion. The Golgi receives substances from the endoplasmic reticulum and packages them for transport out of the cell.

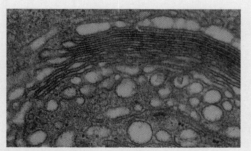

FIGURE C2.8 The Golgi apparatus modifies molecules and prepares them for transport. Transmission electron micrograph (approx. ×110 000)

Mitochondria are rod-like structures where reactions occur to convert chemical energy in sugars into energy the cell can use. This process is called **cellular respiration**. The chemical equation for cellular respiration is:

$$C_6H_{12}O_{6(aq)} + 6O_{2(g)} \longrightarrow$$
$$6CO_{2(g)} + 6H_2O_{(l)} + energy$$

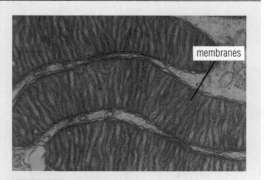

membranes

FIGURE C2.9 Mitochondria have an inner and an outer membrane and a liquid matrix. Transmission electron micrograph (approx. ×130 000)

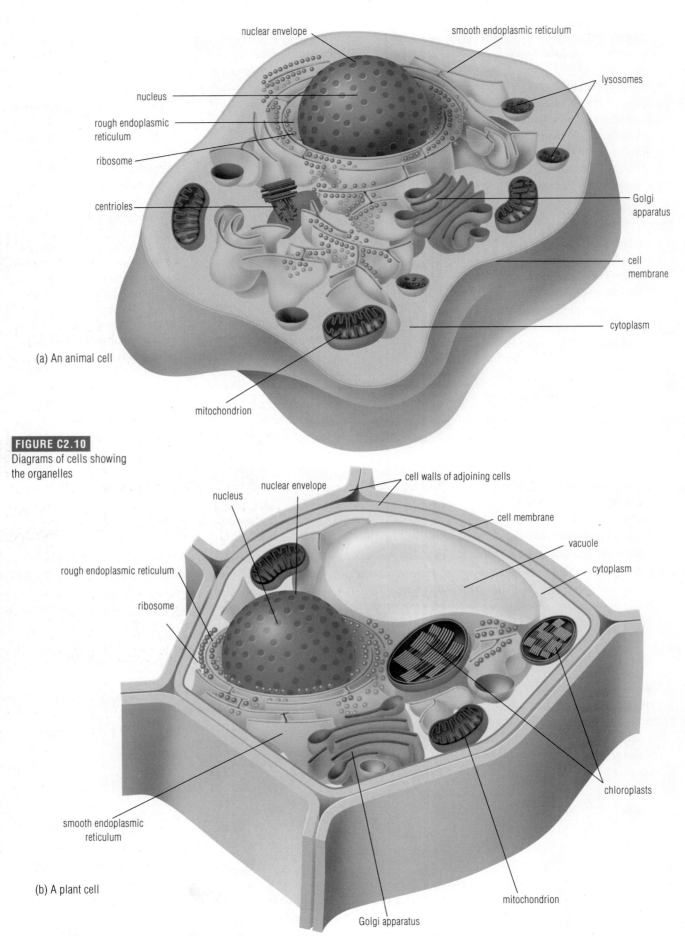

nuclear envelope

smooth endoplasmic reticulum

nucleus

lysosomes

rough endoplasmic reticulum

ribosome

centrioles

Golgi apparatus

cell membrane

cytoplasm

(a) An animal cell

mitochondrion

FIGURE C2.10
Diagrams of cells showing the organelles

nuclear envelope

cell walls of adjoining cells

nucleus

cell membrane

vacuole

rough endoplasmic reticulum

cytoplasm

ribosome

chloroplasts

smooth endoplasmic reticulum

mitochondrion

(b) A plant cell

Golgi apparatus

Inquiry Lab

Required Skills
- Initiating and Planning
- Performing and Recording
- Analyzing and Interpreting
- Communication and Teamwork

Comparing Structures in Plant and Animal Cells

The Question

Are there differences between plant and animal cells that are observable through the light microscope?

The Hypothesis

State a hypothesis concerning the differences between plant and animal cells that you will be able to see through the light microscope.

Materials and Equipment

compound light microscope

prepared slides: plant and animal cells

CAUTION: To avoid cuts, use proper technique when handling the microscope and glass slides.

Procedure

1. Set up the compound light microscope. Refer to Student Reference 8: The Compound Light Microscope.

2. Observe the prepared slides of both animal cells and plant cells. Use the low-, medium-, and high-power objective lenses.

3. Draw and label one plant and one animal cell. Use the magnification where the whole cell is visible and the cell parts are clearest. Use the technique you learned in Activity C2 to estimate the actual size of the cells. For each diagram indicate the magnification and the scale of the drawing.

Analyzing and Interpreting

1. Make a chart of the cell structures that you were able to see in the animal cells and the plant cells.

2. Compare the following cell structures in animal and plant cells: cell membrane; nucleus; cytoplasm.

3. Describe the differences in the image you see when using the high-power objective lens instead of the low-power objective lens.

Forming Conclusions

4. Use your observations to reach conclusions about the differences between plant and animal cells that are visible through the light microscope.

Applying and Connecting

5. Suggest reasons why certain organelles shown in Figures C2.10(a) and C2.10(b) are not visible through the light microscope.

6. Use Table C2.1 and Figures C2.10(a) and C2.10(b) to review the structure and function of these cell organelles that you could not see through the light microscope.

In Activity C7, you would have observed that some of the cell organelles are visible when you use the compound light microscope, but some are not. The electron microscope provides images of these structures, and inferences can be made about their function. Figures C2.4–C2.9 on pages 268–269 show electron micrographs of the structures that cannot be seen in detail through a compound light microscope.

The Chemical Composition of Cell Structures

The major elements making up the structure of plant and animal cells are carbon, hydrogen, oxygen, and nitrogen. These are organized into four major organic compounds: **lipids** like fats and oils; **carbohydrates** such as sugars, starches, and cellulose; **protein**, for example, muscle fibre; and **nucleic acids** such as DNA, the genetic material. Water is the other major compound found in all plant and animal cells. Many other substances are dissolved in water, so we say that water is the **solvent** that provides the environment for all biological reactions inside and outside cells. In addition, there are substances called **trace elements** present in tiny amounts that are essential for the health of the cell. Magnesium (Mg), zinc (Zn), manganese (Mn), and iron (Fe) are examples of trace elements.

There are similarities and differences between plant and animal cells in terms of chemical composition. Similarities are:

- animal and plant cells have a cell membrane and an internal network of fibres, the **cytoskeleton**, made up of proteins and lipids;
- animal and plant cells have genetic material (DNA) made up of sugars, nitrogen bases, and phosphate.

Some of the differences are:

- animal cells have **centrioles**, which are involved in cell division; plant cells do not have centrioles.
- plant cells have a rigid cell wall made of cellulose, a type of carbohydrate, whereas animal cells do not have cell walls;
- plant cells contain a specialized chemical compound called **chlorophyll**, a pigment that makes photosynthesis possible;
- some animal cells have other specialized compounds; for example, hemoglobin in red blood cells and cholesterol in other cells;
- some plant cells store energy in the form of starch or oils, for example, cornstarch and canola oil; for energy storage, animal cells may contain glycogen, another form of carbohydrate, or lipids in the form of fats.
- plant cells have a large central vacuole; vacuoles and vesicles in animal cells tend to be small.

A Model of the Cell Membrane

The electron microscope has provided very detailed images of the cell membrane that allowed scientists to gain a better understanding of the role of the membrane in maintaining **equilibrium** or balance inside the cell. The cell needs to keep this equilibrium while allowing some substances in and keeping others out. The membrane, sometimes referred to as the **plasma membrane**, consists of a **phospholipid bilayer**. This is a double layer of lipids that each have a phosphate group attached. The phosphates face out into the watery fluids on either side of the membrane while the lipids face toward each other in the inner part of the membrane. A technique used to split the two layers, with the aid of electron microscopy, positively identified the structure of the cell membrane. Figure C2.12(a) shows the two layers of the cell membrane separated and laid side by side, as seen through the electron microscope. Proteins are suspended in the phospholipid bilayer, some attaching to the outside of the cell membrane, some attaching to the inside of the cell membrane, and some running through the membrane. Some surface proteins have sugar molecules attached. The currently accepted structure of the cell membrane was suggested in 1972 and is referred to as the **fluid-mosaic model**. A mosaic is a collection of different substances held together

FIGURE C2.11 A Roman mosaic floor has small pieces of tile held together by a common material. Scientists suggest that the cell membrane has some aspects similar to a mosaic.

by a common material (Figure C2.11). From above, the cell membrane looks like a mosaic of tiles (the proteins) held together by a fluid, flowing grout (the lipid bilayer). The model is shown in Figure C2.12(b). Each part of the membrane has a role to play in allowing the movement of nutrients, gases, and wastes into and out of the cell. These roles will be discussed in section C2.2.

The cell membrane is a protective barrier between the environment and the cell's fragile contents. Inside the cell membrane is the cytoplasm, a gel-like substance that contains primarily water, salts, dissolved gases, dissolved nutrients, and organelles. The cytoplasm is often compared to a gelatin dessert with one important difference: the cytoplasm moves and flows inside the cell membrane.

re SEARCH

Investigate how sugar molecules attached to membrane proteins may enable cells to recognize foreign substances or to interact with each other. Begin your search at

www.pearsoned.ca/school/science10

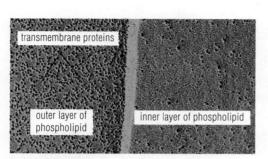

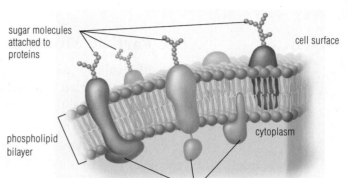

FIGURE C2.12 (a) A TEM showing that the cell membrane can be split into inner and outer layers laid side by side. Most proteins stay with the outer layer of phospholipids. (approx. ×200 000)

(b) The fluid-mosaic model of the cell membrane

C2.1 Check and Reflect

Knowledge

1. What is meant by a system?

2. Describe what makes the cell an open system.

3. Draw a diagram of a plant cell. Label the organelles and state the function of each.

4. Using your own words, describe the appearance and state the function of the following cell structures:
   a) cell membrane
   b) vacuoles
   c) mitochondria
   d) chloroplasts

5. Identify the organelle associated with the following life processes: intake of nutrients; exchange of gases; removal of wastes.

6. What are trace elements in the cell?

7. List three similarities and three differences in the chemical composition of plant and animal cells.

Applications

8. Construct a chart showing the organelles in a cell and identify a human organ that performs the same or similar function in the body as a whole.

9. Consider what happens to the human body if an organ fails. What would happen if one of the cell organelles failed? In a short paragraph, provide the reasoning for your prediction.

10. Compare the structure and function of an animal cell and a plant cell.

Extensions

11. Create a concept map to show the relationships between the organelles.

12. Create a three-dimensional model of a cell using any materials of your choice. Use your knowledge to attempt to make the organelles as correct to scale as possible.

C 2.2 The Role of the Cell Membrane in Transport

The transport of gases, nutrients, and wastes into and out of the cell is essential for the cell's survival. The cell membrane is the organelle responsible for transport. The substances that enter and leave the cell may be ions or molecules or, in some cases, micro-organisms or other cells. In a physical sense, all of these substances can be regarded as particles, and their behaviour can be examined with reference to the particle model of matter.

The Particle Model of Matter

You will recall the particle model of matter, which helps us to explain the nature of matter, from your studies in previous grades. We can use this model to help us understand the process of transport in a cell. The particle model has four main points:

1. All matter is made of particles but the particles in different substances may be different in size and composition.

2. The particles of matter are constantly moving or vibrating; particles move least in solids and most in gases. Adding or taking away energy will affect the movement of particles.

3. The particles of matter are attracted to one another or are bonded together.

4. Particles have spaces between them that are smallest in solids, except for ice, and greatest in gases. The spaces may be occupied by the particles of other substances.

As you learn about the transport of material in cells in this section, try to relate to the particle model of matter to help your understanding of the different types of transport.

Minds On ... Diffusion

Try this in your class.

1. Spread out through the classroom.

2. Have one student draw a map of the location of each person or group of people on the board.

3. Have another student, standing in one corner of the room, open a sealed package of coffee or a sealed bag of microwaved popcorn.

4. Have individuals indicate when they smell the coffee or popcorn by raising their hands. Record the order of students' signals on the map.

Questions

1. Using the particle model of matter, explain what has happened and why. Be as specific as possible.

2. Refer to Figure C2.13. Use the particle model to explain what has happened in the Petri dish.

3. List the similarities and differences between the coffee or popcorn aroma in the room and the food colouring in the Petri dish.

Diffusion

Roasted coffee contains as many as 800 flavour compounds, which may vaporize, releasing aroma molecules into the air when a fresh package of coffee is opened. The process you observed with the coffee demonstrates **diffusion**, the natural movement of particles from an area of high concentration to an area of low concentration. The place where the coffee was opened had many aroma particles. Since these particles are in constant motion, some of them are able to move into the spaces between the particles of the air, spreading out until they are equally spaced throughout the room. This process may take a few seconds or continue for a longer period of time. The end result is a state of equilibrium, in which the particles are still moving but maintain an overall balanced, even distribution. Figure C2.13 shows diffusion in the liquid state. The coloured liquid will eventually spread evenly throughout. The **rate of diffusion** can be increased by adding energy and increasing molecular movement, for example, by stirring or heating, but the process of diffusion will continue even in the absence of added energy.

Diffusion also occurs in cells. As discussed earlier, water is a major component in plant and animal cells. It is the solvent that provides the environment for all biological reactions. Diffusion of water or **solutes** can occur across a cell membrane if there is a difference between the concentrations of water or solutes on either side of the membrane, or within the cytoplasm if there is a concentration difference between areas of the cytoplasm. This difference between the concentrations is called a concentration gradient. The **concentration gradient** determines the direction in which water or solutes will move. In the cell, the cell membrane is the gatekeeper trying to maintain equilibrium of particles on either side.

Movement of material by the process of diffusion is considered to be **passive transport** because no added energy is required for it to occur. The energy inherent in the particles themselves is sufficient for the movement along the concentration gradient to occur.

The essential things for the cell are to allow needed substances to enter, to keep other substances outside, and to maintain substances at an equilibrium that is favourable to the life processes. The cell membrane is considered to be **selectively permeable** because it allows certain particles to pass through it, but not all particles. The membranes used in desalination and water treatment, discussed earlier in this unit, mimic the natural functioning of the cell membrane. Membranes that do this are called **semi-permeable** membranes. Generally, the passage of materials through the cell membrane is determined by the size of the molecules, their charge, and whether they are soluble in lipids. Particles that are too large will not get through. Only particles that are soluble in lipids or that are small enough to pass through the pores of the cell membrane will diffuse. Carbon dioxide, a waste product of cells, leaves the cell by diffusion because the concentration of the gas inside the cell is greater than its concentration outside the cell. Living cells require oxygen, a gas that is usually in higher concentration outside the cell. Oxygen diffuses across the cell membrane into the cell. In general, particles move from an area of high concentration to an area where their concentration is lower.

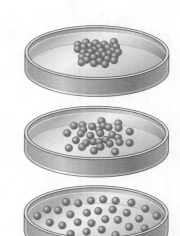

FIGURE C2.13 The movement of particles in a liquid will result in an even distribution.

*info***BIT**

The particle model states that the particles of a gas have more energy and move more rapidly than the particles of a liquid. In addition, the particles of a gas have larger spaces between them than the particles of a liquid. Therefore, diffusion will occur more quickly in a gas than in a liquid.

Movement across a Semi-Permeable Membrane

The Question

What happens when a model cell containing starch is placed in water containing iodine?

The Hypothesis

State a hypothesis based on what you know about semi-permeable membranes.

Materials and Equipment

zipper lock plastic bag
500-mL beaker
cornstarch solution prepared by your teacher
iodine tincture in a dropper bottle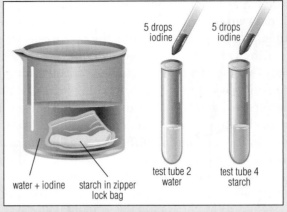
test tube rack
4 test tubes
1 dropper
10-mL graduated cylinder or graduated pipette

FIGURE C2.14 The experimental set-up for steps 3–5

Labels: 5 drops iodine; 5 drops iodine; water + iodine; starch in zipper lock bag; test tube 2 water; test tube 4 starch

Procedure

1. Add approximately 200 mL of tap water and one dropperful of iodine tincture to the 500-mL beaker.

2. Half fill a zipper lock plastic bag with tap water and seal. Observe the bag to be sure that it does not leak by tipping it upside down and checking for openings.

3. When you are sure that the bag is leak-proof, empty the water and add starch solution so that it fills half of the bag. Remove as much air as possible, seal the bag, and rinse it thoroughly with tap water. Place the bag in the beaker of water containing iodine tincture. Set aside for 20–30 minutes.

4. In the meantime, set up four clean test tubes in a test tube rack. Add 2.5 mL of water to test tubes 1 and 2, and 2.5 mL of starch solution to test tubes 3 and 4.

5. Add 5 drops of iodine tincture to test tube 2 containing water and to test tube 4 containing starch solution. See Figure C2.14.

6. Record your observations for the four test tubes.

7. Return to the 500-mL beaker and observe the starch solution in the bag.

8. Record your observations.

Analyzing and Interpreting

1. What is the result of adding iodine tincture to water (test tube 2) and to starch (test tube 4)? What can you infer from these results?

2. What is the reason for having test tubes 1 and 3 in the activity?

3. Describe the colour changes that result from placing the plastic bag containing starch into the beaker of water plus iodine. Which substance was able to pass through the plastic bag? Write a short paragraph to explain your results.

4. Consider the 'tightness' of the bag at the beginning and end of the experiment. What does this indicate about the volume of solution inside the bag at the end of the experiment? What substance is causing this change in volume? Explain your observations.

Forming Conclusions

5. Did the results of the experiment support your hypothesis? State a conclusion.

Concentration Gradients

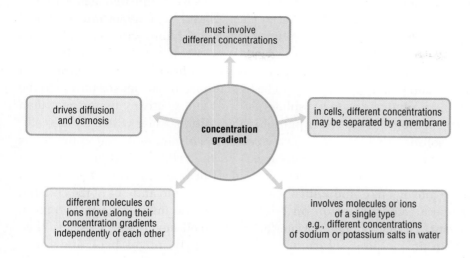

Figure C2.15 shows the concepts related to a concentration gradient. The operation of a concentration gradient can be demonstrated by using a plastic bag containing cornstarch solution as a model for a cell and cell membrane. The plastic has pores of a particular size that allow ions and small molecules to pass through, but prevent large particles such as starch molecules from passing. If iodine ions are in higher concentration outside the bag than inside, they will move along their concentration gradient into the bag. The passage of the iodine ion from the solution outside the bag into the starch solution is indicated by a change in colour of the cornstarch solution. Water also can move down its concentration gradient into the bag, as is indicated by the change in volume of solution inside the bag. The starch molecules cannot move along their concentration gradient because they are prevented from leaving the bag by the semi-permeable plastic membrane.

Osmosis

Because the cell is an open system, it always responds to the conditions of its environment. If there is a concentration gradient across the cell membrane but the solute molecules are not able to pass through, there will be a net movement of water molecules through the cell membrane. Water molecules move along their concentration gradient from an area of high water concentration to an area of lower water concentration (Figure C2.16). The diffusion of water across the cell membrane is called **osmosis**; it is another example of passive transport.

*info***BIT**

The ancient Egyptians, Greeks, and Aztecs used honey as a medicine to promote the healing of wounds. Until recently it was believed that honey's antibacterial properties were due to its high sugar content. However, natural honey kills bacteria three times more effectively than an artificial sugar solution of the same concentration; this new evidence suggests other active ingredients are present in this traditional medicine.

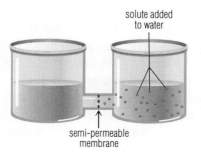
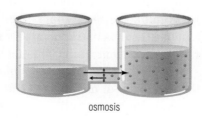

solute added to water

semi-permeable membrane

osmosis

FIGURE C2.16 Osmosis is the movement of water through a membrane in response to its concentration gradient. The membrane is not permeable to the solute.

(a) Hypertonic
The concentration of solutes outside is higher than it is inside the cell.

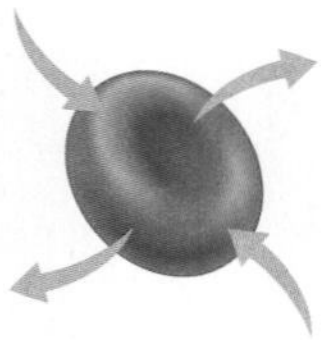

(b) Isotonic
The concentration of solutes outside the cell is equal to that inside the cell.

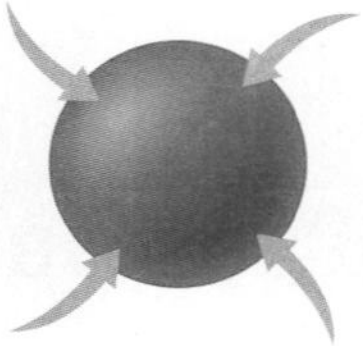

(c) Hypotonic
The concentration of solutes outside is lower than it is inside the cell.

FIGURE C2.17 The movement of water molecules, when a cell is placed in solutions that are hypertonic, isotonic, and hypotonic to the cell contents, results in changes in cell shape.

To predict the direction in which a net movement of water will occur, we need to compare the solute concentration. A solution that has a higher concentration of solutes than that in a cell is said to be **hypertonic** ("hyper" means over) to the cell. This solution has more solute particles and, therefore, relatively less water than the cell contents. If the cell is put into this solution, water will leave the cell. A solution that has a lower concentration of solutes than that in a cell is said to be **hypotonic** ("hypo" means under) to the cell. This solution has fewer solute particles and relatively more water than the cell contents. If the cell is put into this solution, water will enter the cell.

A solution that has the same concentration of solutes as that in the cell is said to be **isotonic** ("iso" means equal) to the cell. If a cell is put into an isotonic solution, there is no net movement of water molecules. There will still be movement of individual water molecules into and out of the cell, but the overall concentration on both sides of the membrane will remain constant. The movement of water across the cell membrane is so easy that, even in an isotonic solution, water constantly moves back and forth. Figure C2.17 shows the response of an animal cell to three different conditions in the environment. In a plant cell, the maximum volume is determined by the rigid cell wall. The tendency of water to move into the plant cell creates a pressure, called turgor pressure, that acts to support the plant's structure. Figures C3.13 on page 309 and C3.21 on page 320 show some of the effects of turgor pressure in plants.

Facilitated Diffusion

Only substances that are soluble in lipids can pass through the lipid bilayer by diffusion. Substances that are soluble in water but not in lipids need some way of crossing the cell membrane. The protein part of the membrane is involved. **Channel proteins** create pores or channels through which small water-soluble particles are able to move. These small molecules move in response to the concentration gradient. **Carrier proteins** have the ability to attach to larger molecules that are not able to diffuse across the membrane. The carrier protein changes shape and physically moves the molecule across the membrane and into the cell. Once the molecule has been transported, the protein returns to its original shape. This process is called **facilitated diffusion**, because the movement is in response to the concentration gradient but needs the presence of the protein facilitator. These two forms of protein-mediated transport are examples of passive transport, because no added energy is needed for the process to occur.

Active Transport

At times, transport by way of a protein carrier in the cell membrane requires energy input because, in some cases, it is necessary for the cell to move particles against the concentration gradient, from an area of low concentration to an area of high concentration. This method is called **active transport**. It may be necessary for the concentration of materials such as nutrients inside the cell or for the expulsion of materials even though they are at a higher concentration on the outside of the cell. The carrier proteins work almost as a pump to move molecules or ions across the membrane. This is like swimming upstream. It is very difficult and requires energy.

Unlike the passive processes of diffusion, osmosis, and facilitated diffusion, which do not require energy, active transport requires energy from the cell to move materials against the concentration gradient. The energy needed is produced in the mitochondria through the process of cellular respiration and comes from a substance called **adenosine triphosphate** or **ATP**. A series of chemical reactions occurs, first in the cytoplasm and then in the mitochondria, to break down glucose and produce the ATP. A comparison of diffusion, facilitated diffusion, and active transport is shown in Figure C2.18.

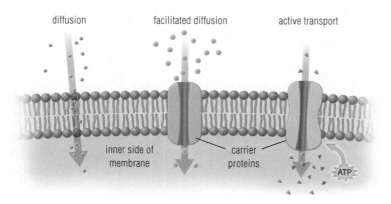

FIGURE C2.18 A comparison of the processes of diffusion, facilitated diffusion, and active transport

Skill Practice   Linking Conclusions to Hypotheses

In any science inquiry activity, you will follow a series of steps from an initial question to the formation of a conclusion. This Skill Practice gives you the opportunity to review the skills needed to perform these steps.

A student was asked an initial question. Why do vegetables like carrots and celery become crispy when placed in a container of water?

1. State a hypothesis to answer this question.

The student designed an experiment to investigate the question above. The experimental design used potato slices of the same initial mass placed in salt solutions of various concentrations. After a standard time period, the mass of each slice was obtained and the percent change in mass was calculated. Figure C2.19 shows the graph of the data obtained in the experiment.

2. a) If the data were analyzed, what would a zero percent change in mass indicate? What could you infer if you obtained this result?

   b) What would a positive percent change in mass indicate? What could you infer if you obtained this result?

c) What would a negative percent change in mass indicate? What could you infer if you obtained this result?

3. Interpret the graph of Percent Change in Mass of Potato Slices vs. Concentration of Salt Solution shown in Figure C2.19, and draw inferences from the data.

4. State a conclusion about the problem of vegetable crispiness and whether your hypothesis was accepted or rejected.

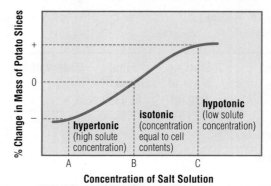

FIGURE C2.19 Graph of change in mass versus concentration

The Incredible Egg

A hen's egg is a very large cell. This cell has the nucleus attached to a food source, the yolk. The egg white or albumen surrounds the yolk and contributes materials to the growing chick. A very thin membrane surrounds the yolk and albumen. You can see the colourless membrane when you carefully crack an egg and peel away the shell. The membrane allows oxygen to get to the chick and moves carbon dioxide out of the egg. These gases are able to get to the membrane through more than 7000 tiny pores in the eggshell. When eggs are laid, they are covered with a thin mucous layer to prevent water loss. Eggs sold in stores have a mineral oil coating for the same reason.

Purpose

To observe the movement of materials into and out of a hen's egg

Materials and Equipment

one egg—shell dissolved

distilled water

10% salt solution

two 250-mL beakers

top-loading or pan balance (measuring in grams (g))

plastic spoon

paper towel

CAUTION: Wear gloves when handling the eggs. Wash your hands at the beginning and end of this activity.

Procedure

1. Set up a data table similar to the table below in your notebook. Remember to give your table a title.

Step	Starting Mass of Egg (g)	Final Mass of Egg (g)	Observations
Submerge in 10% salt solution			
Submerge in distilled water			

2. Obtain a hen's egg prepared by your teacher. The eggs are in distilled water but were previously placed in a weak acetic acid solution to dissolve the shell. Carefully remove the egg with the spoon and pat dry with a paper towel. Record the mass of the egg and your observations of the egg at the start of the activity in your table.

3. Submerge the egg in a beaker containing a 10% salt solution. Allow the egg to sit for 8 minutes.

4. Carefully remove the egg with the spoon and rinse it under running water. Pat dry with a paper towel and record the final mass of the egg after treatment with the salt solution. Record any changes that you observe in the egg due to submerging in the salt solution.

5. Submerge the egg in a beaker of distilled water for 15 minutes. The starting mass of the egg for this section will be the same as the final mass for the previous section. Record this mass in your table.

6. Carefully remove the egg with the spoon and rinse it under running water. Pat dry with a paper towel and record the mass of the egg and any changes that you observe in the egg due to submerging it in distilled water.

7. Dispose of the egg as indicated by your teacher.

Questions

1. In a short paragraph explain what happened to the egg when it was placed in the salt solution. Include the appearance and mass of the egg following this step.

2. Explain what happened to the egg after it was placed in the distilled water for 15 minutes.

3. Draw a diagram to show the movement of substances across the membrane of the egg in the two experimental treatments.

4. Use the particle theory and your understanding of concentration gradients to explain the indirect evidence of osmosis provided by this experiment.

5. Explain why water was able to move across the membrane but salt was not.

You can use a hen's egg to demonstrate osmosis, the movement of water in response to its concentration gradient. When an egg is immersed in an acidic solution the shell will dissolve, leaving the membrane intact. If the shell-less egg is placed in a 10% salt solution, water will leave the egg by osmosis and the mass of the egg will decrease. If the egg is transferred to distilled water, the concentration gradient will be reversed. Water will enter the cell through the membrane and the mass of the egg will increase.

Endocytosis and Exocytosis

In some cases, molecules that need to be taken in by the cell, or secreted from it, are too large to pass across the cell membrane, even with the help of protein carriers. In these cases, the cell has another option—to use vesicles, sacs that surround the large particle and contain it. These sacs are similar to vacuoles in structure, but are usually small and temporary. When an amoeba, for example, comes upon a food particle, it engulfs the particle by folding pseudopods around it. A vesicle forms around the particle and the cell membrane pinches off around it so that the vesicle is inside the cell. This process is called **endocytosis** (Figure C2.20).

Similar steps, but in the reverse order, occur when the cell must rid itself of large waste particles, or when a secretory cell releases product molecules. A vesicle surrounds the particle, then moves to the plasma membrane and fuses with it. The vesicle then ruptures, releasing its contents into the surroundings, as shown in Figure C2.21. This process of secretion is called **exocytosis**. Both exocytosis and endocytosis require energy from ATP for the rearrangement of the cell membrane.

*re*SEARCH

You may be interested in researching some aspects of endocytosis:

Phagocytosis: a form of endocytosis that occurs in specialized cells and involves the ingestion of large particles (e.g., bacteria) within a vacuole. The bacterium is destroyed by enzymes that enter the vacuole.

Pinocytosis: a form of endocytosis that occurs in almost all cells. The cells engulf minute molecules and ions in the environment.

Receptor-mediated endocytosis: receptor proteins bring specific molecules into the cell by endocytosis.

Begin your search at

www.pearsoned.ca/school/science10

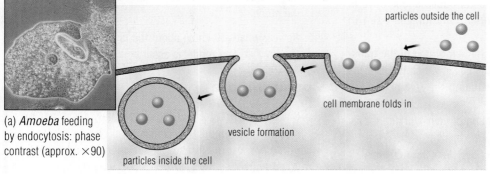

FIGURE C2.20 The process of endocytosis

(a) *Amoeba* feeding by endocytosis: phase contrast (approx. ×90)

particles outside the cell

cell membrane folds in

vesicle formation

particles inside the cell

(b) Particles are brought into the cell by the folding-in of the cell membrane to form a vacuole or vesicle.

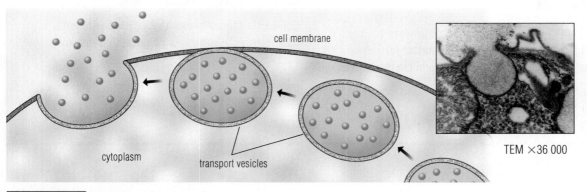

cell membrane

cytoplasm

transport vesicles

TEM ×36 000

FIGURE C2.21 In the process of exocytosis, a vesicle fuses with the cell membrane and then ruptures to release its contents outside the cell.

Problem-Solving Investigation

Building Exhibit Models

A model is a working representation of a concept, object, or process. The use of models helps in visualization of abstract concepts. An example is the use of a globe as a model of Earth.

Recognize a Need

The Science Alberta Foundation is developing a travelling exhibit aimed at describing how knowledge of cellular functions is used in industry and medicine. Your class has been asked to design, build, and test models to demonstrate diffusion, osmosis, facilitated diffusion, endocytosis, and exocytosis for the display.

The Problem

Divide into groups with each group taking one of the processes to be demonstrated in the exhibition. Collaboration and teamwork will be essential in designing, constructing, and testing your model.

Criteria for Success

- Inform and educate the general public about ways in which knowledge of cellular functions is used in industry and medicine.
- Provide an accurate representation of one of the transport mechanisms used by the cell in which the process is clearly demonstrated, including the role of the cell membrane in this process.
- Provide a poster or explanation of your working model to assist people who stop at the exhibit.
- Appeal to a large audience of people of various ages.

Build a Model

1. Review everything you know about the process you are modelling, and jot down the most important characteristics that you will need to demonstrate in the model.

2. Discuss the materials available to you and what you would like to use.

3. Decide on the responsibility of each member of the group and determine how you will apportion your time to meet the deadline set for fabrication of the display (your teacher will provide this information).

4. Choose your own materials.

5. Design your model.

6. Obtain approval from your teacher.

7. Build your model.

> **CAUTION: Consider and follow safety precautions while building your model. Remember that others will be using the model also, so you have a responsibility for their safety as well.**

Test and Evaluate

8. Test your model at least three times to ensure that it will work over and over again in the exhibition. Evaluate each test and re-design or re-work as required. You may want to get input from other groups as you perfect the model.

9. Review what you know about the biological process to ensure that your model is accurate.

Communicate

1. Set up your model and the accompanying poster or explanation. Conduct a "staff testing" by having each group work through each of the models and provide constructive feedback to the group who designed the model. Make the necessary changes.

2. Conduct a "focus group testing" with students from other classes, teachers, or parents. Your display is now ready to go on tour!

Knowledge

1. Explain the four points of the particle model of matter.

2. Explain how the processes of diffusion, facilitated diffusion, and active transport occur and why each one is important to cells.

3. Using your own words, explain what is meant by the terms "concentration gradient" and "equilibrium."

4. Explain how you would ensure that the celery you bought three days ago will be crisp and fresh for your dinner tonight.

5. What are the differences between passive and active transport?

6. Draw two diagrams showing the processes of endocytosis and exocytosis. Indicate the similarities and differences.

Applications

7. Imagine three identical animal cells, each placed in one of three beakers labelled A, B, or C. Beaker A contains a solution that is hypertonic to the cell contents; Beaker B contains a solution that is hypotonic to the cell contents; Beaker C contains a solution that is isotonic to the cell contents. Predict what will happen to the cells in each beaker. Give reasons for your prediction.

8. The principles of osmosis are used in food preservation. Certain foods are stored in strong salt solutions (brine) or in syrups to prevent infection by microbes.
   a) Explain how the principles of osmosis apply to this situation.
   b) What effect will these solutions have on the micro-organisms?

9. Use the particle model to explain how the size of particles would affect the rate of diffusion.

Extensions

10. Give some examples of how the cell membrane helps the cell to maintain equilibrium through exchange of materials with its environment.

11. Research an example of active transport in a cell. Present your findings in a poster or PowerPoint presentation.

12. Using a plastic grocery bag to represent the cell membrane, and wrapped candies as a food source, demonstrate the process of endocytosis. You may use your hands inside the bag as the movement of the cytoplasm, and scissors and tape to accomplish the pinching off of the membrane. Do not turn the bag inside out or expose the cytoplasm. You must be able to demonstrate the vesicle formation. Draw a diagram of your model to explain what you did.

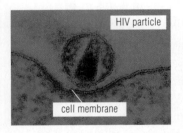

FIGURE C2.22 Recognition proteins on the cell surface allow cell communication.

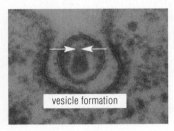

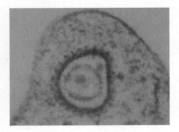

FIGURE C2.23 Viruses like HIV can enter cells by endocytosis. Transmission electron micrographs (approx. ×450 000)

C 2.3 Applications of Cellular Transport in Industry and Medicine

Knowledge about the make-up and functions of the cell membrane and about methods of transporting substances into cells has advanced research in both industry and medicine. Efficient natural systems are often the model for manufactured systems, and the cell membrane is an excellent example of a selective gatekeeper. Knowledge about the cell membrane has prompted industrial use of synthetics to mimic natural functions. This area of research and development is known as **membrane technologies**.

The molecules associated with the cell membrane on the surface of the cell are important for many cell activities. Some proteins, called **recognition proteins**, are embedded in the cell membrane, but stick out into the cell's surroundings. They allow cells to recognize one another; for example, when egg and sperm cells link together, or when cells of the human immune system recognize and destroy invading bacteria and viruses or destroy newly arisen cancer cells. Figure C2.22 shows a model of the link between recognition proteins on the surface of different cells

Other proteins called **receptor proteins** may bind specifically with certain molecules to bring them into the cell by endocytosis. Some of these proteins have sugar groups attached to them that make the binding specific and allow the cell to identify a particular bacteria or virus. In a reverse way that has a negative effect on humans, some viruses like human immunodeficiency virus (HIV), hepatitis, and influenza, use the binding reaction to target human cells (Figure C2.23). In other cases, the binding reaction on the surface of the cell acts like a molecular switch and triggers many different activities in the cell.

Pharmaceutical research draws on this understanding of cell membrane proteins to develop and test new drug therapies, making use of the cell's ability (either that of the disease-causing organism or of the host) to recognize molecules. This is one of the reasons why studies of the three-dimensional shape of molecules are important to health research as well as being of interest in themselves.

Membrane Proteins and Disease

Researchers have been working long and hard to find treatments and cures for constantly changing viruses such as HIV. New discoveries focus on recognition or receptor proteins in human cell membranes that appear to be the attachment point for the virus. In understanding these proteins, scientists suspect that they may be able to produce a lock-and-key scenario that would prevent the virus getting into the cell. The process would work to block or close off the receptor protein so that the "key" produced by the virus would not work—the virus would essentially be locked out (Figure C2.24). Imagine covering the keyhole of a padlock with cement so that even if you had the right key for the lock, you would be unable to use it. Being able to turn the virus away in this manner would mean that it would not be necessary to deluge the body with drugs that could affect healthy cells as well as infected ones. The disease could be stopped before it takes hold.

Cancer research has also targeted the study of recognition proteins. Common treatments for cancer are not able to single out only the defective cells; they affect healthy cells as well. If it were possible to identify the unique proteins of cancer cells, it might be possible to develop drugs specific to these proteins, and therefore specific only to cancer cells. Further, if certain recognition proteins specific to cancer cells could be identified, they could be used to stimulate the immune system to detect and destroy the cancer. The ability to be specific and target only cells of the cancer would mean less overall discomfort to the patient.

Synthetic Membrane Technology

While protein research continues, drug therapies also use a structure manufactured to act like the cell membrane. **Liposomes**, as shown in Figure C2.25, are fluid-filled sacs surrounded by a phospholipid bilayer identical to the cell membrane in human cells. Liposomes were first produced in the early 1960s and have since become important agents in the delivery of drugs to infected body tissue. They can be produced for almost any need by manipulating the composition of the membrane. Liposomes are microscopic, about 1/1000th the diameter of a human hair. Water trapped on the inside can hold water-soluble medications while the membrane layer is able to hold fat-soluble medications. The tiny sacs can be introduced into the bloodstream and circulate throughout the body. Because the membrane is identical to that of human cells, the liposomes can attach to infected cells and deliver the medication.

HIV and cancer therapies make use of liposomes to deliver medication. The advantage of using liposomes is that the spheres may circulate in the bloodstream for longer than the medication on its own, allowing for longer, sustained treatment. Sometimes, liposomes concentrate themselves at the site of a tumour or infection, and in this way deliver the drug directly to the targeted cells without affecting normal cells.

The use of liposomes in gene therapy to inject DNA into tumour cells is another application of liposomes that is actively being researched. The DNA is contained inside the liposome. A molecule on the liposome surface fits on to certain cancer cells to recognize and target the correct cells. In this way, the DNA can be introduced into the tumour cells, and begin the production of toxins to kill the cell. However, more research is required to ensure that healthy cells are not also susceptible to the gene- or drug-carrying liposomes.

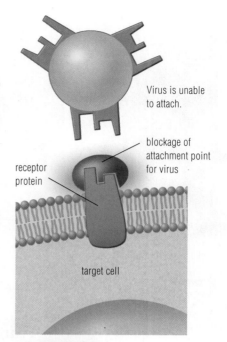

FIGURE C2.24 One possible way of fighting attachment of a virus

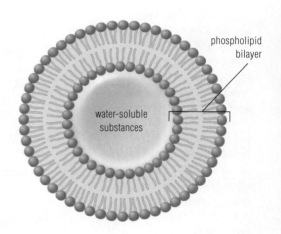

FIGURE C2.25 The phospholipid bilayer forming the liposome allows water-soluble substances to be carried inside the liposome.

infoBIT

Scientists are working on the production of synthetic vaccines using molecules that resemble parts of the cell membrane of disease-causing cells. The aim is protection against disease without any risk of the person becoming ill.

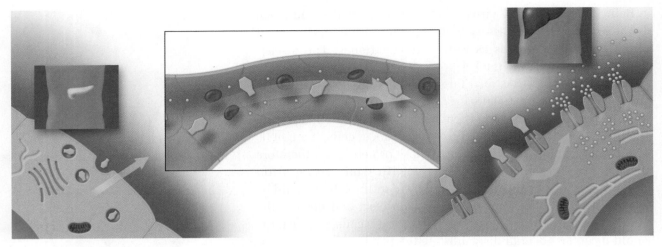

Insulin is released by exocytosis.

Insulin travels through the blood.

Insulin binds to receptor proteins in the target cell.

Binding stimulates processes in the cell.

FIGURE C2.26 A model of the mechanism of insulin action

Transport of Protein Hormones

Insulin is a small protein produced in the pancreas. It is a hormone, meaning that it is secreted into the bloodstream and binds with membrane receptors at a distance from the point of secretion. The complex formed between the hormone and the target cell triggers the target cell to undergo particular processes.

Specialized cells in the pancreas have channels that detect glucose (so-called blood sugar) in the bloodstream. This initiates the excretion of insulin into the blood. Insulin binds to receptor proteins of tissues including liver, muscle, and fat. This binding stimulates the rate of movement of glucose into the cells through facilitated diffusion using a carrier protein. Glucose is then used either directly to produce energy, or stored as a future source of energy as glycogen in the liver, fat in the fat tissue, and protein in the muscle. Figure C2.26 shows a model of the mechanism of insulin action.

Peritoneal Dialysis

Before the process of dialysis was available, people who experienced total kidney failure died. Today, the availability of dialysis and kidney transplants means that many patients can continue to live full lives. Two types of dialysis are possible: peritoneal dialysis and hemodialysis. Both are based on the principles of diffusion and osmosis and the operation of concentration gradients. The purpose of dialysis is to rid the blood of toxins, wastes, and excess fluid produced by the cells of the body. Normally, healthy kidneys would perform this task, sending wastes to be eliminated in the urine.

In humans, cells form a membrane called the **peritoneum**, which lines the abdominal cavity. During dialysis, waste products from the blood pass through these cells into a fluid, the dialysate fluid. This is termed **peritoneal dialysis**. A soft plastic tube (catheter) is surgically inserted into the abdominal cavity. The sterile dialysate fluid is pumped into the cavity. The dialysate has a composition similar to human body fluids and consists of a

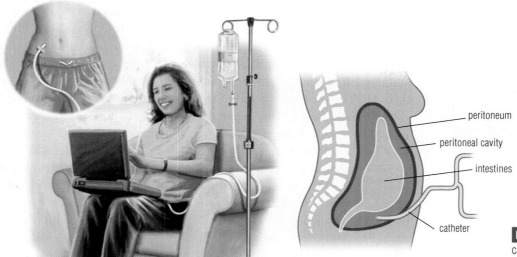

mixture of water, glucose, and certain substances the body needs. Dialysate usually contains sodium, magnesium, chloride, potassium, and calcium salts. The dialysate has no toxins or wastes present, so the concentration of these materials in the blood is much higher than it is in the fluid on the other side of the peritoneal membrane. The movement of toxins and wastes is down the concentration gradient. The wastes diffuse across the membrane and into the dialysate. As the cleansing fluid becomes saturated or full of wastes, it is removed from the body, disposed of, and replaced with fresh dialysate until the entire exchange process is complete.

The patient is able to perform peritoneal dialysis at home while carrying on most activities. **Hemodialysis**, on the other hand, is a more complicated procedure and must be performed in a health facility. The blood must be removed from the body, cleansed using a dialysate fluid in a special machine, and returned to the body. The patient is not able to move around during hemodialysis.

Minds On ... Simulating Peritoneal Dialysis

In groups, discuss what you know about diffusion, osmosis, and semi-permeable membranes. Consider how knowledge of these concepts was used to develop the technology of dialysis that is now used to save so many lives.

Design a representation of the movement of materials across the peritoneum. You may choose a diagram, poster, model, role play, or another format of your choice to explain the workings of dialysis.

Reverse Osmosis

Antarctica is a frigid and remote continent, not easily accessible for most of the year. Researchers and other workers living at the research facilities there must be in good physical, emotional, and mental health. As well, the technologies used must be reliable and efficient. The McMurdo Research Station is charged with meeting the needs of the people living there and addressing the question of how to provide potable water.

Osmosis:

Solvent enters solution along concentration gradient.

Reverse Osmosis:

Solvent is forced out of solution against concentration gradient.

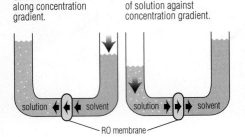

FIGURE C2.28 Reverse osmosis pumps water against its concentration gradient to remove charged particles.

re**SEARCH**

Find out how membrane technology is used in the modern dairy industry. Begin your search at

www.pearsoned.ca/school/science10

Desalination is the process of removing salt from sea water in order to make it suitable for drinking. Sea water in Antarctica is very cold, so it is first warmed slightly and then pumped through a 25-μm filter to eliminate coarse materials. The filter contains layers of anthracite coal, sand, garnet, and limestone. The water is pumped through progressively smaller filters that allow only smaller and smaller particles to pass through. The process is referred to as **reverse osmosis (RO)** because the water moves from a low water concentration (high concentration of solute) to a high water concentration (low concentration of solute) and therefore requires the force of pressure of a pump (Figure C2.28).

RO makes use of semi-permeable membranes that allow the water to be forced through but filter out other molecules or micro-organisms of progressively smaller and smaller size. As this process proceeds, the rejected materials continue to increase in solute concentration, requiring more force to push the water through. Reverse osmosis is affected by charged particles, like salts, so that the larger the molecule and the greater the charge on it, the less likely it will be to move through the membrane. "Backwash" from the filtration process helps to keep the filter clean. Following the RO process, the pH levels of the water are adjusted and chlorine is added to kill any bacteria still present. RO is an efficient, but expensive, method of desalinating and purifying water in Antarctica and other places of the world where fresh water is in extremely short supply. RO systems are now available for home water-purification.

C2.3   Check and Reflect

Knowledge

1. *The transport of wastes out of the blood during dialysis depends on the composition of the dialysis solution.* Explain this statement. You should include the particle model of diffusion and the role of the cell membrane in your answer.

2. Draw and label a diagram of a liposome. How are liposomes used in the treatment of HIV and cancer patients?

3. Describe the role of membrane technologies in the following:
   a) water purification
   b) peritoneal dialysis
   c) gene therapy for cancer

4. List three differences between peritoneal dialysis and hemodialysis.

5. Explain the term "reverse osmosis" as compared with "osmosis."

6. Explain the importance of membrane binding to the action of insulin.

Applications

7. What methods of water treatment are used in your area to provide potable water?

8. Describe some of the limitations of membrane technologies in the treatment of HIV, diabetes, cancer, and kidney disease.

Extensions

9. Write an article for an imaginary science journal, highlighting the importance of the cell membrane in the development of one commercial process.

10. Create a Web site to explain what you know about cell membranes, diffusion, osmosis, and applications in industry and medicine.

C 2.4 Is Bigger Better?

Whether we consider a one-celled amoeba, a giant sequoia tree, or a lumbering elephant, cells are all microscopic in size. Why are cells so small? Wouldn't it make more sense for cells to grow to a larger size? That way, the human body, for instance, could be made up of a few hundred large cells instead of trillions of tiny ones. And yet, the cell is considered to be an efficient system. Is there an explanation for the small size of cells?

The Ratio of Surface Area to Volume

As an efficient, open system, the cell must be able to carry out all of the life processes. The transport of materials into and out of the cell is critical because these materials will determine how the other processes function. The cell membrane is the barrier to free exchange between the outside environment and the cytoplasm. Whatever changes happen to the cell, the ability to transport materials must be kept at a maximum.

If a cell becomes larger and its volume increases, more molecules will need to be transported across the cell surface to take part in the cell's functions. Also, the distance any molecule has to travel from the cell surface will increase. If the cell is to maintain its ability to transport substances, there must be a greater surface area to match the increased need for molecule transport. One way to see how the surface area changes in relation to volume as the cell changes in size is to calculate the surface area to volume ratio for different cell sizes.

Example Problem C2.1

Determine the surface area to volume ratio for cubes that have the following side lengths:

a) 1.0 cm   b) 2.5 cm   c) 4.0 cm

A cube has 6 square faces, each having area s^2, where s is the side length.
Surface area of the cube $A = 6s^2$
Volume of the cube $v = s^3$
Surface area to volume ratio of the cube $\dfrac{A}{v} = \dfrac{6s^2}{s^3} = \dfrac{6}{s}$

a) $s = 1.0$ cm, $\dfrac{A}{v} = \dfrac{6}{1.0} = 6.0$

b) $s = 2.5$ cm, $\dfrac{A}{v} = \dfrac{6}{2.5} = 2.4$

c) $s = 4.0$ cm, $\dfrac{A}{v} = \dfrac{6}{4.0} = 1.5$

The surface area to volume ratios for cubes a), b), and c) are 6.0, 2.4, and 1.5, respectively.

Example Problem C2.1 shows that as a cell increases in size, its surface area to volume ratio decreases. For efficient transport at a cell's surface, the cell must have a large surface area in relation to its volume. The greater the surface area to volume ratio, the more efficient **cell transport** will be.

Practice Problems

1. Determine the surface area to volume ratio for cubes that have the following side lengths:
   a) 3.5 cm   b) 5.5 cm

2. What is the formula for the surface area to volume ratio of a rectangular prism? Determine the surface area to volume ratio of a rectangular prism that has:
   length $l = 2.5$ cm;
   width $w = 2.0$ cm; and
   height $h = 1.0$ cm

3. What is the formula for the surface area to volume ratio of a sphere? Determine the surface area to volume ratio for spheres that have the following diameters:
   a) 4.3 cm   b) 8.6 cm

Inquiry Lab

Required Skills

■ Initiating and Planning
■ Performing and Recording
■ Analyzing and Interpreting
■ Communication and Teamwork

Is Bigger Better?

If you cut a cube of gelatin into pieces, the total volume occupied by all the pieces remains the same as the volume of the initial cube. However, the surface area changes and this means that the surface area to volume ratio also changes. Phenolphthalein is an indicator chemical that is pink in a basic solution but becomes colourless when it comes in contact with an acid. Phenolphthalein was added to a basic solution to make the gelatin cubes that you will be using in this experiment. You will bring dilute hydrochloric acid (0.1 mol/L $HCl_{(aq)}$) in contact with the gelatin cubes and measure diffusion by the change in colour of the gelatin. Accuracy of measurement and calculation is very important in this activity. Be as careful as possible.

The Question

How is the rate of diffusion affected by the surface area to volume ratio of a cell?

The Hypothesis

State a hypothesis indicating how you think diffusion will be affected by differences in the surface area to volume ratio of cells.

> **CAUTION: Acids and bases are corrosive. Handle the base-containing gel carefully. If any acid spills, wash immediately with cold water.**

Materials and Equipment

3 cubes of gelatin containing phenolphthalein (each approximately 4 cm × 4 cm × 4 cm)

dilute hydrochloric acid solution (0.1 mol/L $HCl_{(aq)}$)

metric ruler

plastic knife

plastic spoon or tongs

3 250-mL beakers

graphing calculator or spreadsheet program

clock, watch, or timer

Procedure

1. Prepare a data table similar to the table below. Remember to give your table a title.

2. Take three identically sized pieces of gelatin.

3. Measure the length of the sides of one cube and record the cube side s in the table.

4. Calculate the surface area, volume, and surface area to volume ratio for the cube. Enter your results in the data table. If you are using a graphing calculator or spreadsheet, enter the data there.

Cube Size	Cube Side s (cm)	Surface Area of One Cube (cm^2)	Total Number of Cubes	Total Surface Area A (cm^2)	Total Volume v (cm^3)	Surface Area to Volume Ratio $\frac{A}{v}$
large	4					
medium	2					
small	1					

5. Take a second cube of gelatin. Cut it in half along its length, then in half again across the width, and in half again through the height.

6. Measure and record the length of the sides of one of the eight medium-sized pieces.

7. Calculate the surface area of each cube and the total surface area of all the medium-sized cubes. Enter your data in your table and graphing calculator or spreadsheet.

8. Has the total volume changed? Enter the total volume in your table.

9. Take the third cube of gelatin. Cut it into eight pieces as you did with the second cube and then cut each of the eight pieces again into eight equal pieces, resulting in 64 equal cubes.

10. Measure the cube side of one small cube. Calculate its surface area and the total surface area of all the small cubes. Enter your data in your table and graphing calculator or spreadsheet.

11. Has the total volume changed? Enter the total volume in your table.

12. Place all three sets of gelatin pieces into separate beakers and add just enough 0.1 mol/L $HCl_{(aq)}$ to cover the cubes.

13. Observe the beakers and record the time taken for the cubes to change colour completely from pink to colourless.

Analyzing and Interpreting

1. Explain how the surface area to volume ratio changes in each of the sets of cubes when the length of the side of each individual cube is decreased.

2. The colour change indicates the diffusion of the acid into the cube. The rate of diffusion $r = \frac{\text{total volume (cm}^3)}{\text{time (min)}}$. Calculate the rate of diffusion (cm^3/min) for the three sets of cubes.

3. Summarize the effect on the rate of diffusion of decreasing the size of individual cubes while increasing the number of cubes.

4. Graph your data using the surface area to volume ratio as the manipulated variable and the rate of diffusion as the responding variable.

5. State a relationship between the surface area to volume ratio and the rate of diffusion.

Forming Conclusions

6. Use your data and analysis to suggest conclusions from this investigation. Do these conclusions support your hypothesis?

Applying and Connecting

7. Consider the amount of time it takes to suck on a hard piece of candy until it completely dissolves. Predict how the time would be affected if you took an identical piece of the same candy (same shape and size), but chewed as well as sucked. Give reasons for your hypothesis. Try the experiment to see if your hypothesis is supported.

Extending

8. Is bigger better? Based on your observations, calculations, and conclusions, suggest a reason why cells are so small.

The Size and Shape of Organisms

For the survival of each cell, whether as a single-celled organism or as one cell in a mass of cells, the amount of surface exposed to the environment is crucial. The surface area determines the opportunities for transport of materials. If very little surface is available, the opportunities for intake of needed materials and expulsion of wastes are severely limited. What happens to the cell if it is unable to take in enough nutrients or is unable to remove poisons quickly?

Passive transport is one of the ways in which water, gases, and some dissolved nutrients are able to pass into and out of the cell. These materials must get quickly to all parts of the cell. The investigation of the gelatin cubes in Activity C11 showed that as the surface area to volume ratio increased, the rate of diffusion also increased. The set of cubes with the greatest surface area to volume ratio was the set with the smallest cubes. That means that the smallest cube is the one in which diffusion can be most quickly accomplished. As well, the distances materials have to travel from the surface to the other parts inside a small cube are relatively short. So, in the case of cells, bigger is not necessarily better. However, cells in multicellular organisms perform specialized functions, and their shape and size are determined by these functions.

Maximizing Potential

To maximize efficiency and promote survival, each individual cell needs to have the greatest possible surface area in relation to volume. In this way, there are lots of opportunities for transport of substances to occur, and the distance any molecule must travel within the cell is not too great. Multicellular organisms have evolved and adapted to balance the increased size of the organism against the need for an appropriate surface area to volume ratio. Compare a large plant and a small one, as shown in Figure C2.29. The large plant has more mass and volume. It is a challenge to maintain an optimum surface area to volume ratio in order to meet all the needs of the cells. The plant may have large, flat leaves to create as much surface area as possible for exchange and transport of materials. The smaller plant has less mass and volume. It has less problem to transport materials quickly to all the cells.

Multicellular organisms have developed other internal transport systems to reduce dependence on diffusion and to help in the transport of materials. For example, the circulatory, digestive, and respiratory systems of animals are all involved in the transport of essential materials to all the cells of the body. Transport is not confined only to the surface of the skin. In humans, no cell is more than 0.1 mm away from a capillary that transports blood to bring nutrients and remove wastes.

Plants also have transport systems for essential materials. These are different from the systems in animals. The **xylem** is concerned with the delivery of water from the roots to all parts of the plant while the **phloem** distributes sugars throughout the plant according to conditions operating at any particular time. The transport systems may carry substances long distances, up to 100 m in large trees.

FIGURE C2.29 Despite size differences the two plants must use similar processes to supply their cells with nutrients and remove wastes.

*re***SEARCH**

Investigate the range of surface to volume ratios in different types of human cells and plant cells. Relate your findings to the functions of the cells. Begin your search at

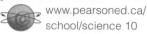 www.pearsoned.ca/school/science 10

Some organisms or specialized structures have features that help to increase the overall surface area to volume ratio. The alveoli in your lungs are small sacs that increase the total surface area for transport of oxygen and carbon dioxide. Tiny finger-like projections, called villi and microvilli, extend from the lining of your small intestine to provide more surface for the absorption of nutrients. The roots of plants have tiny, thin extensions called root hairs that increase the surface area of the cell available for the uptake of water.

C2.4 Check and Reflect

Knowledge

1. Define the following terms:
   a) surface area
   b) volume
   c) surface area to volume ratio

2. As a cell gets larger, how does its surface area to volume ratio change?

3. What is the limiting factor when it comes to the size of a cell? Explain.

4. As the cell grows larger and increases in volume, will it need more or less cell membrane to survive? Explain.

5. How does the surface area to volume ratio of a cell affect the rate of diffusion of materials across the cell's surface?

6. What determines the size and shape of cells in multicellular organisms?

Applications

7. Assuming a spherical balloon and a cylindrical balloon both contain the same amount of air, which one would represent the more efficient cell? Explain your answer.

8. Assume that you have a perfect cube of side 4 cm.
   a) Calculate the surface area of the cube.
   b) Calculate the volume of the cube.

   Cut the cube in half so that you have two identical rectangular prisms.
   c) What is the surface area of each of the two new rectangular prisms?
   d) What is their combined surface area?
   e) What is the volume of each new piece? What is the combined volume?
   f) Describe how cutting the cube in half affects surface area, volume, and the relation between surface area and volume.

Knowledge

1. What are the life processes necessary for an organism to survive?

2. What is the function of:
   a) the cell membrane?
   b) mitochondria?
   c) chloroplasts?

3. Name the four major types of organic compounds found in the cell and give examples of each.

4. Draw a diagram of the cell membrane to show the arrangement of the phospholipid bilayer.

5. List the four points of the particle theory.

6. Define the term "semi-permeable."

7. Describe the differences between the following terms when comparing concentrations in solutions:
   a) isotonic
   b) hypotonic
   c) hypertonic

8. What factor determines whether or not transport across the cell membrane is "active" or "passive"?

9. Describe similarities and differences in the processes of diffusion, facilitated diffusion, and active transport.

10. List two situations where a cell would use endocytosis and two situations where a cell would use exocytosis.

11. What is a hormone? Give an example.

12. What are recognition proteins? Give two examples of the operation of recognition proteins.

13. Identify a drawback to the use of liposomes for the treatment of tumours.

14. What is a scientific model? How do models assist our understanding of concepts? Give an example.

15. Distinguish between surface area, volume, and surface area to volume ratio. Include formulas.

16. Onion cells are rectangular prisms, not cubic or spherical. Use the information below to calculate the surface area, volume, and surface area to volume ratio of the onion cell models.

Cell #	Length (cm)	Width (cm)	Height (cm)	Surface Area (A)	Volume (v)	Surface Area to Volume Ratio (A/v)
1	5	3	2			
2	12	5	1			
3	40	27	20			

17. Predict which one of the models in question 16 will have the fastest rate of diffusion across the surface. Give reasons for your answer.

18. Explain how diffusion takes place, using an example.

19. What is meant by a concentration gradient?

20. A container has two compartments, A and B, separated by a permeable membrane inserted vertically through the middle. A 10 g/L NaCl solution is placed in compartment A and a 12 g/L NaCl solution is placed in compartment B.
   a) Describe the movement of particles that will occur across the membrane.
   b) Draw a diagram to illustrate the movement of particles across the membrane.

21. What is osmosis?

22. Explain the process of reverse osmosis. Contrast this with osmosis.

Applications

23. Identify each part of a plant cell. Compare the parts to the operation of a factory or to the services provided in a community. Include at least four organelles and an explanation for your choice of comparison. Choose a way to present your comparison: poster, diagram, model, electronic presentation, skit, or another format of your choice.

24. Use a Venn diagram to illustrate the similarities and differences between plant and animal cells.

25. Explain how a cell's plasma membrane functions.

26. Identify ways in which the rate of diffusion can be changed. Explain each factor using the particle model.

27. How is peritoneal dialysis based on our understanding of the function of the cell membrane? Find out more about peritoneal dialysis and hemodialysis from the Kidney Foundation of Canada. Prepare a report.

28. What is the purpose of a hypothesis in an investigation?

29. Why do grocery store owners spray fresh vegetables with water? Are there any vegetables for which this is not a good idea?

30. Describe how recognition proteins are or may be used in cancer treatment.

31. For a cell to be able to carry out the life processes, materials must be able to move in and out of the cell, as well as within the cell. What is the advantage of having a large surface area?

32. Dialysis tubing will allow small molecules like water and glucose to pass through but will prevent large molecules like starch. Examine the diagram below. Determine what will happen in each situation.

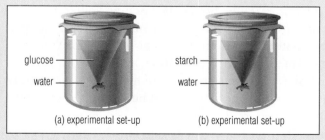

(a) experimental set-up   (b) experimental set-up

(a) Dialysis tubing containing a glucose solution placed in a beaker of water

(b) Dialysis tubing containing a starch solution placed in a beaker of water

33. Your teacher has set a challenge for the class. You must dissolve 10 g of salt in 300 mL of water in the shortest possible time. Half the

class has been given coarse rock salt, while the other half has been given fine table salt.
a) Predict which half of the class will win the race.
b) Explain your answer with regard to surface area and rates of diffusion.

34. Is there anything that the students who have been given the coarse rock salt could do to increase their chance of winning? Use your knowledge of the particle model and surface area to suggest possible strategies.

Extensions

35. If the members of a shipwrecked crew drink sea water, they will probably die. Why?

36. Relate the functions of the cell membrane to the fluid-mosaic model of the membrane.

37. Design and build a model of a semi-permeable membrane.

38. Provide an analogy for facilitated diffusion. Explain how the analogy serves to represent the work of channel and carrier proteins.

39. Research other current uses of membrane technologies in industry or medicine, apart from the examples used in the text. Write a paragraph describing one of these applications.

40. Using electronic and print resources, find out about current research and breakthroughs in cancer and HIV treatments. Write a report illustrating how this research is related to our understanding of the way cells function.

41. As organisms increase in size, they have proportionately less surface area per unit volume. Find out how large organisms compensate for the small surface area to volume ratio.

42. Identify one significant thing that you learned from this section and one topic that you would like to know more about.

43. Why would enormous insects, often seen in science fiction movies, be unlikely to survive in our present-day environment?

Plants are multicellular organisms with specialized structures.

Key Concepts

In this section, you will learn about the following key concepts:

- use of explanatory and visual models in science

- cell specialization in multicellular organisms; i.e., plants

- mechanisms of transport, gas exchange, and environmental response in multicellular organisms; i.e., plants

Learning Outcomes

When you have completed this section, you will be able to:

- explain why, when a single-celled organism or colony of single-celled organisms reaches a certain size, it requires a multicellular level of organization, and relate this to the specialization of cells, tissues, and systems in plants

- describe how the cells of the leaf system have a variety of specialized structures and functions

- explain and investigate the gas exchange system in plants

- explain and investigate the transport system in plants

- explain and investigate phototropism and gravitropism as examples of control systems in plants

- trace the development of theories of phototropism and gravitropism

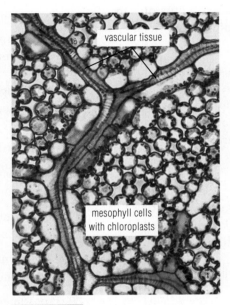

FIGURE C3.1 This section of a lilac leaf cut parallel to the surface shows cells in tissues specialized for different functions within the leaf. Light micrograph (approx. ×250)

Imagine being stranded on a desert island with a group of your family and friends. You would have two choices. You could look out only for yourself and be responsible for all of your own needs, including food and shelter, or you could work with the others on the island, giving each person a particular responsibility for the community. In the second scenario, everything does not depend on one person alone, and each person works for the good of the whole group. On the other hand, individuals lose some of their independence by specializing in one area and not having control over all aspects of their survival.

These ideas can in some ways be applied to cells. The protists you examined in the pond water exist as single-celled individuals, each responsible for carrying out all life processes. Each cell maintains an efficient surface area to volume ratio in order to sustain life. If a cell becomes too large to function efficiently, it will usually divide to produce two new cells. Both cells are now able to flourish. However, many of the prepared slides and photomicrographs you have viewed show material from multicellular organisms. You are a multicellular organism. So are a tree, an onion, an earthworm, and an elephant. Multicellular organisms are made of many cells (your body has trillions), but the cells are not all alike. When an organism grows in size, it is essential that some specialization occurs to deal with different functions. In a multicellular organism, different types of cells facilitate the movement of nutrients, gases, essential molecules, and wastes.

The understanding of life processes at the microscopic level can also be applied to a multicellular organism. This section will focus on plants as examples of multicellular organisms with specialized structures at the cellular, tissue, and system levels. Figure C3.1 shows a variety of tissues present in a leaf.

C 3.1 Cells, Tissues, and Systems

Organisms, small or large, unicellular or multicellular, such as those shown in Figure C3.2, can survive if both their needs and the challenges of their environments are met. To survive, the *Euglena* depends on the normal function of a single cell, while the lodgepole pine depends on the normal function and interaction of countless cells that make up its large structure. There are advantages and disadvantages to having a large structure that depends on countless single cells. These are listed below.

- Division of labour—when cells are specialized for one particular function, they can perform it more effectively and efficiently. It is like having the luxury to concentrate on just one task and so doing it perfectly. Contrast this situation with the single-celled organism, which must be a multi-tasker, performing all necessary functions at the same time.

- Size—the surface area to volume ratio and the related rate of diffusion restricts the size of a unicellular organism. In multicellular organisms, internal transport systems allow efficient exchange of materials. These transport systems permit the organism to grow to a larger size.

- Interdependence of cells—the life of a multicellular organism does not depend on a single cell. When a single-celled organism dies, that is the end of that particular organism. If one cell of a multicellular organism dies, it does not kill the entire organism. There is a cost, however. If one type of cell functions abnormally, for example becomes cancerous, it is possible that as the cancer increases, the whole organism will suffer.

Plant Structure

Plants are multicellular organisms; they can be regarded as living systems made up of many parts, each performing its own important function. As plants grow and increase in size, the cells begin to have specialized functions. Although every cell contains the same genetic information, individual cells perform particular jobs within the organism. Groups of cells performing the same function together are called **tissues**. Tissues contributing to the same function form **organs** which are part of a **system**. The plant has two organ systems, as shown in Figures C3.3 and C3.4. The **shoot system** is everything that is above ground; it includes the stem, leaves, buds, flowers, and fruits. It also includes **tubers** (swollen stems that store food, for example potatoes) even though they are under the ground. The **root system** is everything underground, but also includes aerial roots even though they are above ground.

Cells divide for the growth of new tissue and repair of damaged tissue. Mitosis is the process of cell division that allows growth and repair; in this process, one cell literally divides into two cells.

(a) Unicellular *Euglena*. Light micrograph (approx. ×250)

(b) Very large lodgepole pines

FIGURE C3.2 The challenges of survival can be solved in very different ways.

*info*BIT

Multicellular animals, like plants, are also composed of tissues made up of many cells performing the same task. In humans, we refer to nervous tissue, muscle tissue, and connective tissue, for instance. Tissues grouped together to perform similar tasks form organs. The skin is the largest organ of your body. Organs work together to form a system. The heart, arteries, veins, and capillaries are made of different tissues, but all are connected and depend on the efficient functioning of each cell to form the circulatory system.

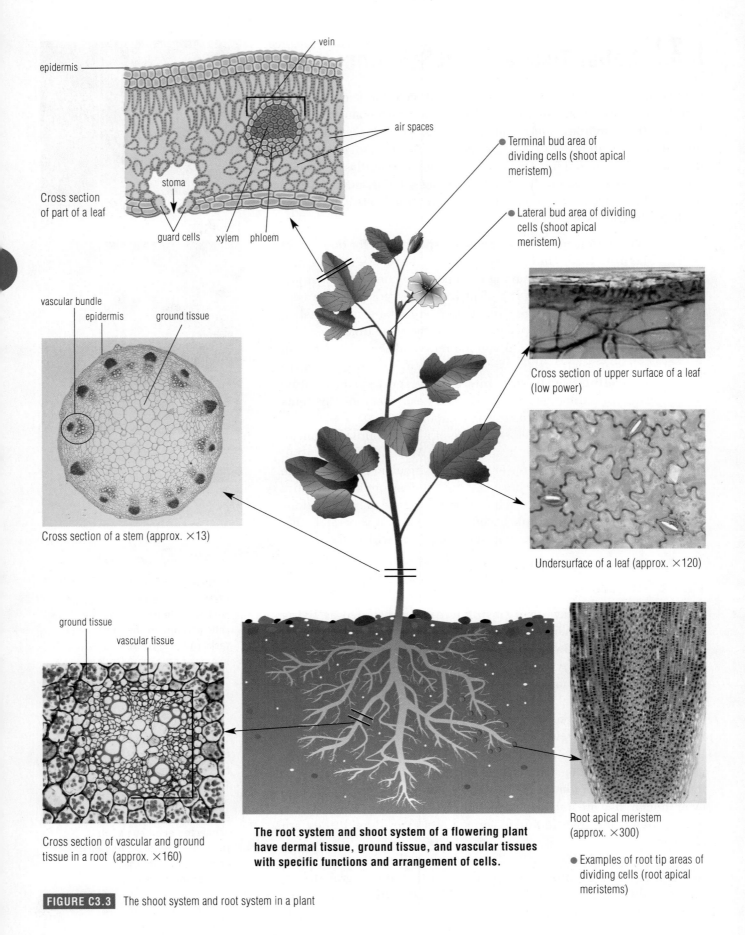

vein

epidermis

air spaces

Cross section
of part of a leaf

stoma

guard cells   xylem   phloem

● Terminal bud area of
dividing cells (shoot apical
meristem)

● Lateral bud area of dividing
cells (shoot apical
meristem)

vascular bundle

epidermis   ground tissue

Cross section of a stem (approx. ×13)

Cross section of upper surface of a leaf
(low power)

Undersurface of a leaf (approx. ×120)

ground tissue

vascular tissue

Cross section of vascular and ground
tissue in a root (approx. ×160)

**The root system and shoot system of a flowering plant
have dermal tissue, ground tissue, and vascular tissues
with specific functions and arrangement of cells.**

Root apical meristem
(approx. ×300)

● Examples of root tip areas of
dividing cells (root apical
meristems)

FIGURE C3.3   The shoot system and root system in a plant

Cell division does not occur at the same rate throughout the organism. In plants, increase in size results from cell division in particular growth areas called **meristems**. Different meristems produce root tissue and shoot tissue (Figure C3.3). The process is one of constantly creating new building blocks that add to one another almost endlessly. The giant Douglas fir tree is an example of the meristems doing their work continually over a long period of time to produce an enormous organism.

The root and shoot systems are made up of tissues specialized for different activities such as gas exchange, transport of materials, and photosynthesis. In their turn, the tissues are made up of individual, specialized cells that each contribute to the function of the tissue. There are three main types of plant tissues. Figure C3.3 shows the relationship of these tissues in different parts of a flowering plant.

Dermal tissue or **epidermis** is the outer layer of cells that covers all **herbaceous** (non-woody) plants. This tissue is generally one cell-layer thick and is responsible for the exchange of matter and gases into and out of the plant. In woody plants, the epidermis of the stem is replaced by cork and bark during the secondary growth stage of development. The dermal tissue of the shoot system organs, the leaves and stem, is primarily involved in gas exchange of carbon dioxide and oxygen. This dermal tissue also protects the plant from disease. The cells of the leaves and stem secrete a waxy substance called the **cuticle** that resists attack from micro-organisms and helps to reduce water loss from the plant. The cuticle is shown in Figure C3.5(a). Dermal tissue of the root system organs is responsible for the uptake of water and mineral salts from the soil.

Ground tissue makes up the majority of the plant and is found as a layer beneath the epidermis. Ground tissue has several important functions. In the stem, it provides strength and support to the plant; in the roots, it is involved in food and water storage; and in the leaves, it is the location where photosynthesis occurs. The cells of the ground tissue are loosely packed together and the air spaces between cells allow gases to diffuse rapidly through the ground tissue. Figure C3.5(b) shows the ground tissue in a root.

FIGURE C3.4 The shoot system and root system in the developing bean plant

cuticle

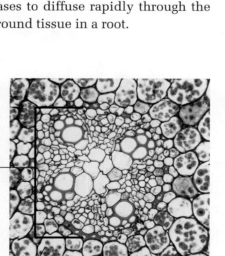

vascular tissue

epidermis

ground tissue

(a) The cuticle protects the surface of the leaf. (LM polarized light; low power)

(b) Ground tissue in the root is important for storage. Light micrograph (approx. ×200)

FIGURE C3.5 Tissues in leaf and root

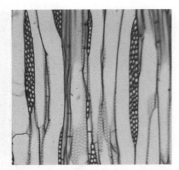

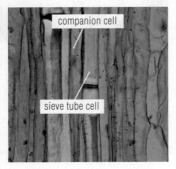

(a) The xylem of the stem is made up of parallel tubes. Light micrograph (approx. ×200)

(b) The phloem tissue of the stem is made up of sieve tube cells with associated companion cells. Light micrograph (approx. ×200)

FIGURE C3.6 Vascular tissues

Vascular tissue is responsible for the transport of materials throughout the plant. **Xylem tissue** moves water and dissolved minerals from the roots up the stem to the leaves where these substances are used in photosynthesis. Xylem vessels are thick-walled tubes of varying diameters, the thickening being the result of cellulose and possibly lignin being deposited in the cell wall. As the cylindrical cells mature, they fuse together and the walls at each end become perforated. As a result, the contents of the cytoplasm break down, and the cells die, leaving the non-living cell walls attached together like a long straw. Imagine stacking paper towel rolls one on top of the other and taping them together to form one long tube. These non-living ducts are responsible for the movement of water and minerals up the stem. Figure C3.6 shows the composition of the xylem and phloem.

Phloem tissue transports sucrose and other dissolved sugars from the leaves to other parts of the plant. The phloem is formed from individual long **sieve tube cells**, which have perforated end walls, through which the cytoplasm extends. The sieve tubes form continuous ducts. Imagine the same tower of stacked paper tubes, except this time there are pinholes along the length of the rolls, and in between every two tubes there is a piece of gauze to allow the flow of materials from one roll to another. The sieve tube cells remain alive, but lose their nuclei. In many plants, sieve tube cells are connected to small, nucleated **companion cells** that appear to direct their activities. The sugars transported by the phloem are used to provide energy for cellular processes such as protein manufacture, or are converted into cellulose. Cellulose forms fibrous structures for strength and support and may become associated with lignin in the formation of wood. Some of the transported sugars may be stored as starch in roots (carrots, sweet potatoes), stems (ginger, potatoes), or leaves (green onions, rhubarb). Figure C3.7 shows the organization of the three tissue types in the stem of herbaceous plants.

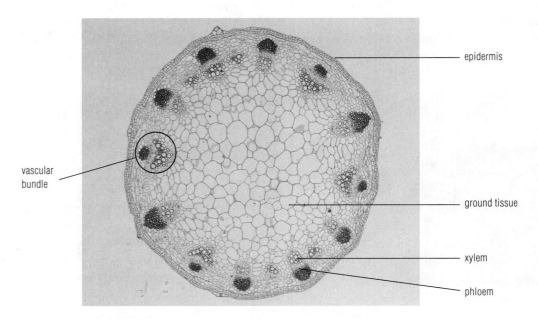

FIGURE C3.7 Cross section of a herbaceous stem, showing the tissue types as seen through the light microscope (approx. ×20)

Specialization in Plant Cells

Cells that are no longer part of the meristem show the characteristics of only certain parts of their genetic code. Cells become specialized for a particular function and produce only the products needed for that function. The following are some examples of specialization in plants.

(i) Cells that become part of the root system and are responsible for the absorption of water and minerals from the soil, produce tiny hair-like projections called **root hairs** (Figure C3.8(a)). The root hairs increase the surface area for absorption of water—more cell surface is exposed to the soil and therefore the amount of water that is able to enter the root by osmosis is maximized. You may have noticed these tiny root hairs when you pull a carrot or radish from the garden.

(ii) Dermal cells of the shoot system produce cuticle (Figure 3.8(b)) to protect the cells from water loss.

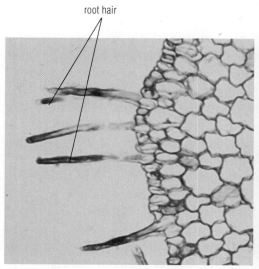

(a) Cells of the root showing root hairs as seen through the light microscope (approx. ×100)

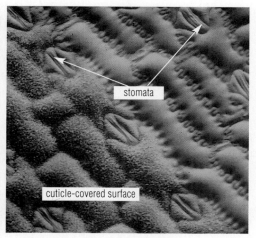

(b) Scanning electron micrograph of cells in the upper epidermis of a leaf showing the cuticle and stomata (approx. ×1800)

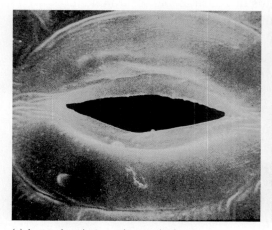

(c) A scanning electron micrograph of a stoma (approx. ×12 000)

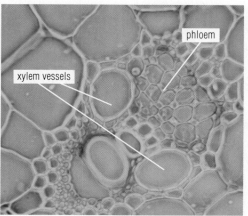

(d) Cells in a vascular bundle seen through the light microscope (approx. ×200)

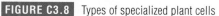 **FIGURE C3.8** Types of specialized plant cells

Investigate the different functions of the ground tissue in plants. What specializations make these functions possible? Begin your search at

www.pearsoned.ca/
school/science10

(iii) The lower epidermal surface of leaves develops specific cells, called **guard cells**, that form tiny pores called **stomata** for gas exchange (Figures C3.8(b) and C3.8(c)). The guard cells are the only cells in the epidermis that contain chloroplasts. The upper epidermis usually has fewer stomata than the lower.

(iv) Cells that become part of the xylem in the vascular tissue specialize to be able to conduct water and to allow the transport of water to adjacent cells. These cells die during differentiation of the xylem and therefore are empty inside (Figure C3.8(d)). They form long tubes that behave almost like straws to move water and dissolved salts throughout the plant. For example, the long fibres in celery are the vascular tissue of the plant.

C3.1 Check and Reflect

Knowledge

1. Define the following terms:
   a) unicellular
   b) multicellular
   c) tissues
   d) organ
   e) organ systems
   f) meristems

2. Name and describe each of the organ systems in plants. Draw a diagram to illustrate your description.

3. Prepare a chart to outline the advantages and disadvantages of being multicellular.

Applications

4. In plants, as in other multicellular organisms, cells specialize to perform specific functions. List four examples of ways that specialization provides for the life processes of the plant.

5. Explain why plant stems and leaves have a layer of cuticle but plant roots do not.

6. Draw a diagram of a tomato or bean plant to show all of the tissue types described in section C3.1. Describe how each of these tissues contributes to the overall function of the plant.

Extensions

7. Humans have cultivated and bred plants for centuries to provide food, fibre, fuel, and medicine. For many years, as a result of plant research, crop yields have increased. Recently, however, yields are less able to keep up with demand, as fertile land is lost and the population increases. Plant researchers must find ways to meet the challenges of production and to fight famine worldwide while attempting to maintain a sustainable environment and prevent any further decline in biodiversity.

   a) Suggest how research into plant structure and the relationships between different plant tissue types may aid scientists in meeting the challenge of increasing crop yields in a sustainable environment.

   b) Plants share similar physical structures and tissue relationships, as outlined in this section, but they also show a huge diversity. How can understanding both the similarities and differences assist scientists in their research?

8. There is growing concern about climate change and the degradation of the environment and about ways that human activity may be important to these changes. In what ways could research into plant structures and their possible uses for food and fibre address these issues?

C 3.2 The Leaf and Photosynthesis

The leaf is a collection of tissues whose main purpose is to carry out or support the process of photosynthesis. Within the overall requirements, each type of tissue—dermal, ground, and vascular—has a particular purpose and function. The survival of the whole organism requires every cell and tissue to perform its function.

The Chloroplast: A Unique Plant Organelle

Unlike animal cells, many plant cells have organelles called chloroplasts that contain the green pigment, chlorophyll. Chloroplasts are easily identified in the cytoplasm by their colour. Cells containing chloroplasts are found in the ground tissue of leaves and sometimes in stems. Chloroplasts are very important to the functioning of the cell and the organism. These organelles are where the plant carries out photosynthesis, a chemical process in which carbon dioxide from the air and water from the soil, in the presence of light energy, produce glucose and oxygen. **Photosynthesis** means putting together with light ("photo" = light; "synthesis" = putting together). The word equation for photosynthesis is:

$$\text{water} + \text{carbon dioxide} \xrightarrow{\text{chlorophyll + light}} \text{glucose} + \text{oxygen}$$

The balanced chemical equation for photosynthesis is:

$$6H_2O_{(l)} + 6CO_{2(g)} \xrightarrow{\text{chlorophyll + light}} C_6H_{12}O_{6(aq)} + 6O_{2(g)}$$

In photosynthesis, the light energy is absorbed by the chlorophyll and converted into chemical energy that is stored in the molecules of glucose for future use in fuelling cellular processes. Light and chlorophyll are not considered to be reactants or products. Figure C3.9 shows chloroplasts as seen through the light microscope.

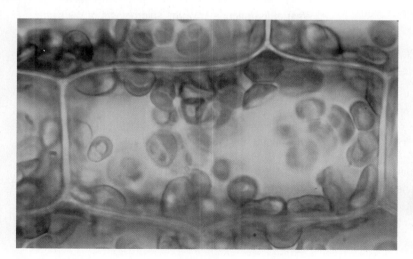

FIGURE C3.9 Chloroplasts in plant cells seen through the light microscope (approx. ×3000)

Counting Chloroplasts

In this activity, you will be using an aquatic plant called *Elodea canadensis* which is native to Western Canada. *Elodea* grows in ponds, anchored to the pond floor. It has a tube-like stem with many small, thin leaves growing from it. Similar South American species are used in aquariums. Small fish eat the leaves, but primarily the many leaves of the plant provide protection and shelter.

The Question

How many chloroplasts are present in a typical cell of an *Elodea* leaf?

Materials and Equipment

compound light microscope

glass slides and coverslips

droppers

forceps

Petri dishes

Elodea canadensis, Java Moss, or other aquatic plants

CAUTION: Wash your hands at the end of the lab activity.

Procedure

1. Transfer some water from the aquarium where the plants are kept into a Petri dish. Using the forceps, transfer a section of the plant into the water you collected.

2. Using the forceps, carefully remove one small, thin leaf from the plant and place it on a clean glass slide.

3. Make a wet mount of the leaf. Be careful not to include air bubbles under the coverslip.

4. Examine the slide through the microscope using the low-power objective. Find an area where the cells are clearly visible. Switch to high power so that you can see organelles in the cell. The round, green organelles are chloroplasts. The leaf is two cell-layers thick. Use the fine adjustment knob to focus up and down through the layers.

5. Draw what you see in the field of view. Set up a data table and record the number of chloroplasts present in each of 10 cells. Find the mean number of chloroplasts per cell.

6. Compare the number of chloroplasts in cells near the edge of the leaf and in cells in the middle of the leaf.

7. Draw one chloroplast. Label your diagrams with the name of the plant and the total magnification used.

8. Estimate the actual size of the chloroplast by comparing it with the diameter of the field of view, using the technique you learned in Activity C2.

9. Try to distinguish the cell wall in these chloroplast-packed cells. The central vacuole is also present but it is difficult to see because it is transparent and filled with water.

10. Continue to observe the chloroplasts. What do you notice about their position in the cell? Are they moving or stationary?

Analyzing and Interpreting

1. What was the mean number of chloroplasts in the cells you observed? Were there significant differences in the number of chloroplasts in cells near the edge of the leaf compared with the middle of the leaf? Provide a possible explanation of your observation.

2. Describe the movement of the chloroplasts in the cell. This movement is often termed cytoplasmic streaming. What is its function? Are the chloroplasts of the same cell moving in the same direction? Are the chloroplasts of all the cells in the field of view all moving in the same direction?

Forming Conclusions

3. Write a statement to answer the question posed at the beginning of the inquiry, based on your observations.

Applying and Connecting

4. Plant cells have three structures that are absent from animal cells. Suggest reasons why animals do not need these structures, but plants do.

Movement of chloroplasts within cells has given indirect evidence that the cytoplasm behaves like a fluid. This type of movement of the cytoplasm and its contents is termed cytoplasmic streaming. It is a mechanism that circulates materials and speeds up their distribution within the cell. Robert Brown, who discovered the nucleus, also discovered and demonstrated cytoplasmic flow in plant cells. His experiments with *Tradescantia* pioneered the study of the flow of matter within the living cell. Figure C3.10(a) shows hair cells in stamens of *Tradescantia*, observed in a repeat of Brown's experiments. Figure C3.10(b) shows strands of cytoplasm in onion cells undergoing cytoplasmic streaming.

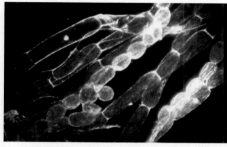

(a) Robert Brown discovered cytoplasmic streaming in *Tradescantia* stamen hairs, here viewed through his microscope. (approx. ×40)

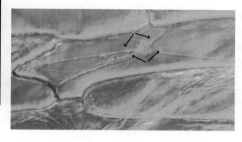

(b) A section through onion cells showing cytoplasmic streaming seen through the light microscope. Arrows indicate strands of cytoplasm. (approx. ×600)

FIGURE C3.10 Cytoplasmic streaming

Gas Production in Plants

There are two important reactions that take place in plants and produce gases as products. These reactions are in many ways the opposite of each other. Photosynthesis occurs in the chloroplasts of plants in the presence of light energy and carbon dioxide, producing glucose and oxygen. The light energy is converted to chemical energy stored in the bonds within the glucose molecules.

To obtain energy to fuel the cell's activities, a second general reaction is needed. This process is called **cellular respiration**, and is a set of reactions in which bonds are broken and other bonds formed in new compounds, with the result that energy is released.

Cellular respiration begins in the cytoplasm but is completed in the mitochondria by way of a series of reactions that release energy and produce carbon dioxide and water. The word equation for cellular respiration is:

glucose + oxygen $\longrightarrow$ carbon dioxide + water + energy

The chemical equation for cellular respiration is:

$$C_6H_{12}O_{6(aq)} + 6O_{2(g)} \longrightarrow 6CO_{2(g)} + 6H_2O_{(l)} + energy$$

These reactions produce the energy needed by the cell to carry out its life processes. Cellular respiration using the same chemical reactions is also carried out in animal cells to provide energy for the life processes. However, plant tissues respire at a much lower rate than animal tissues, and the CO_2 produced during cellular respiration is not an obvious product during the day, when photosynthesis is going on.

In the dark, photosynthesis cannot take place. The plant stops manufacturing food but the process of cellular respiration continues and any carbon dioxide that is produced is released.

Inquiry Lab

Evidence of Carbon Dioxide Production

Gas production differs in plants and animals. During photosynthesis, plants use carbon dioxide and produce oxygen. During cellular respiration, both plants and animals produce carbon dioxide. When aquatic organisms produce carbon dioxide, it dissolves to produce a weak acid called carbonic acid. Carbon dioxide production can be detected by using an indicator solution called bromothymol blue (BTB), which responds to changes in acidity. As carbonic acid is produced, the BTB in solution will change from blue to green (low concentration of acid) to yellow (higher concentration of acid). This colour change gives indirect evidence of the production of carbon dioxide. In this investigation you will consider the effect of light on carbon dioxide production in systems containing plants and animals.

The Question

Does light have an effect on carbon dioxide production by plants and animals?

The Hypothesis

Predict whether the presence or absence of light will affect carbon dioxide production in an aquatic plant and an aquatic animal.

Materials and Equipment

10 glass screw-cap vials

4 sprigs of an aquatic plant (e.g., *Elodea canadensis* or Java moss), of the same size and with the same number of leaves

4–6 aquarium snails

plastic straws

water

bromothymol blue indicator solution in a dropper bottle

grease pencil or marker

NaOH solution, 0.01 mol/L

Area of the lab that will be lit for 24 hours (i.e., under grow lamps)

Area of the lab that will be darkened (i.e., inside closed cabinet)

CAUTION: Wear gloves for this activity. Bromothymol blue stains skin. Wash your hands at the end of the lab activity. Sodium hydroxide (NaOH$_{(aq)}$) is corrosive. Avoid contact with skin. If NaOH gets on your skin, flush immediately under running water and inform your teacher.

Procedure

1. Number the vials 1–10. Add water to each vial, allowing approximately 1.5 cm of air space.

2. Add an equal number of drops of BTB to each vial so that the colour of the solution remains consistently blue. If the solution turns green, carefully add 0.01 mol/L NaOH$_{(aq)}$, one drop at a time, until the solution becomes and stays blue.

3. Loosely secure the caps on vials 1 and 2 and set aside.

4. Add carbon dioxide to vials 3, 4, 7, and 8 by blowing through a straw until the solution turns yellow. Loosely secure the caps. Set vials 3 and 4 aside.

5. Place a sprig of the aquatic plant, with cut end upward, in vials 5, 6, 7, and 8 and loosely secure the caps. Set aside.

6. Place one snail in each of vials 9 and 10 and loosely secure the caps. Set aside. The contents of the vials are shown in the table on page 307.

7. Prepare a data table in which to record observations for each of the 10 vials. Remember to give your table a title. List the contents of each vial, the colour of the solution in each vial, and whether the vial is placed in the light or dark. Leave space for your observations before and after the experiment.

8. Place vials 1, 3, 5, 7, and 9 in a lighted area for 24 hours (Figure C3.11).

9. Place vials 2, 4, 6, 8, and 10 in a completely dark area for 24 hours (Figure C3.11).

10. Record the colour of the solution in each vial, after 24 hours of dark or light treatment, in your data table.

Contents of Vials 1–10

Vial Number	Vial Identification
1	water + BTB (control)
2	water + BTB (control)
3	water + BTB + CO_2 (control)
4	water + BTB + CO_2 (control)
5	water + BTB + plant
6	water + BTB + plant
7	water + BTB + CO_2 + plant
8	water + BTB + CO_2 + plant
9	water + BTB + snail
10	water + BTB + snail

Analyzing and Interpreting

1. Describe the colour observed in each vial. Use labelled diagrams to illustrate your observations.

2. Explain the need for vials 1, 2, 3, and 4 as controls in this experiment.

3. What colour change occurs in bromothymol blue solution if carbon dioxide is dissolved in the solution? Explain why.

4. Based on the colour changes observed, which of the vials showed the presence of carbon dioxide?

Forming Conclusions

5. From the results of your experiment, what can you infer about the production of carbon dioxide by plants and by animals in the light and the dark?

6. Write a statement to answer the question posed.

Extending

7. Suggest a possible experimental procedure to determine whether the carbon dioxide produced by the snail could be used by the aquatic plant in conditions of light or dark.

8. If your lab is equipped with oxygen-sensing probes, propose an experimental procedure using the aquatic plant, to record the production of oxygen under conditions of light and dark.

9. How might the techniques used in this inquiry be applied to a study investigating the effects of changes in carbon dioxide concentration on plants?

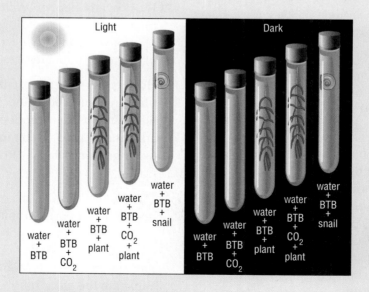

FIGURE C3.11 Set-up of vials for light and dark treatments

re**SEARCH**

The complex process of photosynthesis has been investigated through cell research based on the understanding of how molecules function. Find out more about cellular research on plants. Begin your search at

www.pearsoned.ca/
school/science10

Experiments to investigate gas production in organisms under various conditions may focus on the formation of the product or on the consumption of the reactants. For example, in a study of photosynthesis students may observe oxygen production by counting the bubbles of oxygen produced by an aquatic plant, or by measuring the volume of water displaced by the oxygen gas produced. Alternatively, photosynthesis may be studied by measuring the amount of carbon dioxide consumed in the process. Cellular respiration in plants or animals may be studied as the amount of oxygen consumed in the reaction or the amount of carbon dioxide produced as a product of the reaction. Oxygen-sensing probe ware can provide a measure of the change in the gas volume over the course of an experiment.

C3.2 Check and Reflect

Knowledge

1. Describe the process of photosynthesis. Include the word equation and the chemical equation.

2. What essential role does chlorophyll play in photosynthesis?

3. Explain the differences in activity of plant cells in the dark and in the sunlight.

Applications

4. Why is it useful to know the actual size of a cell or organelle?

5. *The chloroplasts and the mitochondria in a cell have opposite functions.* Agree or disagree with this statement. Explain your answer.

6. An important part of Alberta's economy is related to the oil and gas industry. Oil and gas, used to power our vehicles, heat our homes, and cook our meals, can be traced back to pre-historic plants and animals that died and were buried under layers of rock for millions of years. In fact, almost everything we eat or use can be traced back to plants because of their ability to take energy from the Sun to produce sugar and starch.

   Trace each of the following items back to plants. Draw a schematic to show the number of "degrees of separation" for each item.
   a) cotton shirt
   b) ham and cheese sandwich
   c) coal (the main source of electricity in Alberta)
   d) an item of your own choosing—see if you can get "6 degrees of separation"

Extensions

7. What would happen in the process of photosynthesis if:
   a) more carbon dioxide was available?
   b) the light intensity was increased?

8. Heat energy was not identified in the photosynthesis equation, yet gardeners will tell you that the warmth of a greenhouse is advantageous in producing healthy and faster growing plants. How do you explain this?

9. Have you ever been lazing on an air mattress on a lake or pool? Without using any energy of your own, you are able to drift around quite easily. Relate this experience to the movement of the chloroplasts in the cell. What are the chloroplasts drifting on? Design and build a model to mimic the fluidity of the cytoplasm and the movement of organelles within the cell.

C 3.3 The Leaf Tissues and Gas Exchange

Air can enter cells by passive diffusion. However, it would take a long time to get the needed volume of air into a plant that way, especially with the cuticle covering the surface of most of the plant. To solve this problem, the leaf has specialized cells to maximize its ability to exchange gases. There are also other specialized cells that function to provide the reactants and remove the products of the leaf's cellular activities.

Dermal Tissue

The epidermis on both the top and underside of the leaf is clear and very thin. Specialized cells called guard cells form tiny openings or pores called stomata that allow gas exchange to happen easily. The stomata regulate the movement of gases. They open into air chambers that connect with the cells of the ground tissue. Carbon dioxide and oxygen can therefore enter and leave the leaf by diffusion at any time. The direction of the movement of these gases depends on their concentration gradients. The majority of stomata are found in the lower epidermis on the underside of the leaf. Figure C3.12 shows the arrangement of stomata in a leaf.

It would not be efficient to have the stomata open all of the time. The guard cells that surround the stomata control whether they are open or closed. The guard cells are kidney bean-shaped and, depending on conditions, swell up to open the stomata, or shrink away so that the stomata are closed. Light striking the leaf stimulates the guard cells to accumulate potassium ions by active transport. As a result, the number of particles present in the guard cells increases, water enters by osmosis, and the guard cells swell up under increased turgor pressure. The outer walls of the guard cells are thinner than the inner walls, so the cell under pressure bulges outward and is drawn into a crescent shape. In this way, the stoma opens.

Guard cells function to allow materials in and out when necessary, but also to protect the leaves from losing too much water through open stomata. Because all gases must dissolve in a film of water to pass across cell membranes, a film of water is always on the surface of cells. This means that water is continually being lost from the plant by evaporation through the stomata. In conditions where water is not readily available, the guard cells become limp and this closes the stomata. A model of the mechanism for opening and closing the stomata is shown in Figure C3.13. The process of water vapour leaving the leaf through the stomata is called **transpiration**. Without the control system operated by the guard cells, transpiration could dangerously dehydrate a plant.

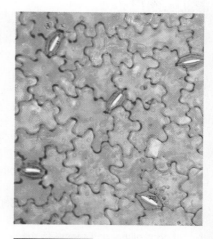

FIGURE C3.12 Stomata and guard cells in a leaf seen through the light microscope (approx. ×120)

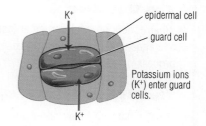

epidermal cell
guard cell

Potassium ions (K^+) enter guard cells.

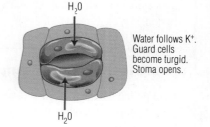

Water follows K^+. Guard cells become turgid. Stoma opens.

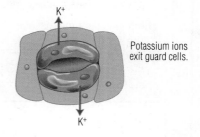

Potassium ions exit guard cells.

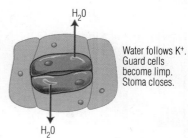

Water follows K^+. Guard cells become limp. Stoma closes.

FIGURE C3.13 The opening and closing of the stomata are controlled by changes in the cell contents, followed by movement of water.

Activity C14
Inquiry Lab

Student Reference **5, 8**

Required Skills

- Initiating and Planning
- Performing and Recording
- Analyzing and Interpreting
- Communication and Teamwork

Analyzing Stomata

Transpiration is the movement of water vapour out of the leaf through the stomata. By controlling the opening and closing of stomata, the guard cells provide the control system necessary to reduce water loss from the plant. In the first part of this activity you will observe plants, which your teacher provides, to obtain indirect evidence of this process of controlling water loss. In the second part of the activity, you will use prepared slides to make an analysis of the numbers of stomata present in different plants. You will use the data from both parts of the activity to form a conclusion.

The Question

What effects do environmental factors have on the number and appearance of stomata and on their ability to monitor the process of transpiration?

The Hypothesis

Using what you know about the role of stomata in plants, state what you think would happen to the number and appearance of stomata in conditions that are (a) dry or (b) humid.

Materials and Equipment

3 potted plants covered with clear plastic bags (e.g., cactus, jade, geranium)

prepared slides of leaf epidermis (e.g., cactus, geranium, pine needles, *Elodea*)

compound light microscope

CAUTION: Observe proper technique with the microscope and slides to ensure safe handling of equipment.

Procedure

1. Examine the three potted plants provided by your teacher. These plants have been covered with clear plastic bags for a few days, as shown in Figure C3.14.

2. As a large group, discuss the differences between the plants. Record your observations in a table of class results.

3. Examine each of the prepared slides of leaf epidermis provided by your teacher. Using the low-power objective, examine the slide and draw and label what you see. Include the name of the plant and the total magnification.

4. Move to the medium- and high-power objectives. Observe epidermal cells, presence or absence of stomata, cell nuclei, and chloroplasts.

5. Set up a data table in your notebook. Count and record the number of stomata in your field of view. Draw and label what you see, and include the name of the plant and the total magnification. Repeat this step twice more for each slide, observing cells in two other fields of view.

6. Using a spreadsheet or graphing calculator, enter the number of stomata per unit area found in each plant. Include the average of the three fields of view for each plant. Generate a bar graph to allow a comparison of the plants.

FIGURE C3.14 Set-up of plants for observing transpiration activity in step 1

Sensitivity of Stomata

The number and appearance of stomata in the epidermis are sensitive to environmental conditions. Since plants must regulate the loss of water through transpiration, those growing in hot, dry climates with low humidity have adapted to having fewer stomata. In places where humidity is high, water loss is not a problem and plants may have many stomata. Similarly, if carbon dioxide is in short supply, stomata may be open to the maximum to obtain whatever carbon dioxide is available. If there is a normal level of carbon dioxide available for photosynthesis, the stomata will be less stressed.

Ground Tissue

Between the upper epidermis and the lower epidermis of the leaf are specialized ground tissues called **mesophyll**. There are two very different types of mesophyll tissues. The **palisade tissue cells** are found just below the upper epidermis. They are long, rigid, rectangular cells that are tightly packed together and arranged so that a large number of cells are exposed to the Sun's rays. The palisade tissue cells are responsible for photosynthesis, so as you would expect, there are many chloroplasts in this layer of tissue. These cells require carbon dioxide as a reactant during photosynthesis and produce oxygen as one of the products.

Between the palisade tissue cells and the lower epidermis are loosely packed, irregularly shaped, less rigid cells making up the **spongy mesophyll tissue**. The increased space between these cells allows for the primary function of the spongy mesophyll tissue: gas exchange by diffusion throughout the leaf. The mesophyll cells will move oxygen toward the stomata for expulsion from the plant and will move carbon dioxide from the air toward the palisade cells. Figure C3.15 shows a cross section through a leaf.

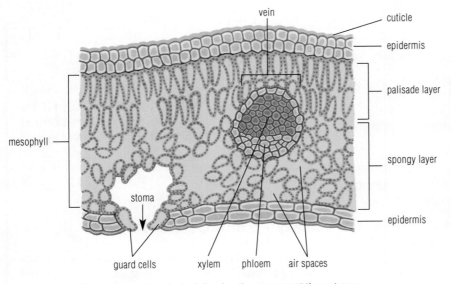

vein
cuticle
epidermis
palisade layer
mesophyll
spongy layer
stoma
epidermis
guard cells   xylem   phloem   air spaces

(a) A cross section of a leaf showing the component tissue types

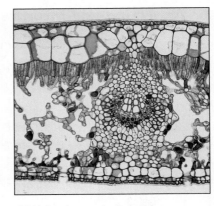

(b) Light micrograph of a leaf in cross section (approx. ×70)

FIGURE C3.15 Tissue relationships in a leaf

Activity C15

QuickLab

Airtight

Purpose

To observe the ability of leaves to exchange gases

Materials and Equipment

narrow-necked glass bottle	leaves similar to geranium leaves
straws	modelling clay
	water

FIGURE C3.16
Set-up of Quicklab experiment step 4

Procedure

1. For this activity, you will work in pairs. Partially fill the bottle with water as shown in Figure C3.16.

2. Cut a fresh leaf from the plant your teacher provides. Be sure to have a long stem attached to the leaf.

3. Wrap modelling clay around the stem, close to the leaf. Place the stem into the bottle so that the end of the stem is submerged in the water. Wrap the clay around the bottle opening to seal.

4. Poke a small hole in the clay and insert the straw. The straw should not touch the water. Re-seal the clay around the straw so that there is no air leakage. Figure C3.16 shows the experimental set-up.

5. Suck on the straw to pull the air out of the bottle. If you are having difficulty, check for holes in the straw or air leaks around the clay seal.

6. Have a partner observe what is happening in the water. Record the observations.

7. Exchange the straw for a clean one and re-seal the opening. Switch roles with your partner. Record your observations.

Questions

1. Describe what happened when air was withdrawn from the bottle.

2. Offer an explanation for your observations.

The process of diffusion is very efficient in plants because of the air spaces present in the spongy mesophyll of the leaf and within the stem. Air diffuses through the stomata and into air spaces in the leaf, through the intercellular spaces and down the stem. Activity C15 shows evidence of this airflow. As air is sucked out of the bottle, a vacuum is created and air from outside enters the bottle through the leaf and stem.

Vascular Tissue

The vascular tissue provides the leaf with the water needed for transpiration and for photosynthesis, and also removes the sugars formed in photosynthesis. If you observe a leaf, you will see a network of ribs running through it. These ribs, called leaf veins, contain the vascular tissue of the leaf. The xylem and phloem tissues are bunched together like a handful of straws in a **vascular bundle**. The xylem transports water, necessary for photosynthesis, and dissolved salts from the roots to the leaf. The phloem transports the sugar manufactured in photosynthesis to the rest of the plant. The vascular bundles are direct extensions of the vascular bundles of the stem. They branch into finer veins within the spongy mesophyll. Examine Figure C3.15 again to see the relationships between all the tissues in the leaf.

Gas Exchange in Plants

In plants, all gas exchange occurs by diffusion. There are no organs specifically concerned with gas exchange. Diffusion of gases occurs through air spaces and then across cell membranes. In the leaf, the stomata, regulated by guard cells, allow for more efficient intake of gases and therefore for more rapid diffusion of carbon dioxide into the palisade and spongy mesophyll cells. Diffusion of oxygen out of the leaf is also maximized by the air spaces in the ground tissue and the presence of stomata in the epidermis.

The leaf is not the only place where gas exchange occurs. You may have noticed what appear to be blisters or slashes on the stems of trees and herbaceous plants, as shown in Figure C3.17. These are natural openings. They are pores along woody stems and mature roots, the result of a split in the secondary outer tissues that replace the epidermis. These pores are called **lenticels** and, like the stomata, provide a pathway for gas exchange. Like the stomata, the lenticels also provide an opening for transpiration to occur.

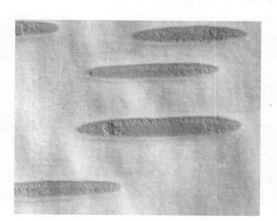

FIGURE C3.17 Photograph of lenticels as seen on the inner surface of a piece of birch bark. Lenticels allow gas exchange to and from the inner parts of the tree trunk. (approx. ×4)

Knowledge

1. Draw a cross section of a leaf and label the upper and lower epidermis, palisade tissue, spongy mesophyll tissue, and chloroplasts.

2. Describe the functions of the following leaf structures:
   a) epidermis
   b) guard cells
   c) palisade tissue
   d) spongy mesophyll tissue
   e) xylem tissue
   f) phloem tissue

3. What is the function of stomata?

4. Describe circumstances that would affect the number of stomata. Explain your answer.

5. Explain why the palisade cells are tightly compacted while the spongy mesophyll cells are more loosely organized.

6. Identify two environmental stresses that would cause stomata to close. Provide an explanation for each response.

Applications

7. What is the advantage of having the palisade tissue directly below the upper epidermis?

8. Stomata are found mainly on the lower epidermis. Propose a reason for this.

9. In a paragraph, state the relationship between lenticels, stomata, guard cells, and the process of diffusion.

10. Greenhouse plants often have trouble surviving when placed in a natural environment. Provide a possible explanation why this is so.

Extensions

11. Using any materials of your choice, design and build a model that will demonstrate the workings and purpose of the stomata.

12. "Stomatal density" is the term used by scientists to refer to the number of stomata found within a certain area of the surface of a plant. In Activity C14 you determined stomatal density in various plants. This type of analysis can provide insights into the environmental conditions in which the plant was found.

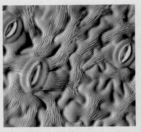 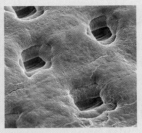

(a) Broad leaf (approx. ×500)   (b) Needle (approx. ×300)

a) As you move from the foothills to the mountains deciduous trees intermingle with coniferous trees until at higher elevations the trees are primarily coniferous with needles rather than broad leaves. Needle shape is an adaptation of the leaf to climate. Needles contain less sap and are less likely to freeze. Being dark in colour and staying on the tree year-round, they can use whatever sunlight is available to the full. Using the results of Activity C14 or additional research, explain how stomatal density and needle structure also contribute to the survival of coniferous trees at higher elevations or latitudes.

b) A scientist has proposed that elevated CO_2 levels will result in decreased stomatal density while depressed CO_2 levels will result in increased stomatal density. Suggest a possible controlled experimental procedure to test this hypothesis.

c) Paleobotanists study fossil imprints of plants. In some cases the imprints provide evidence of stomatal density.
   i) How might this data be used to suggest the environmental conditions of prehistoric times?
   ii) How might the research of paleobotanists be used in the context of current studies of climate change?

C 3.4 Transport in Plants

How is it possible for a plant like the tall Aspen shown in Figure C3.18 to transport the water it absorbs through its roots to the leaves in its uppermost branches so far away? This is obviously a difficult task and, one might infer, a task that must require energy input. The tree must accomplish this task, because photosynthesis occurs only in the leaves and requires water, and without photosynthesis the tree would die.

Many factors are involved in the movement of water in plants. In section C2.0, you learned about the processes of osmosis, diffusion, active transport, and transpiration. These processes result in the movement of materials through plants. Earlier on in section C3.0, you learned about the structures involved in the movement of materials through plants, such as cell membranes, vacuoles, and the vascular tissues. How do all these work together to bring about the movement of water? To answer this, you need to connect the processes and the structures—just like putting together the pieces of a jigsaw puzzle.

FIGURE C3.18 Very tall Aspens like the ones shown here are a feature of the Alberta landscape.

Activity C16
QuickLab

Capillary Action

The ability of the surface of a liquid to cling to the surface of a solid, causing the liquid to move along that solid, is called **capillary action**. Capillary action is at work when you place one corner of a paper towel on a spill and the liquid moves along the towel until it is completely absorbed.

Purpose

To demonstrate a property of water and capillary action

Materials and Equipment

beaker of concentrated food colouring	pennies
3 capillary tubes of same length but different diameters	liquid dish detergent
	potted herbaceous plant
	droppers
	water

Procedure

1. Clean a penny, and using a dropper, add one drop of water at a time, very gently, to the top of the flat coin. How many drops can you get to stay on the penny: 1, 10, 100, 1000? When you think you have reached the maximum, add just one drop of liquid dish detergent. Record your results.

2. Place all three capillary tubes into the beaker of food colouring. Allow them to sit for a day. Observe and record the results.

3. Using the plant provided, cut the stem off close to the level of the soil. Your teacher may do this as a demonstration. Observe for a few minutes. You should begin to see water flowing out of the stem.

Questions

1. How many drops of water were you able to get to stay on the penny? Was this number more or less than what you had expected?

2. Describe what happened when dishwashing liquid was added. Do you think you would have been able to continue adding water if you had not added the dishwashing liquid?

3. Compare the three capillary tubes in step 2. Which tube transported the food colouring the greatest distance?

4. State a relationship between the diameter of the capillary tube and the distance of transportation.

5. Explain why you were able to observe water moving out of the cut stem. Why did the water not drain back into the roots?

Take a moment to review what you know about the structures and processes that move materials in plants and the ways in which they may all be connected. Draw a diagram of a plant in your notebook showing the shoot system and the root system. On the diagram, identify the structures involved in the transport of materials and place the processes where you think they occur. You will have an opportunity to revise your drawing later in this section.

Cohesion and Adhesion

You have probably been aware since you were a small child that water is transported up the plant from the roots to the leaves. The question to consider now is, what structures and mechanisms allow the plant to pump water to the leaves, often a very great distance, against the force of gravity?

The experiments in Activity C16 appear simple, but they illustrate the complex property of water that allows water molecules to cling to each other and to other molecules. This property aids in the transport of water in plants. As you added more and more drops of water to the penny, you probably noticed that the water was forming a dome on top of the penny. Each droplet was clinging to the last one. The attraction of water molecules to other water molecules is called **cohesion**. This property is due to the polar nature of the water molecule. The slightly positive end of one water molecule attracts the slightly negative end of other water molecules with the result that the molecules tend to hold together. Each droplet that you added was attracted to the other droplets and they held together forming the dome shape. When the dishwashing liquid was added, the attraction between molecules was broken and a mini-flood was the result.

Because of their polar nature, water molecules are also attracted to molecules of other substances. In the capillary tubes, the water was able to inch up the tube partly due to cohesion, but also because the water particles were holding on to the glass sides of the tubing. Imagine rock climbers grabbing on with hands and feet to anything on the rock surface that will assist them in inching up the face of the rock. Some of the water molecules are attracted to the glass and pull themselves and other molecules up the tubing. The attraction of water molecules to molecules of other substances is called **adhesion**.

Root Pressure

In the early morning, you may have seen droplets of water on the tips of blades of grass or at the edges of small plants like strawberries. The movement of water into these areas occurs at night when the rate of transpiration is low, but root cells are still accumulating minerals. This movement is the result of **root pressure**. In Activity C16, you would have observed water flowing from the cut stem of the plant. The fluid coming out of the stem is also due in part to root pressure, a pressure created in the xylem in the following manner. Dissolved minerals are present in the cells of the root as a result of active transport, thus producing a higher solute concentration inside the cell. Through the process of osmosis, water is drawn into the cells, creating positive pressure that forces fluid up the xylem. Water is forced from a higher pressure in the roots, toward the lower pressure in the leaves.

Examine the photos of a carnation and a celery stalk after immersion of the stems in food colouring.

1. In a short paragraph, describe what you observed in the carnation and celery stalk (Figure C3.19).

2. What are you able to infer from the results of this experiment? Explain your inference.

3. Are you able to identify any of the cells in the celery stalk cross section? Are all the cells of the stalk stained?

4. Develop a statement to explain how adhesion and cohesion are involved in moving the food colouring up the stem of the carnation and the celery stalk.

(b) A celery stalk

(a) A carnation

FIGURE C3.19 Appearance of plant tissues after immersion in solutions of food colouring

Root pressure, while important in some plants, is not the complete explanation for water movement. It is able to push water to a maximum of only a few metres and many plants are over 100 m tall. The overall process of water movement is affected in a major way by transpiration, which has the effect of pulling water up the stem.

The properties of adhesion and cohesion are at work in moving the food colouring in the carnations and celery stalks. In growing plants, transpiration occurring at the stomata and lenticels has the additional effect of "sucking" the water up. As water is lost in the stem and leaves, it must be replaced, and so water from below is drawn up the stem as a result of transpiration. This is the reason that only certain cells, those present in the xylem, are stained in the celery stalk preparation (Figure C3.19(b)).

From Root to Leaf: Water Transport in Plants

Earlier in this section, you drew a diagram trying to place all the pieces of the jigsaw puzzle called *transport* together. Pull out that diagram and as you work through this discussion make changes, additions, or deletions to it. See if you can create your own study guide for the flow of matter in plant systems. Keep in mind that substances (gases, minerals, sugars) must be dissolved in a film of water to be transported in plants. In addition, transport has costs for the plant in the form of energy expended in active transport across membranes, in the growth and development of vascular tissue, and in the replacement of the water lost through transpiration.

The transport of water in the plant is the result of a combination of factors. Differences in pressure are caused by osmosis and transpiration. At the root, root hairs absorb minerals from the soil by active transport. Water then enters the root hairs through osmosis because of the high concentration of solutes inside the root cells. This leads to root pressure, which forces water through the cells or along cell walls into the xylem. Once the water is in the xylem tubes, it must be moved against gravity up the stem to the leaves, sometimes a distance of as much as 100 m.

The evaporation of water through the stomata and lenticels in the process of transpiration creates a **tension** or **transpiration pull**. As each water molecule evaporates into the surroundings, it creates a pull on the adjacent water molecules. Combined with the forces of adhesion and cohesion, this transpiration pull is enough to draw the water up the xylem vessels to the leaves. Once the water arrives at the leaf, the transpiration pull is enough to move the water from the xylem into the ground tissue. A high proportion of the water is lost from the plant as evaporation through the stomata. In this way, the transpiration pull is maintained to continue drawing water up the stem. Transpiration depends on temperature; if the temperature is high, the rate of evaporation through the stomata will be high and movement through the xylem will be rapid. In ideal conditions, water can rise 75 cm per minute.

The rest of the water in the leaf is used to manufacture sugars in the process of photosynthesis. These sugars in solution then move into the phloem tissue for distribution to other parts of the plant. Figure C3.20 indicates the direction of water movement, based on the pressure gradients.

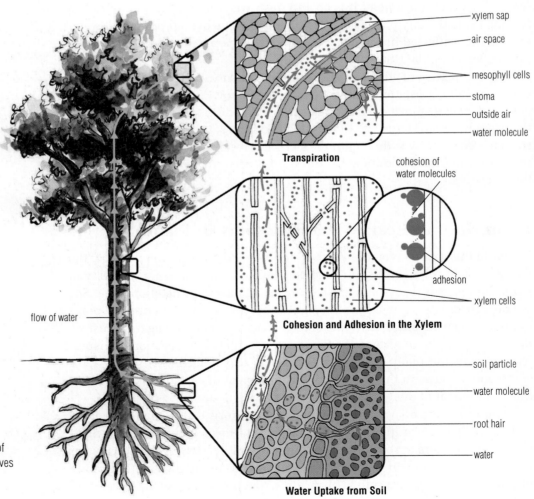

Transpiration

xylem sap
air space
mesophyll cells
stoma
outside air
water molecule

cohesion of water molecules

adhesion

xylem cells

Cohesion and Adhesion in the Xylem

flow of water

soil particle
water molecule
root hair
water

Water Uptake from Soil

FIGURE C3.20 The flow of water from the roots to the leaves

Inquiry Lab

Tonicity and Plant Cells

Tonicity refers to the concentration of solute particles in any solution. If the environment of a cell has a higher concentration of solute particles than the cell contents, the cell environment is said to be hypertonic or to have a higher tonicity. Living cells continuously respond to the tonicity of their environment.

The Question

What is the effect of tonicity on plant cells?

The Hypothesis

Develop a hypothesis for the effect of increased tonicity of the environment on plant cells.

Materials and Equipment

compound light microscope

Elodea canadensis leaves or suitable alternative

glass slides and coverslips

droppers

water

concentrated salt solution

CAUTION: Observe proper technique with the microscope to ensure safe handling of equipment. Wash your hands at the end of the lab activity.

Procedure

1. Remove a leaf from the *Elodea* plant and prepare a wet mount slide.

2. On low power, focus on an area of cells near the leaf's edge. Find an area in which you can clearly identify the following cell structures: cell wall, nucleus, chloroplasts, and vacuoles. The cytoplasm is colourless, so it is not directly visible. Switch to a higher power objective lens to see all of the cell structures.

3. Draw a diagram of your field of view. Calculate the size of a single *Elodea* cell using the procedure from Activity C2. Label the cell structures on your diagram and include total magnification and actual size.

4. Continue to observe the slide for a few more minutes and record observations that relate to moving materials around the cell or into and out of the cell.

5. Place a drop of concentrated salt solution at one end of the coverslip. With a paper towel at the opposite end of the coverslip, slowly draw the salt solution under the coverslip as you would if you were staining the cells. In this way, you will change the tonicity of the environment of the cells.

6. Carefully observe the slide for any changes in the cell structures. Pay particular attention to the vacuoles. Adjust the light to maximize the contrast between cell structures. Vacuoles may be difficult to distinguish, as they are transparent and full of water when the cell is turgid. Record your observations.

Analyzing and Interpreting

1. What movement did you notice inside the cells in step 4? Explain what was causing the movement.

2. State a relationship between the length of time taken to make the observation in step 4 and the amount of movement inside the cell. What variable is responsible for the relationship you have stated?

3. How was the tonicity of the environment changed in step 5?

4. What did you observe in steps 5 and 6? What happened to the cell?

Forming Conclusions

5. Based on your knowledge of cell structures and the mechanisms involved in transport, state which of the structures and mechanisms respond to an increase in the tonicity of the cell's surroundings. Support your statement with evidence from the experiment.

Applying and Connecting

6. Use a water balloon as a model to explain what happens to the central vacuole as it gains and loses water.

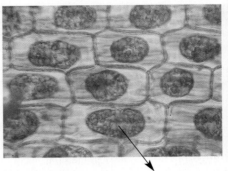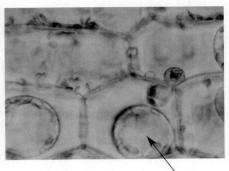

Differences in the salt concentration of the environment affect structures in plant cells.

(a) In a hypertonic environment, plant cells become plasmolysed and the plant appears wilted. Light micrograph (approx. ×700)

H_2O leaves cell

(b) In a hypotonic environment, water enters by osmosis and the cells become turgid. Light micrograph (approx. ×700)

H_2O enters cell

The Effect of Tonicity on Plant Cells

Changes in the tonicity of the environment have an effect on osmosis and on the arrangement of structures in plant cells. You will be able to observe these effects if you place some plant cells, for instance, an *Elodea* leaf, in a concentrated salt solution. The higher solute concentration on the outside of the cell causes water to pass by osmosis from the cell into the surroundings. The effect on the cell is called **plasmolysis**. The water contained inside the vacuole leaves the vacuole and the cell, with the result that the vacuole appears shrunken. Imagine the appearance of a water balloon if you slowly let out the water. As the vacuole shrinks, the cell contents begin to pull away from the cell wall. The cell membrane may become visible because it is no longer pushed up against the cell wall. The result of plasmolysis of the cells is a leaf that is wilted or limp, because it is no longer being held out by the pressure of fluid against the walls of each individual cell.

If the leaf is returned to fresh water, the water will re-enter the cell by osmosis, with the result that the vacuole swells, and the internal pressure increases until the vacuole cannot increase in size. At this point, the cell is said to be turgid. Water can continue to pass in and out of the vacuole but there is no net increase in volume. Turgidity is important to plants because the pressure in all of the cells combines to hold the green parts of the plant up to the sunlight. This allows the chloroplasts to trap light energy. Maintaining turgidity or pressure within cells allows the plant to hold itself up. For this reason, it is beneficial for plant cells to be in a hypotonic environment. Figure C3.21 shows the effects of hypertonic and hypotonic environments on plant cells.

From Source to Sink: Sugar Transport in Plants

If you were to remove a ring of phloem tissue from the stem of a plant, the plant would die because the cells would not be receiving the products of photosynthesis where they are needed. If phloem cells are killed, through dehydration or excessive heat for instance, the movement of sugars stops. The mechanism of phloem transport is a critical process for multicellular plants. It takes the products of photosynthesis from the place where they are manufactured, the leaves, also called the **source**, to the places where they will be used or stored, called the **sink**.

Recall the structure of the phloem tissue discussed on page 300. Sieve tube cells are cylindrical cells that lack nuclei and have perforated sides and end walls that allow the cytoplasm to stream between cells. These sieve tube cells depend on the companion cells for many functions, including the movement of sugars into and out of the sieve tube cells.

At the leaf, that is, the source, the phloem becomes loaded as companion cells use carrier proteins and active transport to take in sugar molecules from the sites of photosynthesis. Water then moves into the cells by osmosis. In turn, the water moves into the sieve cells. The increased water pressure inside the sieve cells pushes the water and sugars through the phloem to the rest of the plant. Imagine increasing the pressure inside a hose. As the pressure builds, the water is forced through the hose until it finds a place to escape. In the case of phloem transport, the end is a sink, which may be a root, a tuber, or another part of the plant such as a fruit. This description of moving materials through the phloem is called the **pressure-flow theory**.

Sugars are actively transported across cell membranes from the sieve tube cells into adjacent cells. The sugar molecules may be used in growth, respiration, or other life processes, for example, at the growing tips (meristems). Sugars may also be stored in the roots, stems, or leaves. As the sugars leave the sieve tube cells, water also moves out into surrounding cells. The water may increase the turgidity of the surrounding cells, or leave the plant through transpiration, or move into the xylem tissue for transport through the plant. As the water pressure in the sieve tube is decreased at the sink, more water and sugar is pushed into these cells from the cells above. The **pressure differences** produced by active transport and osmosis maintain a constant flow of food down the sieve tube, as shown in Figure C3.22.

re**SEARCH**

The companion cells are thought to support the living sieve tube cells. Find out how the interaction of these cells makes phloem transport possible. Begin your search at

www.pearsoned.ca/ school/science10

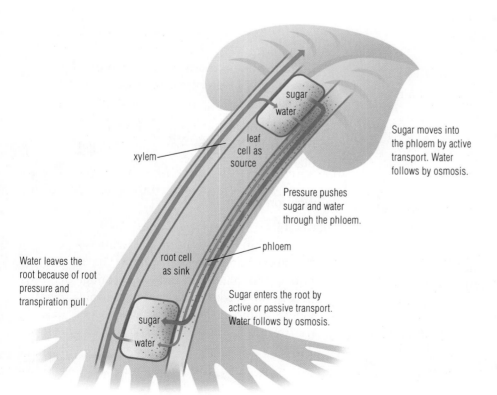

FIGURE C3.22 Movement of sugar and water through the phloem and xylem. Arrows show the direction of movement.

sugar
water
leaf cell as source
xylem

Sugar moves into the phloem by active transport. Water follows by osmosis.

Pressure pushes sugar and water through the phloem.

phloem
root cell as sink

Water leaves the root because of root pressure and transpiration pull.

sugar
water

Sugar enters the root by active or passive transport. Water follows by osmosis.

Design a Lab

Environmental Conditions and Water Movement

Environmental conditions that cause an increased rate of water loss from the plant will have an impact on the movement of water.

The Question

How do environmental conditions affect the movement of water in plants?

Design and Conduct Your Investigation

1. Make a list of variables that you think may affect the amount of water lost from the plant and therefore the movement of water in the plant.

2. For each variable on your list, write a hypothesis to predict how changing that variable will affect movement of water in the plant.

3. Choose one of the variables on your list. Plan and write the procedure for an investigation to test your hypothesis. Outline the steps of your investigation, including safety precautions, and identify the variables that you will control and those that will be manipulated.

4. List all the materials and equipment you will need to carry out your investigation.

5. Submit your lab design to your teacher. Once your teacher has approved your design, perform the investigation.

6. Analyze your results. Do your data support your hypothesis?

7. Compare your experimental design with the designs and procedures used by your classmates. How might you adapt or improve upon your design?

8. Identify any new questions that arose from your experiment and that you would like to explore.

C3.4   Check and Reflect

Knowledge

1. What are the properties of water that aid in water transport in plants?

2. Explain how the vacuoles of a plant cell are affected when the cell is placed in a hypertonic solution and in a hypotonic solution.

3. Water loss could be a danger to the survival of the plant. Explain the control mechanisms the plant uses to reduce water loss.

4. What are the two types of plant vascular tissues? What is the function of each?

5. Suggest a role for turgidity in photosynthesis.

6. Refer to the Minds-On Activity on page 317. Explain why only certain of the cells were dyed by the food colouring.

7. Describe the processes involved in the movement of water from the roots to the leaves.

8. Explain how sugars from photosynthesis are transported from the leaves to other parts of a plant.

Application

9. Create a concept map showing the relationships between the following structures and processes involved in the transport of materials and gas exchange in plants: roots, root hairs, root epidermis, xylem, phloem, stomata, ground tissue, transpiration.

C 3.5 Control Systems

Animals have both instinctive and learned behaviours that allow them to respond to internal and external stimuli. If you touch something hot, you pull your hand away. In the presence of a loud noise, you cover your ears. You and other animals respond to changes in your environment as well as to signs from your body. When you react to these signals in some way, you are responding to the **stimuli**. The way in which you react is based on the type and direction of the stimulus. If you are hungry and you smell pizza, you will most likely follow your nose to the food.

Plants are not as obviously responsive as animals but they do have definite responses to specific stimuli. Think about the needs of a plant and the changes in a plant's surroundings that would require it to respond. The plant needs to be able to carry out photosynthesis and therefore requires water, carbon dioxide, and light. Plants grow toward the light. This growth movement is a response of the plant to the stimulus of light and is called **phototropism**. "Photo" means light and "tropism" refers to the movement of the plant in response to the stimulus. Stems exhibit **positive phototropism**, meaning that they grow toward light. Roots show a weak **negative phototropism** because they grow away from the light.

You may be less aware of another external stimulus to which growing plants respond. Observe the photo in Figure C3.23 showing a germinating bean seed. You will notice that growth is occurring in two directions. The shoot system is growing up toward the light, and the root system is growing down away from the light. There is another factor at play—gravity. Plants respond to Earth's gravitational force through growth movement as well. This is called **gravitropism**. Stems grow against the gravitational force and so show **negative gravitropism** while roots grow toward the gravitational force and so show **positive gravitropism**. An older term for gravitropism is **geotropism**. The responses to these factors are summarized in Table C3.1 below.

infoBIT

Over time, a houseplant kept in one location will show signs of growing toward the light. To avoid having the plant grow entirely in one direction, it is necessary to move the plant occasionally, either to a new location or simply to rotate it.

FIGURE C3.23 A germinating bean seed showing the opposite directions of the growth of the shoot and root

TABLE C3.1 Responses of Plant Parts to Stimuli

Plant Part	Stimulus	Tropism
stem	light	positive phototropism
root	light	weak negative phototropism
stem	gravity	negative gravitropism
root	gravity	positive gravitropism

The observed growth responses to light and gravity are most probably due to the plant's attempt to meet its needs. Roots growing away from the light and in the same direction as gravity are more likely to find soil, water, and minerals. Stems growing toward the light and against gravity will receive the energy required by the chloroplasts in their leaves for the photosynthesis reaction. Tropisms are important **control systems** to ensure survival of the plant.

Inquiry Lab

Investigating Gravitropism and Phototropism

The Questions

1. What evidence is there to indicate that roots respond to gravity?

2. Which part of the stem is responsible for producing a positive phototropic response?

The Hypothesis

1. Read Procedure Part 1 and propose a method to determine that gravity, and not some other variable, is responsible for the growth of roots downward.

2. Based on your observations, propose the location in the plant where the phototropic response is initiated.

Materials and Equipment

oat seeds

corn seeds (pre-soaked for 48 hours)

planting tray

potting soil

light source

Petri dishes

paper towel

cotton batting

aluminium foil

grease pencil

gloves

Part 1
Procedure

1. Imagine the Petri dish as the face of a clock. Mark four positions on the underside of the Petri dish at 12:00, 3:00, 6:00, and 9:00 positions.

2. Place corn seeds at the marked positions in the Petri dish, narrow side facing into the centre of the dish. Try to keep the seeds positioned this way throughout the set-up. See Figure C3.24.

3. Place a wet paper towel on top of the seeds.

4. Add cotton batting on top of the paper towel so that when you place the lid on the Petri dish, the seed and paper towel do not move.

5. Close the lid on the Petri dish and seal the dish with tape.

6. With the seeds facing out, tape the dish to the inside of a closet or cupboard door that will be in complete darkness.

7. Leave the Petri dish untouched for several days in the dark.

8. Observe the germination of the seeds and record your observations.

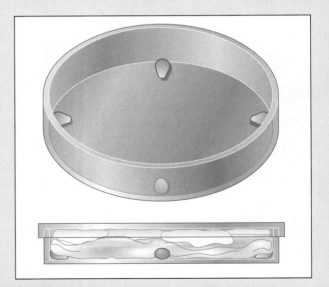

FIGURE C3.24   Placement of corn seeds for steps 2–5.

Analyzing and Interpreting

1. Draw a diagram to show the corn seed germination. Label what you believe to be the shoot and the root.

Forming Conclusions

2. Make a statement relating the germination response of the seed to gravity. Include an explanation of how you can be sure that what you observed is not a phototropic response.

Part 2
Procedure

1. Fill the planting tray with potting soil. Scatter oat seeds into the tray and cover them lightly with soil.

2. Keep the tray in a location so that only one side of the tray is facing the light source.

3. Keep watering the oats lightly and allow the oats to grow 2–3 cm above the soil.

4. Transplant approximately one-third of the oat seedlings to a deeper pot and cover them with soil, exposing only their tips.

5. Keep the deeper pot of covered seedlings in the original setting relative to the light source.

6. Cover the tips of another third of the oat seedlings in the tray with aluminium foil. Make sure that only the tips are covered, not any of the parts below the tips. Leave these in the tray in its original setting.

7. Allow the remaining third of the seedlings to remain untouched in the tray in its original setting.

8. Allow the seedlings to grow for several days, watering them and making observations daily.

9. Carefully observe the growth of the oat seedlings in the three conditions and record your observations.

Analyzing and Interpreting

1. Draw a diagram of your observations.

2. Use a chart similar to the one below to record your explanations of the observations. Remember to give your chart a title.

Growth Condition	Observation of Tropism	Explanation for the Observation
control group		
seedlings covered in soil exposing only the tip		
seedlings' tips covered with aluminium foil		

Forming Conclusions

3. Where is phototropic response initiated in the seedlings?

Extending

4. This activity is similar to one that Charles and Francis Darwin conducted. They concluded that the phototropic stimulus was detected by the tip of the plant, but that the actual growth response of bending was carried out at another location. Do your data support their conclusion? Explain.

Investigations of Phototropism

Positive phototropism is easy to observe but more difficult to explain. The series of investigations that revealed the mechanism of phototropism are classic examples of scientific inquiry, in which observations lead to questions and questions lead to controlled experiments. The scientists who formulated the questions and conducted the experiments were:

- Charles Darwin and his son Francis, who asked in 1880: *Which part of the plant detects and responds to the phototropic stimulus?*
- Peter Boysen-Jensen, who asked in 1913: *What is the signal that initiates the phototropic response?*
- F. W. Went, who asked in 1926: *What is the specific substance responsible for initiating the phototropic response?*

All these scientists focussed their experiments on a particular part of the shoot system in the developing seedling of the oat plant, *Avena sativa*, and various other grasses. The outer sheath of an oat or grass seedling covers the developing leaves. The shoot grows as a result of the lengthening of the cells of this outer sheath. Once the shoot reaches 4–6 cm, the sheath stops growing and the enclosed stem and leaves split through and continue growing. If light comes from one direction only, the seedlings will show phototropism by bending of the sheath toward the light source. The Darwins, Boysen-Jensen, and Went conducted their experiments during the growth period when the outer sheath lengthens rapidly.

The experiment that you performed in Part 2 of Activity C19, in which you used oat seedlings under different conditions of growth, was very similar to the one performed by Charles and Francis Darwin. Figure C3.25 shows their results. They found that the seedlings with the tips covered did not respond to light, and so they were able to conclude that the tip of the stem was the area responsible for the detection of the light stimulus, but it was not the place where the response was carried out. The plants with everything except the tips buried still showed a growth response toward the light. The Darwins inferred that the cells of the tip were somehow communicating with the cells in the area of the bending. Charles Darwin documented their findings in his publication, *The Power of Movement in Plants*.

By 1913, Peter Boysen-Jensen, a Dutch plant physiologist, was trying to determine how the tip was communicating with the area of elongation. The **area of elongation** was lower on the leaf and facing away from the light source. It was called the area of elongation because the phototropic response was created by the elongation of cells on the side of the leaf facing away from the light, causing the leaf to bend toward the light as demonstrated in Figure C3.26.

Boysen-Jensen snipped off the tip of the grass seedlings, covered the stump with gelatin, and replaced the tip. Phototropism continued normally. The gelatin had not interfered with the plant's detection of the stimulus, nor with the growth response. He then tried the same procedure using a thin slice of the mineral mica instead of the gelatin. Phototropism was not observed in this experiment.

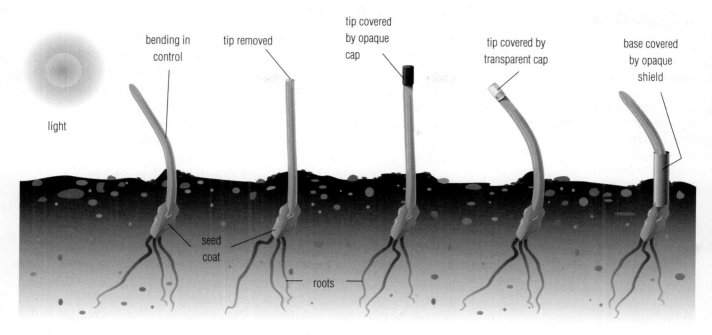

FIGURE C3.25 Stages in the Darwins' experiment on phototropism

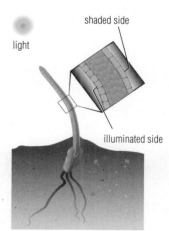

FIGURE C3.26 The effect of changes in cells in the area of elongation on the bending of the plant toward the light

Boysen-Jensen concluded that whatever was responsible for communicating stimulus information from the tip to the area of elongation was able to diffuse through the gelatin, but not through the mica. He suggested that the growth response could only be accomplished as a result of a chemical moving from the tip to the area of elongation.

In 1926, a graduate student in Holland, F. W. Went, was able to isolate this chemical substance. It was later given the name **auxin**. Since then, analysis of the chemical substance has indicated that the auxin is a **hormone**, a chemical compound that is manufactured in one area and transported to another location where, in low concentrations, it has the ability to initiate a physiological response—in this case, cell elongation. Other plant hormones have been isolated since Went's discovery and are used in horticulture.

The Mechanism of Gravitropism

How does a root know to grow toward the gravitational force? If a plant gets knocked over, how do the roots know which way is down? Scientists believe that plants rely on heavy starch particles in specialized cells as indicators of gravity. If a plant is tipped, the starch grains shift and settle in a new location due to gravity. Think of a jar partially filled with jellybeans. As long as the jar is standing upright, the jellybeans are at the bottom. What happens if the jar is knocked over? The jellybeans shift and settle on the new bottom. When the starch grains do this in the root cells, it is thought that the movement is detected by the plant, and a growth response results. This hypothesis received considerable support from microgravity studies in space shuttle experiments.

*re*SEARCH

Investigate the plant hormones that have been described since the discovery of auxin. Begin your search at

 www.pearsoned.ca/school/science10

reSEARCH

Using the data from *PlantWatch* and any additional information you can find on a plant of your choice, compile and organize data on flowering time. Analyze the data based on variables that might influence flowering time. Begin your search at

www.pearsoned.ca/
school/science10

Other Control Mechanisms

Other tropic responses apart from phototropism and gravitropism have been identified in plants. The tendrils of a pea plant that come in contact with a chain-link fence will attach to it and so receive support as the plant grows upward. This is a response to touch. Plants also respond to temperature, chemicals, and water.

To reproduce, the plant must flower and produce seeds. The flowering of plants at particular times of the year is often in response to the length of darkness the plant is exposed to. This is another control mechanism. Some plants require long nights (more than 12 hours of darkness) to produce flowers. Examples include chrysanthemums, poinsettias, and Christmas cactus. Other plants require more than 12 hours of light to flower. These include coneflowers, lettuce, spinach, and potatoes. Some plants will flower regardless of the length of dark and light periods, if they have all of their other needs met. These plants include tomatoes, strawberries, and corn.

Some scientists believe that climate change is affecting the blooming of plant species. By tracking bloom times in different locales over many years, it may be possible to determine if there are links between climate changes and plant responses. The Alberta Wildflower Survey was started in 1987 and has expanded to become *PlantWatch*, organized through the University of Alberta Devonian Botanic Gardens. The program, coordinated by University of Alberta research scientist Elizabeth Beaubien, includes amateur scientists in the work of tracking bloom times of common plants. To participate, you must adhere to recording and reporting protocols established by the program. Such protocols are important to the process of scientific inquiry because they set the rules of the study and ensure accurate data collection.

C3.5 Check and Reflect

Knowledge

1. Define tropism in your own words.

2. Explain what is meant by the terms "positive phototropism" and "negative gravitropism."

3. What are the benefits of phototropism and gravitropism for plants?

4. Explain the results of Charles and Francis Darwin's work. How did their observations further the study of plant physiology?

5. Describe how the work of Boysen-Jensen is an example of scientific inquiry.

Applications

6. Explain the statement: *Tropisms are the plant's control mechanisms.*

7. Why was it important in your experiment with the corn seeds to ensure that the seeds were not exposed to light?

Extensions

8. Plant physiologists are able to produce synthetic plant hormones. Suggest possible purposes for these chemical compounds. Use print or electronic media to research your answer.

9. Create a list of plants with different light requirements for flowering that grow in your area.

10. Imagine that you are making the rules or protocol for data collection and reporting for *PlantWatch*. Create a format for the compilation of data that will be useful in determining whether bloom dates are changing over time for particular species of plants found in Alberta. Compare and discuss your format with a classmate. After your discussion, is there anything you would change to improve the data collection?

Dr. Olga Kovalchuk— Biotechnology Research Scientist

Dr. Olga Kovalchuk

Plants are not able to move away from conditions that threaten their survival. A single plant cannot adapt to changes in its environment, but over time, a species can adapt to survive. Dr. Olga Kovalchuk studies genetic adaptation of plants to environmental stress. Her research at the University of Lethbridge focusses on environmental pollutants such as ionizing and UV-B radiation, heavy metals, and toxic chemicals, and their potentially damaging effect on DNA.

Dr. Kovalchuk has an M.D. degree and received her Ph.D. from the Ukrainian Genetics and Hygiene Research Centre in Kiev. Her Ph.D. research involved development and testing of plant-based systems to monitor genetic effects of radioactive contamination. These systems were later called "biological Geiger counters" because they were able to provide information on the levels and effects of radiation. With researchers at the Chernobyl Research Centre, Dr. Kovalchuk showed that certain communities of plant species are adapted for survival in radioactively contaminated soil. One of her long-term goals is to find the molecular mechanisms that allow these plants to adapt and survive.

Combining her interests in genetics and medicine, Dr. Kovalchuk is conducting the first-ever detailed study to compare cellular responses to varying and sustained doses of radiation and is involved in research to find new approaches to the use of radiation therapy in the treatment of cancer. In her investigations, she works in collaboration with other scientists. She shares her passion for science with her husband, Dr. Igor Kovalchuk, whose research focusses on how a plant responds to attack from bacteria or viruses. World centres of biotechnology and cancer research are interested in their collaborative research at the University of Lethbridge.

Dr. Kovalchuk's message to students is, "The more you know, the more doors will be opened to you in your life. Currently, there are exciting opportunities for young scientists in all areas of research. Get involved and you may contribute to developing hardier crops, feeding the poor, fighting climate change, or finding a cure for cancer. This is very challenging and satisfying work. By encouraging young people to become involved in research, we will ensure Canadian leadership in many scientific fields. Let's be the first!"

1. Why is the ability to work on a team important for a research scientist?

2. What part of Dr. Kovalchuk's research is most interesting to you? What else would you like to know?

3. Identify a question, problem, or issue related to plants, that you would like to research.

Knowledge

1. What are the benefits to an organism of being multicellular?

2. Describe the difference between cells, tissues, and organs. Give examples of each.

3. Name the two main plant systems. How do they differ?

4. Define the following terms:
   a) dermal tissue
   b) ground tissue
   c) vascular tissue
   d) xylem tissue
   e) phloem tissue

5. What are the roles of the cuticle in plants?

6. Compare cells in the meristems to cells in other areas of the plant.

7. Write a short paragraph to describe the characteristics, location, and function of chloroplasts.

8. Write the word and chemical equations for photosynthesis.

9. What evidence is there for cytoplasmic streaming? Is this direct or indirect evidence? Explain.

10. Apart from photosynthesis, what other sequence of reactions occurs in plants to produce a gas?

11. Draw a cross section of a leaf showing spongy mesophyll and palisade tissues.

12. What is the difference between cohesion and adhesion? Explain how each process is involved in the transport of water in a plant.

13. The flowering of certain plants may be affected by the length of daylight that they are exposed to. Identify the three categories of daylight requirements that plants divide into, and give an example of the type of plant that belongs to each category.

14. Briefly describe changes that occur in cells during the formation of xylem vessels.

15. What are the functions of sieve tube cells and companion cells in phloem?

Applications

16. Consider the similarities and differences between plant and animal cells. Why are animals not able to manufacture their own food?

17. Compare and contrast the processes of photosynthesis and cellular respiration. Include reactants, products, and energy requirements.

18. Plant cells respond to a change in tonicity with increased or decreased turgor pressure. In the absence of a cell wall, predict what would happen to a blood cell placed in a hypotonic solution.

19. Using diagrams, describe how guard cells use turgor pressure to regulate the exchange of gases into and out of the leaf.

20. What important physiological role is played by air spaces located in the spongy mesophyll?

21. Using the terms cohesion, adhesion, pressure difference, and transpiration pull, explain the movement of water from the roots to the leaves.

22. What would happen to the growth of a shoot if a strong light source were placed below the plant? Explain your prediction.

23. Would you expect significant water movement to the leaves during the night? Explain your answer.

24. Discuss the transport of sugars, including the loading of phloem at the source. Include the role played by active transport.

25. Describe how the dermal tissue regulates gas exchange. How does it regulate the movement of water into and out of the plant? How are these two processes opposed to one another?

Extensions

26. Design an experiment to test whether phototropism or gravitropism has a greater effect on the growth of a plant.

27. If you were to attempt to improve on the experiments of the Darwins, Boysen-Jensen, and Went, what changes would you propose?

Help Wanted

Background Information

The application of engineering principles to cellular and molecular research is a rapidly growing field. Scientific and technological advances have given us an increased ability to understand how the cell works, opening the door to new treatments at the tissue, organ, and whole-body levels. People who have strong engineering skills and a background in biochemistry and cell biology have an opportunity to influence the future development of health care as well as industrial applications. Developing the right knowledge and skill sets begins with an interest in cutting-edge research and a desire to be part of a team that has the ability to shape the future.

Scenario

BIOMEDICAL ENGINEER

Biomedical Engineer required for new research facility. The successful candidate will have completed a degree in cellular and molecular biology and have an appreciation of engineering applications of transport systems in cells. This position requires teamwork, collaboration, and exceptional abilities in research and investigation. Applicants should be prepared to identify and explain a specific area of research related to the application of cellular transport in medicine or industry.

Research the Issue

Research current applications of cellular transport in industry or medicine in preparation for your job interview. Refer to the following guidelines to help you get started:

1. Identify an area of research to focus on. Will you choose an example from medicine or industry? Perhaps it is an area of particular interest to you because it has a direct impact on you, a friend, or a family member.

2. Use the Internet to locate current information on your area of study.

3. Try to connect with scientists, researchers, or practitioners in the field. Professional organizations and research facilities may be able to help. Check with your teacher for appropriate ways to contact scientists through Web sites or organizations in your area.

4. Find out if any of this research is being done in Canada, and specifically in Alberta. Who are the people involved and what can you find out about them?

5. What educational programs are available that would prepare you for a career in the field of your choice?

Analyze the Issue

6. Prepare a presentation for your job interview that will impress upon the interviewers your knowledge and interest in the area of research you have chosen. Include a discussion of:
   - why you chose the particular area of research
   - what you have found out concerning new, cutting-edge advances
   - who is involved in the research and where they are located
   - how this application of cellular transport could be adapted for practical use in medicine or industry

Address the Issue

7. Present your findings to the interview committee (your teacher and classmates). You may support your presentation with a short report, diagrams, posters, or electronic media.

The Impact of Environmental Factors on Plant Function

The short- and long-term effects of climate change on living organisms are subjects of certain areas of environmental research. Some plants and animals are considered to be **bioindicators**, because they respond quickly to environmental change in clearly defined ways. Plants, as primary producers in the food chain, have an important role in demonstrating the effects of climate change.

The ability of a plant to produce glucose depends on the number and activity of the chloroplasts present in its cells. Chloroplasts are the sites where photosynthesis occurs. Chemical energy, stored in the glucose produced through photosynthesis, is then used or stored by the plant. Animals that eat the plants are able to use this stored chemical energy in their own metabolic activities. For the production of glucose, cells require water and carbon dioxide in the presence of light energy. Are plant cells able to respond to their environments when the levels of carbon dioxide fluctuate?

Criteria for Success

As a research scientist you are asked to write a proposal to investigate whether plant cells are able to respond to their environments when the level of carbon dioxide fluctuates. Not all research proposals are accepted for funding and support. You must meet several criteria for approval of the proposal.

- Design an experiment to determine how the number of chloroplasts found in leaves of *Elodea canadensis* changes with exposure to different levels of carbon dioxide in the water.
- Use the knowledge and skills you have developed to consider how to monitor the levels of carbon dioxide in your experiment, and how to determine the number of chloroplasts present in the cells at the various carbon dioxide concentrations.
- Consider your hypothesis, the variables involved (controlled, manipulated, and responding), the procedure, and appropriate forms of data collection.
- Ensure that your proposal has all the elements necessary for a scientific investigation and can be efficiently and effectively carried out to provide quantitative data.

Procedure

1 State your question and hypothesis. Based on these, review what you learned in this unit that will help you to answer the question and test your hypothesis. Identify the variables involved and ways to control major factors in the experiment. Design an experimental procedure to test your hypothesis. Involve at least two other people (classmates, teacher, friends, family) in a peer review to provide you with feedback on your procedure. You may wish to try your procedure if time and materials allow.

2 Determine the best format for presenting your research proposal—PowerPoint presentation, written report, oral presentation, poster, etc. Identify ways to present your key points that will encourage the approving body, made up of your teacher and/or classmates, to accept your proposal. Develop your proposal.

3 Consider how your results will address concerns about the impact of environmental conditions on plants, specifically the effect of carbon dioxide concentration. You may want to do some research to support your thinking. Address this matter of environmental impact in your proposal.

Analysis

Your research proposal will be assessed on problem-solving technique and communication skill using the rubric supplied by your teacher.

1. Review the rubric and the criteria for success. Assess your proposal and look for modifications to improve it.

2. Use the rubric for peer review prior to submitting the proposal for approval.

3. Consider other variables that may affect the number of chloroplasts present in *Elodea* leaves and may need to be controlled in your experiment. List these factors and suggest alternative experimental designs to address these factors.

4. Consider whether these other factors will affect your discussion of concerns about environmental conditions, climate change, and their effect on plants.

Reporting

5. Present your work in your chosen format.

6. Write a one-page summary report.

Unit Summary

C 1.0 Our current understanding of the cell is due in part to developments in imaging technology.

Key Concepts
- microscopy and the emergence of cell theory

Learnings
- From the time of Aristotle, people have been intrigued by the structure of living things. Van Leeuwenhoek, Hans and Zacharias Janssen, and Robert Hooke contributed to the understanding of structure through the development and use of microscopes.
- It is possible to estimate the size of any object viewed under a compound light microscope.
- Over time, scientists tried to support or disprove the theory of spontaneous generation. Louis Pasteur concluded that new organisms did not arise from spontaneous generation.
- The cell theory was developed after the discovery of the nucleus by Robert Brown and through the contributions of Schleiden, Schwann, and Virchow.
- Various imaging technologies and staining techniques were invented to identify the parts and functions of the cell more clearly. These include contrast and resolution enhancement, fluorescence microscopy, confocal technology, and electron microscopy.
- Many types of cell research at the molecular level are now possible. These include gene mapping, studies of transport across cell membranes, the three-dimensional structure of molecules, and investigations using green fluorescent protein (GFP) technology.

C 2.0 Living systems are dependent upon the functioning of cell structures and organelles.

Key Concepts
- cellular structures and functions, and technological applications of semi-permeable membranes
- active and passive transport of matter
- relationship between cell size and shape, and surface area to volume ratio
- use of explanatory and visual models in science

Learnings
- The cell operates as a functioning open system that uses processes involved in the acquisition of nutrients, excretion of wastes, and exchange of matter and energy.
- Plant and animal cells contain organelles with characteristic chemical structures and functions.
- The fluid-mosaic model suggests that the plasma membrane consists of a phospholipid bilayer with surface and transmembrane proteins suspended in it.
- The particle model of matter is useful to explain the role of the cell membrane in the transport of materials.

- Models and representations are useful to explain and illustrate the processes of diffusion, osmosis, endo- and exocytosis, and the role of the cell membrane in passive and active transport. Some important concepts are: concentration gradients, equilibrium, and the action of protein carrier molecules.
- Tonicity can be explained in terms of the concentration of solute, with different concentrations being described as hypotonic, hypertonic, and isotonic to each other.
- Knowledge about semi-permeable membranes, diffusion, and osmosis has been applied in industry and medicine in ways such as pharmaceutical research, synthetic membrane technology, peritoneal dialysis, and reverse osmosis.
- The ratio of surface area to volume is important to cell size and shape and may limit cell size.

C 3.0 Plants are multicellular organisms with specialized structures.

Key Concepts
- use of explanatory and visual models in science
- cell specialization in a multicellular organism (plants)
- mechanisms of transport, gas exchange, and environmental response in a multicellular organism (plants)

Learnings
- Multicellularity has advantages and disadvantages. Increase in an organism's size may necessitate the move to a multicellular level of organization. This size/organization relationship can be related to the specialization of plant cells, tissues, and organ systems.
- The structure of plants includes organ systems, the shoot system and root system; tissues, dermal, ground, and vascular tissues; and cells specialized for particular functions as a result of cell specialization.
- The leaf has specialized structures and functions. These include: chloroplasts, the sites of photosynthesis; palisade cells; spongy mesophyll cells; and vascular tissue, which consists of phloem and xylem.
- Gas exchange in plants in the light and the dark involves the action of guard cells and stomata, lenticels, and the process of diffusion through intercellular spaces.
- Water transport in plants can be explained in terms of cohesive and adhesive properties of water, root pressure in root hairs, and the process of transpiration through the xylem. Important concepts include turgor pressure and osmosis, diffusion, and tonicity.
- The pressure-flow theory explains sugar transport in terms of moving sugars from the source of production to the sink for use or storage.
- In plants, control systems and mechanisms include phototropism, gravitropism, and other types of tropisms. The understanding of these mechanisms is based on theories developed by the Darwins, Boysen-Jensen, and Went.

Vocabulary

1. Using your own words, define the following terms:

adhesion
auxin
cell theory
cellular respiration
cohesion
compound light microscope
concentration gradient
confocal laser scanning microscope
control systems
controlled experiment
cytoplasmic streaming
electron microscope
fluid-mosaic model
guard cells
gravitropism
hormone
open system
organ
organelles
photosynthesis
phototropism
plasmolysis
pressure difference
spontaneous generation
stomata
system
tissue
tonicity
transpiration
turgor pressure

Knowledge

C 1.0

2. Explain the differences between the microscopes used by Hooke and van Leeuwenhoek.

3. What problems in the use of early compound light microscopes were associated with lens technology? How were these problems overcome?

4. In what way was Francesco Redi's investigation a controlled experiment?

5. Outline the investigations conducted in the attempts both to prove and disprove the theory of spontaneous generation.

6. What were the contributions to the cell theory made by each of the following?
   a) Robert Brown
   b) Matthias Schleiden
   c) Theodor Schwann
   d) Rudolf Virchow

7. Define resolving power. What factor limits the extent of resolving power in the light microscope?

8. Explain the advantages and disadvantages of using an electron microscope.

9. What are the advantages of conducting cell research at the molecular level?

10. State one advantage and one disadvantage of treating cells with stains.

11. Describe how the use of fluorescence microscopy can increase our knowledge of cell structure.

12. What is the unit of measurement most commonly used in measuring cells and their component parts?

C 2.0

13. What is meant by an open system and why is a cell considered to be one?

14. Consider the structures in a plant cell. Describe the function of the:
   a) nucleus
   b) central vacuole
   c) cell wall

15. How is the rate of diffusion affected by the surface area to volume ratio of a cell?

16. What cell structures are visible through a light microscope?

17. Compare the terms "diffusion" and "osmosis."

18. What processes must cells use to be able to survive as living systems?

19. Describe how the particle model is useful in understanding the movement of matter in living systems.

20. Explain the term "concentration gradient" by referring to solutes, solvents, membranes, diffusion, and osmosis.

21. Review the results of Activity C8. From these results, what inference can you make about the movement of iodine ions and starch across the membrane of the plastic bag? How do you account for this?

22. What is a vesicle? How do cells use vesicles in transport?

23. Explain how liposomes can transport both fat-soluble and water-soluble medications.

24. Describe the process by which water is desalinated at the McMurdo Research Station in Antarctica.

25. Use your textbook as a sample cell. Calculate the surface area, volume, and surface area to volume ratio. Would your "book cell" be efficient in the transport of materials? Explain your answer.

C 3.0

26. Define the following terms:
    a) meristem
    b) shoot system

27. Give examples of the products of cell specialization. Explain how the cells in each example perform specialized functions in the organism.

28. List the three main types of plant tissue and state their functions.

29. Explain why light and chlorophyll are not considered to be reactants or products in the photosynthesis reaction.

30. What is the meaning of turgor pressure? Why is it important to plant cells?

31. Define transpiration. What effect does transpiration have on the movement of water in a plant?

32. Describe the component parts of a vascular bundle.

33. Explain how root pressure moves water up a plant stem.

34. How are xylem and phloem the same? How are they different? Consider both structure and function in your answer.

35. Which transport tissue in plants is composed of dead cells? Explain your answer.

36. What is a tropism? Name two tropisms and describe how they regulate plant growth.

37. Describe a method for determining the presence of carbon dioxide in water.

Applications

38. Explain the importance of conducting controlled experiments, maintaining detailed records of observations, and connecting results to conclusions. Give an example of each of these aspects of the scientific process using your experience of the lab work from this unit.

39. If 16 protists fit across a low-power field of view having a field diameter of 4800 μm, what is the approximate size of each protist?

40. Describe three examples of the relationship between developments in imaging technology and the current understanding of the cell.

41. Using the particle model and the fluid-mosaic model, explain what is known about the cell membrane and transport of materials.

42. Draw a diagram showing the movement of water along a concentration gradient.

43. If a bowl of fresh strawberries is sprinkled with sugar, a few minutes later the berries will be covered with juice. Why?

44. Explain the process of facilitated diffusion and give an example.

45. Desert plants like cacti have prickly spines or needles, not large leaves. Chloroplasts are found in the cells of the stems. By contrast, rainforest plants tend to have large, flat leaves. Use what you know about surface area and diffusion to explain what may have influenced the structure of each plant.

46. Compare the surface area to volume ratio of various types of cells (i.e., nerve cells, blood cells, root hair cells) and relate your findings to the function of each cell type.

47. What is the advantage to the plant of cytoplasmic streaming that allows chloroplasts to move around in the cell?

48. Describe the means plants have for maintaining firm cells, able to hold the plant upright in the absence of a skeleton.

49. What is the advantage to the plant of having the palisade mesophyll cells arranged in a fence-like pattern?

50. Describe the experiment(s) you performed to determine the effect of control mechanisms in plants. Include your observations and conclusions.

51. Explain what happens during plasmolysis in plant cells and why it happens. What are the consequences for the plant? How can this process be reversed?

52. Explain the pressure-flow theory. According to this theory, what drives the movement of substances in the phloem?

53. *Plants act like animals at night!* Do you agree or disagree with this statement? Explain your answer.

54. Discuss the differences between water transport and sugar transport in plants.

55. Why is it important for cells in the stem, in particular, to be turgid? What control mechanism does a pea plant use to supplement the turgidity of the cells in its stems?

56. Explain how plants use specialized cells and processes to accomplish on a larger scale the same functions that a single cell carries out alone.

57. How did the cell theory replace the concept of spontaneous generation and revolutionize the study of life sciences?

58. Grade 8 students are just beginning to use the compound light microscope. Prepare a study sheet for them on the use, care, and handling of the instrument. Be sure to include the proper names of each of the parts.

Extensions

59. In terms of transport of materials, what problems might land-plants face that water-plants do not?

60. Would transport in the phloem tissue or xylem tissue require more energy input? Explain your answer.

61. How might hydroponics be used to determine whether or not a specific mineral is necessary for plant growth?

62. In the face of rising concerns over climate change and greenhouse gas emissions, describe how plants may be used as bioindicators of environmental conditions.

63. Stomata are usually found on the undersurface of leaves. Suggest reasons for this relationship and conditions that could affect the position of the stomata, as well as their number.

64. Bioethical issues are constantly in the news. Find a current article related to an issue in cell research. Identify and explain the two or more perspectives on the issue. Based on the information provided in the article, are you able to make an informed decision? What further information would you want to have?

65. What do you think was the most significant breakthrough in the study of living cells? Justify your choice by stating the implications of the breakthrough for future study.

66. Most cells have specialized shapes and sizes to make them suited to their particular function. Some have long appendages, some are cubic or cylindrical, and blood cells have a donut shape. Very few are spherical in shape, the yeast cell being an exception. Propose an explanation for the fact that few cells are spherical.

67. An exposed cut stem is left out of water for an extended period of time. Predict the effect on its ability to transport water. Justify your reasoning.

68. Design an experiment for the Canadian Space Agency to test the effects of gravitropism on germinating seeds under zero gravity conditions.

69. How do the following big ideas from this unit relate to one another: development of the microscope, understanding of molecular transport processes (diffusion, osmosis, active and passive transport), functioning of multicellular organisms in transporting materials? Use a presentation form of your choice to describe and illustrate the ways in which these ideas are connected.

70. Write the experimental procedure you would use to determine how a particular type of plant would react to various levels of fertilizer. Identify the controlled and manipulated variables in this investigation.

71. Find out about one plant research project currently being conducted at the Crop Diversification Centre South in Brooks, Alberta or at the Crop Diversification Centre North in Edmonton, or at Olds College in Olds, Alberta. Write a short report on the project of your choice.

Skills Practice

72. Write instructions, in your own words, for making a wet mount slide. Give your instructions to a friend or family member who has never made a wet mount. Are they able to follow your directions?

73. What is the purpose of making a hypothesis?

74. Using any five solid objects found in your classroom, complete the following table:

Object Name	Formula and Calculation of Surface Area	Formula and Calculation of Volume	Surface Area to Volume Ratio

75. Using instructions, mathematical formulas, and examples, explain the proper method for estimating the size of an object under low- and high-power magnification.

Self Assessment

76. In this unit, you have seen the relationship between increased scientific understanding and advancements in technology. How are science and technology dependent on one another? What role did societal values, needs, and wants have on the development of microscopy and knowledge of cell functioning?

77. Identify a possible career in each of the areas of plant study: gardening, horticulture, or agriculture. In a chart like the one below, identify what you would find to be interesting, challenging, or difficult about the job.

Career Choice: _____

Interesting	Challenging	Difficult

Would you like to have a career related to the study of plants? Why or why not?

78. Identify the topic in this unit that you found most interesting and explain why.

Energy Flow in Global Systems

Precipitation, such as the rain that accompanies this
electrical storm over Calgary, Alberta, is one of the factors
that make up climate.

In this unit, you will cover the following ideas:

D 1.0 Climate results from interactions among the components of the biosphere.
  D1.1 Earth—Our Biosphere
  D1.2 Climate

D 2.0 Global systems transfer energy through the biosphere.
  D2.1 Energy Relationships and the Biosphere
  D2.2 Thermal Energy Transfer in the Atmosphere
  D2.3 Thermal Energy Transfer in the Hydrosphere
  D2.4 Earth's Biomes
  D2.5 Analyzing Energy Flow in Global Systems

D 3.0 Changes in global energy transfer could cause climate change, and impact human life and the biosphere.
  D3.1 Climate Change—Examining the Evidence
  D3.2 International Collaboration on Climate Change
  D3.3 Assessing the Impacts of Climate Change

Focus on Social and Environmental Context

During this unit, you will study how solar energy sustains life and drives global climate systems on Earth. Without solar energy, Earth would be cold and lack precipitation, so life as we know it could not exist. You will investigate how absorption and transfer of energy at and near Earth's surface results in a variety of biomes with specific climates. Once you understand the factors that affect Earth's global energy systems, you will be able to assess the evidence that has brought scientists to conclude that human activity can cause climate change—a change that could potentially harm the environment and our economy. As you work through this unit, think about the following questions:

1. Are there relationships between solar energy, global energy transfer processes, climate, and biomes?
2. How do global systems transfer energy through the lithosphere, hydrosphere, and atmosphere?
3. What evidence suggests our climate may be changing more rapidly than living species can adapt?
4. Is human activity causing climate change, and in meeting human needs, how can we reduce our impact on the biosphere and on global climate?

At the end of the unit, you may be asked to do these tasks:

Case Study Risky Solutions
You will research the costs and benefits of an emerging technology aimed at reducing or reversing the impact of human activity on Earth's climate. You will then analyze your findings, and decide whether further research on this technology deserves funding.

Project A Personal Plan for Reducing Carbon Dioxide Emissions
Using information provided, you will develop your own plan to reduce your and your family's carbon dioxide emissions by 2%. You will assess the economic and social costs of your plan on your family members, then report on your plan and its predicted outcome.

Exploring

■ Open water at the North Pole is a normal climatic event, and not a result of climate change.

In August of 2000, visitors to the North Pole were greeted by open water, instead of the usual solid ice. The thinning of the ice pack at the pole was picked up by the world's media as another example of the consequences of climate change. In fact, thawing of the polar ice sheets has always occurred periodically. However, the media response to this one event underlined the limits of our knowledge about climate, climate change, and its consequences.

We know that the average temperature on Earth's surface has increased over the last century. What is not yet clear is how quickly the climate is changing or its consequences. Climate change already appears to be causing significant consequences in some areas of Earth. For example, Inuit families in Canada's northern reaches are finding that their traditional igloo hunting shelters are no longer able to protect them from the cold. Warmer daytime temperatures are melting the snow of the igloos, which then refreezes to ice at night. Snow has better insulating properties than ice, so the refrozen igloos are much colder. In addition, meat from winter hunting is no longer staying frozen, but is thawing and rotting before it can be used.

These and other changes taking place in the Arctic are examples of the potentially global consequences of climate change. Climate affects many aspects of daily life, so scientists and governments are working to understand more about climate change and its causes. You might be surprised to learn that Earth's climate has changed before. Learning more about the causes and consequences of past changes in climate can help us to understand what is happening to our climate today, and also to predict its results. Scientists look for clues about Earth's past climate in many places. For example, one good source of information about past climatic conditions is the thick ice at Earth's polar regions. The ice in these areas has not melted for many thousands of years. Scientists drill out core samples from the lowest parts of this ice to get a glimpse of the conditions that existed when the ice first formed, about 2.6 million years ago. Evidence from ice core samples suggests that the climate at the poles was much warmer in the past. Fossil evidence also supports this theory. For example, fossils of an extinct dinosaur, called a Champsosaur, have been found in the Arctic. The Champsosaur, a crocodile-like creature with a long nose and razor-sharp teeth, could survive only in regions with a warm climate, similar to that of present-day Florida.

Today, climate change may also be affected by human activities. To determine the extent to which we are affecting our climate, we need to understand the global systems that give Earth its climate in the first place, and the factors that can cause climate to change. This knowledge will help scientists to identify the causes of climate change today, and to predict its consequences.

■ A group of scientists, including members of Alberta's Royal Tyrell Museum of Paleontology, found fossils of Champsosaur in Canada's Arctic.

Activity D1

QuickLab

Climate and Tree Growth

For every year of its growth, a tree produces a single ring of new wood in its trunk. The width of each growth ring is affected by the average temperature and moisture conditions during that year. Since trees can live many years, tree rings can be used to identify changes in the climate conditions of a region over long spans of time. In order to see the growth rings, scientists drill out core samples that extend from the centre of the tree (the pith) to the outer bark.

Purpose

To deduce the changes that occurred in the local climate of an area from the growth rings in core samples

Procedure

1. Since trees produce new wood just below their bark, the growth ring beneath the bark was produced in the last year of growth. The figure below shows how to determine the age of a tree from a core sample. Start counting from the bark inwards to the pith. The area between the lines in each core sample counts as one ring, or 1 year's growth, so this tree is 10 years old.

2. Create a chart with the following column headings: Sample, Age, Wet and Cool, Dry and Hot.

3. Look at the drawings of core samples taken from four different trees growing in the same area. Determine the age of each tree, and record it in your chart.

4. When a year was cool and wet on average, the trees produced wider growth rings. When a year was hot and dry on average, the trees produced narrower growth rings. For each of the core samples, deduce the time periods when each tree experienced cool and wet conditions and when each experienced hot and dry conditions. Record your deductions in your chart.

Question

1. Why would a scientist studying climate change be interested in the core samples from trees?

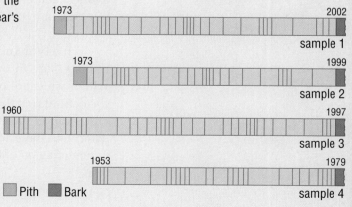

Climate results from interactions among the components of the biosphere.

Key Concepts

In this section, you will learn about the following key concepts:

- social and environmental contexts for investigating climate change

Learning Outcomes

When you have completed this section, you will be able to:

- describe the major characteristics of the atmosphere, the hydrosphere, and the lithosphere, and explain their relationship to Earth's biosphere
- explain how climate impacts on the lives of people and other species, and explain the need to investigate climate change; investigate how a species may be affected by an increase or decrease in average temperature

FIGURE D1.1 Scientists aboard the icebreaker *Des Groseilliers* spent a year collecting data on climate in the Arctic.

From October 1997 to October 1998, the Canadian Coast Guard icebreaker vessel *Des Groseilliers* drifted on the Arctic Ocean (Figure D1.1). Onboard, scientists and technicians from five different nations collected data on the Arctic's climate, as part of an international research project called the Surface Heat Energy Budget of the Arctic Ocean, or SHEBA. Their research was part of the ongoing worldwide effort to better understand climate, and the causes and potential consequences of climate change.

How is climate different from weather? **Weather** refers to the conditions of temperature, air pressure, cloud cover, precipitation (rain or snow), and humidity that occur at a particular place at a particular time. For example, today the weather in your area could be cold and sunny, but tomorrow the weather may be overcast and warmer. **Climate** is the average weather conditions that occur in a region over a long period of time, usually a minimum of 30 years. To describe the climate of Alberta, for example, you might say that the average temperature in summer ranges from 14°C to 20°C and in winter from −24°C to −9°C, and the average annual precipitation is 442 mm.

Why is it important to know about climate? What role does climate play in our lives and the lives of the other organisms with which we share our planet? In this section, you will find out about the central role that climate plays in keeping planet Earth a place that can support life. You will also learn about some of the evidence scientists have found that indicates our climate is changing, and consider some of the consequences climate change may have.

D1.1 Earth—Our Biosphere

Earth appears to be unique in our solar system in that it is the only planet that supports many different living things. The **biosphere** is a relatively thin layer of Earth that has conditions suitable for supporting life as we know it. The biosphere is composed of all the living things on Earth and the physical environment that supports them.

The biosphere is made up of three interacting components: the atmosphere, the lithosphere, and the hydrosphere (Figure D1.2). The **atmosphere** is the layer of gases that surround Earth. The **lithosphere** is the solid portion of Earth, composed of rocks, minerals, and elements. The **hydrosphere** is all the water on Earth, whether it is present as liquid, water vapour, or ice. Living things are found in parts of all three components of the biosphere, wherever environmental conditions exist that can support life. These environmental conditions are in part created by the interactions between these components and incoming energy from the Sun, and between the components themselves, which you will study in this unit. These interactions create Earth's climate, which helps to maintain an environment that supports life.

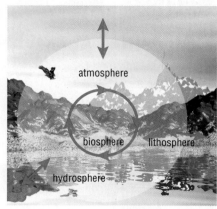

FIGURE D1.2 The biosphere is composed of all living things on Earth and the physical environment that supports them.

The Atmosphere

The atmosphere rises over 500 km from the surface of Earth, and is mainly composed of a mixture of different gases (Table D1.1) that is commonly referred to as air. Figure D1.3 is a graph of the relative composition of the main gases in the atmosphere. Water vapour is also a gas found in the atmosphere, but in extremely variable levels. In this textbook, water vapour is considered to be part of the hydrosphere, and so is not included in Table D1.1 or Figure D1.3. The atmosphere also contains varying amounts of suspended particulate matter called **atmospheric dust** (solid particles less than 0.66 mm in diameter). These particles may include non-living particles, such as soot, or living particles, such as pollen and micro-organisms.

TABLE D1.1 Percent Composition of Gases in Earth's Atmosphere (excludes water vapour)

Gas	Percent of Atmosphere by Volume
nitrogen	78.08
oxygen	20.95
other gases*	0.97

*includes argon, carbon dioxide, neon, helium, methane, and krypton

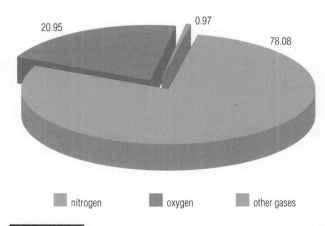

Percent of Atmosphere

20.95   0.97   78.08

nitrogen   oxygen   other gases

FIGURE D1.3 Most of Earth's atmosphere is composed of nitrogen gas.

Modelling Atmospheres

Purpose

To generate models of the atmospheres of Earth, Venus, and Mars, and compare their gas compositions

Materials and Equipment

graph paper, graphing calculator, or spreadsheet software

Procedure

1. The data in the table show the percent composition of gases in the atmospheres of Venus, Earth, and Mars. If you have access to a computer spreadsheet software or a graphing calculator, enter these data. Gases present in trace amounts should be entered as 0% for the purposes of this investigation.

2. Create graphs that visually summarize the differences in the atmospheres of the three planets. Test the effects of using different types of graphs in communicating these differences. For example, you could construct a pie chart for each planet using same colours for each type of gas on each planet chart. You might instead plot the data for all three planets on one bar graph, or generate one bar graph for each planet.

3. Choose the graph you think most clearly communicates the difference between the relative amounts of gases in the atmospheres of Venus, Earth, and Mars. Print out or redraw that graph in final form.

Percent Composition of Three Atmospheres

Gas	Venus	Earth	Mars
carbon dioxide	96.5%	0.04%	95%
nitrogen	3.5%	78%	2.7%
oxygen	trace	21%	0.13%
argon	0.007%	0.9%	1.6%
methane	0%	0.002%	0%

Questions

1. Explain why you think your choice of graph is most effective in communicating the differences between the atmospheres of the three planets.

2. Mars and Venus do not appear to have a biosphere. Summarize the main differences in the gas composition of Earth's atmosphere and of the atmospheres of Mars and Venus. Based on your summary, would you predict that Mars and Venus would be able to support life as we know it? Why or why not?

The most abundant gas in our atmosphere is nitrogen gas. Nitrogen is required for plant growth. Certain bacteria convert nitrogen gas into nitrogen compounds that can be taken up by plants. Oxygen is the second most abundant gas in Earth's atmosphere. Life as we know it would not exist without these levels of oxygen in the atmosphere. Living cells obtain energy through the process of cellular respiration, which uses oxygen to break down glucose molecules. The levels of oxygen gas are maintained through the process of photosynthesis, which uses the carbon dioxide that is produced by respiration and produces oxygen gas and sugars. Oxygen gas is also involved in many other chemical reactions, including combustion reactions (burning). Burning is the most common way that we release energy from fuel. The levels of nitrogen gas in our atmosphere help to control the amount of combustion that takes place, since nitrogen gas does not support combustion.

Earth's atmosphere can be divided into four layers, which are determined by the average air temperature. These layers are found at different altitudes (Figure D1.4). **Altitude** is the distance above Earth's surface, measured from sea level (the surface of the oceans). The altitudes shown are average values for Earth as a whole. The exact altitude at which a particular layer begins or ends above any point on Earth will be different for different locations or at different times of the day.

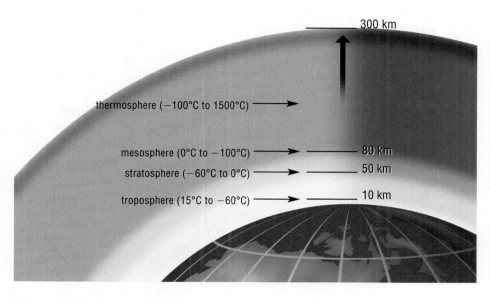

thermosphere (−100°C to 1500°C) ⟶

mesosphere (0°C to −100°C) ⟶ — 80 km

stratosphere (−60°C to 0°C) ⟶ — 50 km

troposphere (15°C to −60°C) ⟶ — 10 km

300 km

FIGURE D1.4 The layers of Earth's atmosphere do not have distinct boundaries, but blend into one another. Values are average altitudes for all of Earth, as stated by the Centre of Atmospheric Science at the University of Cambridge, U.K.

Troposphere

The **troposphere** is the layer of atmospheric gases at 0 km to 10 km from Earth's surface. The troposphere has an average temperature of 15°C at Earth's surface. The temperature of the troposphere decreases with increasing distance from the surface of Earth, and reaches a minimum of −60°C at the top.

The troposphere contains about 80% of the atmospheric gases by mass. It is the only layer of Earth's atmosphere with a temperature range and concentration of oxygen that can support many living organisms, including humans. The troposphere contains most of the carbon dioxide and water vapour in the atmosphere, and is the layer in which most weather occurs. The root of the word "troposphere" is the Greek word *tropos*, which means, "to change." The troposphere also contains almost all of the atmospheric dust. Atmospheric dust may be produced by natural events such as volcanoes and forest fires, and by human activity.

Stratosphere, Mesosphere, and Thermosphere

The **stratosphere** is the atmospheric layer above the troposphere, from about 10 km to 50 km above Earth's surface. The temperature in the stratosphere increases with distance from Earth's surface, starting at −60°C at the lowest part, to about 0°C at the top. Scientists have found clumps of cells in the stratosphere, but no other life.

The stratosphere contains most of the ozone gas in the atmosphere. **Ozone** is a molecule made up of three atoms of oxygen (Figure D1.5). Ozone gas forms a layer in the stratosphere called the **ozone layer**. Ozone absorbs large amounts of energy from the Sun's rays, which causes the temperature in the stratosphere to increase with altitude. The ozone layer protects living organisms from damaging high-energy radiation.

The **mesosphere** is the third atmospheric layer above Earth's surface. The temperature of the mesosphere decreases from 0°C at the bottom to −100°C at the top. The **thermosphere** is the farthest layer from Earth's surface. The temperature in this layer increases from −100°C to as much as 1500°C. There is very little gas in these layers, and these temperature changes are not yet fully understood.

FIGURE D1.5 Ozone is composed of three atoms of oxygen. Its formula is $O_{3(g)}$.

The Lithosphere

The lithosphere is the solid portion of Earth that floats above the semi-fluid portion of the upper mantle (Figure D1.6). The lithosphere is home to many micro-organisms, plants, and animals, including humans. It can be thought of as the outer surface of Earth and any solid portions of Earth's interior. The lithosphere extends from Earth's surface to about 100 km below, and runs under Earth's continents and oceans. The lithosphere is warmed mainly by incoming energy from the Sun and, to a lesser degree, by the molten material in the mantle.

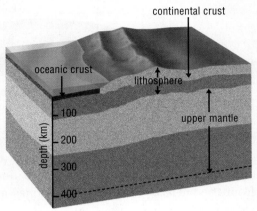

FIGURE D1.6 The lithosphere is the solid portion of Earth's crust. The lithosphere varies in thickness from as little as 5 km deep beneath parts of the oceans, to as deep as 100 km beneath the continents.

The Hydrosphere

The hydrosphere accounts for all the water on Earth. About 97% of this water is salt water in Earth's oceans. The other 3% is fresh water, and includes unfrozen water such as in lakes and streams, and frozen water, such as the ice in snow and glaciers. The amount of water on Earth always remains the same. Many different organisms, from whales to algae, live in the large water bodies of the lithosphere. However, the vast majority of the living organisms found in the lithosphere or atmosphere need water to survive, and so also depend on the hydrosphere. Like the lithosphere, the hydrosphere is warmed mainly by incoming sunlight and, to a small degree, by the molten material in the mantle.

The Components of the Biosphere Interact

Thinking about the atmosphere, lithosphere, and hydrosphere separately can be helpful for understanding the processes that occur on Earth. However, to understand the global systems of our planet fully, it is important to remember that these components continuously interact with one another. For example, water does not exist only in the hydrosphere. Water is also present in the atmosphere as water vapour, where it plays a role in cloud formation and other processes. It is present in the soil and minerals of the lithosphere, where, among other things, it dissolves plant nutrients and weathers rock. These interactions can change daily. For example, there may be as little as 1% water vapour in the atmosphere over a prairie ranch on a cold winter day, but as much as 4% over a large lake on a hot summer day (Figure D1.7).

FIGURE D1.7 Differences in the lithosphere can affect the amount of water vapour in the atmosphere, which changes the cloud cover.

Inquiry Lab

Required Skills
- Initiating and Planning
- Performing and Recording
- Analyzing and Interpreting
- Communication and Teamwork

Air Temperature and Altitude

If you have visited or seen pictures of high mountains, such as the Rocky Mountains in North America, you have probably noticed that some mountains are capped with snow year-round. Why are the tops of mountains always colder than the lower levels? In this investigation, you will create a graph of the air temperature measured on Sept. 3, 2002 at increasing altitudes above two Canadian cities. You will use this graph to explore the differences in air temperature at the top and bottom of a mountain.

The Question

How does air temperature vary with altitude above Port Hardy, BC, and Edmonton, AB?

Altitude and Air Temperature on Sept. 03, 2002

Port Hardy, BC		Edmonton, AB	
Altitude (m)	Air Temp. (°C)	Altitude (m)	Air Temp. (°C)
17	14.6	—	—
610	9.1	766	18.0
914	6.7	914	16.3
1 829	0.6	1 829	7.3
3 658	−11.0	3 658	−5.3
5 443	−23.9	4 914	−11.3
9 100	−42.3	8 535	−36.3
10 668	−45.4	10 621	−51.5

Source: University of Wyoming, Department of Atmospheric Science

Variables

Temperature is the responding variable. What is the manipulated variable?

Materials and Equipment

graph paper, spreadsheet software, or graphing calculator

pencils

Procedure

1. Graph the altitude and air temperature for both cities on a single graph.

Analyzing and Interpreting

1. Which city had the higher temperature at an altitude of 914 m? Which had the higher temperature at an altitude of 10 668 m?

2. Determine the air temperature at an altitude of 4000 m for both cities.

Forming Conclusions

3. Describe the general relationship between air temperature and altitude above these two cities.

4. Relate the trend of your graph of temperature versus altitude to the characteristics of the troposphere.

Applying and Connecting

5. Evergreen trees, such as firs and pines, cover much of the Rocky Mountains in Alberta. In contrast, much of the Laurentian Mountains in Quebec is covered with deciduous trees, such as maples and birch. The mountains of Alberta's Rockies have elevations up to 3700 km, but the mountains of the Laurentians have an elevation no higher than 520 m. Suggest one reason for the difference in the types of trees between these two mountain ranges.

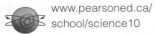

re SEARCH

Find out what causes inversions, and why they often occur in mountainous regions. Begin your search at

www.pearsoned.ca/ school/science10

Altitude and Temperature

Altitude is the distance above Earth's surface, measured from the upper surface of the oceans (sea level). In the troposphere, the temperature of the air tends to decrease with altitude. The temperature at high altitudes can be so cold that the tops of some mountains remain covered in snow year-round. In general, regions that are at higher altitudes tend to be cooler on average than regions at lower altitudes.

Sometimes, conditions in the atmosphere cause this pattern to change. An **inversion** is a reversal of normal temperature patterns seen in the troposphere. Inversions may trap unusually cold air close to the ground. Inversions tend to occur more often in areas close to mountains, where the air is forced to travel up over the higher elevations. There is also less air circulation during an inversion, which can cause pollutants to become trapped close to the ground. High levels of pollutants can affect the health of some people.

D1.1   Check and Reflect

Knowledge

1. Identify the following statements as examples of weather or of climate:
   a) Today is very hot.
   b) We usually get a lot of rain this time of year.

2. Write a short paragraph explaining the difference between climate and weather.

3. Describe the components of the biosphere.

4. What characteristics of the troposphere make it unique?

5. Identify the most abundant gas in the atmosphere.

6. How are the layers of the atmosphere classified?

7. In which part of the atmosphere does most of Earth's weather occur?

8. Does the lithosphere include just the land making up Earth's continents? Explain your answer.

9. Explain why temperature increases with altitude in the stratosphere.

10. Agree or disagree with the following statement: *The hydrosphere comprises only the water in the world's oceans, streams, and rivers.* Explain your answer in a short paragraph.

Applications

11. Make a chart that compares and contrasts the three parts of the biosphere.

12. Explain how each part of the biosphere supports life.

13. Using the data in the table below, construct a graph that clearly illustrates any similarities and differences between the gas composition of the atmospheres of Earth and Saturn.

Gas	Earth (percent by volume)	Saturn (percent by volume)
nitrogen	78	0
oxygen	21	0
helium	trace	11
hydrogen	trace	88
other	1.0	1.0

Referring to your graph, outline why our atmosphere is important to the existence of life as we know it.

Extension

14. Imagine that as part of your summer job, you are to participate in a scientific study of the biosphere. Write a short persuasive letter to the supervisors of the study, explaining which part of the biosphere you would like to study and why.

D 1.2 Climate

If you ever have travelled between places with different climates, you have some idea of how climate affects your life. Your daily activities, clothing choices, even what you eat can change in areas with different climates. Climate also affects all other living organisms on Earth.

Climate Affects Daily Life

Alberta's climate has four seasons. In general, the summers are warm, winters are quite cold, and fall and spring can be very brief. The Northwest Territories, which share Alberta's northernmost border, are generally a lot colder than Alberta. How do differences in climate affect people's daily lives?

According to data from Statistics Canada, in 2001, Alberta had a population of 3 064 249 people in an area of 642 317 square kilometres, which is an average of 4.8 people per square kilometre. In the same year, the Northwest Territories had a population of 42 083 in an area of 1 183 085 square kilometres, or 0.036 people per square kilometre. A similar pattern is seen worldwide: regions with severe climates tend to have fewer people than regions with more moderate climates.

One reason that fewer people live in these regions is that severe climate causes additional challenges to everyday life. People cannot survive outdoors in extreme heat or extreme cold without adequate clothing (Figure D1.8). In Alberta's climate, people need one set of clothing to protect them from the summer heat, and a second set to protect them from the cold of winter.

Even with adequate clothing, people living in severe climates must seek shelter after a relatively short time in order to avoid injury, such as frostbite or sunburn. Their shelter must also suit the climate. Albertans' homes usually have some form of heating device, such as a furnace, which is used throughout the winter. In summer, heating is seldom used. Homes in Alberta generally are well insulated and have tightly sealed windows and doors, to help keep the temperature indoors different from that outdoors. The climate of Alberta also causes Albertans to use more fuel (and spend more money) to heat their homes than people who live in milder climate zones. For example, homes in regions of California often have only a space heater. The climate is so mild that residents may use their space heaters for only a few days in a year. Californians therefore use much less fuel and spend less money for home heating than Albertans. People in warmer climates may use more fuel or spend more money on air conditioning, however. Homes must also be able to withstand the amount and type of precipitation of a climate zone. Whereas homes in Alberta must be able to withstand the considerable weight of snow that can fall during winter, homes in areas with heavy rainfalls, such as in parts of Brazil, must be able to withstand these conditions (Figure D1.9).

Climate can determine the types of foods that are available in a region and the cost of that food. It is generally more expensive to buy fresh fruit in northern Alberta in January than it is in Florida, for example. Most fruit trees are unable to withstand the climate conditions of northern Alberta, so fruit must be transported to the region. The cost of transport increases the price of

FIGURE D1.8 The climate of the area in which we live determines what we need to survive.

The first official weather observations in Canada were taken at King's College, University of Toronto, Toronto, Ontario, by members of the British Royal Artillery on September 6, 1840.

the fruit. Florida's climate provides good growing conditions for fruit trees, so this area produces many different fruits. These cost far less to transport to residents of Florida than to residents of Alberta.

The economic opportunities of an area can also be affected by climate. Think again about the example of producing fruit. In regions in Canada with warmer climates, such as the Okanagan Valley of British Columbia or the Niagara region of Ontario, fruit production is an important part of the economy. The economies of regions with colder climates, such as Fort Fitzgerald near Alberta's northernmost border, have little or no agricultural components. Tourism and recreation industries can also be affected by climate. Activities such as skiing or ice fishing are possible only in regions with a cold winter season. People in regions such as the Caribbean Islands depend on the year-round warmth of their climate to attract tourists interested in swimming and sunbathing.

Climate Affects All Organisms

Climate affects environmental conditions, and so all living things in any region are affected by climate. The species of plants that can survive in a region are determined by the climate. However, some characteristics of plants and animals can make them more suited or less suited to a particular climate. An **adaptation** is any change in the structure or functioning of an organism that makes it more suited to its environment. Different plants and animals have various adaptations that make them more suited or less suited to a particular climate. Think about the plants and animals of Alberta. How are they suited to Alberta's climate? How would their adaptations affect their ability to live in other climates?

Plant life in Alberta must be able to survive the seasonal changes in the climate. For example, many plants undergo a period of dormancy during the winter. Dormancy is a period in which growth of the plant ceases or becomes very slow. Deciduous trees, such as poplars, shed their leaves when they go dormant. This helps to protect them from freezing, and minimizes the amount of moisture they need. Plants cannot use frozen water, so winter is also a period of extreme dryness. Plants in Alberta will flower and reproduce only when temperatures are warmer and more moisture is available, usually

FIGURE D1.9 Home designs are altered to match the climate of the region in which the homes are to be built.

during spring and summer. In contrast, the climate in some tropical regions is warm and moist year-round. Plants in such tropical areas do not undergo a period of dormancy (Figure D1.10). Tropical plants continue to grow year-round, and many also reproduce throughout the year. Many plants in tropical climates cannot survive long dry periods, whereas plants found in dry climates are often unable to tolerate wet conditions.

The native animal life of a region is also affected by climate. Through food webs, plants ultimately supply food energy to all other organisms in a region. Earth's different regions, therefore, support different species of animals. For example, grizzly bears can find food in Alberta's mountains, but would be less able to find food in a desert. Animals also have adaptations that make them more suited to particular environmental conditions. Grizzlies can put on as much as 200 kg of fat during the summer months. This fat layer helps to insulate their organs from the cold of winter, as well as providing fuel. Grizzlies also make a den in a protected spot, such as a cave, and become extremely inactive during the winter. Contrast these adaptations with those of an animal native to a tropical region, the green iguana. The green iguana is cold-blooded, so it seeks out sunlight when the temperature is too cold and finds shade when the temperature is too warm. Instead of fur and insulating fat, the green iguana has a thick, water-resistant skin to protect it from the warm, wet climate of its home. Green iguanas are active all year round, since the seasons do not bring significant changes in temperature.

FIGURE D1.10 Plants and animals have adaptations that make them suited to the climate conditions of their home.

(a) Arctic wolf

(b) Trumpeter swan

(c) Purple lilac

FIGURE D1.11 What kind of climate do these species need to survive?

The organisms in Figure D1.11 have adaptations that enable them to survive in the climate conditions of their home. The Arctic wolf has a white coat year-round, which provides camouflage against ice and snow. The trumpeter swan nests only in wetland areas, which provide food and protection for its young. The purple lilac blooms very early in the spring, at the first hint of warmth, before many other plants.

In a group of two or three, brainstorm the effects of an increase in the average temperature of the regions where these organisms live. Consider factors such as the ability of the organisms to find food, water, and suitable shelter, and to compete with other organisms.

Write a summary statement on the importance of climate to living things, and the potential effects if the climate were to change quickly.

Climate Change

If one day in April happens to have a temperature of 29°C, does this mean that the climate is changing? No: the temperature on any one day is just a part of that day's weather. **Climate change** is change that occurs in the climate of a region over time, usually a minimum of 30 years. Scientists determine if the climate in an area has changed by comparing the average weather over the last 30 or more years with the average weather conditions over a similar period of time in the past. If every day in April had been warmer for the last 30 years than the average temperature in Aprils over the last 100 years, that would be strong evidence that the climate is changing.

Earth has experienced climate change a number of times in its history, according to evidence such as that from ice core samples and fossils. During some periods, the climate became cooler, and warmer during others. Today, the average surface temperature of Earth is increasing, according to two kinds of evidence: anecdotal evidence and scientific evidence.

Anecdotal evidence of climate change relies on reports from people about particular weather events and how they interpret these events changing over time. Anecdotal evidence is often useful, but it has not been carefully tested to ensure it is unbiased and that it applies to situations other than the particular events reported. For example, farmers in Alberta report that the growing season begins earlier now than it did years ago. Aboriginal and Inuit elders and leaders in Canada's north have also reported changes in weather events over time, including the first frost date, the start of animal migration, and the thickness of ice. These observations all suggest that the average temperature of Earth is increasing. **Scientific evidence** of climate change relies on evidence collected in a manner that, as much as possible, ensures it is unbiased and that reflects general situations, instead of just particular events. Scientific evidence is usually collected by trained scientists and is checked by other scientists. It often involves data collected using specialized instruments. Much of our evidence about historical climate conditions relies on anecdotal evidence, since keeping formal records and using specialized equipment to determine specific climate conditions in the past or present are relatively recent inventions. Anecdotal evidence and scientific evidence may provide information about the same or similar events. For example, scientists at Environment Canada have graphed the average yearly temperature in Canada from 1948 to 1999 (Figure D1.12). This graph provides scientific evidence that agrees with the anecdotal evidence: the average yearly temperature in Canada tends to be higher now than in the past. The data for this graph were collected from weather stations across Canada. The collected data were then used to calculate an average value for the whole of Canada, which was then plotted on the graph.

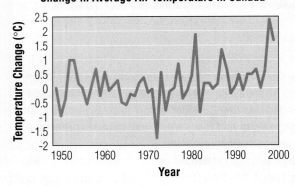

Data Source: Environment Canada

FIGURE D1.12 This graph provides scientific evidence of a warming trend in Canada's average air temperature, from 1948 to 1999. The zero point indicates that no temperature change occurred.

Activity D4
Decision-Making Investigation

Student Reference **10**

Required Skills
- Initiating and Planning
- Performing and Recording
- Analyzing and Interpreting
- Communication and Teamwork

Climate Change Today

The Issue

Is climate change affecting present-day life in Canada?

FIGURE D1.13 Loss of permafrost is linked to increases in average temperature in northern regions and can cause significant damage to some structures, such as this railroad.

Background Information

As scientists collect and analyze data from many different sources, their understanding of climate increases. Some scientists predict that climate change may occur so quickly that some organisms will be unable to adapt. Even as you read this, the world's scientists are publishing new information related to climate and climate change.

For example, scientists at Environment Canada have suggested that if the average global temperature continues to increase, the amount of moisture in many regions in Alberta would decrease. These changes would affect the types of plants that can survive, which would in turn affect the organisms that depend on them for food and shelter. However, warmer temperatures would also increase the length of the growing season, which would allow some plants to grow in areas where they previously could not. In northern regions of Canada, such as the Yukon, Nunavut,

and Northwest Territories, an increase in average temperature is predicted to cause melting of permafrost. **Permafrost** is permanently frozen ground, and thawing of permafrost can cause the ground to become unstable (Figure D1.13). A rise in the average temperature is also predicted to change the position of the tree line, the boundary between regions where trees can and cannot survive.

Working in small groups, collect articles and reports of current events related to climate change for regions in Canada. Use as many different types of information sources as you can to get current information, such as science journals and magazines, newspapers and news magazines, and Internet articles. When research is complete, create a class information board that incorporates all the information you have found. Arrange the information in a manner that will allow you to compare the information about the impact of climate change in different regions of Canada. You can create your information board electronically, using print materials, or both.

Analyze and Evaluate

1. Review the information on the class information board. In which region was human life most affected by climate change? Justify your choice.

2. In which region were other living organisms most affected by climate change? Justify your choice.

3. Severe or unusual weather events are not always due to climate change. Choose one severe or unusual weather event that is included on your information board. Summarize the evidence that links this event to climate change. Do you think the evidence is convincing? Why or why not?

4. You and your classmates can continue to add to the information board throughout this unit. At the end of sections D2.0 and D3.0, review any new information that has been added to the board, and repeat steps 1 and 2.

Interpreting Climate Data

The graph in Figure D1.12 also demonstrates how difficult it is to detect changes in climate. According to scientists from Environment Canada, the data in the graph indicate that the average temperature in Canada increased by 1.0°C from 1948 to 1999. This was determined from the line of best fit for the data points on the graph. This was not a straightforward task, since the average temperature for some years was much warmer than previous years, and sometimes was much cooler. Also, not all regions of Canada experienced the same variations in temperature, which made the analysis even more difficult.

We do not have a complete record of Earth's past climate, and we do not yet fully understand all the factors that affect climate today. What is known, however, is that climate is very important to the biosphere and climate change could have consequences to all life on Earth.

re SEARCH

Using the Internet, find evidence related to global climate change from current sources. This evidence may be about global climate change in the past or today. Begin your search at

www.pearsoned.ca/ school/science10

D1.2 Check and Reflect

Knowledge

1. Describe one example of how climate affects people.

2. Describe how climate affects the life of a grizzly bear, or of another organism of your choice.

3. Could trumpeter swans survive in a hot, dry climate? Explain your answer.

4. Define climate change.

5. Explain why scientists use data from time periods of at least 30 years to look for evidence of climate change.

6. Give one example of anecdotal evidence of climate change, and one example of scientific evidence of climate change.

Applications

7. A foreign exchange student is coming to visit your class. This student has never before lived in a climate similar to yours. Write a letter in which you recommend what clothes the student should bring with him/her. Complete your letter by inviting the student to join you in one winter sport and one summer sport. Explain why each of the two sports is played only in one season.

8. Each year, a bird-watching club records the first spring sighting of a migratory bird, the golden-crowned kinglet. Their observations from 1973 to 2003 were:

1973	May 15	1984	May 8	1995	May 4
1974	May 14	1985	May 10	1996	May 2
1975	May 14	1986	May 9	1997	May 1
1976	May 13	1987	May 7	1998	Apr 30
1977	May 15	1988	May 6	1999	May 1
1978	May 11	1989	May 8	2000	Apr 29
1979	May 12	1990	May 7	2001	May 2
1980	May 10	1991	May 6	2002	Apr 30
1981	May 11	1992	May 4	2003	Apr 29
1982	May 9	1993	May 5		
1983	May 10	1994	May 3		

a) Create a graph of these observations.

b) Describe any trends you find in your graph.

c) Write a hypothesis to explain any trend you observed.

d) What kind of information could you collect to gather evidence that might support your hypothesis?

Extension

9. Although the temperature of the Okanagan Valley supports the production of fruit, there is too little rain for these trees to survive naturally. Growers therefore supply extra water by irrigation. Using print and electronic resources, find out how irrigation changed the types of plants that can survive in the Okanagan Valley. If the climate were to become even drier, which would be more affected, the native plants or the plants that depend on irrigation? Why?

Section Review

Knowledge

1. What is the biosphere?

2. How is climate different from weather?

3. In a brief descriptive paragraph, distinguish between the hydrosphere, lithosphere, and atmosphere.

4. Explain the relationship between the troposphere and the survival of humans.

5. Where in the atmosphere does the ozone layer occur?

6. Where is atmospheric dust found?

7. What two gases in Earth's atmosphere are most important to supporting life?

8. What two sources of energy warm the lithosphere?

9. What forms of water are found in the biosphere, and where are they located?

10. Describe one example of the way climate affects animals.

11. What is the difference between anecdotal and scientific evidence?

12. Identify which of the following would be examples of anecdotal evidence and which of scientific evidence of climate change.
   a) Rocky Mountain glaciers are smaller than 100 years ago.
   b) Inuit people are finding that the Arctic ice floes are breaking up earlier in the spring.
   c) Farmers are saying their crops ripen earlier now than in the past.
   d) The average temperature of Earth increased by 0.6°C over the 20th century.

Applications

13. It is difficult to include water vapour in a chart or table of the composition of Earth's atmosphere. Why is this?

14. A researcher is studying the changes in the width of growth rings in trees from a particular region, using tree cores that were collected previously. Some of the data from two core samples are presented in the following table:

Year	Width of Growth Ring (mm)	
	Sample 1	Sample 2
1959	—	2.0
1960	3.0	2.0
1961	2.0	2.0
1962	2.5	2.0
1963	2.0	2.0
1964	9.0	9.0
1965	4.0	4.0
1966	7.5	7.5
1967	3.0	3.0
1968	3.0	3.0

a) If the trees produce wider rings under cool, wet conditions and thinner rings under dry, hot conditions, which years were hot and dry? Which were cool and wet?

b) The researcher plans to measure the growth rings from at least 20 core samples that contain rings produced over this same time period. This work will take a long time. Why would the researcher measure so many trees?

c) The researcher found newspaper articles from 1961 to 1963 in which local farmers reported that their crops had failed due to lack of water. What kind of evidence are these reports? Why might the researcher also be interested in this kind of evidence?

d) The data for 1964 are very different from that from 1959 to 1963. Is this evidence of climate change? Why or why not?

Extensions

15. Create a model of the region of the biosphere that is within a 50-km radius of your school. Include the lithosphere, hydrosphere, atmosphere, and the living things that can be found.

16. Create a multi-media presentation that shows the ways in which an animal or plant of your choosing is affected by the climate of Alberta.

17. Create diagrams of a house in Alberta and a house located in a village near the equator. Show how the buildings must be different to address different climates.

Global systems transfer energy through the biosphere.

FIGURE D2.1 Life on Earth depends on the transfer of energy between the lithosphere, hydrosphere, and atmosphere.

Virtually all the energy on Earth initially comes from the Sun; that is, from **solar energy**. Life as we know it depends on this incoming solar energy. A small amount of the incoming solar energy is converted to food energy through photosynthesis, but most is converted to thermal energy. **Thermal energy** is the energy possessed by a substance by virtue of the kinetic energy of its molecules or atoms. A quantity of a substance at a high temperature has more thermal energy than the same quantity of that substance at a low temperature.

Different regions on Earth's surface have different amounts of thermal energy. In general, regions at or near the equator tend to be warmer, or have more thermal energy, than regions closer to the poles. What causes this general relationship and what consequences does it have for the biosphere?

Although the average temperature of Earth's surface generally decreases as one moves away from the equator, there are many exceptions. For example, consider the following cities in Canada: Vancouver, BC, Lethbridge, AB, and Gander, NF. According to Environment Canada, between 1971 and 2000, Vancouver had an average annual temperature of 10.1°C. During the same period, the average annual temperature in Lethbridge was 5.7°C, and 3.8°C in Gander. What factors contribute to these variations in climate?

In this section, you will learn about factors that affect the amount of solar energy that reaches our planet's surface. You will explore how differences in Earth's atmosphere, lithosphere, and hydrosphere can affect the absorption of solar energy and its conversion to thermal energy. You will also discover how thermal energy is transferred between regions of Earth by the atmosphere and the hydrosphere. You will use this knowledge to analyze the climates of different regions on Earth called biomes, and then explain why biomes with similar characteristics can exist in different locations on Earth.

D 2.1 Energy Relationships and the Biosphere

Solar energy is **radiant energy**, or energy that is transmitted as electromagnetic waves. Solar energy consists of electromagnetic waves at different wavelengths, which together make up the electromagnetic spectrum (Figure D2.2). The electromagnetic spectrum can be divided into classes of waves that fall within a certain wavelength range. The radiation at wavelengths in the range that we can see is called visible light. The amount of energy carried per wavelength also varies across the spectrum. For example, waves of radiation in the gamma ray range will carry far more energy than an equal number of waves in the radio wave range.

Although virtually all the energy on Earth comes from the Sun, all regions do not receive the same amount of solar energy. **Insolation** is the amount of solar energy received by a region of Earth's surface. Insolation depends on latitude, and on specific characteristics of the lithosphere, atmosphere, and hydrosphere in a region, some of which can change from day to day.

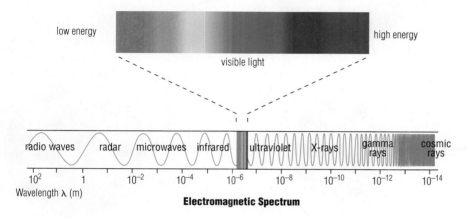

FIGURE D2.2 The electromagnetic spectrum contains many different types of radiation, which are distinguished from one another by their wavelengths. Solar energy is composed of all the types of radiation in the electromagnetic spectrum.

Insolation and the Angle of Inclination

If you were to line up Earth's poles relative to the plane of its orbit around the Sun, you would find that the poles would be slightly tilted, rather than perpendicular (straight up and down) to the orbital plane. The **angle of inclination** refers to the degree by which Earth's poles are tilted from the perpendicular of the plane of its orbit. Earth has an angle of inclination of 23.5° (Figure D2.3).

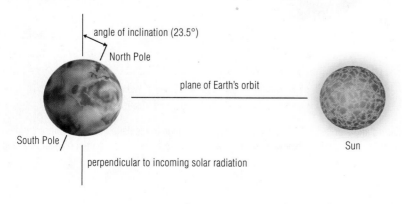

FIGURE D2.3 The tilt of Earth's axis is 23.5° from the perpendicular of the plane of its orbit.

Earth orbits the Sun once per year. On the first day of summer in the Northern Hemisphere (June 21), the angle of inclination causes the North Pole to be tilted toward the Sun (Figure D2.4). On the first day of winter in the Northern Hemisphere (December 21), however, the North Pole is tilted away from the Sun. The North Pole therefore receives more insolation during our summer, whereas the South Pole receives more insolation during our winter. Regions in the Northern Hemisphere, such as Canada, therefore have warmer temperatures from about March to September, whereas regions in the Southern Hemisphere, such as Australia, have warmer temperatures from September to March.

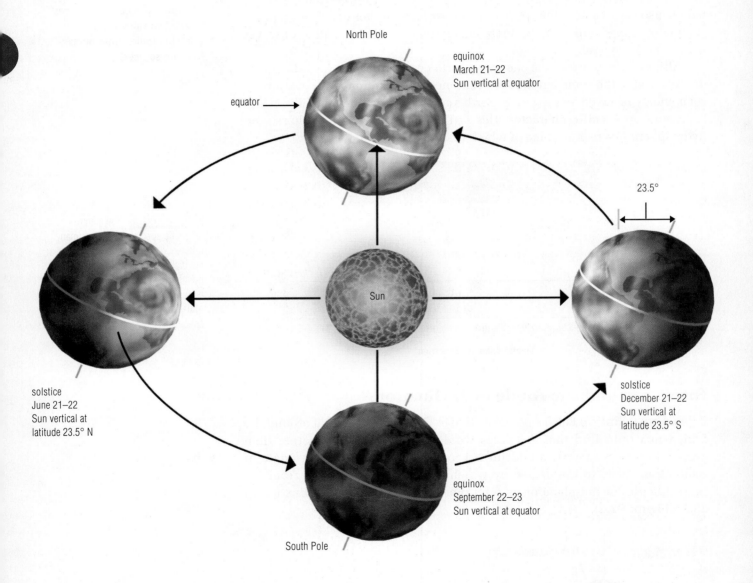

FIGURE D2.4 Earth's angle of inclination causes the seasonal change in insolation at more polar latitudes. The dates of the equinoxes and solstices may vary by one day, depending on whether a particular year is a leap year.

Earth can be divided into different **latitudes**, which are imaginary lines that run parallel to the equator. The equator is at latitude 0°, and the poles are at latitudes 90° N and 90° S. The remainder of Earth's surface is divided equally with parallel lines between these points. The angle of inclination also causes variation in the number of hours of daylight at different latitudes. At more northern latitudes, such as in Canada, there are more hours of daylight as the North Pole becomes tilted toward the Sun. A **solstice** is one of two points in Earth's orbit at which the poles are the most tilted toward or away from the Sun. The solstice that occurs on June 21–22 is the day that has the most hours of daylight in northern latitudes, but the least hours of daylight in the southern latitudes. Regions of Earth at or near the equator experience little variation in the number of hours of daylight. An **equinox** is one of two points in Earth's orbit when the number of daylight hours is equal to the number of hours of night.

Insolation and the Angle of Incidence

The shape of Earth also affects the insolation of regions at different latitudes. Earth is roughly spherical. As a result, most incoming solar radiation is not perpendicular to Earth's surface. The **angle of incidence** is the angle between a ray falling on a surface and the line of the perpendicular to that surface. At the equator, the angle of incidence of incoming solar radiation is 0°. As you move from the equator to the poles, the angle of incidence of the Sun's rays increases. At larger angles of incidence, the same amount of radiation is spread out over a greater surface area (Figure D2.5). Therefore, areas at more polar latitudes always receive less solar energy per square kilometre than areas at or near the equator.

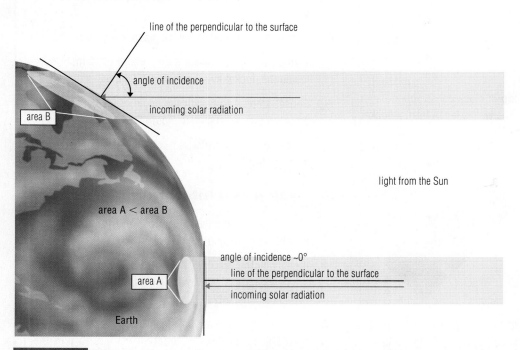

FIGURE D2.5 The angle of incidence increases with distance from the equator. As a result, the same amount of solar energy is spread over a larger surface area at more polar latitudes, such as area B, than at or near the equator, such as area A.

Angle of Incidence and Rate of Temperature Change

> **CAUTION: To avoid a burn injury, be careful not to touch the light bulb.**

The Question

How does the angle of incidence of radiant energy affect the rate of temperature change along a surface?

The Hypothesis

Create a hypothesis that answers the question.

Variables

Which is the manipulated variable in this experiment: the angle of incidence or the rate of temperature change?

Materials and Equipment

thermometer or temperature probe

100-W lamp

black construction paper

protractor

books or blocks

Procedure

1. Cut a 5 cm by 10 cm strip of black construction paper. Fold the paper, and tape the two sides to form a pocket, as shown in Figure D2.6.

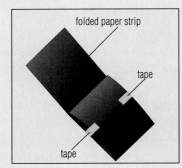

FIGURE D2.6
Fold your paper strips to form a pocket.

2. You will be directing radiant energy from a lamp onto the pocket, at angles of incidence of 0°, 45°, and 90°. Create a data table that will allow you to record the temperature inside the pocket every minute for 15 min, for each of these angles.

3. Place the pocket on books or blocks so that it is level with the lamp bulb, and at a distance of 30 cm (Figure D2.7). Using another book or block to support the pocket, position the pocket so the rays from the lamp hit the pocket at an angle of incidence of 0°.

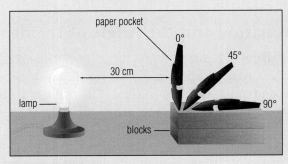

FIGURE D2.7 The experimental set-up

4. Place the thermometer or temperature probe inside the pocket, ensuring that the black paper surrounds the bulb or probe end.

5. Record the initial temperature inside the pocket.

6. Turn on the lamp. Measure and record the temperature inside the pocket every minute for 15 min.

7. Repeat steps 4 to 6 with the angle of incidence at 45° and then 90°, as shown in Figure D2.7.

8. Switch off the lamp when you have completed your investigation.

Analyzing and Interpreting

1. Identify the manipulated variable and the responding variable in this experiment.

2. Identify all the variables that were held constant during the investigation. Why was it important to keep these variables constant?

3. Create a line graph of your data. Use solid, dashed, and dotted lines, or lines of different colours to plot the results for each of the angles of incidence.

Forming Conclusions

4. Describe how the angle of incidence affected the rate of temperature change.

5. Identify the angle of incidence that exposed the pocket to the most radiant energy. Which angle exposed the pocket to the least radiant energy? Describe the evidence you used to come to your conclusion.

Applying and Connecting

6. Consider your experiment as a model of Earth. Describe the consequences of the angle of solar radiation incidence on average temperature at different latitudes on Earth, using your data to illustrate your answer.

Extending

7. In this experiment, the black paper absorbs most of the radiant energy from the lamp. Design an experiment that would allow you to test whether the rate of temperature change of a substance that reflected more radiant energy (such as another colour of paper) was affected by the angle of incidence in a similar way as was the black paper. Include a hypothesis in your experimental design.

The Earth's shape and the angle of incidence play a large role in creating Earth's climate. From the equator to the pole, there is a progressive decrease in insolation year-round. As a result, the average annual air temperature is highest at the equator, and decreases as you move toward the poles. There is little variation in the number of hours of daylight with the seasons at the equator, but the number of hours of daylight varies progressively with the seasons at increasingly higher and lower latitudes. There is therefore more variation in average daily temperature throughout the year as you move closer to the poles (Figure D2.8).

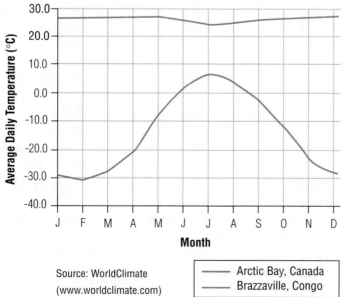

Average Daily Temperature per Month

Source: WorldClimate
(www.worldclimate.com)

Arctic Bay, Canada
Brazzaville, Congo

FIGURE D2.8 This graph shows the variation in average daily temperature per month for Arctic Bay, Nunavut, which is at latitude 73.00° N, and Brazzaville, Congo, at latitude 4.25° S. The data for Arctic Bay are the averages of temperatures recorded from 1937 to 1976. Data for Brazzaville were recorded from 1941 to 1972.

Absorption and Reflection by the Biosphere

As soon as the radiation from the Sun reaches Earth's outer atmosphere, it may be reflected or absorbed by particles of matter. When particles **reflect** energy, they simply change the ray's direction. When particles **absorb** energy, the energy is converted into another form of energy, such as kinetic energy of the particles. When a substance absorbs energy, the temperature of that substance will increase.

Absorption and reflection of solar radiation occurs in all three components of the biosphere. The reflected radiation either goes back into space, or is absorbed elsewhere in the biosphere. Some of the absorbed solar energy is re-emitted as thermal energy, which warms the atmosphere, lithosphere, and hydrosphere. Some of the kinetic energy resulting from energy absorption is used to drive the movement of water through the hydrologic cycle, and the movement of air as wind. A small amount of the solar energy is converted to chemical energy by the process of photosynthesis, and is then passed on to other organisms through food webs.

The layers of the atmosphere (troposphere, stratosphere, mesosphere, and thermosphere) contain different mixtures of gases. These different gas mixtures absorb or reflect the energy from different areas of the electromagnetic spectrum. High-energy radiation, such as X-rays and gamma rays, are absorbed by oxygen and nitrogen gases, mostly in the mesosphere, thermosphere, and stratosphere. Ozone absorbs most of the ultraviolet radiation. Carbon dioxide and water vapour in the atmosphere absorb infrared radiation, as do other gases such as methane. Visible light and radio waves make it to Earth's surface with very little absorption by the atmosphere.

FIGURE D2.9 Clouds reflect some of the incoming radiation, but also absorb energy from Earth's surface.

Cloud Cover and Atmospheric Dust

Most clouds and atmospheric dust (particles less than 0.66 mm in diameter) are found in the troposphere. The amount of cloud cover and atmospheric dust over any region varies daily, but some regions will commonly have cloudy skies, and some regions usually have relatively high levels of atmospheric dust. Human activity has also caused an overall increase in the amount of atmospheric dust in some regions, especially those over industrialized nations.

Clouds reflect some incoming solar radiation back into space. As a result, the air temperature is cooler on a cloudy day (Figure D2.9). However, clouds also absorb energy that is emitted by Earth's surface, which helps to warm the planet. Atmospheric dust behaves in a similar way. It can shade Earth's surface from incoming radiation, reducing the amount of solar energy that reaches the lithosphere and hydrosphere. Atmospheric dust also absorbs some of the incoming energy from the Sun and some of the thermal energy emitted by Earth's surface. When a natural or human-made event, such as a volcanic eruption or a large forest fire, expels large volumes of dust into the atmosphere, the effect on climate can be significant. Such effects can be very difficult to predict (Figure D2.10).

FIGURE D2.10 Large amounts of atmospheric dust affect the amount of radiation that reaches Earth's surface.

FIGURE D2.11 The albedo of an area can vary with the seasons. This variation affects the amount of solar energy that reaches Earth's surface at that locale.

Albedo—Reflection by the Lithosphere and Hydrosphere

The solar radiation that reaches Earth's surface is either reflected or absorbed. The amount of solar energy that is reflected versus the amount absorbed depends on the type of surface encountered by the incoming radiation. Scientists have invented a scale to measure the reflectivity of a surface, called the albedo. The **albedo** of a surface is the percent of solar radiation that it reflects. Light-coloured, shiny surfaces, such as snow, reflect more solar energy than darker, duller surfaces such as forests or soils.

The average albedo for Earth's surface is 30%, or 0.30. Each region of Earth has a different albedo value, depending on its surface features. For example, the albedo of the polar icecaps is much higher than the albedo of the forests of northern Alberta, or of the deserts of Africa. Albedo can also vary with the seasons. Most areas in Canada have a higher albedo in the winter than in the summer (Figure D2.11), due to the change in the amount of snow cover.

Figure D2.12 shows the albedo of Earth's surface according to data collected from April 7–22, 2002, by certain NASA satellites. In this image, regions with the highest albedo are red. The snow and ice cover of northern latitudes causes these regions to have a high albedo year-round. Areas that lack forest cover, such as the Sahara desert of Africa, also have a high albedo. Yellows and greens show regions with intermediate albedo values, and regions with low albedo are coloured blue or violet. No data were available for regions that are white, or for oceans.

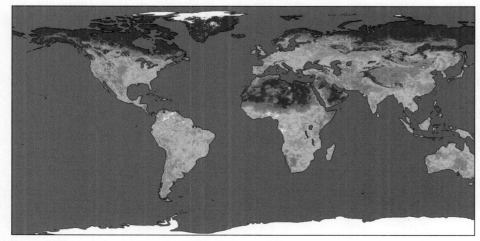

Source: NASA

FIGURE D2.12 The average albedo of Earth's surface from April 7 to 22, 2002. Polar regions with high amounts of snow have a high albedo. Cloud cover, atmospheric dust, and forest cover also affect the albedo of an area.

Modelling Albedo in the Biosphere

CAUTION: To avoid burn injury, do not touch the light bulb.

The Question

When two samples with differing albedo, white and green sugar, are exposed to equal amounts of radiation, will the amount of temperature change above and below the surface of the samples differ?

The Hypothesis

Create a hypothesis that relates the albedo of white sugar and green sugar to the change in temperature above and below the surface of the sugar samples.

Variables

Identify the responding and manipulated variables, and the variables that must be controlled in this experiment.

Materials and Equipment

3 paper baking cups
3 thermometers or temperature probes
reflector lamp with a 200-W bulb
white sugar
green-dyed sugar
timer
graph paper, spreadsheet software, or graphing calculator

Procedure

1. Fill one baking cup with white sugar, and a second baking cup with green sugar. Both baking cups should be filled as close to the top as possible, and the surface of the sugar should be flat. Leave the third baking cup empty. This will be your control.

2. You will be measuring the temperature of the air just above the sugar samples and just below the surface of the sugar samples every 2 min for 10 min. You will also be measuring the temperature of the air in the control at these same times. Using paper or spreadsheet software, create a data table that will allow you to record these data. If you are using a graphing calculator, open the appropriate application to collect or enter temperature data.

3. Place the lamp so that it is about 30 cm above the containers.

4. Place the bulb of one thermometer or one temperature probe just under the surface of each sugar sample. Place the third thermometer or temperature probe inside the empty baking cup so that it is not touching any surface. Record the initial temperature of each.

5. Using the same thermometers or temperature probes, measure and record the temperature of the air just above the surface of each sugar sample.

6. Turn on the lamp and start the timer. Repeat the temperature measurements in steps 4 and 5 every 2 min for 10 min with the light on. After 10 min, carefully turn off the lamp.

Analyzing and Interpreting

1. Using the data in your table, create a graph of the temperature versus time. Your graph should include temperatures above and below each sugar sample and in the control, for each time point.

2. Using your graph, describe the changes that occurred in the temperature above and below the surface of the white sugar and the green sugar, and in the control. Outline any differences among the two samples and the control.

3. According to your graph, over which sugar sample did the air temperature change more when the light was on? Relate this to the albedo of the two sugar samples.

4. According to your graph, which sugar sample absorbed more radiation when the light was on? Relate this to the albedo of the two sugar samples.

5. Why did you need to determine the temperature of the air in the empty baking cup?

Forming Conclusions

6. Review your hypothesis. Write a paragraph that explains whether your data and analysis support or refute your hypothesis.

Applying and Connecting

7. Imagine you are in a park in the summer. The Sun is shining on a grassy area and on the sand beach. Will the air just above the sand or just above the grass be warmer? Why?

8. The far north of Canada is mainly covered with ice and snow year-round, whereas the more southern regions are covered with snow only during the winter. Would the northern or the southern regions of Canada absorb more solar radiation? Explain your answer by referring to the results of this experiment.

Extending

9. Using green and white sugar, design an experiment that would model how albedo varies between the summer and winter months in your area. When your teacher approves your experimental design, conduct your investigation.

Natural Greenhouse Effect

Some of the radiant energy that is absorbed by Earth's surface is re-emitted into the atmosphere as infrared radiation, which has high thermal energy (Figure D2.13). This re-emitted thermal energy helps to keep the temperature of our planet in the range that supports life.

Most of the thermal energy is absorbed in the atmosphere by clouds, water vapour, and gases such as carbon dioxide and methane. Without the atmosphere, this thermal energy would escape into space, and Earth would be significantly cooler. The absorption of thermal energy by the atmosphere is known as the **natural greenhouse effect**. Without the natural greenhouse effect, the average temperature on Earth would be about 33°C lower.

Greenhouse gases are gases that contribute to the greenhouse effect. Since it is present in such high amounts in the atmosphere, the main contributor to the natural greenhouse effect is water vapour. However, carbon dioxide and other gases, methane and nitrous oxide (N_2O, also called dinitrogen monoxide), also absorb significant amounts of thermal energy.

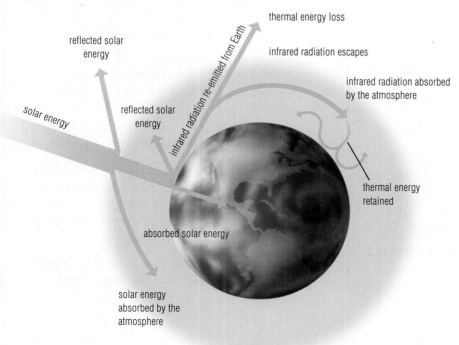

thermal energy loss

reflected solar energy

infrared radiation re-emitted from Earth

infrared radiation escapes

infrared radiation absorbed by the atmosphere

solar energy

reflected solar energy

thermal energy retained

absorbed solar energy

solar energy absorbed by the atmosphere

FIGURE D2.13 The natural greenhouse effect keeps Earth warm enough to support life by absorbing some of the infrared radiation re-emitted from Earth's surface.

The Greenhouse Effect

CAUTION: To avoid burn injury, do not touch the lamp.

The Question

How does the greenhouse effect help to maintain temperature?

The Hypothesis

The greenhouse effect results in more absorption of thermal energy, and reduces the amount of thermal energy that radiates back into space.

Variables

In this experiment, you will be measuring the temperature change inside and outside a model greenhouse over time. Identify the manipulated, responding, and all controlled variables.

Materials and Equipment

2-L clear plastic bottle

tape

one-hole stopper to fit bottle

2 thermometers or temperature probes

reflector lamp with 200-W bulb

retort stand

clamp

graph paper, spreadsheet software, or graphing calculator

Procedure

1. Carefully insert one of the thermometers or temperature probes into the one-hole stopper. Fit the stopper assembly snugly into the top of the 2-L bottle. The bulb should be as far down into the bottle as possible.

2. Secure the thermometer or temperature probe in place with tape.

3. With the clamp, attach the second thermometer to the retort stand so that its bulb is at about the same height as the one inside of the bottle. Position the stand and thermometer near the bottle.

4. Position the heat lamp so it is at an equal distance from both thermometers. Your model should look like Figure D2.14.

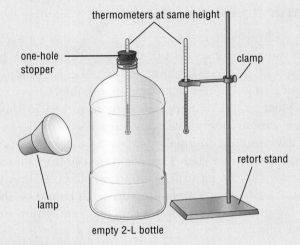

FIGURE D2.14 The completed model

5. Create a data table that will allow you to record the temperature change inside and outside of the bottle every minute for approximately 15 min.

6. Turn on the lamp. Record the initial temperature, then the temperature at 1 min intervals. When the temperature stops rising, continue to record the temperature for another 3 to 5 min.

Analyzing and Interpreting

1. Graph your results. Plot the time in minutes on the horizontal axis and the temperature in °C on the vertical axis. Use solid and dashed lines to distinguish the temperature inside the bottle from the temperature outside the bottle. Include a legend.

2. Compare the temperature changes that occurred inside the bottle to those outside. Explain any differences you observed.

Net Radiation Budget

Earth is a warm, habitable planet because incoming solar radiation is absorbed by Earth's surface and the atmosphere. However, not all the incoming solar energy is absorbed. Some is reflected out to space, and some is re-emitted as thermal energy by Earth's surface and atmosphere. The **net radiation budget** is the difference between the amount of incoming radiation and of outgoing radiation re-emitted from Earth's surface and atmosphere. Incoming radiation is all the solar energy that reaches Earth's surface, not including the solar radiation that is reflected by the atmosphere and by the albedo of Earth's surface. Outgoing radiation is the thermal radiation re-emitted by Earth's surface and atmosphere that is not absorbed by the greenhouse gases of the atmosphere. The net radiation budget of Earth can be written as a word equation:

net radiation budget = incoming radiation − outgoing radiation

Activity D8

QuickLab

Earth's Net Radiation Budget

Purpose

To analyze Earth's net radiation budget

Materials and Equipment

graph paper, graphing calculator, or spreadsheet software

Procedure

1. Using the information in Figure D2.15, create a pie chart that illustrates what happens to incoming radiation. Use different colours to represent reflected solar energy, absorbed solar energy, and re-emitted solar energy.

Questions

1. What is the total amount of solar energy reflected back into space, in percent?

2. What percent of solar energy is re-emitted from Earth back into space?

3. What is the total amount of solar energy absorbed by Earth, in percent?

4. Describe what happens to the solar energy coming to Earth. Your description should include the following terms: solar energy, energy input, and energy output.

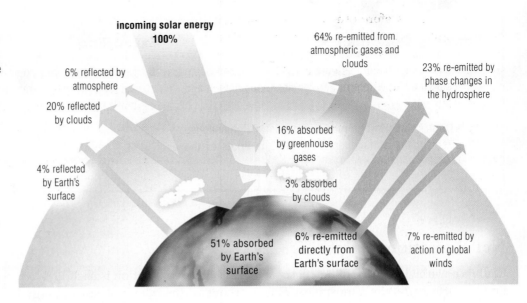

FIGURE D2.15 For Earth as a whole, the net radiation budget is in balance. In other words, the amount of radiation coming in to Earth is the same as the amount that goes back into space.

incoming solar energy
100%

6% reflected by atmosphere

20% reflected by clouds

4% reflected by Earth's surface

64% re-emitted from atmospheric gases and clouds

23% re-emitted by phase changes in the hydrosphere

16% absorbed by greenhouse gases

3% absorbed by clouds

51% absorbed by Earth's surface

6% re-emitted directly from Earth's surface

7% re-emitted by action of global winds

Figure D2.15 shows the relative contribution of different aspects of Earth's average net radiation budget, based on data collected by NASA for the Earth Radiation Budget Experiment project. When solar energy reaches Earth, some of the radiation is immediately reflected back out to space by the atmosphere (6%), clouds (20%), and Earth's surface (4%). The remaining incoming radiation is absorbed directly by greenhouse gases in the atmosphere (16%), clouds (3%), and the Earth's surface (land and water: 51%). On average, all the energy absorbed by the atmosphere, lithosphere, and hydrosphere is eventually emitted and radiated back into space as thermal energy. Absorbed solar energy is radiated from clouds and atmospheric gases (64%), by phase changes in the hydrosphere (23%), by the action of global winds (7%), and directly from Earth's surface (6%). You will learn more about some of these events later in this unit.

On average, the amount of incoming radiation is equal to the outgoing radiation for all of planet Earth. In other words, incoming radiation minus outgoing radiation equals zero. If this balance were to change, then the average global temperature would either increase or decrease, until the net radiation budget was balanced again. For example, if the amount of radiation re-emitted back into space were to decrease and the amount of incoming radiation remained the same, Earth's average global temperature would increase.

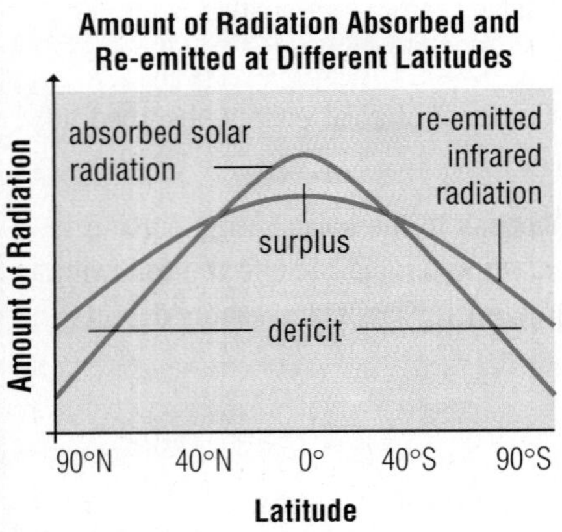

Net Radiation Budget and Latitude

Although the net radiation budget is balanced for Earth as a whole, some regions on Earth have an unbalanced net radiation budget. Latitude is an important factor in predicting whether the net radiation budget of a region will be out of balance. For example, polar regions tend to always have lower insolation and higher albedo than other regions on Earth. As a result, at polar latitudes (90° S or 90° N), there tends to be less incoming radiation than outgoing radiation (Figure D2.16).

Amount of Radiation Absorbed and Re-emitted at Different Latitudes

absorbed solar radiation

re-emitted infrared radiation

surplus

deficit

Amount of Radiation

90°N   40°N   0°   40°S   90°S

Latitude

FIGURE D2.16 Average distribution of absorbed and re-emitted radiation on Earth

The poles therefore always have a net radiation budget deficit. Regions near the equator (latitude 0°) tend to have higher insolation, which results in more incoming radiation relative to outgoing radiation. Regions on and near the equator always have a net radiation budget surplus.

If the only factor that determined climate were differences in net radiation budget, then the average temperature in regions with a net radiation budget surplus, such as at the equator, would be expected to increase over time, since the excess radiation would be converted to thermal energy. Similarly, in regions with a net radiation budget deficit, such as at the poles, the average temperature would be expected to decrease over time, since the amount of emitted thermal energy would be greater than the amount of absorbed radiation. These trends do not occur, however. In the following sections, you will find out how thermal energy is transferred from latitudes with a net radiation surplus to latitudes with a net radiation deficit.

*re*SEARCH

The Earth Radiation Budget Experiment (ERBE) was started in 1984. Find out how this project monitors Earth's radiation budget, and how the information is used. Begin your search at

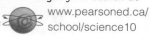 www.pearsoned.ca/school/science10

D2.1 Check and Reflect

Knowledge

1. Describe how the amount of solar energy reaching the poles varies during the year.

2. How does cloud cover influence the amount of solar radiation that reaches Earth's surface?

3. What determines the albedo of a material?

4. What is the electromagnetic spectrum?

5. Describe the source(s) of energy that reach the troposphere.

6. Explain what is meant by the term "Earth's net radiation budget."

7. When does the North Pole receive the highest insolation? What is happening to the insolation at the South Pole at this time?

8. Compare the albedo of an area that is covered in snow to an area covered with dark soil.

9. Describe what happens to the solar energy that is absorbed by Earth's surface.

10. Distinguish between the angle of inclination and the angle of incidence.

11. What happens to the solar energy that reaches Earth's surface, but is not reflected back into space?

12. Identify the factors that affect the amount of radiation that reaches a region of Earth's surface.

13. Outline the effect of the angle of inclination on the amount of solar energy that reaches Earth.

Applications

14. The city of Ynnus is located on the equator, and Ywons is at the North Pole. In a table, compare the relative number of hours of daylight and amount of insolation that would be received by these two cities on December 21 and on March 21 of any year.

15. Using an illustration in your answer, explain the natural greenhouse effect.

16. Two cities located in the desert have the same altitude and latitude, but have different surface features. The city of Rocky Peaks is surrounded by a dark rocky surface. The city of Sandy Beach is surrounded by light-coloured sand. Neither city ever has snow. Which city will have the higher average temperature in the summer? Which will have the higher average temperature in the winter? Explain your answers.

Extensions

17. Create an illustration to show as many factors as possible that would likely affect the amount of solar radiation that reaches Earth's surface in your area.

18. The amount of solar energy reflected by water at midday is 5% to 10%. Explain why this percent would vary during the day.

D 2.2 Thermal Energy Transfer in the Atmosphere

infoBIT

A resting person transfers about 100 J of thermal energy every second into the atmosphere. This is the same amount of energy emitted per second by a 100-watt light bulb.

Thermal energy transfer is the movement of thermal energy from an area of high temperature to an area of low temperature. Suppose you brought a bicycle outdoors on a cold day. The temperature of the bicycle would fall to the same temperature as the air outside. If you were then to bring the bicycle back inside, the temperature of the bicycle would increase to the indoor temperature. In this example, thermal energy first was transferred from the bicycle to the air, and then from the air to the bicycle. Thermal energy transfer can occur by conduction or convection.

Conduction and Convection

Radiation is the emission of energy as particles or waves. When radiant energy encounters particles of matter, it may be reflected or absorbed. Absorbed energy can increase the movement of the particles (their kinetic energy). An increase in kinetic energy increases the temperature of the matter. Any substance at a higher temperature than its surroundings will emit radiant energy, usually as infrared radiation. For example, the Sun radiates energy in the form of electromagnetic waves (solar energy), some of which travels to Earth. When this radiant energy reaches Earth's atmosphere, some of it is absorbed by particles of matter, such as molecules of carbon dioxide gas. The absorbed radiant energy increases the kinetic energy of the carbon dioxide molecules, and the temperature of the carbon dioxide gas increases. The warmed carbon dioxide gas may then transfer some of its thermal energy to substances at lower temperatures, or re-emit it as infrared radiation.

Conduction is the transfer of thermal energy through direct contact between the particles of a substance, without moving the particles to a new location. Thermal energy transfer by conduction usually takes place in solids. Recall that particles in a solid all have a certain average kinetic energy. During conduction, particles with more kinetic energy transfer some of their energy to neighbouring particles with lower kinetic energy. This increases the kinetic energy of the neighbouring particles, which may in turn transfer energy to other neighbouring particles, increasing their kinetic energy. For example, in Figure D2.17, the burner is radiating energy to the solid metal pan. The particles of metal closest to the burner absorb some of this radiated energy and increase in kinetic energy. These particles can then transfer energy to neighbouring particles, causing an increase in temperature.

FIGURE D2.17 In this illustration, energy is radiated from the heating element and is absorbed by the lower surface of the pan. The absorbed radiant energy increases the kinetic energy of the particles in this part of the pan. Thermal energy is then transferred to other parts of the pan by conduction. Conduction transfers thermal energy from one particle to another through direct contact.

Convection is transfer of thermal energy through the movement of particles from one location to another. Thermal energy transfer by convection usually occurs in **fluids**, which are substances with no definite shape (such as gases and liquids). During convection, the movement of the particles forms a **current**, or a flow from one place to another in one direction. For example, when the water in the pot in Figure D2.18 absorbs energy from the burner, the water molecules increase in kinetic energy. The water molecules then begin to move apart from one another, causing the water to expand in volume. This expansion lowers the **density**, or mass per volume, of the water. The less dense water will rise to the top, forming an upward convection current. When it contacts the cooler air at the surface, the water will cool and contract, which increases its density and forms a downward convection current (Figure D2.18).

FIGURE D2.18 Convection transfers thermal energy through the movement of particles from one location to another.

QuickLab

Convection

CAUTION: To avoid being scalded, do not touch the apparatus.

Materials and Equipment

paper and pen

watch or clock

assembled apparatus as shown

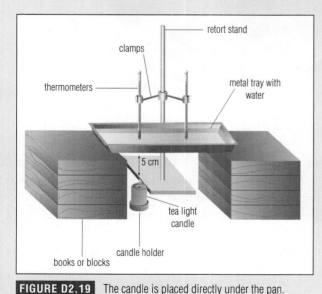

FIGURE D2.19 The candle is placed directly under the pan.

Procedure

1. On a clean sheet of paper, create a table that will allow you to record the two temperature readings from each thermometer. You will use the rest of the sheet to record your observations.

2. Your teacher will measure the initial temperature of the water with both thermometers. Record these measurements.

3. Your teacher will now add one drop of food colouring below each thermometer. Observe and record the movement of the food colouring.

4. You teacher will light the tea light and place it at the centre of one end of the pan. Observe and record what happens to the food colouring over the next 10 min.

5. After 10 min, your teacher will measure the final temperature of the water with both thermometers. Record these measurements.

Questions

1. In a table, compare and contrast the movement of the food colouring before and after the water was heated.

2. Write a paragraph to summarize your observations. In a second paragraph, discuss how this activity illustrated thermal energy transfer in the atmosphere.

3. If an open bottle of perfume were heated, would the effect be similar to the results of this activity? Explain your reasoning.

Effects of Thermal Energy Transfer in the Atmosphere

The temperature of the atmosphere tends to increase in areas close to or on the equator. As the heated atmospheric gases gain energy and expand, the air becomes less dense and rises. In areas close to or at the poles, the temperature of the atmosphere tends to decrease. Here, the cooling atmospheric gases lose energy and contract, and the air becomes denser and falls. If the Earth were not spinning, there would be a continuous convection current between the polar and the equatorial regions (Figure D2.20).

Atmospheric pressure is the pressure exerted by the mass of air above any point on Earth's surface. Since warm air is less dense than cold air, warmer regions of the atmosphere exert less atmospheric pressure than cooler regions. **Wind** is the movement of cool air from these areas of high pressure to areas of low pressure. The rising and sinking masses of air in convection currents cause changes in atmospheric pressure, which cause wind.

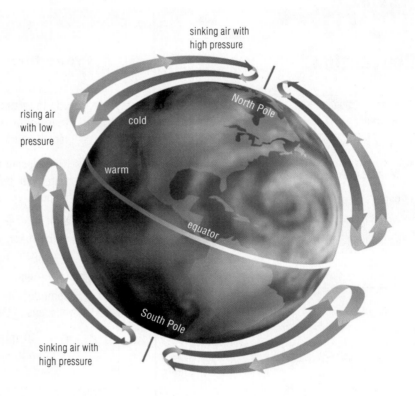

sinking air with high pressure

rising air with low pressure

cold

warm

North Pole

equator

South Pole

sinking air with high pressure

FIGURE D2.20 Differences in thermal energy in the atmosphere would cause these convection currents, if Earth did not rotate.

The Coriolis Effect

The difference between the net radiation budget at the poles and at the equator tends to cause air to move directly north and south. However, since Earth is rotating on its axis, the winds are deflected either toward the right or toward the left. The **Coriolis effect** is the deflection of any object from a straight line path by the rotation of Earth. The Coriolis effect causes moving air or wind to turn right in the Northern Hemisphere and left in the Southern Hemisphere.

QuickLab

The Coriolis Effect

Purpose

To model the Coriolis effect

Materials and Equipment

piece of cardboard at least 30 cm wide

nail or large pin

pen or marker

Procedure

1 Cut a circle of at least 30 cm in diameter from a piece of cardboard. Put the nail or pin into the exact centre of the circle so that it spins freely.

2 Label the centre of the circle as the North Pole, and the outer edge as the equator.

3 Draw a clockwise arrow on the circle at the edge, to indicate the direction of Earth's rotation.

4 To demonstrate the Coriolis effect, have a partner rotate the circle as you draw a straight line from the North Pole to the equator.

Questions

1. Look at the line drawn on the cardboard circle. Which direction does the line twist?

2. What does the twisting line represent?

3. How did this activity model the Coriolis effect?

4. If you repeated this activity on the underside of the circle, which way would the lines twist?

To better visualize the Coriolis effect, imagine you were to launch a rocket at high speed southward from the North Pole. Your rocket would not just travel a straight line south from where you launched it. As the rocket travelled south, Earth would be rotating beneath it, deflecting the path of the rocket westward to the right. If you launched the rocket from the South Pole to the equator instead, the Earth's rotation would again deflect the path of the rocket westward, which is now to the left (Figure D2.21).

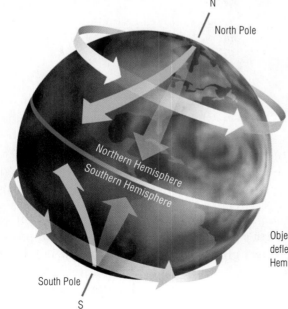

N
North Pole

W

Northern Hemisphere
Southern Hemisphere

Objects moving toward the equator deflect to the right in the Northern Hemisphere.

E

Objects moving toward the equator deflect to the left in the Southern Hemisphere.

South Pole

S

FIGURE D2.21 Winds in the two hemispheres of Earth move in opposite directions because of the Coriolis effect.

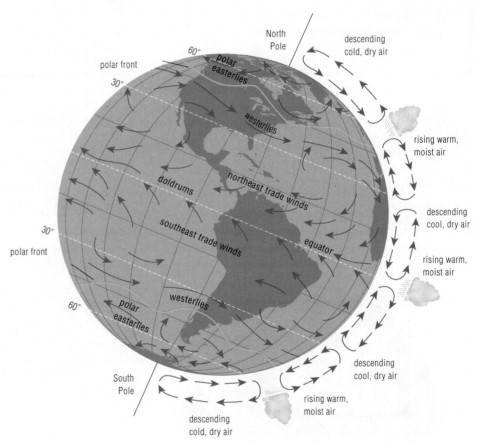

infoBIT

The Cape Denison-Commonwealth Bay region of Adelie Land, Antarctica is the windiest place on Earth. The mean annual wind speed is 90 km/h, but winds can reach speeds up to 320 km/h.

Global Wind Patterns

The convection currents in the atmosphere and the Coriolis effect result in the global wind patterns shown in Figure D2.22. Global winds transfer thermal energy from areas of net radiation budget surplus to areas of net radiation budget deficit. If this did not occur, areas at or near the equator would grow very hot while the rest of Earth would become much colder.

In regions at and near the equator, the rising current of air causes winds that blow steadily northeast and southeast, called the trade winds. Trade winds are caused by the action of the Coriolis effect, which deflects the rising currents of air to the northeast in the Northern Hemisphere and the southeast in the Southern Hemisphere. At latitudes of about 30° N and 30° S, some of the warm air from the equator is sufficiently cooled that it begins to sink and move back toward the equator. The rest of the warm air moves toward the poles and is pushed east by the Coriolis effect, which causes cold air to rush in, in a westward direction. This gives rise to the westerly winds that prevail at the latitudes between 30° and 60° in both directions from the equator. At the poles, sinking cold air is pushed eastward, forming easterly winds.

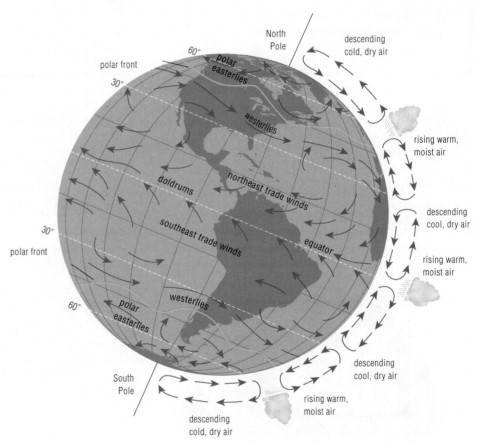

FIGURE D2.22 Global wind patterns are caused by the unequal heating of Earth's atmosphere and the deflection of winds by the Coriolis effect. The trade winds and polar easterlies tend to blow to the east, and the westerlies tend to blow to the west. The doldrums are a region of very low winds in a band about the equator.

Jet Streams

Local conditions such as the presence of continents or large bodies of water also affect wind patterns. Earth's surface and the density of the troposphere produce friction, which slows global winds. A **jet stream** is a band of fast-moving air in the stratosphere. Because of their high altitude, these winds are not subject to as much friction, and so are much faster than winds closer to Earth's surface.

Earth has several jet streams, which circle Earth at various latitudes. There are usually two or three jet streams in the Northern Hemisphere and in the Southern Hemisphere. Like the surface winds, jet streams are also formed by the convection currents in Earth's atmosphere. Their speed and temperature vary with the amount of thermal energy in the atmosphere. During the cooler months, the jet streams tend to be closer to the equator and to move more quickly. Changes in the jet streams affect the formation of severe weather events such as squalls, storms, and cyclones. The movements of the jet streams, particularly those in polar regions, can also affect the movement of the air at lower levels of the atmosphere. Changes in the jet streams are therefore very important to predicting weather changes, and so you are likely to hear them mentioned during weather forecasts.

re SEARCH

Jet streams were first discovered by pilots during the Second World War. The pilots noticed that it took less time to fly to Britain from the United States than it did to fly from the United States to Britain. Using print and electronic resources, find out how the aviation industry uses jet streams today. Begin your search at

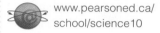
www.pearsoned.ca/school/science10

D2.2 Check and Reflect

Knowledge

1. Describe the effect of the unequal distribution of thermal energy on Earth on the temperature of the atmosphere.

2. Name three methods of thermal energy transfer.

3. Compare and contrast conduction and convection.

4. Identify what is transferred by global winds.

5. Explain why air moves from areas of high atmospheric pressure to areas of low atmospheric pressure.

6. Describe the Coriolis effect.

7. Explain how the Coriolis effect influences the direction of wind in the Northern Hemisphere.

8. What are the trade winds and where do they occur?

9. What are jet streams?

10. Explain why jet streams are faster than other global winds.

Applications

11. Create a diagram to illustrate how convection transfers heat.

12. If a high-pressure system is approaching from the west, predict the direction in which the winds will most likely be blowing. Explain your answer.

13. Explain why the air at the equator moves toward the poles.

14. Draw an illustration showing the deflection of the path of a rocket launched in a direct line from the equator toward the North Pole. Would the path of the rocket be deflected in the same way if it were launched in a direct line from the equator toward the South Pole? Explain.

Extensions

15. Describe how conditions in the biosphere might differ if air transferred thermal energy by conduction, instead of by convection.

16. Suppose a planet was discovered that was Earth's twin in all physical and geographic features, except that the planet did not rotate. How would the pattern of global winds on this planet compare to those of Earth?

17. The trade winds were once very important to sailing ships that travelled between Europe and South America. Suggest a reason to explain this fact.

D 2.3 Thermal Energy Transfer in the Hydrosphere

The hydrosphere transfers thermal energy from the warmer latitudes near to the equator to cooler areas near the poles, through the action of global winds. Figure D2.23 shows the major pattern of the surface currents of Earth's oceans. The warmer waters near the equator are driven by the trade winds that prevail between the equator and latitudes 30° N and 30° S. The westerly winds that prevail between latitudes 30° and 60° N and S tend to bring warm waters down toward the poles, and the easterlies that prevail from latitudes 60° N and S to the poles tend to drive cooler waters up toward the equator. As with global winds, the pattern of surface ocean currents is modified by the Coriolis effect. Currents in the Northern Hemisphere are driven clockwise, and currents in the Southern Hemisphere are driven counterclockwise. Earth's continents also affect the general pattern of the ocean's currents, however. The currents change direction when they encounter a large land mass. Some coastal regions, such as the west coast of British Columbia, experience a continuous current of warm water, whereas other regions, such as the east coast of Labrador, experience a continuous current of cold water.

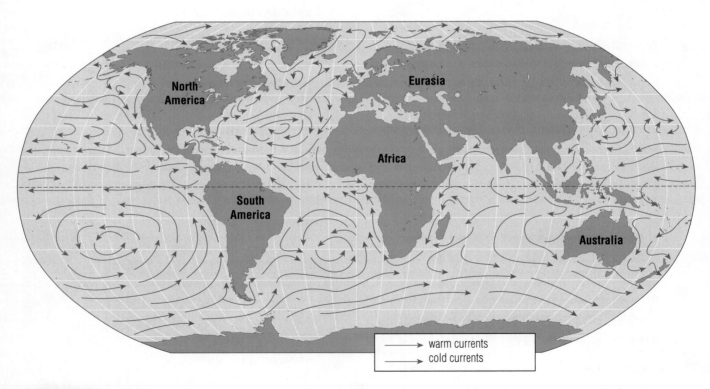

FIGURE D2.23 The surface ocean currents extend from the surface of the ocean to a depth of about 100 m, and reflect the pattern of Earth's global winds.

Thermal energy is also transferred vertically through the oceans and other bodies of water, through convection currents (Figure D2.24). As does air, the density of water decreases when its temperature increases, so warm water tends to rise. Cooler water is more dense, so it tends to sink.

Specific Heat Capacity

Earlier in this unit, you were asked to consider the climates of three Canadian cities: Vancouver, BC (latitude 49.11° N), Lethbridge, AB (49.38° N), and Gander, NF (48.56° N). Since they are at similar latitudes, you now know that these three cities receive similar insolation, and experience similar winds (westerlies). Yet the average temperatures of these cities between 1971 and 2000 varied considerably, according to Environment Canada records (Table D2.1).

TABLE D2.1 Climate Data for Three Canadian Cities

City	Latitude	Average Annual Temperature (°C)	Average January Temperature (°C)	Average July Temperature (°C)
Vancouver, BC	49.11° N	10.1	3.3	17.5
Lethbridge, AB	49.38° N	5.7	−7.8	18.0
Gander, NF	48.56° N	3.8	−7.4	16.0

Data Source: Environment Canada

Vancouver is situated on the west coast (next to a warm ocean current), Lethbridge is in southern Alberta (an area with no large bodies of water), and Gander is situated on the east coast (next to a cold ocean current). Large bodies of water can have a profound effect on climate.

Climate variations in regions at similar latitudes can be caused by differences in the thermal properties of substances in those regions, which can lead to uneven heating and cooling. Every substance has particular thermal properties, one of which is the amount of energy that the substance can absorb before it changes temperature. For example, suppose you have an aluminium lawn chair. One hot summer day, you leave the lawn chair in direct sunlight with a glass of water beside it. If you were to return to the chair in an hour, you would likely find that the aluminium chair was too hot to touch. The water would likely be very warm, but it would not be too hot to touch. Water can absorb a large quantity of thermal energy before it changes temperature.

The **specific heat capacity (*c*)** of a substance is the amount of energy required to raise the temperature of 1 g of the substance by 1°C. The theoretical specific heat capacity of water is 4.19 J/g·°C, whereas the theoretical specific heat capacity of aluminium is 0.897 J/g·°C. Regions on Earth's surface that have little water tend to heat and cool more rapidly than regions at similar latitudes with a lot of water.

Because water has a relatively large specific heat capacity, it takes a considerable amount of energy to increase the temperature of a mass of water (Figure D2.25). Similarly, a large amount of energy is released from a mass of water when the temperature of the water decreases. Water therefore heats up and cools down slowly compared to many other substances. About 70% of Earth's surface is covered by water, so the capacity of water to absorb thermal energy has a great effect on climate. Substances that make up the lithosphere generally have a lower specific heat capacity than water. This in part is why the air temperature tends to vary more with the seasons in Lethbridge than in Vancouver.

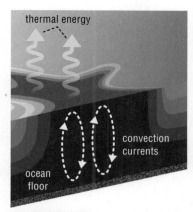

FIGURE D2.24 Convection currents transfer thermal energy between the upper and lower depths of the oceans.

FIGURE D2.25 Specific heat capacity is the amount of energy required to raise the temperature of 1 g of a substance by 1°C. It therefore takes far more thermal energy to increase the temperature of the water in an ocean than in a single glass.

The specific heat capacity of water is also much higher than that of air. As a result, the average air temperature over a body of water varies far less than the air temperature over land in the same region. Water can absorb a large quantity of thermal energy from the atmosphere without changing temperature. As a result, coastal areas experience less variation in temperature than inland areas. Coastal areas also tend to be warmer than non-coastal regions when they are close to warm ocean currents, and cooler when they are close to cool ocean currents. For example, in Vancouver, the warm ocean currents help to maintain relatively warm air temperatures in January, and the relatively warm average annual temperature of 10.1°C. In Gander, the cool ocean currents help to maintain relatively cool air temperatures in July, and the relatively cool average annual temperature of 3.8°C.

Quantity of Thermal Energy, Q

The **quantity of thermal energy**, Q, is the amount of thermal energy absorbed or released when the temperature of a specific mass of substance changes by a certain number of degrees. Q can be calculated by the following equation:

$$Q = mc\Delta t$$

where Q is the quantity of thermal energy, in J,

m is the mass of the substance, in g,

c is the specific heat capacity of the substance, in J/g·°C, and

Δt is the change in temperature, in °C.

To determine Q, you must know the value for the specific heat capacity, c, of the substance. The specific heat capacity of a substance can be determined using a calorimeter. A **calorimeter** is any device used to determine the transfer of thermal energy. A calorimeter can be as simple as nested foam coffee cups, like the device shown in Figure D2.26. When you use a calorimeter, you assume that any energy that is released can be detected as a change in the temperature inside the calorimeter. Scientists use calorimeters to determine the specific heat capacities of many substances, which are then published in reference materials.

The other two variables in the equation can be directly measured. Mass is measured in grams, using a balance. The change in temperature is determined by measuring the temperature of a substance before energy is added or removed, and the highest temperature that substance reaches at the end of the experiment.

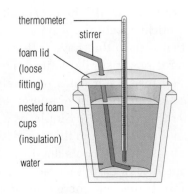

thermometer

stirrer

foam lid (loose fitting)

nested foam cups (insulation)

water

FIGURE D2.26 A simple foam cup calorimeter

Example Problem D2.1

A 50.0-g mass of water at 25.0°C is heated to 50.0°C on a hot plate. Given that the theoretical specific heat capacity of water is 4.19 J/g·°C, determine the value for Q.

$$\Delta t = 50.0°C - 25.0°C$$
$$= 25.0°C$$

The mass, m, is 50.0 g, and the specific heat capacity, c, is 4.19 J/g·°C. Therefore:

$$Q = mc\Delta t$$
$$= (50.0\ \cancel{g})\ (4.19\ J/\cancel{g}·°\cancel{C})\ (25.0°\cancel{C})$$
$$= 5237.5\ J$$
$$= 5.24\ kJ$$

The amount of thermal energy added, Q, was 5.24 kJ.

Practice Problems

1. A 200-g mass of water at 4.00°C is allowed to warm to 22.0°C. Determine the amount of thermal energy, Q, absorbed. The theoretical specific heat capacity of water is 4.19 J/g·°C.

2. A 100.0-g mass of water is at 23.0°C. Determine the quantity of thermal energy, Q, required to increase the temperature of the water to 100.0°C. The theoretical specific heat capacity of water is 4.19 J/g·°C.

Example Problem D2.2

How much thermal energy must be released to decrease the temperature of 1.00 kg of water by 10.0°C, given that the theoretical specific heat capacity of water is 4.19 J/g·°C?

Mass, m, is 1.00 kg or 1000 g. Therefore:

$$Q = mc\Delta t$$
$$Q = (1000\ \cancel{g})\ (4.19\ J/\cancel{g}·°\cancel{C})\ (10.0°\cancel{C})$$
$$= 41\ 900\ J$$
$$= 41.9\ kJ$$

To decrease the temperature of 1.00 kg of water by 10°C, 41.9 kJ of thermal energy must be released.

Practice Problems

3. Calculate the amount of thermal energy that must be released to decrease the temperature of 20.0 g of water by 15.0°C, given that the theoretical specific heat capacity of water is 4.19 J/g·°C.

4. Determine the quantity of energy required to warm a 1.00-kg block of ice from −15.0°C to 0°C. The theoretical specific heat capacity of ice is 2.00 J/g·°C.

Provided that three of the variables are known, this equation can be solved for any of Q, m, c, or Δt.

Example Problem D2.3

Calculate the change in temperature, Δt, that occurs when 8.38 kJ of thermal energy is added to 100.0 g of water. The theoretical specific heat capacity of water is 4.19 J/g·°C.

First, convert the amount of energy from kJ to J.

$$8.38 \text{ kJ} = (8.38 \text{ kJ}) (1000 \text{ J/kJ})$$

$$= 8380 \text{ J}$$

Then, rearrange the equation as follows:

$$Q = mc\Delta t$$

$$\text{or, } \Delta t = \frac{Q}{mc}$$

$$= \frac{8380 \text{ J}}{(100.0 \text{ g}) (4.19 \text{ J/g·°C})}$$

$$= 20.0°C$$

When 8.38 kJ of thermal energy is added to 100.0 g of water, the temperature changes by 20.0°C.

Practice Problems

5. Calculate the change in temperature, Δt, that occurs when 255 kJ of thermal energy is added to 3.0 kg of water. The theoretical specific heat capacity of water is 4.19 J/g·°C.

6. Calculate and compare the changes in temperature, Δt, that occur when 500 J of thermal energy is removed from 1.00 kg of water, and when 500 J of thermal energy is removed from 1.00 kg of iron. The theoretical specific heat capacity of water is 4.19 J/g·°C, and the theoretical specific heat capacity of iron is 0.449 J/g·°C.

Example Problem D2.4

When 21.6 J of thermal energy is added to a 2.0-g mass of iron, the temperature of the iron increases by 24.0°C. What is the experimental specific heat capacity of iron?

First, rearrange the equation to solve for specific heat capacity, c:

$$Q = mc\Delta t$$

$$\text{or, } c = \frac{Q}{m\Delta t}$$

$$= \frac{21.6 \text{ J}}{(2.0 \text{ g}) (24.0°C)}$$

$$= 0.45 \frac{\text{J}}{\text{g·°C}}$$

The experimental specific heat capacity of iron is 0.45 J/g·°C. Although the theoretical specific heat capacity of iron is 0.449 J/g·°C, the experimental value is slightly higher. The difference is due to the limits of accuracy in measurement. Accuracy is indicated by the number of significant digits.

Practice Problems

7. When 574 J of thermal energy is added to 20.0 g of aluminium, the temperature of the aluminium increases by 32.0°C. What is the experimental specific heat capacity of aluminium?

8. Calculate the experimental specific heat capacity of an object of mass 1.00 kg, given that the object releases 1.95 kJ of heat when its temperature decreases by 15.0°C.

Inquiry Lab

Student Reference **5**

Required Skills
- Initiating and Planning
- Performing and Recording
- Analyzing and Interpreting
- Communication and Teamwork

Investigating Specific Heat Capacity

> **CAUTION: In this lab, you will work with solids and liquids heated to 100°C. Use extreme care. If you are unsure of any steps in the procedure, ask before you proceed.**

Changes in the quantity of thermal energy, Q, of any substance can be determined by measuring the change in temperature of the water within a simple calorimeter. This method assumes that, when the substance is placed inside, all the thermal energy released or absorbed by the substance is absorbed or released by the water in the calorimeter. In this investigation, you will raise the temperature of two substances from room temperature to 100.0°C. You will then use a calorimeter and the equation $Q = mc\Delta t$ to determine the specific heat capacities of the substances from your experimental data. Finally, you will compare your experimental values with the theoretical values.

The Question

How different are the specific heat capacities of iron and copper?

Variables

The manipulated variable is specific heat capacity. What is the responding variable?

Materials and Equipment

small piece of iron	thermometer
small piece of copper	tongs
2 foam cups	stirring rod
foam lid to fit foam cups	100-mL graduated cylinder
250-mL beaker	balance
hot plate	

Procedure

1. Read through the procedure, and then design a data table to record your observations. Your data table will need space for at least five entries for each substance.

2. Make a simple calorimeter by first placing one of the foam cups into the other. Then make a hole in the foam lid that is large enough to insert the thermometer. Make a second hole to fit the stirring rod.

3. Using the balance, determine the masses of the iron and the empty calorimeter. Record the masses in your data table.

4. Add 100 mL of water to a 250-mL beaker. Place the beaker on the hot plate and bring the water to a boil. One person in your group must always monitor the water.

5. Determine the temperature of the boiling water to the nearest 0.1°C. Record your observation.

6. Place the piece of iron into the boiling water for 5 min.

7. While the iron is in the boiling water, pour 50 mL of room-temperature water into the calorimeter. Determine the initial temperature of the water in the calorimeter to the nearest 0.1°C, and record your observation.

8. After 5 min have passed, use the tongs to carefully remove the iron from the boiling water. Immediately place the iron into the calorimeter so that the iron is completely submerged. If necessary, add additional room-temperature water. Attach the lid, and insert the thermometer and stirring rod. Make sure the thermometer is not touching the piece of iron.

9. Gently stir the water in the calorimeter with the stirring rod. Measure and record the maximum temperature reached by the water in the calorimeter, to the nearest 0.1°C.

10. Remove the metal, thermometer, and stirring rod, and then determine the mass of the water in the calorimeter.

11. Repeat steps 1 through 10, using a small piece of copper.

Analyzing and Interpreting

1. Calculate the temperature change, Δt, of the water in the calorimeter after the iron was added.

2. Determine the amount of heat, Q, that was absorbed by the water in the calorimeter after the iron was added. The theoretical specific heat capacity of water is 4.19 J/g·°C.

3. Calculate the temperature change, Δt, for the piece of iron.

4. Using the mass of the iron and the equation $Q = mc\Delta t$, calculate your experimental value for the specific heat capacity of iron. Assume that the quantity of thermal energy, Q, released by the iron is equal to the quantity of thermal energy absorbed by the water.

5. Repeat steps 1 to 4, using your data for the piece of copper.

6. The theoretical value for the specific heat capacity of iron is 0.449 J/g·°C. The theoretical value for the specific heat capacity of copper is 0.385 J/g·°C. Determine the percent error of your experimental values for the specific heat capacity of iron and of copper. Percent error can be calculated from the following formula:

$$\text{percent error} = \left| \frac{(\text{experimental value} - \text{theoretical value})}{\text{theoretical value}} \right| \times 100\%$$

Forming Conclusions

7. Compare the specific heat capacities of iron and copper, referring to your data. Write a lab report summarizing your experiment.

8. In a paragraph, compare the temperature change of the iron to the temperature change of the water. Assuming that all the thermal energy lost by the iron was transferred to the water, comment on the effect of the specific heat capacity of water on maintaining Earth's average global temperature.

9. Discuss how differences in the specific heat capacity of substances can contribute to uneven heating and cooling of Earth's surface.

The Hydrologic Cycle and Energy Transfer

The water of the hydrosphere may be present as liquid water, as solid ice or snow, or as water vapour in the atmosphere. Water molecules are also found within the cells and tissues of the living organisms found in the biosphere. Water molecules are constantly moving among the components of the biosphere through the action of the **hydrologic cycle** (also called the **water cycle**). At various stages in the hydrologic cycle, water molecules undergo change in **phase** (state), from solid to liquid to vapour, and back again

As shown in Figure D2.27, water leaves the atmosphere as precipitation, either as a solid (snow or hail) or as a liquid (rain). Some of the solid precipitation then melts and returns to the liquid phase. Most of the liquid water from precipitation collects in large bodies of water such as lakes and oceans, and a smaller amount stays in the soil of the lithosphere. All living organisms, including plants, take in water for use in cellular processes and then release water back to the atmosphere as water vapour during respiration. Plants also take up a proportion of the liquid water in the biosphere and use it for photosynthesis. Transpiration brings water up from the soil in the lithosphere through the roots. Any water that is not used by the plant is then returned to the atmosphere as water vapour, through microscopic pores in the plant's leaves. Most water (about 90%) returns to the atmosphere through evaporation from large bodies of water on Earth's surface. During evaporation, water changes from the liquid phase to the vapour phase. The hydrologic cycle therefore moves water between the components of the biosphere.

info BIT

It is estimated that there are about 1.39 billion cubic kilometres of water on Earth, but only 12 900 cubic kilometres are in the atmosphere at any one time. If all the water were to fall out of the atmosphere, the lithosphere would be covered in an average depth of water of 2.5 cm.

Whenever water changes phase, thermal energy is either released or absorbed. The temperature of the water remains the same during a phase change, even though the quantity of thermal energy increases or decreases. Thermal energy is released when water goes from liquid to solid. When liquid water changes to water vapour, thermal energy is absorbed. Through such changes of state, the hydrologic cycle therefore also transfers thermal energy through the biosphere.

The hydrologic cycle also moves thermal energy, through absorption and release of energy by the attractive forces (bonds) that hold the water molecules together. Recall that during the hydrologic cycle, water changes phase many times. When any substance changes from solid phase to liquid phase, or from liquid phase to vapour phase, the bonds between the particles become weaker and break. Breaking bonds always requires absorption of energy. In contrast, when any substance changes from vapour phase to liquid phase, or from vapour phase to solid phase, new bonds are formed between the particles. Bond formation always releases energy. When energy is released or absorbed by the bonds between particles during a phase change, energy is transferred. However, when bonds break or form during a phase change, the temperature of the substance does not change. Temperature change only occurs when there is an increase or decrease in the kinetic energy of the particles. Since the energy is used to break bonds between the particles, this energy is not available to increase the kinetic energy of the particles.

Since water molecules undergo many phase changes during the hydrologic cycle, a lot of energy is transferred in the biosphere without any changes in temperature of the water. This helps to keep the average temperature of Earth relatively stable. For example, incoming solar energy used to break bonds, and so evaporate water molecules from the ocean or melt snow on land, is not available to increase the temperature of any component of the biosphere.

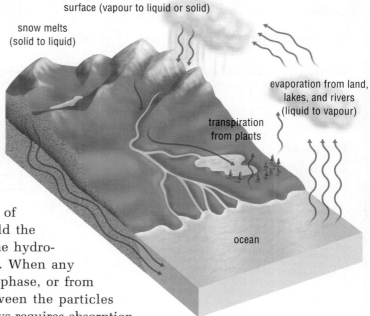

precipitation returns water to Earth's surface (vapour to liquid or solid)

snow melts (solid to liquid)

evaporation from land, lakes, and rivers (liquid to vapour)

transpiration from plants

ocean

FIGURE D2.27 The hydrologic cycle involves many phase changes.

FIGURE D2.28 Thermal energy is released when water changes from the liquid phase to the solid phase.

FIGURE D2.29 Thermal energy is absorbed by water as it changes from the liquid phase to the vapour phase.

Heat of Fusion and Heat of Vaporization

The **heat of fusion** of a substance is the amount of energy absorbed when 1 mol of the substance changes from solid phase to liquid phase, without a change in temperature. The energy released during the reverse phase change, when 1 mol of a solid forms, is referred to as the **heat of solidification** (Figure D2.28). The **heat of vaporization** of a substance is the amount of energy absorbed when 1 mol of the substance changes from liquid phase to vapour phase, without a change in temperature (Figure D2.29). The energy released during the reverse phase change, when 1 mol of a vapour condenses to a liquid, is called the **heat of condensation**.

Temperature and Phase Change

> CAUTION: To avoid a burning injury, handle the heated water carefully.

Purpose

To observe the temperature changes of water as it changes phase

Materials and Equipment

250-mL beaker

hot plate

retort stand

clamp

thermometer or temperature probe

crushed ice

timer or clock

graph paper, graphing calculator, or spreadsheet software

Procedure

1. In your notebook or a spreadsheet file, construct a data table similar to the one shown. You will need more rows than in the example.

2. Add crushed ice to the beaker until it is about half full.

Time (s)	Temperature (°C)

3. Place the beaker on a hot plate. Carefully place the thermometer in the ice. The bulb of the thermometer should be just above the bottom of the beaker. Attach the thermometer to the clamp on the retort stand. Turn on the hot plate to its highest setting.

4. Wear heat-proof protective gloves while working. Measure and record the temperature of the ice–water mixture every 30 s, until the water in the beaker has boiled for 3 min.

5. Turn off the hot plate.

Questions

1. Construct a line graph of your data.

2. In one or two sentences, describe the shape of your graph.

3. Based on your data, explain what happens to the temperature of water as it changes phase from solid to liquid and from liquid to gas (water vapour).

4. Identify the manipulated and the responding variable in this investigation.

In Activity D12 QuickLab, you heated a beaker of ice until the water turned to steam. During heating, the water underwent two phase changes: first from solid to liquid, then from liquid to gas. The temperature of the water remained at about 0°C for all the time that ice remained in the beaker. While the water was boiling, the temperature remained at about 100°C. These results are shown graphically in Figure D2.30, the heating curve of water.

When thermal energy was first added to the ice, the temperature of the ice increased. During this stage of the experiment, the absorbed thermal energy was converted to kinetic energy of the water molecules. This was detected as an increase in temperature. When water changed phase from solid to liquid, the temperature of the water remained at 0°C for some time,

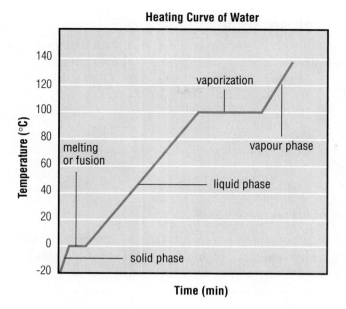

Heating Curve of Water

melting
or fusion

vaporization

vapour phase

liquid phase

solid phase

Temperature (°C)

Time (min)

FIGURE D2.30 The temperature of water remains constant during a phase change. The temperatures shown are for water at sea level. The exact temperatures at which phase changes occur will vary slightly with changes in altitude. The shape of the graph will always be the same, however.

which is shown by the first flat area in the heating curve, and is labelled "melting or fusion." At this stage, the absorbed thermal energy was no longer being converted to kinetic energy, but was absorbed by the forces between the water molecules. When these forces gained sufficient potential energy, they became disrupted, and the water changed from solid phase to liquid phase. After this phase change was completed (when all the ice was melted), the thermal energy absorbed by the liquid water was again converted into kinetic energy, so the temperature of the liquid water rose. At the boiling point of water, the absorbed thermal energy again was absorbed by the intermolecular forces, causing them to break. We know this because the temperature of the water again remained constant, giving rise to the second flat area on the heating curve, at 100°C.

Calculating Heat of Fusion and Heat of Vaporization

The amount of energy absorbed or released during a phase change from solid to liquid by a known amount of any substance can be calculated from the following formula:

$$H_{fus} = \frac{Q}{n},$$

where H_{fus} is the heat of fusion, in kJ/mol,

Q is the quantity of thermal energy, in kJ, and

n is the amount of the substance, in mol.

To determine H_{fus}, you must know the quantity of thermal energy that was added and the molar amount of the substance. Scientists have determined the heats of fusion of many substances, and these values are available in reference sources. The equation for H_{fus} may be rearranged and used to solve for either the quantity of thermal energy or the molar amount of a substance, using these published values. The theoretical heat of fusion of ice is 6.01 kJ/mol.

Example Problem D2.5

When 27.05 kJ of thermal energy is added to 4.50 mol of ice at 0.0°C, the ice melts completely. What is the experimental heat of fusion of water?

$$H_{fus} = \frac{Q}{n}$$

$$= \frac{27.05 \text{ kJ}}{4.50 \text{ mol}}$$

$$= 6.0111111 \; \frac{\text{kJ}}{\text{mol}}$$

$$= 6.01 \; \frac{\text{kJ}}{\text{mol}}$$

The heat of fusion of ice is 6.01 kJ/mol.

Although the theoretical value for H_{fus} of ice is 6.01 kJ/mol, the experimental value is slightly higher than this before rounding, due to the limits of accuracy in measurement. The level of accuracy is indicated by the number of significant digits in the final answer.

If the mass (m) of a substance is given or required, the amount (n) must first be determined by converting from g to mol, using the equation below:

$$n = \frac{m}{M}$$

where n is the amount of the substance, in mol

m is the mass of the substance, in g, and

M is the molar mass of the substance, in g/mol.

Example Problem D2.6

When 5.00 g of ice melts, 1.67 kJ of thermal energy is absorbed. Calculate the experimental heat of fusion of ice. The molar mass, M, of ice is 18.02 g/mol.

First determine the number of moles, n, in 5.00 g of ice:

$$n = \frac{m}{M}$$

$$= \frac{5.00 \text{ g}}{18.02 \text{ g/mol}}$$

$$= 0.2774694 \text{ mol}$$

You can now determine H_{fus}

$$H_{fus} = \frac{Q}{n}$$

$$= \frac{1.67 \text{ kJ}}{0.2774694 \text{ mol}}$$

$$= 6.01868 \; \frac{\text{kJ}}{\text{mol}}$$

$$= 6.0 \; \frac{\text{kJ}}{\text{mol}}$$

The experimental heat of fusion of ice is 6.0 kJ/mol, given to the correct number of significant digits.

Practice Problems

9. When 0.751 kJ of thermal energy is added to 0.125 mol of ice at 0.0°C, the ice changes phase. Calculate the experimental heat of fusion of ice.

10. How much thermal energy is required to completely melt 3.20 mol of ice at 0.0°C?

11. Calculate the amount in moles of ice at 0.0°C that can be melted by addition of 15.0 kJ of thermal energy.

Practice Problem

12. Determine the experimental heat of fusion of copper, given that it takes 0.606 kJ of thermal energy to melt 100 g of solid copper at its melting point. The molar mass of copper is 63.55 g/mol.

The second flat area on Figure D2.30 is due to the absorption of thermal energy required to vaporize the water. The heat of vaporization for water is 40.65 kJ/mol. The heat of vaporization can be calculated by:

$$H_{vap} = \frac{Q}{n}$$

where H_{vap} is the heat of vaporization, in kJ/mol,

Q is the quantity of thermal energy, in kJ, and

n is the amount of the substance, in mol.

As for H_{fus}, if the mass (m) of the substance changing phase is given or required, the amount (n) of the substance can be determined by converting from grams to moles, using the molar mass (M) of the substance, before the equation for H_{vap} is used.

re**SEARCH**

Investigate why farmers spray their crops with water if there is chance of frost during the growing season. Begin your search at
www.pearsoned.ca/ school/science10

Example Problem D2.7

When 150 g of water changes from liquid to vapour phase, 339 kJ of energy is absorbed. Determine the experimental heat of vaporization of water, given that the molar mass, M, of water is 18.02 g/mol.

First determine the number of moles, n, in 150 g of water, using the molar mass:

$$n = \frac{m}{M}$$

$$= \frac{150 \text{ g}}{18.02 \text{ g/mol}}$$

$$= 8.32 \text{ mol}$$

You can now determine experimental H_{vap}.

$$H_{vap} = \frac{Q}{n}$$

$$= \frac{339 \text{ kJ}}{8.32 \text{ mol}}$$

$$= 40.745192 \frac{\text{kJ}}{\text{mol}}$$

$$= 40.7 \frac{\text{kJ}}{\text{mol}}$$

The experimental heat of vaporization of water is 40.7 kJ/mol.

Note that the theoretical value for H_{vap} is 40.65 kJ/mol. The experimental value is slightly higher than this, due to the limits of accuracy in measurement, indicated by rounding the final answer to the correct number of significant digits.

Practice Problems

13. When 8.70 kJ of thermal energy is added to 2.50 mol of liquid methanol, all the methanol enters the vapour phase. Determine the experimental heat of vaporization of methanol.

14. When 250 g of liquid water evaporates, 564.0 kJ of thermal energy is absorbed. Determine the experimental heat of vaporization of water, given that water has a molar mass, M, of 18.02 g/mol.

15. Calculate the amount of thermal energy required to change 500 g of water from the liquid phase to the vapour phase. The molar mass of water is 18.02 g/mol, and the theoretical heat of vaporization of water is 40.65 kJ/mol.

Inquiry Lab

Thermal Energy and Melting Ice

The Question

How much thermal energy is required to change the phase of water from solid to liquid?

Materials and Equipment

2 foam cups	thermometer
stirring rod	ice cubes
balance	paper towels
100-mL graduated cylinder	water

Procedure

1. Make a calorimeter by placing one foam cup inside the other.

2. Using the balance, measure and record the mass of the empty calorimeter, including the thermometer and stirring rod. Ensure that the calorimeter does not tip over.

3. Using the graduated cylinder, add 50 mL of hot tap water to the calorimeter. The temperature of the water should be about 50°C.

4. Measure the mass of the calorimeter and water, including the stirring rod and thermometer. Calculate and record the mass of the water alone.

5. Measure and record the temperature of the water in the calorimeter to the nearest 0.1°C.

6. With a paper towel, dry any water from two or three ice cubes and then add them to the calorimeter. Stir the mixture with the stirring rod. As soon as the ice cubes melt, measure and record the temperature of the water.

7. Using the balance, determine the mass of the full calorimeter. Calculate and record the mass of the melted ice cubes.

Analyzing and Interpreting

1. Calculate the amount of heat transferred from the water to the ice cubes, using the mass of the melted ice cubes and the equation $Q = mc\Delta t$.

2. Given that the molar mass, M, of water is 18.02 g/mol, calculate the number of moles of ice that you added, using the following equation:

$$n = \frac{m}{M}$$

3. Use your data to calculate the experimental heat of fusion of ice in kJ/mol, using the following equation:

$$H_{fus} = \frac{Q}{n}$$

4. The theoretical value of H_{fus} of ice is 6.01 kJ/mol. Determine the percent error of your value using the following formula:

$$\text{percent error} = \left| \frac{(\text{experimental value} - \text{theoretical value})}{\text{theoretical value}} \right| \times 100\%$$

Forming Conclusions

5. Write a summary of your findings. Compare the accepted value for H_{fus} of water with the value you calculated from your data. Identify the sources of error for your experimental value.

Design a Lab

Required Skills
- Initiating and Planning
- Performing and Recording
- Analyzing and Interpreting
- Communication and Teamwork

Variables Affecting the Evaporation of Water

Many variables can affect the rate at which water evaporates. In this investigation, you will design a controlled experiment that will allow you to determine how one variable, that you select, affects the rate of water evaporation.

The Question

How does one particular variable affect the rate of evaporation of water?

Design and Conduct Your Investigation

1. Make a list of variables that you think are likely to influence the rate of evaporation of water.

2. For each variable on your list, write a hypothesis that predicts how changes in that variable will affect the rate of evaporation of water.

3. Write a plan for an investigation that will test the effect of one of these variables on the rate of evaporation of water. Clearly outline all the steps that you will follow to complete your investigation. Identify the variables that you will control and the variable that will be manipulated.

4. List all the materials and equipment you will need to carry out your investigation. Include only materials that you can find at home or in the science classroom.

5. List all the safety precautions that need to be followed in your experiment.

6. Turn in your completed procedure to your teacher. Do not proceed until your teacher has approved your procedure.

7. Perform your experiment.

8. Analyze your results. Do your data support your hypothesis?

9. Compare your experimental design and procedure with those of your classmates. Identify any strengths and weaknesses that are in the different experimental designs.

11. State any problems or questions that you found during your investigation or analysis, that would need additional investigation to answer.

Phase Changes and Global Energy Transfer

The phase changes that occur in the hydrologic cycle play a significant role in the global transfer of thermal energy. When it evaporates, water absorbs 40.65 kJ of thermal energy per mol. When water vapour condenses into liquid water, an equivalent amount of thermal energy per mol is released into the atmosphere, which warms the air. This warmed air becomes less dense and rises. Rising air can sometimes start thunderstorms (Figure D2.31), or even hurricanes.

FIGURE D2.31 Thermal energy released by phase changes in water can cause severe weather events.

Knowledge

1. Describe how thermal energy is transferred through the hydrosphere.

2. Show how water moves through the biosphere in a cyclic manner.

3. Identify the sources of water vapour in the atmosphere.

4. State the percent of Earth's surface that is covered by water.

5. Create a pie chart illustrating the sources of water vapour in the atmosphere.

6. Define the term "specific heat capacity."

7. Identify the factors that must be considered in order to determine the specific heat capacity of any substance.

8. The theoretical specific heat capacity of water is 4.19 J/g·°C. Aluminium has a theoretical specific heat capacity of 0.897 J/g·°C. If 1.00 g of water and 1.00 g of aluminium are both heated to 50.0°C, which substance will contain the greater quantity of thermal energy?

9. Write an equation for the heat of fusion, and define each term in the equation.

10. Define the term "heat of vaporization."

11. What is the difference between the heat of fusion and the heat of vaporization of a substance?

Applications

12. Describe any similarities between global wind patterns and global ocean current patterns.

13. A large island, surrounded by ocean, has two cities at the same latitude. One city is situated on the west coast, and the other on the east coast. Cold ocean currents travel along the west coast of the island, and warm ocean currents travel along the east coast. Which city do you predict would have the warmer average annual temperature? Explain your answer.

14. Calculate the amount of thermal energy required to raise the temperature of 3.0 kg of aluminium from 20.0°C to 80.0°C. The theoretical specific heat capacity of aluminium is 0.897 J/g·°C.

15. Calculate the amount of thermal energy required to increase the temperature of 2.00 kg of water by 20.0°C. The theoretical specific heat capacity of water is 4.19 J/g·°C.

16. A 2.50-g mass of iron is at 24.0°C. Determine the final temperature of the iron after it absorbs 13.5 J of thermal energy. The theoretical specific heat capacity of iron is 0.449 J/g·°C.

17. When 60.0 J of thermal energy is added to a mass of copper, the temperature of the copper increases by 10.4°C. The specific heat capacity of copper is 0.385 J/g·°C. What mass of copper was heated?

18. Calculate the experimental heat of vaporization of water, given that it requires 81.4 kJ of thermal energy to vaporize 2.00 mol of liquid water at 100.0°C.

19. Explain why 100.0 g of liquid water at 100.0°C contains less thermal energy than 100.0 g of water vapour at 100.0°C.

20. Calculate the amount of energy absorbed when 45.0 g of ice at 0.0°C melts. The theoretical heat of fusion of water is 6.01 kJ/mol, and the molar mass of water is 18.02 g/mol.

21. Determine how many moles of water at 100.0°C will change from the liquid to the vapour phase by absorption of 488 kJ of thermal energy. The theoretical heat of vaporization of water is 40.65 kJ/mol.

Extensions

22. Explain why water in a lake is warmer in the fall than in the spring.

23. A glass of water with ice cubes in it is left in a room at 24.0°C. Explain why the temperature of the water will remain at 0.0°C, until all the ice is melted.

D 2.4 Earth's Biomes

Although the biosphere provides environmental conditions that support life, these conditions are not the same everywhere on Earth. As a result, the types of life that can survive in a particular place are also not the same. A **biome** is a large geographical region with a particular range of temperature and precipitation levels, and the plants and animals that are adapted to those climate conditions.

*info*BIT

Depending on the specific factors used, our planet can be divided into as few as six and as many as twelve different biomes.

Biomes Are Open Systems

Biomes function as a **system**, or a set of interconnected parts. The **surroundings** of a system is everything that is outside the system. Any system that exchanges matter and energy with its surroundings is an **open system**. Biomes are open systems because they exchange both matter and energy with their surroundings. A **closed system** does not exchange matter with its surroundings, but does exchange energy. Earth's hydrosphere is an example of a closed system, in which space is the surroundings.

A cell is also an open system, since it exchanges matter and energy with its surroundings. Cells take in nutrients and energy and export wastes to their surroundings, which is the region outside the cell membrane. The cell system does this while maintaining conditions within a range necessary for life. For example, a cell would die if it were to allow too little or too much water to move inside. Biomes are similar to cells in that they also exchange matter and energy with their surroundings (Figure D2.32). Like cells, biomes allow matter to move into and out of their boundaries. This matter comes from other biomes, and may be in the form of organisms that travel from one biome to the next, or chemicals that move through the hydrosphere, lithosphere, or atmosphere.

Like cells, biomes also need energy to survive. Virtually all the energy for a biome is supplied by solar energy, or energy from the Sun. This energy maintains the temperature of the biome, and is also used to provide food for organisms living in the biome. Energy can also leave the biome. Some energy is radiated out into space, and the rest is transferred to the other biomes.

FIGURE D2.32 Cells and biomes are open systems that exchange matter and energy with their surroundings.

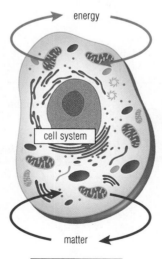

energy

cell system

matter

cell surroundings

energy

biome system

matter

biome surroundings

As a class, choose any two biomes in Figure D2.33 that are located next to one another. For each biome, brainstorm ways in which energy and matter can be moved in and moved out of the biome. Make your suggestions as specific as possible. For example, you might name species of organisms that are found in each or both of the biomes. Keep a list of all the suggestions.

Working in small groups, make a chart or point-form summary that describes how each of the exchanges on the class list might occur. For example, you might suggest that pollen from a plant in one biome is blown into the second biome.

How would your suggestions change if biomes were closed systems? Explain your answer.

Earth's Biomes

Figure D2.33 shows regions of Earth's surface divided into six different biomes. Although biomes have a defined range of temperature and precipitation to which the plants and animals in the biome are adapted, the particular plants and animals found in various regions of these biomes may vary, due to

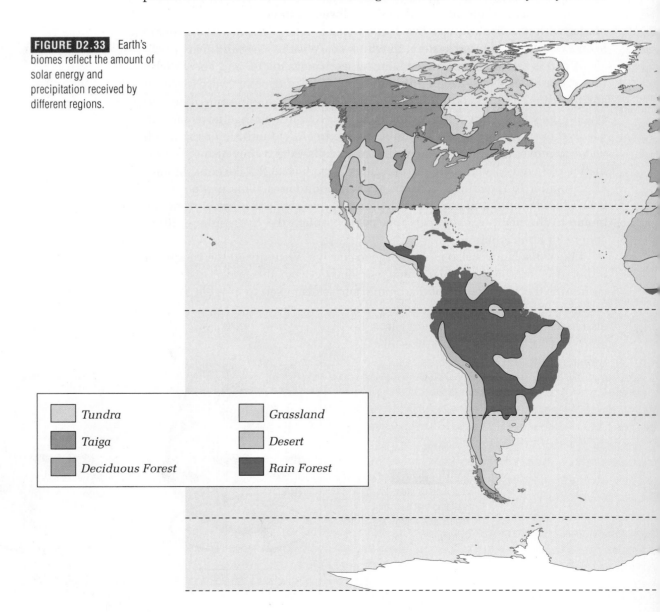

FIGURE D2.33 Earth's biomes reflect the amount of solar energy and precipitation received by different regions.

Tundra

Taiga

Deciduous Forest

Grassland

Desert

Rain Forest

additional factors such as soil types, topography, and human activity. For example, in the Rocky Mountains, the topography changes dramatically. Here, the valleys and foothills usually are covered with thick coniferous forests, which support animals such as grizzly bears, marmots, and hawks. As the elevation increases, however, the air becomes colder and can hold less moisture, so eventually there is not enough water to support tree growth. Above a certain elevation (the tree line), only low-lying, drought-resistant plants, such as mosses, and small animals, such as mice and other rodents, are found.

Dividing Earth into biomes helps scientists to study and understand the interactions between the living and non-living components of each biome, and how the biomes interact with one another. Biome divisions also make it easier for scientists to predict how different groups of organisms may be affected by changes that may occur in a region, such as a decrease in precipitation. You may come across maps that show different biomes than in Figure D2.33. This is because scientists sometimes classify biomes in ways other than in this textbook, depending on the nature of their studies.

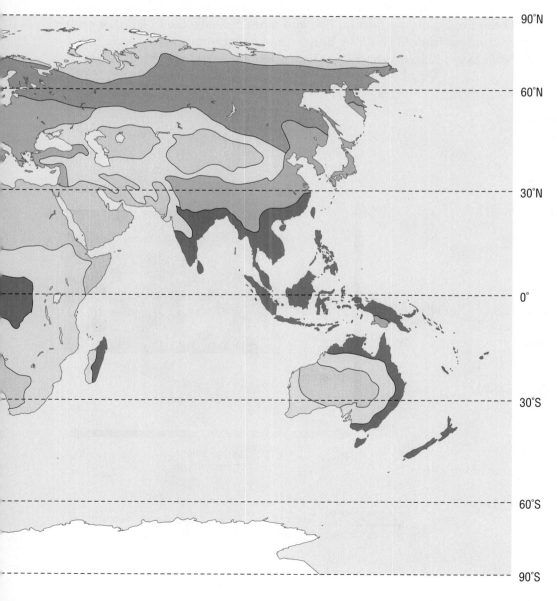

Tundra

Tundra can be found in the arctic regions of North America and Eurasia. Most tundra is found around the Arctic Circle, which is at latitude 66.33°N. At these latitudes, the number of hours of daylight varies greatly over the year. At the summer solstice, daylight lasts for 24 hours, but at the winter solstice, there is no daylight at all. Tundra biomes therefore receive very little solar energy during the winter months. The annual amount of insolation in tundra biomes is the lowest of all the biomes, and ice and snow cover most of the tundra year-round. As a result, lower layers of the ground are permanently frozen (permafrost). The low insolation and high albedo from year-round ice- and snow-cover maintain very cold temperatures in tundra biomes.

Tundra also has very little precipitation (Figure D2.34). As a result, relatively few plants and animals inhabit the tundra (Table D2.2). The plants and animals that live in the tundra are adapted to the conditions of that environment, including the climate. Plants have a very short life cycle so they may complete reproduction during the brief summer season. Many are very small and lie close to the ground, to limit their exposure to the cold and the high winds that are common in the tundra. Since there are few plants, the animals of the tundra mostly feed on fish and other animals. Small animals protect themselves from the cold by burrowing underground, while larger animals often have thick coats and squat bodies to reduce loss of thermal energy.

TABLE D2.2 Characteristics of Tundra Biomes

Climate
• precipitation > 20 cm/y; mostly as snow
• average annual temp. −15°C to 5°C
• very short summer season (20–30 days)

Plants
• lichens, mosses, sedges
• few dwarf woody shrubs

Animals
• ptarmigan, migratory birds in summer
• arctic fox, snowshoe hare, lemming
• caribou, reindeer, musk ox
• wolves, polar bear

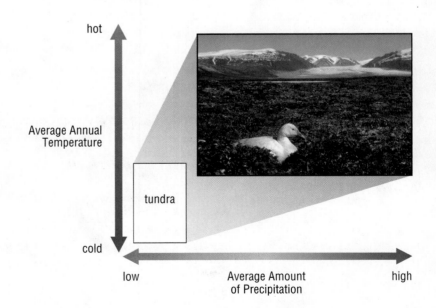

FIGURE D2.34 Tundra biomes are very cold and dry, and have extremely short summer and long winter seasons.

Taiga

Taiga is found in a broad belt around Earth, just south of the region of tundra biomes. Taiga is dominated by evergreen conifer trees, such as fir, pine, and spruce. Taiga may also be called boreal forest. There are few shrubs or bushes in taiga, because the thick conifer branches tend to block out most of the light. A few lichens, mosses, and ferns may be found in more open areas, however. Taiga has more precipitation and higher temperatures on average than tundra (Figure D2.35). Because of the insolation at these latitudes of Earth, taiga also has a longer growing season than tundra. As a result, more plants can survive in taiga than in tundra, which in turn support more animals (Table D2.3). Taiga covers much of Alberta, and is of great economic value as a source of forest products, such as lumber.

TABLE D2.3 Characteristics of Taiga Biomes

Climate
• precipitation 40 to 100 cm/y; much as snow
• average annual temp. 4°C to 14°C
• cool summers, cold winters

Plants
• cone-bearing evergreens
• few lichens and mosses

Animals
• woodpeckers, chickadees, grosbeaks, hawks, eagles
• rodents, rabbits, squirrels
• moose, bear, lynx, fox, wolves

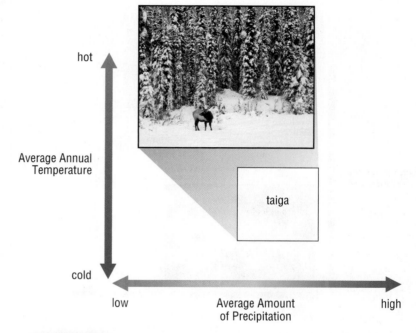

FIGURE D2.35 Taiga biomes have cool summers, and long, cold winter seasons with much snow. There is little water available for plants during the winter due to freezing.

The leaves of evergreen conifers, such as fir, cedar, and spruce, are needle-shaped and contain large amounts of resin, an adaptation which makes them resistant to the freezing and drought conditions of the long winter season. Evergreen conifers therefore can undergo photosynthesis year-round. Animals found in taiga biomes also have adaptations to increase their chances of surviving the long winter season, when food can be scarce and the weather cold. Most are relatively inactive during the winter, either hibernating or remaining in burrows. The coat colour of some animals, such as the arctic fox, changes from brown in the summer to white in the winter, providing year-round camouflage to help them to hunt or to avoid hunters. Birds of the taiga usually migrate in the fall, avoiding most of the winter weather.

Deciduous Forest

Deciduous forest biomes are distinguished by trees that lose their leaves each fall, such as oaks, maples, and ash. Deciduous forests are found in parts of North and South America, Europe, Asia, Japan, and Australia, predominantly between latitudes 30° N and 60° N. This type of biome has a more moderate climate (Figure D2.36) and a longer growing season than taiga. The variation in the amount of insolation during the year at these latitudes results in very distinct winter and summer seasons. Deciduous trees allow light to penetrate to the forest floor, so shrubs, mosses, lichens, and ferns are also common. This rich mixture of plants provides food and habitat for many kinds of animals (Table D2.4).

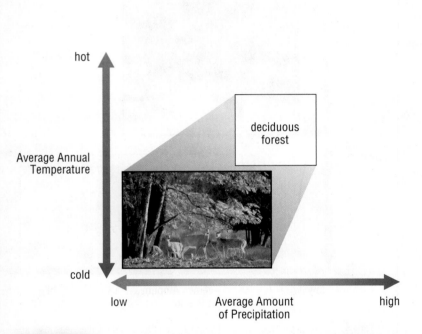

TABLE D2.4 Characteristics of Deciduous Forest Biomes

Climate
• precipitation 75 to 150 cm/y   • average annual temp. 14°C to 27°C   • well-defined summer and winter seasons
Plants
• broad-leaved deciduous trees   • mosses, lichens, ferns
Animals
• insects and birds; ground-dwelling birds (turkey, pheasant)   • squirrels, rabbits, skunk, chipmunks   • white-tailed deer, black bear, timber wolf, red fox

FIGURE D2.36 Deciduous forest biomes have a moderate climate with distinct winter and summer seasons. Water is limited during winter, since most is frozen.

The annual average temperature of deciduous forests is higher than taiga, which enables broad-leaved trees to survive. Broad leaves, such as those of the maple, are more efficient at photosynthesis than needle-shaped leaves, but also freeze easily and lose high amounts of water through transpiration. By losing their leaves each fall, deciduous trees are protected from freezing and require little water during the winter season. Many animals in deciduous forests remain active year-round, but most time their reproduction to coincide with the spring or summer seasons, when food is plentiful and temperatures are milder.

Grassland

Grassland biomes are grassy regions with few or no trees. Trees require far more water than grasses. This biome type occurs in any region where precipitation is at least 20 cm per year, and yet still too low to support the growth of trees (Figure D2.37). The average annual temperature of grassland biomes ranges from 4°C to 30°C. Grasslands occur on all continents, and may be known by different names, depending on other distinguishing factors.

FIGURE D2.37 All grasslands receive little precipitation throughout the year, and also have periods of drought, either in winter (prairies) or during the dry season (savannas). Savanna grasslands have warm temperatures, whereas prairie grasslands have moderate temperatures.

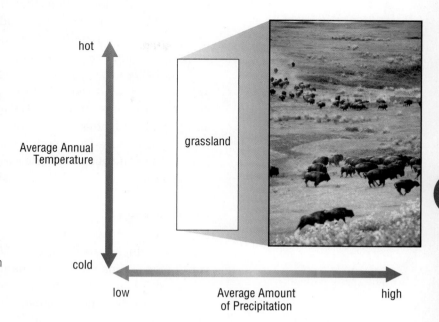

TABLE D2.5 Characteristics of Grassland Biomes

Grassland Type	Climate	Plants	Animals
prairie	• precipitation 25 to 57 cm/y • average annual temp. 4°C to 18°C • winter and summer seasons	• grasses • some forbs	• hawks, snakes • mice, gophers, rabbits • buffalo, deer, elk, antelope • coyotes, badgers, kit foxes
savanna	• ppt. 25 to 57 cm/y • average annual temp. 18°C to 30°C • wet season and dry season	• grasses • scattered trees	• insects, birds, reptiles • elephants, giraffe, antelopes, zebras, wildebeest, rhinoceros • cheetah, lion, hyena

In North America, grasslands are often referred to as **prairie**. Natural prairies are dominated by tallgrass or shortgrass plants, and may also contain drought-tolerant flowering plants known as forbs. Prairie regions have warm summers and cold winters. Most of the natural prairie of North America has disappeared and been replaced by agricultural land. In Alberta, for example, most crops are grown in regions that were once natural prairie. **Savannas** are grasslands found in regions such as Africa, Central America, and Australia. The temperature in these regions does not vary much with the seasons, but there are pronounced seasonal differences in precipitation (a wet season and a dry season). As a result, savannas usually have scattered, drought-tolerant trees as well as grasses.

Although the particular species found in grassland regions can be very different (Table D2.5), they all are adapted to dry climate conditions. Grasses have extensive root systems that allow quick recovery from drought, cold, or grazing. Most die off each year and start from seed when weather conditions are suitable, thus avoiding the more difficult weather of the winter season of prairie grasslands or the dry season of savannas. Most grassland animals are grazers. Large grazers must be able to travel great distances, in order to find sufficient food. Grasslands also support small burrowing animals, which construct underground burrows to protect themselves from harsh weather and predators. Humans also rely on grasslands for much of their food, either directly as grasses (e.g., wheat and corn) or as products of grazing animals (e.g., cattle and sheep). Alberta's agricultural industry depends on plants and animals that are adapted to a grassland biome.

Rain Forest

Rain forests contain the richest diversity of plants and animals of all the biomes. Rain forests have over 200 cm of rain every year and are always warm, conditions that allow plants to grow year-round (Figure D2.38). The dominant plants of rain forests are broad-leaved trees, which may be either evergreen or deciduous, depending on the location of the rain forest. Many other plant species grow under and on these trees, such as vines that travel up entire tree trunks, or rootless air plants, which take up moisture through their leaves from the humid air. This rich plant life supports an equally rich population of animals (Table D2.6).

TABLE D2.6 Characteristics of Rain Forest Biomes

Climate
• precipitation > 200 cm/y • average annual temp. 25°C to 30°C • may have short dry season

Plants
• broad-leaved trees, evergreen and deciduous • vines and shrubs • air plants

Animals
• hummingbirds, parakeets, parrots, toucans • snakes, lizards, frogs • paca, agouti, peccary, armadillo, coatimundi • monkeys, gorillas, jaguars, tigers

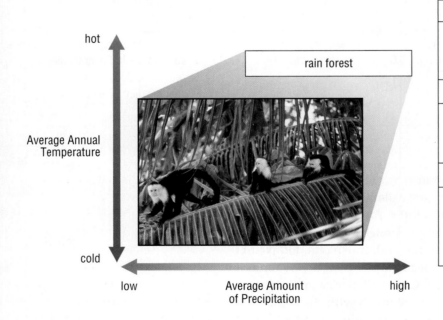

FIGURE D2.38 Rain forests are usually warm and moist throughout the year, although some may be relatively dry for short periods.

Since rain forests have so many plants in any one area, the amount of shade varies at different levels of the forest. Many plants are adapted to maximize their exposure to sunlight, which may include broad leaves, great height, or the ability to climb (e.g., vines). Others are adapted to life in relative shade, and rely on larger plants to produce these conditions. Animals in the rain forest are active year-round, and have a wide variety of adaptations. Each species is specialized for life in a particular part of the rain forest, such as on the ground, at mid-tree level, or in the treetops.

Desert

A desert biome always has less than 25 cm of rainfall per year (Figure D2.39), and so has relatively little plant life. Some deserts, such as the Sahara, have as little as 2 cm of rain per year. Deserts receive high levels of insolation, and so are quite hot during the day. Since deserts lack water and plants, there is not enough material with sufficient heat capacity to retain thermal energy, so deserts are quite cold at night. The most recognizable plants of the desert are the succulents, such as cacti, which store water in fleshy stems and leaves. Non-succulent plants are also found, such as drought-tolerant trees (Table D2.7). Deserts support a number of unique animal species adapted to the hot, dry climate, such as camels and running birds. Animals of the desert require relatively little water, and are often active only at night.

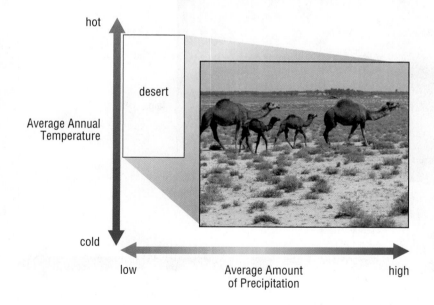

FIGURE D2.39 Desert biomes are the driest biomes. Temperature varies considerably during the day in deserts, with very hot days and cold nights.

TABLE D2.7 Characteristics of Desert Biomes

Climate

- precipitation < 25 cm/y
- average annual temp. 12°C to 27°C
- days hot, nights cold

Plants

- succulent plants (cacti)
- non-succulent, drought-tolerant plants (sagebrush, mesquite tree)

Animals

- millipedes, centipedes, scorpions, spiders, lizards, snakes
- running birds (ostrich, roadrunner)
- antelope, goats, sheep, camels
- bats, rodents, rabbits
- coyote, kit fox, dingo dog

Biomes and Climate

The climate of each of Earth's biomes plays a major role in determining the plants and animals that can survive in a region, and the types of adaptations they need. Figure D2.40 summarizes the relationship between the six biomes and average temperature and precipitation. On the horizontal axis, precipitation levels increase from left to right. On the vertical axis, temperature levels increase from bottom to top. Each biome is placed on the graph according to its average yearly precipitation and temperature range. Note that this graph shows very general trends only. Since climate conditions change gradually, there is no distinct line between one biome and another, and many regions on Earth have characteristics intermediate between two biomes.

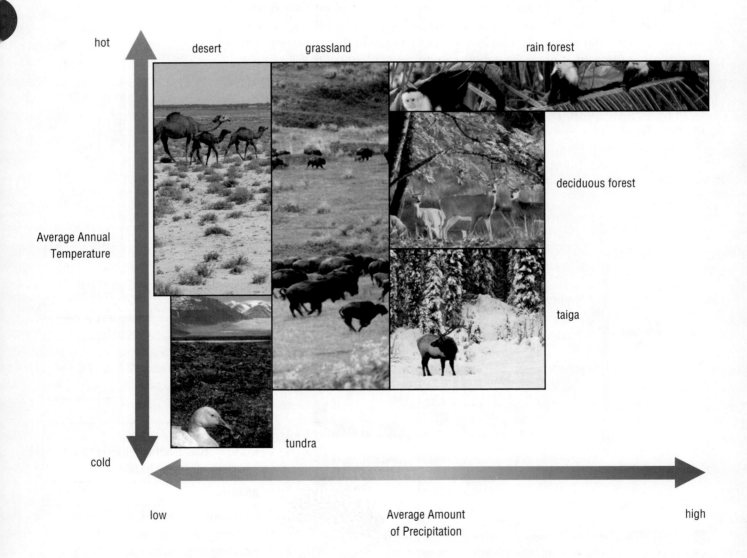

FIGURE D2.40 The characteristics of each of Earth's biomes are related to the climate conditions.

Problem-Solving Investigation

Student Reference 7

Planning for Climate

 Begin your search at www.pearsoned.ca/school/science10

Recognize a Need

A research group is studying the living organisms found at various sites in Alberta (Figure D2.41). This year, one group will be at Wood Buffalo National Park (near Fort Smith weather station) and a second group at Dinosaur Provincial Park (near Brooks weather station). The researchers will live in the park for one year, and most of their work will be conducted outdoors. They will spend some of their time in remote regions of the park.

The Problem

Before the project can move ahead, all the needed supplies for each park must be identified. Since there is a limited amount of funding, only the minimum number of necessary items can be included. Research the climate conditions and identify the biome of each park. Based on this information, plan out how to meet the basic needs for each month of the year for each of the two research teams.

Criteria for Success

To be successful, your two plans must meet the following criteria:

- Identify the biome in which each park is located.
- Describe the climate conditions in each park for each month, including the average temperature, average amount of rain, and average amount of snow.
- List specific supplies that will be needed to work outdoors in each park for 12 months. Assume that researchers will need to stay at least 2 nights in the shelter in a remote area each month.
- Communicate your choices, and clearly and accurately describe the connection to climate conditions.

Brainstorm Ideas

1. Work with a partner or in a small group. Brainstorm ideas that would fit the criteria. All ideas should be considered.

2. Incorporate the best ideas into one list of potentially useful supplies for each park.

FIGURE D2.41 These two parks are in different biomes.

Design a Presentation

3. Decide what additional information you need to decide on the most appropriate items to include on your supply list for each park. Conduct further research if necessary.

4. When all research is complete, design an effective presentation of your supply list that will clearly show how differences in the climate of the two parks impacted the supplies needed by the researchers. Remember to keep track of your decisions as you work, since they will form part of your presentation. Your presentation may be done on paper or with the aid of a computer.

5. Create your presentation.

Evaluate and Communicate

1. What are the main differences in climate between the two sites?

2. How was your list of supplies affected by these climate conditions?

3. Two important factors in climate are the average temperature range and the average amount of precipitation. Which of these do you think is most important to the living things in each park? Why?

4. Share and compare your presentation with others in the class.

*re*SEARCH

Determine the biome of your community. Find another city in the world in the same type of biome, and compare the plants and animals that are found in the two areas. Begin your search at

www.pearsoned.ca/
school/science10

Canada's Biomes

Canada has four biomes: tundra, taiga, grassland, and deciduous forest (Figure D2.42). Most of Canada is a taiga biome, but grassland and deciduous forest regions are very important. Most of our agricultural crops are grown in these regions, since they support the growth of the plants and animals on which we rely.

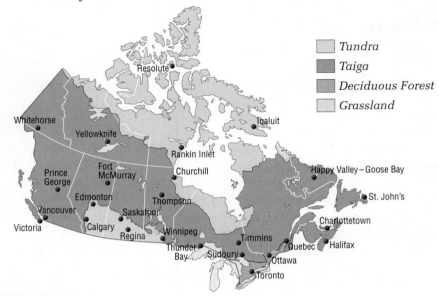

Legend:
- ☐ Tundra
- ■ Taiga
- ■ Deciduous Forest
- ☐ Grassland

FIGURE D2.42 Canada can be divided into four biomes; two of these biomes are found in Alberta.

D2.4 Check and Reflect

Knowledge

1. What is a biome?

2. Explain why a biome is an open system.

3. Describe the surroundings of a biome.

4. Explain how dividing Earth into biomes helps scientists to study and understand Earth.

5. Describe the characteristics of the biome in which you live.

6. Name two biomes that have very low average annual precipitation.

7. Compare and contrast the plants and animals that would be found in a grassland biome in Alberta, Canada to those found in a grassland biome in the country of Sudan, in Africa.

8. Identify the biome in which organisms with the following adaptations are most likely to be found:
   a) large, leafy plants that do not lose their leaves

   b) animals that change coat colour from white to brown each year
   c) animals that time reproduction to have young only in spring and summer
   d) plants that can store water
   e) animals that feed mostly on fish and other animals

Applications

9. In a paragraph, compare a biome to a cell.

10. Using the information in Figure D2.42, create a map of the biomes of Alberta. Use print and electronic resources to identify at least three species of plants and three species of animals that are found in each biome.

Extension

11. In 2001 and 2002, Alberta farmers experienced droughts so severe that some were unable to feed their livestock or harvest any crops. Wild species were also affected. Which of Alberta's biomes do you think was most impacted by this drought? Explain your choice.

D 2.5 Analyzing Energy Flow in Global Systems

In previous sections, you learned that the climate of any area on Earth is determined by many interacting factors. The insolation of an area is determined by that area's latitude, the number of hours of daylight, and the time of year. The albedo, cloud and dust cover, and the natural greenhouse effect interact with insolation to give each area a particular net radiation budget. Convection currents and the Coriolis effect cause predictable global wind patterns in the atmosphere, which transfer thermal energy between areas at or near the equator and those at or near the poles. The world's ocean currents moderate air temperature due to the large specific heat capacity of water. The hydrologic cycle also contributes to thermal energy transfer, through the release and absorption of thermal energy that occurs when water warms, cools, and changes phase.

To fully understand climate, all these interactions must be considered. One of the simplest tools for analyzing the relative impact of these factors on an area is a climatograph. A **climatograph** is a summary of the average temperature and precipitation for each month of the year for a given location, presented as a graph. Figure D2.44 shows a climatograph for Grande Prairie, Alberta, and for Manokwari, Indonesia. Grande Prairie is in a taiga biome, whereas Manokwari is in a rain forest biome. The vertical axis on the left of a climatograph shows the average precipitation (ave. ppt.) in millimetres. The vertical axis on the right shows the average temperature (ave. temp.) in degrees Celsius, and the months of the year are shown on the horizontal axis. The values for average precipitation are always plotted as a bar graph, and values for average temperature are plotted as a line graph.

FIGURE D2.43 Biomes result from the patterns of thermal energy transfer on Earth.

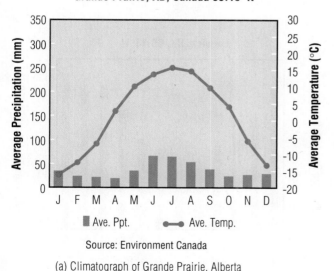

(a) Climatograph of Grande Prairie, Alberta

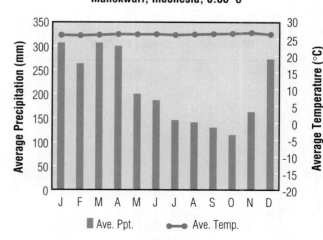

(b) Climatograph of Manokwari, Indonesia

FIGURE D2.44 A climatograph provides a visual summary of climate conditions of an area.

To compare the climates of different areas, the scale of the vertical axes on each climatograph must be the same. In Figure D2.44, the precipitation scales of both climatographs reflect the range of the data for Manokwari, since this area has the higher precipitation levels. The temperature scales reflect the maximum temperature in Manokwari, and the minimum temperature in Grande Prairie. If you compare the two climatographs, you can see that the monthly average temperature of Grande Prairie changes significantly with the seasons, but Manokwari experiences little variation in monthly average temperature from month to month. Also, precipitation levels in Grand Prairie are relatively low year-round, and are highest from May to September. Precipitation levels in Manokwari are high year-round, and are highest from December to April.

Climatographs can also help to identify the factors that determine the climate of an area. In this unit, you have learned how the following factors can affect climate:

- Insolation, which is mostly related to the latitude of a region; other factors can cause daily changes in insolation, including cloud cover, albedo, and the level of atmospheric dust.
- The pattern of global winds that prevail over a region
- The pattern of the warm and cold currents in Earth's oceans, and the effect of differences in specific heat capacity of water and of air on cooling and heating of a region

Of all these factors, insolation has the strongest effect on climate. The differences between the climates of Grande Prairie and Manokwari are primarily due to the insolation at their different latitudes. However, the other factors can also significantly affect climate in some regions. For example, look at the climatographs shown in Figure D2.45, for Whitehorse, Yukon, and Lerwick, a city in the Shetland Islands of the United Kingdom.

FIGURE D2.45 Although they are at similar latitudes, the climates of Whitehorse and Lerwick are very different.

These two cities are at almost the same latitude, and so receive similar insolation. However, the climatographs clearly show that the climates of these two regions are quite different. Lerwick is warmer and wetter than

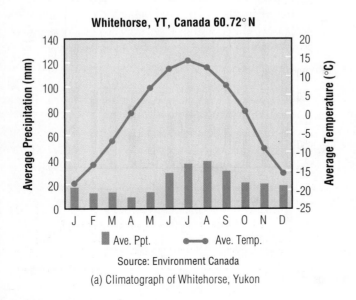

Whitehorse, YT, Canada 60.72° N

Source: Environment Canada

(a) Climatograph of Whitehorse, Yukon

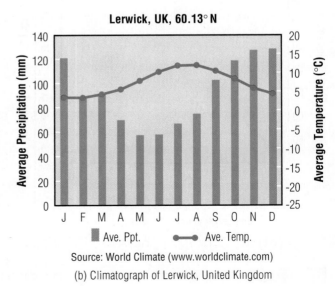

Lerwick, UK, 60.13° N

Source: World Climate (www.worldclimate.com)

(b) Climatograph of Lerwick, United Kingdom

Whitehorse year-round. The prevailing winds for both regions are the polar easterlies (see Figure D2.22). However, if you look at the pattern of Earth's ocean currents in Figure D2.23, you will see that the Shetland Islands are located in the path of a warm ocean current moving up from the Atlantic Ocean. This warm ocean water warms the air temperature throughout the year and increases the precipitation. Whitehorse, in contrast, is inland, and so its climate is affected mostly by the amount of insolation at that latitude. These two cities are therefore in different biomes. Lerwick is in a deciduous forest biome, whereas Whitehorse is in a taiga biome.

You could also predict the biomes of these two regions by examining their climatographs. The evergreen tree species that survive in boreal forest biomes have adaptations such as needle-like leaves that allow them to survive in a relatively dry, cold climate. Deciduous trees require higher levels of precipitation and higher temperatures than evergreens.

*re*SEARCH

Find out how climates are influenced by local factors. What factors influence the climate in your community? Begin your search at

www.pearsoned.ca/ school/science10

Activity D16

QuickLab

Constructing a Climatograph

Purpose

To construct and interpret a climatograph

Materials and Equipment

graph paper or spreadsheet software

Procedure

1. Copy the data in the table below into a new spreadsheet file or graph it on a clean sheet of graph paper.

2. Begin your climatograph by marking the months of the year along the horizontal axis of the graph.

3. Determine the range of the temperature data for the year. Construct and label a vertical axis on the right side of your graph according to this temperature range.

4. Plot the average temperature for each month as a line graph.

5. Determine the range of the average precipitation data over the year. Construct and label a vertical axis on the left side of your graph according to this precipitation range.

6. Plot the average precipitation data for each month as a bar graph.

7. Write a legend and title for the climatograph. The title should include the location and the latitude.

Questions

1. From the patterns in your climatograph, describe how average temperature varies during the year in Jasper.

2. From the patterns in your climatograph, describe how average precipitation varies during the year in Jasper.

3. Identify the biome of Jasper.

Average Temperature and Precipitation in Jasper, Alberta (latitude 53° N)

Month	Jan	Feb	Mar	Apr	May	June	July	Aug	Sept	Oct	Nov	Dec
Average Temperature (°C)	−10.7	−5.9	−1.6	3.8	8.1	12.8	15.1	14.6	9.8	4.7	−4.0	−9.7
Average Precipitation (mm)	31.1	17.4	15.7	21.2	28.6	49.9	56.2	50.6	37.0	30.9	28.2	26.8

Source: Environment Canada

Required Skills
- Initiating and Planning
- Performing and Recording
- Analyzing and Interpreting
- Communication and Teamwork

Using Climatographs to Compare Biomes

Begin your search at
www.pearsoned.ca/school/science10

The Question

What does the information in a climatograph tell us about the biome of an area?

The Hypothesis

A climatograph summarizes the climate conditions of an area, which determine the type of vegetation.

Materials and Equipment

Internet access (optional)

atlas

graph paper or spreadsheet software

Average Climate Conditions

Month	Victoria, BC		Edmonton, AB	
	Average Temp. (°C)	Average Ppt. (mm)	Average Temp. (°C)	Average Ppt. (mm)
Jan	3.4	141.1	−12.5	23.3
Feb	4.8	99.3	−8.9	16.8
Mar	6.1	71.9	−3.6	17.0
Apr	8.4	41.9	4.9	22.1
May	11.4	33.4	11.6	43.5
June	14.3	27.3	15.6	79.9
July	16.2	17.6	17.5	94.3
Aug	16.2	23.7	16.6	67.0
Sept	13.8	36.6	11.1	41.6
Oct	9.7	74.4	5.9	17.3
Nov	6.0	139.2	0.6	16.1
Dec	3.8	151.6	−8.4	22.2

Source: Environment Canada

Procedure

1. Using data from the given table, create a climatograph for these two cities in Canada. Alternatively, find and use climate data from the Internet, for two cities that interest you.

2. Complete the following steps for the climate data for each city:
   a) Write the names of the months along the horizontal axis.
   b) Determine the range of temperature in the data. Label the vertical axis on the right side to fit this range.
   c) Plot the average temperature for each month as a line graph.
   d) Determine the range of average precipitation, and label the vertical axis on the left side to fit this range.
   e) Plot the average precipitation as a bar chart.
   f) Prepare a legend and a title for your climatographs. Your title should include the name of the location, the latitude of the location, and the type of biome being represented. Carry out any research necessary to obtain all the information you need.

Analyzing and Interpreting

1. For each city, use your climatograph to summarize the type of climate found in that area. Identify the biome of each city.

2. Suggest reasons to explain the differences in the climates of the two cities you investigated. Justify your answer with facts.

Forming Conclusions

3. Summarize the general trends found in each of your climatographs and describe the characteristics of the biome of each city.

Knowledge

1. In point form, list the factors that play a role in determining the climate of an area.

2. What is a climatograph?

3. What two main factors are used when describing a region in a climatograph?

4. Explain why a coastal region would have a significantly different climate than would an inland region at the same latitude.

5. Construct a climatograph for Medicine Hat, Alberta, using the information in the table below. Medicine Hat is at latitude 50.05° N.

Average Climate Conditions of Medicine Hat, AB

Month	Average Precipitation (mm)	Average Temperature (°C)
Jan	16.8	−11.0
Feb	14.6	−8.8
Mar	17.4	−2.1
Apr	21.9	6.7
May	41.2	12.6
June	59.7	16.9
July	40.7	20.4
Aug	35.3	19.1
Sept	32.1	13.3
Oct	16.5	7.4
Nov	16.0	−1.4
Dec	15.7	−7.3

Source: World Climate (www.worldclimate.com)

Applications

6. Two regions on Earth have the same latitude, but different climates. Suggest two factors that might cause this difference in climate.

7. Why do some regions on Earth have different amounts of insolation?

8. If a region experienced one year in which the weather was much colder than on average, would the climatograph of that region change? Explain your answer.

9. From the climatograph below, describe the relationship between precipitation and temperature in a series of statements.

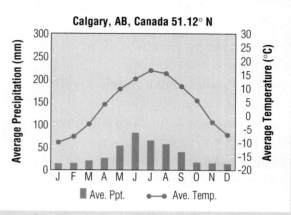

Source: Environment Canada

Extensions

10. Calgary is in a grassland biome. Relate the information in the climatograph in question 9 above to the type of vegetation that occurs in this biome. For example, a desert biome could be described as an area of high temperature and low precipitation.

11. Find the climate data for another city in the world at the same latitude as your city or town. Construct climatographs of the two areas, then compare and contrast the two climates.

Knowledge

1. Identify the two main factors that determine the amount of solar energy a point on Earth will receive.

2. Explain why the albedo of snow is different from the albedo of a forest.

3. Write the word equation for Earth's net radiation budget.

4. Where on our planet is most of the infrared radiation absorbed?

5. Outline how the natural greenhouse effect influences the climate of Earth.

6. The average albedo for Earth is 0.3. What does this value represent?

7. Identify and describe the process that transfers thermal energy from the lithosphere to the atmosphere.

8. Describe the movement of air in relation to atmospheric pressure.

9. Describe how the Coriolis effect influences global wind patterns.

10. In what direction is thermal energy transferred through the hydrosphere?

11. Using an example, explain the hydrologic cycle. Use a diagram in your explanation.

12. What is transferred by the hydrologic cycle, other than water?

13. Define heat of vaporization.

14. Draw a graph of the temperature changes of water as it changes phase from solid to liquid to water vapour. Describe the effects of the heat of vaporization and the heat of fusion on the shape of the curve.

15. Identify three factors that contribute to Earth's climate.

16. Describe two ways in which thermal energy is moved through the biosphere.

17. State the biomes that are found in Canada.

18. Why do grassland biomes have few or no trees?

19. Give two examples of adaptations, one for a plant and one for an animal, that would help the organism to survive in a tundra biome.

20. Which biome supports the highest number of species in the greatest abundance? Why?

21. Sketch and label the key components of a climatograph.

22. State the main factor that determines Earth's biomes. Justify your answer.

Applications

23. Explain why the polar regions of Earth have less insolation than the equator. Use a diagram in your answer.

24. Explain why life on Earth depends on the absorption of infrared radiation by the troposphere.

25. How does the presence of naturally occurring greenhouse gases affect human life? Explain your answer.

26. Describe the process of convection, referring to the motion of particles in your answer.

27. Why does warm air rise?

28. Explain why the temperature of water remains constant when it changes from solid to liquid phase, even though thermal energy is being added.

29. Calculate the final temperature when 100 J of thermal energy is added to 15.0 g of copper at 20.0°C. The theoretical specific heat capacity of copper is 0.385 J/g·°C.

30. Calculate the quantity of thermal energy that is absorbed when the temperature of 12.5 g of nickel increases by 2.5°C. The theoretical specific heat capacity of nickel is 0.444 J/g·°C.

31. The temperature of a mass of tin increases from 24.0°C to 34.0°C when 250 J of thermal energy are added. Calculate the mass of the tin. The theoretical specific heat capacity of tin is 0.228 J/g·°C.

32. Calculate the amount of thermal energy that is released when a 20.0-g mass of zinc at 30°C is cooled to 0.0°C. The theoretical specific heat capacity of zinc is 0.388 J/g·°C.

33. A researcher observes that 7.50 mol of water at 100.0°C is vaporized completely when 305 kJ of thermal energy is added. Using this data, determine the experimental heat of vaporization of water to the appropriate number of significant digits.

34. Calculate the amount of thermal energy needed to change 25.0 mol of water at 100.0°C from liquid to vapour phase, without any change in temperature. The theoretical heat of vaporization of water is 40.65 kJ/mol.

35. How much thermal energy is absorbed when 10.0 g of ice at 0.0°C changes phase to liquid water at 0.0°C? The molar mass, M, of water is 18.02 g/mol and the theoretical heat of fusion, H_{fus}, of water is 6.01 kJ/mol.

36. Saskatoon is located at latitude 52.17° N. The table below presents average climate conditions in Saskatoon.

Average Climate Conditions of Saskatoon, SK

Month	Average Precipitation (mm)	Average Temperature (°C)
Jan	18.2	−17.8
Feb	14.2	−14.4
Mar	16.9	−7.6
Apr	20.1	3.6
May	38.3	11.0
June	62.5	15.7
July	57.4	18.6
Aug	42.8	17.3
Sept	35.0	11.2
Oct	19.4	4.9
Nov	16.5	−5.8
Dec	16.5	−14.2

Source: World Climate (www.worldclimate.com)

a) Draw a climatograph for Saskatoon.
b) Predict the biome in which Saskatoon is located. Give reasons for your prediction.
c) Assume your prediction is correct. What kinds of plants and animals would you expect to find in natural areas around Saskatoon?

Extensions

37. Compare the influence on climate of the albedo of a tundra biome and of a deciduous forest biome by answering the following questions:
a) Which biome would have the greatest average albedo over a 12-month period?
b) Which biome would reflect the most incoming radiation, and which would absorb the most incoming radiation on average over a 12-month period?
c) Would your answers change if you were comparing the albedo of both biomes only in the month of July? Why or why not?

38. The figure below shows climatographs for two cities at similar latitudes: Manchester, United Kingdom, and Hamburg, Germany. Given that Hamburg is further inland than Manchester, deduce reasons for the differences and similarities in the climates of these two cities.

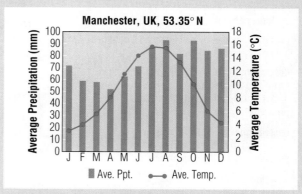

Source: World Climate (www.worldclimate.com)

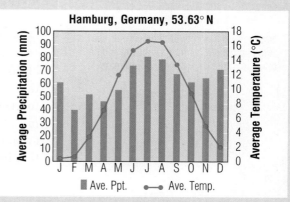

Source: World Climate (www.worldclimate.com)

Changes in global energy transfer could cause climate change, and impact human life and the biosphere.

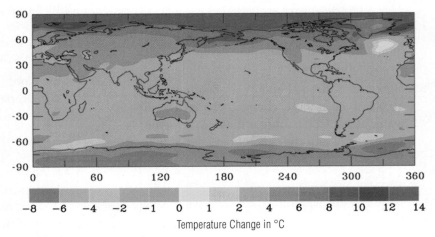

Source: Dai et al. 2001

FIGURE D3.1 Predicted increase in global temperature that could occur from 2170 to 2199, based on expected increases in greenhouse gas levels. The image was generated by computer modelling, using data on average global temperatures and greenhouse gas levels that occurred between 1970 to 1999.

Figure D3.1 shows a computer simulation of the predicted effects of changes in the levels of greenhouse gases in our atmosphere over the next 200 years. The red areas denote warmer than average temperatures. Scientists use current climate data in climate modelling programs, such as the one that produced this simulation, to predict potential changes to our climate. However, just predicting what may happen to climate is not in itself the goal of these studies. Scientists use these predictions to assess the impact that climate change could have on all life on Earth. For example, the Government of Canada publication *Canada Country Study: Climate Impacts and Adaptation 1997* was the first assessment of the social, biological, and economic impacts of climate change to Canada. In this report, scientists suggested that climate change could cause an increase in average air temperature and a decrease in average soil moisture, events that would impact every facet of the life of Canadians. In this section, you will evaluate some of the evidence that indicates we are currently experiencing climate change. You will also investigate evidence that human activity is contributing to climate change, and consider the effects that climate change could have on human society. Some strategies for reducing the effect of human activities on climate change will also be presented.

D 3.1 Climate Change—Examining the Evidence

Is human activity affecting climate? The vast majority of climatologists agree that we are currently experiencing climate change, and that human activity has played a role. However, we do not yet understand enough about long-term climate cycles, or about the interacting factors that control climate, to accurately predict the rate of climate change or its consequences.

FIGURE D3.2 Modern agricultural practices are one contributor of greenhouse gases.

Changes in Greenhouse Gases

In section D2.1, you found out that the natural greenhouse effect keeps our planet warm by absorbing some of the thermal energy radiated by Earth's surface. The natural greenhouse effect is due mainly to the presence of water vapour in our atmosphere, but other greenhouse gases also play a significant role. Some of these gases are produced by human activity, such as agriculture (Figure D3.2).

TABLE D3.1 Global Warming Potential of Three Main Greenhouse Gases

Gas	Global Warming Potential	Persistence (y)
carbon dioxide	1	50–200
methane	23	10
nitrous oxide (N_2O)	296	120

There are four main greenhouse gases: water vapour, carbon dioxide, methane, and nitrous oxide (N_2O). Table D3.1 gives the Global Warming Potential (GWP) of three of these gases. GWP is a measure of the ability of a gas to trap thermal energy in the atmosphere. Since carbon dioxide is the most common greenhouse gas, it is given a rating of 1. All other greenhouse gases are then rated relative to carbon dioxide. The persistence (time the gas remains in the atmosphere) is also given. Gases that persist longer will absorb thermal energy over a longer time period.

Analysis of ice core samples from Greenland and Antarctica, and of atmospheric data collected from the last few decades, has led scientists to conclude that the atmospheric concentrations of carbon dioxide (Figure D3.3), nitrous oxide (N_2O) (Figure D3.4), and methane (Figure D3.5) have increased over the time period of about A.D. 1700 to A.D. 2000.

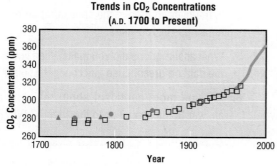

Source: Environment Canada

FIGURE D3.3 This graph shows the changes in worldwide atmospheric carbon dioxide (CO_2) levels over time, from about 1700 to 2000. Data were collected either by analyzing ice core samples from three sites in polar regions (triangles, squares, and circles) or directly measured in atmospheric gases (line).

Changes in Global Energy Transfer Could Cause Climate Change, and Impact Human Life and the Biosphere   411

infoBIT

Every tonne of carbon burned releases 3.7 tonnes of carbon dioxide gas into the atmosphere.

Since greenhouse gases absorb heat, changes in the levels of these gases could change the net radiation budget of Earth. Increased greenhouse gas levels could mean that less thermal energy is released back into space, and the average temperature at Earth's surface could increase as a result.

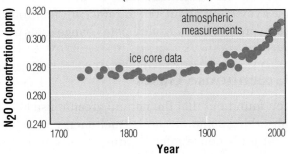

Source: Environment Canada

FIGURE D3.4 This graph shows the changes in worldwide atmospheric levels of nitrous oxide (N_2O) over time, from about 1700 to 2000. Data were collected from ice core samples only for the earlier dates (up to about 1900). Data from about 1900 to 2000 include measurements from ice core samples and directly from samples of atmospheric gases.

FIGURE D3.5 This graph shows the changes in worldwide methane (CH_4) levels in the atmosphere from about 1700 to 2000. Measurements were obtained either through analysis of ice core samples, or by direct determinations from atmospheric gas samples.

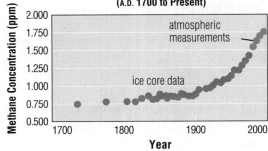

Source: Environment Canada

Skill Practice   Extrapolating Data

To predict the results of the increase in greenhouse gases, scientists extrapolate existing data into the future. **Extrapolation** is the process of estimating the value of a measurement beyond the known or measured values of a set of data. For example, you might estimate how tall you will be next year based on your rate of growth over the last 5 years.

How reliable is extrapolated data? Using the graphs in Figures D3.3, D3.4, and D3.5, respond to the following:

1. How does the change in carbon dioxide gas concentrations over time compare to changes in the other two greenhouse gases?

2. By how much has the concentration of each gas increased since 1750?

3. Express the increase in the concentration of each greenhouse gas as a percent change.

4. Extrapolate to predict the concentration of each greenhouse gas in 100 years.

5. What assumptions did you make when you extrapolated the data on greenhouse gas concentrations?

6. Are you more confident about the accuracy of the answer to question 2 or to question 4? Why?

Greenhouse Gases and Human Activity

The increase in the levels of greenhouse gases since the start of the Industrial Revolution in the late 18th century is a direct result of changes in human activity (Figure D3.6). During this time, human society became more and more dependent on fuel consumption, especially fossil fuels. **Fossil fuels** are fuels that contain large amounts of carbon, that were formed from the remains of living organisms. Coal, oil, and natural gas are the most commonly used fossil fuels. Producing fossil fuels releases methane and carbon dioxide gases into the atmosphere, while burning fossil fuels releases carbon dioxide and nitrous oxide (formed when atmospheric N_2 and O_2 combine during combustion). The most significant increase in concentration of gases from fossil fuel combustion has been in carbon dioxide. Any process that releases carbon dioxide to the atmosphere is called a **carbon source**. Burning fossil fuels is a carbon source, since it releases carbon dioxide to the atmosphere. The respiration of living things is also a carbon source, since this process releases carbon dioxide to the atmosphere.

At the same time, people were migrating into wilderness areas and clearing land of forest to provide timber for fuel and construction and to prepare areas for agriculture. Forests play an important role in removing carbon dioxide from the air, through the process of photosynthesis. Photosynthesis is a **carbon sink**, which is any process that removes carbon dioxide from the atmosphere. Large amounts of atmospheric carbon dioxide dissolve in Earth's oceans and lakes and are removed from the atmosphere. This process is also an important carbon sink. The loss of forest cover during the last two centuries reduced the size of Earth's carbon sinks, and therefore decreased the amount of carbon dioxide being removed from the atmosphere. Loss of forest cover continues today worldwide.

When the release of carbon dioxide to the atmosphere by carbon sources is equal to the amount of carbon dioxide removed from the atmosphere by carbon sinks, the amount of this greenhouse gas remains stable (Figure D3.7). However, the balance between carbon sinks and carbon sources has shifted since the Industrial Revolution, causing the levels of carbon dioxide in our atmosphere to increase. According to scientists at the Carbon Dioxide Information Analysis Center in the United States, the concentration of carbon dioxide gas in the atmosphere has increased by 32% over the last 200 years.

FIGURE D3.6 The Industrial Revolution increased the emission of carbon dioxide at a rate never before seen.

FIGURE D3.7 (a) When the action of carbon sources is equal to the action of carbon sinks, atmospheric levels of carbon dioxide remain stable.

(b) Over the 20th century, the number of carbon sources increased and the number of carbon sinks decreased, causing atmospheric carbon dioxide levels to increase.

*info***BIT**

FIGURE D3.9 Change in the global average surface temperature since 1880 as compared with the average temperature from 1951 to 1980. The zero point on the vertical scale indicates no change from the 1951 to 1980 average surface temperature. Positive values indicate a year in which the average temperature was above the 1951 to 1980 average; negative values indicate years in which the average temperature was below the 1951 to 1980 average.

Agriculture is another human activity that contributes greenhouse gases to the atmosphere. Nitrous oxide is released by the use of manure and chemical fertilizers, a worldwide practice. Methane is emitted from rice paddies and from the digestive systems of cattle and other animals. Other human practices also contribute greenhouse gases to the atmosphere. For example, decaying garbage in landfill sites releases methane, as does decaying vegetation in flooded areas created by dams.

Humans have also contributed greenhouse gases to our atmosphere that have never before occurred. **Halocarbons** are human-made chemicals that can absorb significant amounts of thermal energy. They are used mainly as coolants, and may be found in refrigerators and air conditioners (Figure D3.8). The ability of this group of chemicals to absorb thermal energy also makes them powerful greenhouse gases. For example, the class of halocarbons called chlorofluorocarbons (CFCs) have a Global Warming Potential of 12 000. CFCs were once commonly used in aerosols (spray bottles), air conditioners, and fire extinguishers. CFCs also undergo chemical reactions that destroy the ozone in the stratosphere, so their use is now restricted.

Greenhouse Gases and Climate Change

Most scientists have concluded that the increased emission of greenhouse gases by human activity has influenced global climate. The **enhanced greenhouse effect** is the change in Earth's net radiation budget caused by the increase in human-generated greenhouse gases. Temperature data collected from around the world show that the global average temperature increased by 0.6°C, during the period from 1880 to 1999 (Figure D3.9). This time span was also the period when changes in human activity, such as those of the Industrial Revolution, increased the amount of greenhouse gases emitted to the atmosphere.

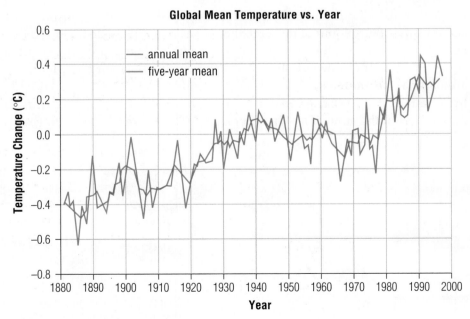

Source: Environment Canada

Global warming refers to the observed increase in Earth's average temperature. Global warming has been detected in all regions of Earth, by global organizations that collect and share information related to climate change. One of the most important of these organizations is the Intergovernmental Panel on Climate Change (IPCC), an international group of scientists brought together by the World Meteorological Organization (WMO) and the United Nations Environment Program (UNEP) to assess information related to climate change. The IPCC has linked global warming to the increase in the amount of greenhouse gases in the atmosphere. The majority of scientists think that if we continue to produce high levels of greenhouse gases and decrease the number of carbon sinks, global warming will continue and eventually result in climate change.

FIGURE D3.10 Severe storms may be one result of climate change.

Global warming is one piece of evidence that Earth is currently undergoing climate change. Other observed changes suggest that climate change may be affecting biomes. Using satellite data and historical records from 1936 to 1998, scientists from the University of Alberta and the Institute of Ocean Sciences have found that, over the past century, flowers in the Northern Hemisphere have begun to bloom an average of 26 days earlier, due to a change in the date that spring-like conditions begin. Many regions on Earth, including Canada, have experienced severe weather-related disasters in the recent past (Figure D3.10), such as the flooding of Manitoba's Red River in 1997 and the crippling ice storm that hit Ontario and Quebec in 1998. Changes in the frequency and severity of storms are one potential effect of a rapid increase in average global temperature. In some areas of Earth, such as in the Canadian Arctic, the amount of snow cover and ice has decreased. The average level of the world's oceans has increased by 2 to 5 cm over the past century, which is most likely related to the decrease in ice cover. Some areas of the world's oceans have also increased in temperature, which may be related to the decline in stocks of fish such as Pacific salmon and Atlantic cod.

Evaluating the Evidence of Climate Change

The IPCC publishes their findings in comprehensive reports that are available to governments, industry, citizens groups, scientists, and the general public. Information from international groups like the IPCC can help us to make more informed decisions related to climate change.

Although most scientists agree we are experiencing global warming, the potential effects on the biosphere are not clear. The study of climate is still a very challenging field. Scientists do not yet fully understand all the interactions between the lithosphere, hydrosphere, and atmosphere in transferring thermal energy. Even seemingly simple factors, such as the effect of cloud cover on the net radiation budget, have turned out to be very complex. As a result, there are limits on the accuracy by which scientists can evaluate the evidence for climate change, and the effect of human activity on climate.

TABLE D3.2 IPCC Confidence Ratings

Confidence Rating	Probability That Result Is True
virtually certain	> 99%
very likely	90–99%
likely	66–90%
medium likelihood	33–66%
unlikely	10–33%
very unlikely	1–10%
exceptionally unlikely	< 1%

Scientists have therefore found ways of estimating their confidence in evaluations and predictions. Through statistical and other means, all analyses of data can be given a particular level of confidence. The IPCC uses the rating scale, shown in Table D3.2, to communicate the level of confidence that can be attributed to events related to climate change. Some of those events are shown in Figure D3.11. Analyses and predictions are given a higher confidence level when there are more data (such as long-term temperature measurements), more accurate measurements (such as temperature measurements of atmospheric temperatures at various altitudes), or if scientists have a greater understanding of the factors involved in a particular climatic event (such as the effect of the time of year on insolation).

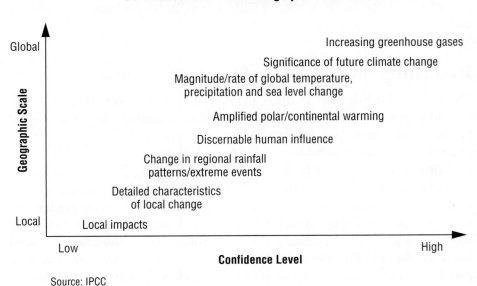

FIGURE D3.11 This graph shows events thought to be related to climate change, arranged according to IPCC levels of confidence (horizontal axis) and whether events are more local or more global in scale (vertical axis). Global events are events that are observed worldwide; local events are events that are observed only in particular regions of Earth. In general, events on a global scale can be linked to climate change with more confidence than can local events.

Decision-Making Investigation

Student Reference **9**

Evaluating the Potential Effects of Climate Change

Begin your search at
www.pearsoned.ca/school/science10

The Issue

Although not all people agree that climate change is occurring, they do agree that climate change would affect our lives in many ways. What are the potential effects of climate change to the environment, economy, and society of Alberta?

Background Information

FIGURE D3.12 What effects would climate change have on Alberta?

Some of the possible impacts of climate change on life in Alberta are obvious and may even appear pleasant (Figure D3.12); for example, warmer winters and less precipitation. However, climate affects every living thing in a biome, so climate change would have negative consequences in areas you might not think about right away. Using the evidence presented in this section and from your own research, you will identify some of the possible impacts of climate change to Alberta.

To help you analyze the impact of climate change, you will use a graphic organizer called an Impact Wheel. An Impact Wheel can be created on a piece of chart paper, in your notebook, or on the chalkboard in your classroom. Follow the directions in the chart to the right.

Analyze and Evaluate

1. Review your Impact Wheel. Describe any patterns you observe in your work.

2. State the impact of climate change in Alberta that was most surprising to you.

Creating an Impact Wheel

Directions	Example
An Impact Wheel starts with an issue at the centre of the wheel. The issue in this activity is climate change.	CLIMATE CHANGE
Around the centre of the wheel, list the evidence for climate change. Circle each piece of evidence. Make a line between each piece of evidence and the centre of the wheel, so that each piece of evidence is part of a spoke on the wheel.	PRODUCTION OF NITROUS OXIDES — CLIMATE CHANGE
For each of the pieces of evidence on your chart, list one or more possible effects of that change. Join the possible effects to the piece of evidence with a double line.	INCREASED SMOG IN URBAN AREAS — PRODUCTION OF NITROUS OXIDES — CLIMATE CHANGE
Finally, list the possible impacts on your community or province. Join each of these points with a triple line.	INCREASED HEALTH RISKS TO PEOPLE WITH RESPIRATORY PROBLEMS — INCREASED SMOG IN URBAN AREAS — PRODUCTION OF NITROUS OXIDES — CLIMATE CHANGE

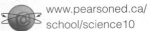

Other Views on Climate Change

Scientists agree the Earth's average temperature has increased over the last century. There remains some disagreement about how much human activity contributed to this global warming, whether global warming will lead to climate change, and the consequences climate change could bring. Evidence from sources such as fossil records and ice cores suggests that Earth's climate has undergone change in the past, well before humans existed. Some scientists argue global warming today could be part of a natural climate cycle that occurs over thousands of years. Until such cycles are fully described, the human contribution to global warming will remain debatable to some people. Predicting the consequences of climate change is also difficult, because our knowledge of the factors that affect climate is limited. Climate change is a relatively new field, so there are not yet enough data to predict how quickly climate change may occur.

D3.1 Check and Reflect

Knowledge

1. What is Global Warming Potential (GWP)?

2. Identify three greenhouse gases that are generated by human activity. Describe how the atmospheric concentrations of these gases have changed over the last 200 years.

3. Describe one method that scientists use to measure changes in the concentration of greenhouse gases over time.

4. State the sources of human-generated nitrous oxide emissions.

5. Define carbon sink and give two examples.

6. What is the enhanced greenhouse effect?

7. Describe three pieces of evidence of climate change during the 20th century.

Applications

8. To assess the work of a scientist or group of scientists, the IPCC sends the work to other scientists to review and evaluate. Explain why this process increases the confidence of the IPCC in work submitted to them for assessment.

9. Explain the difference between natural and human-generated greenhouse gases.

10. Outline the reasons why emission of greenhouse gases increased after the Industrial Revolution.

11. Explain the link between photosynthesis and greenhouse gas levels in the atmosphere.

12. Create a diagram that compares the natural greenhouse effect with the enhanced greenhouse effect.

13. Some scientists and organizations disagree with the evidence presented by the IPCC on climate change. Does this mean that someone is right and someone else is wrong? Explain.

Extensions

14. List as many human activities as you can that take place in your local region that decrease carbon sinks. Make a second list of human activities in your local area that increase carbon sources. Based on your list, do you think that the balance between carbon sinks and carbon sources will change over the next 20 years? Why?

15. Do you think that climate change is occurring? Write a persuasive paragraph outlining and defending your viewpoint.

D 3.2 International Collaboration on Climate Change

Since climate change could have many consequences, the world's scientists, governments, and citizens have agreed to act now on human actions that contribute to climate change (Figure D3.13). As you have seen in the previous sections of this unit, the problem of climate change is complex and not yet fully understood, so it is a challenge just to decide what to do first. Because climate change is a global issue, the political, environmental, and social issues involved can sometimes make action difficult.

Scientific Collaboration on Climate Change

As scientists gather more data and learn more about climate, the confidence level of their predictions increases. Climate research depends on international co-operation. In order to do the best possible job, scientists must share climate data and access to the tools to collect and analyze the data. A recent IPCC report on climate change (Figure D3.14) stated that "confidence in the ability of models to project future climate has increased." This is in large part due to the willingness of the world's scientists to work together.

Advances in technology have also contributed to the increased confidence level. For example, scientists have achieved a better understanding of how water vapour and other greenhouse gases affect global climate. Better computers and software have given us computer simulations and models that can analyze and more accurately predict the effects of human activities, such as the emission of more carbon dioxide into the atmosphere.

There are a number of different types of computer models of climate, but the one that reflects the observed climate data of most climates is the **general circulation model (GCM)**. These highly sophisticated models incorporate the laws of physics to model climate on a global scale. GCMs centre on the effects of changes that affect Earth's energy balance (e.g., changes in insolation, albedo, and/or absorption) on thermal energy transfer in the atmosphere. Since climate modelling is very expensive, scientists must often pool their resources to use this technology to the best advantage.

Since GCMs reflect the world's climate the best, it may seem that all climate modelling should be done using this type of model. When choosing which model to use, scientists consider the problem they are investigating, and the type of data that are available. In some cases, other models will produce a result with a higher level of confidence than will GCMs.

Predictions made by a climate model can be only as good as the data on which the model is based. Satellites, high-altitude jets, and deep-sea submarines now collect data from previously unreachable areas of our planet. The type and quantities of gases and dust in Earth's atmosphere can be measured more accurately because of improvements in scientific instruments. Nations must also share this data in order to get an accurate picture of climatic events.

FIGURE D3.13 Climate change is a global issue that requires international co-operation and personal action.

FIGURE D3.14 The IPCC reports that confidence in computer models is increasing, which is in part due to international collaborations between scientists.

Andrew Weaver

Dr. Andrew Weaver is a world-renowned climate research expert.

Dr. Andrew Weaver is widely known as one of Canada's leading experts on climate change. Dr. Weaver is currently a faculty member at the University of Victoria in British Columbia, where he is developing climate change models of the changes in Earth's climate over the past 400 000 years.

How do you determine what Earth's climate was like 400 000 years ago?
My research group and I have developed the UVic Earth System Climate Model, which contains interactive sea ice, glaciological, ocean, atmosphere, and land surface components. This model will help us to understand the feedbacks between land and ocean surface properties and climate that occurred over the last 400 000 years. We compare modelling results with actual climate data for this same period.

Why did you choose to study climate change?
When I first started, I was studying the role of the ocean in climate. I thought then that the ocean played such an important role that the effect of changes in greenhouse gas levels would be dwarfed by the natural variability of the ocean atmosphere system. In trying to prove this, I proved instead that I was wrong! When I started understanding the problem, I realized that climate change is perhaps the greatest issue facing humanity this century. I am now involved with international committees, such as the IPCC, that are concerned with climate change.

Why should the average Canadian care about the IPCC reports on climate change?
The IPCC provides a comprehensive assessment of our understanding of the science behind climate change. The IPCC reports are extremely influential in providing the scientific foundation on which governmental policy is based.

1. What do you think would be the most challenging part of Dr. Weaver's job?

2. In the future, do you think there will be a greater or lesser need for research scientists like Dr. Weaver in the area of climate change? Why?

3. Why do climate-change scientists often study all fields of science, instead of just one?

Political Collaboration on Climate Change

As our understanding of global energy systems improves, the challenge becomes one of ensuring international co-operation to reduce the contribution of human activity to global warming. The government of Canada has entered into several agreements with other nations to make changes that will benefit the atmosphere and alter Canada's contribution to climate change.

The Montreal Protocol

The **Montreal Protocol** is an international agreement to phase out the production and use of CFCs, and was the first international agreement concerning Earth's atmosphere. It was signed in 1987 by 182 nations, including Canada. CFCs were invented in 1946, to replace many flammable and toxic compounds formerly used by industry. CFCs were used in many products, including aerosol cans, fire extinguishers, and air conditioners. In the 1970s, the chemists Mario Molina and F. Sherwood Rowland showed that CFCs react with the ozone in the atmosphere, converting it to oxygen. Even a very small amount of CFCs can cause a significant loss of ozone. CFC emissions are thought to be the main cause of the thinning of the ozone layer that has been observed over Antarctica (Figure D3.15) and other regions.

Ozone absorbs much of the ultraviolet radiation from the Sun's rays, so loss of ozone results in more ultraviolet radiation reaching the surface of Earth. This could change the net radiation budget of areas of Earth, and cause an increase in the global average temperature. Thinning of the ozone layer could also cause an increase in the rates of cancers caused by exposure to ultraviolet radiation, such as skin cancer.

Hydrochlorofluorocarbons, or **HCFCs**, are chemicals with similar properties to CFCs, but which destroy ozone much more slowly. The Montreal Protocol specifies that nations ban use of CFCs and replace them with HCFCs over a specified time span. HCFCs are still only a temporary solution to the problem of ozone depletion. Scientists are working to find other chemicals to replace HCFCs that do not harm the environment. The Canadian government plans to ban HCFCs by 2020.

United Nations Framework Convention on Climate Change

The **United Nations Framework Convention on Climate Change** (UNFCCC) is an agreement by the world's nations to act to stabilize greenhouse gas emissions caused by human activity (Figure D3.16). The UNFCCC is not an action plan like the Montreal Protocol. Instead, it sets out a process for making international agreements on future actions related to climate change. The UNFCCC marked the first time the world community acknowledged that human activities could cause climate change.

The nations that signed the UNFCCC also agreed that any actions taken to stabilize greenhouse gas emissions must not threaten global food production or the economic interests of any nation, and must support sustainable development. **Sustainable development** is the use of the world's resources in ways that maintain these resources for future generations with minimal environmental impact. For example, to meet the standards of the UNFCCC, the forestry industry in Canada must harvest our forests in a manner that ensures

140 180 220 260 300 340 DU

FIGURE D3.15 This computer simulation shows the thickness of the ozone layer over Antarctica on August 30, 1996. Areas in purple are the thinnest. Ozone levels are given in Dobson units (DU): 1 DU is equal to 2.69×10^{16} molecules per cm^2.

FIGURE D3.16 The United Nations Framework Convention on Climate Change was the first agreement by the world's nations to act on a global problem before having absolute proof that the problem would occur.

that the total amount of forest cover does not decrease. Photosynthesis by forest plants is a carbon sink that removes large quantities of carbon dioxide from the atmosphere, which plays an important role in stabilizing greenhouse gases. Forests also provide habitat for many wildlife species, recreational opportunities for humans, and contribute to the hydrologic cycle. These roles, along with the economic importance of forestry, must be considered whenever Canada proposes any change to its forestry practices.

Kyoto Protocol on Climate Change

The UNFCCC provided the foundation for the **Kyoto Protocol**, an international agreement to reduce the production of greenhouse gases. In 1998, Canada and 160 other countries agreed in principle to set a goal of a 5% reduction in global greenhouse gas emissions by 2012. According to the Kyoto Protocol, Canada must reduce its emissions of greenhouse gases to 6% below 1990 levels. Figure D3.17 shows Canada's past and predicted greenhouse gas emissions, with and without the changes proposed by the Kyoto Protocol.

A key feature of the Kyoto Protocol is a concept called emission-reduction credits. **Emission-reduction credits (ERCs)** are credits given to a country for actions that contribute to the global reduction of greenhouse gas emissions. ERCs are not a reduction in the emissions of that country. ERCs are awarded for the following actions:

- when a developed country helps a developing country to reduce its emissions;
- when a developed country helps another developed country that has a temporary economic problem to reduce its emissions: for example, developed countries recovering from a major war or natural disaster might qualify;
- when a country engages in practices that help to remove carbon dioxide from the atmosphere, such as planting trees to reforest a logged area.

The emission-reduction credit system allows some flexibility in how nations meet their goals, and so allows them to more easily make sustainable changes. However, some people see the ERCs as a way for richer nations to avoid having to reduce the amount of greenhouse gases they emit.

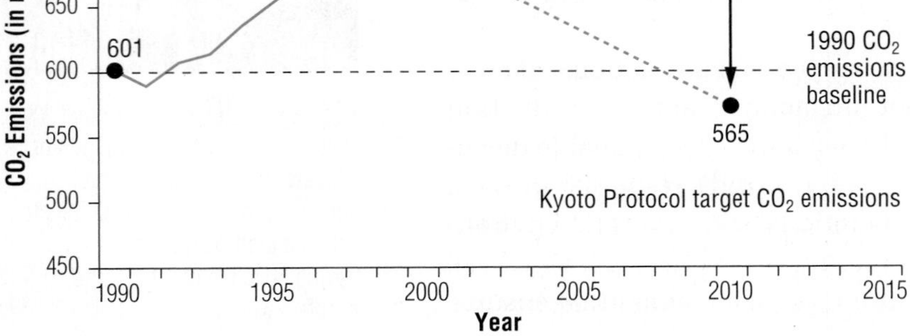

Canadian Emission of Carbon Dioxide per Year

FIGURE D3.17 Since the Industrial Revolution, economic growth was always associated with an increase in greenhouse gas emissions. By meeting the commitments of the Kyoto Protocol, Canada could produce about 25% fewer carbon dioxide emissions in 2012 than would be expected from normal economic growth (business as usual).

Source: Environment Canada

Decision-Making Investigation

Future Options

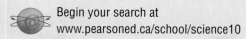

Begin your search at
www.pearsoned.ca/school/science10

The Issue

How are international collaborations and decisions related to climate change important for your future?

Background Information

Throughout this unit, you have been investigating the science of global energy systems and the potential of human activity to influence these systems. Since changes in global energy transfer could lead to climate change, international collaborations between scientists and governments continue to produce new information and new agreements about climate change and the role we play. Issues related to climate change can also be very controversial. Such long-term and complex issues can sometimes be difficult to relate to personally.

Global warming and climate change have the potential to produce short-term and/or long-term impacts on the local and global environment. Each of these changes may potentially have an impact on your life. For example, suppose you plan to work in the agricultural industry in the future. A change in precipitation patterns could influence the type of vegetation growing in your area, which in turn could affect opportunities in your future occupation.

International agreements such as the Kyoto Protocol seek to reduce the impact of human activity on global climate, while allowing for sustainable development. Each agreement that is made may cause disagreement about the relative costs and benefits to segments of the population. For someone working in agriculture, for example, a requirement to reduce emissions by 2% in a year may require investment in more fuel-efficient machinery. This investment may not be financially possible for all people, or may not be possible on the negotiated schedule. Alternatively, the same investment could have great long-term benefit by reducing production costs. Either of these outcomes could affect your ability to find work in this area. In fact, most agreements related to climate or climate change will have political, economic, and social consequences that would impact on you, your friends, and family.

Analyze and Evaluate

1. Using your notes and additional print and electronic information, create an outline of a scenario that describes how changes in climate could potentially impact on your life 15 years from now. This scenario could include descriptions on how the changes in environment impact on your career, family, or personal time. Remember to consider the political, social, and economic factors when creating your scenario.

2. Share your ideas with one or two other classmates. Select at least one of your ideas that can be modified based on what you have learned from them.

3. Illustrate your scenario using your choice of media. This could include an illustrated story, electronic presentation, or poster.

4. After creating your scenario, make a summary of the research that supports and refutes your views. Using your notes, this textbook, and other print and electronic information sources, find examples where your views on climate change are supported. You should also find one opposing view. Your summary can be in paragraph or point form.

5. Share your scenario and research summary with the class. As you listen to other presentations, record how you might modify your work to incorporate at least one idea from someone else into your scenario.

Economics and the Kyoto Protocol

The Kyoto Protocol involves a process of signing the treaty, followed by ratification or acceptance by the voters of each country. Many developed regions, such as Canada, the United States, and the European Union, signed the treaty and agreed to the principles of the protocol. Canada ratified the Kyoto Protocol in 2002, but some other countries have yet to ratify it. The United States indicated in the spring of 2001 that they may withdraw from

FIGURE D3.18 Many nations think that agreeing to the provisions of the Kyoto Protocol would slow down their economic growth.

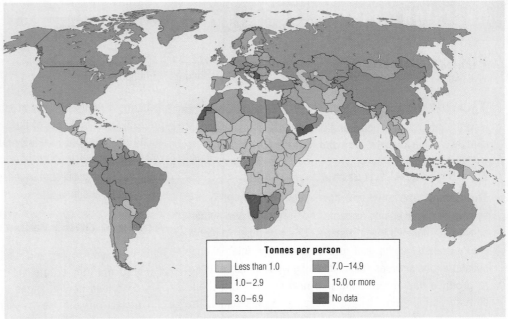

Tonnes per person

Less than 1.0	7.0–14.9
1.0–2.9	15.0 or more
3.0–6.9	No data

Source: New Scientist, 2000

FIGURE D3.19 Most greenhouse gases are emitted by the world's more developed and wealthier nations. This map shows emissions for 1998.

the Kyoto Protocol for economic reasons. China also signed the treaty but did not ratify it, and India has not signed at all. These two less developed countries are experiencing many of the changes and economic growth that more developed nations had experienced earlier in history. This economic growth is linked to increased production of greenhouse gases (Figure D3.18).

Figure D3.19 shows the greenhouse gas emissions by nation in 1998. Most of the emissions still come from the world's richer nations. Some developed nations have decided not to participate in the Kyoto Protocol until developing countries have signed the agreement. Some of these countries have stated they will not sign the Kyoto Protocol until the more developed countries reduce their greenhouse gas emissions.

Stabilizing Greenhouse Gas Levels

Stabilizing the levels of greenhouse gases in the atmosphere depends on achieving a balance between reducing the emission of greenhouse gases and increasing the rate of their removal. For example, levels of atmospheric carbon dioxide are increased by emissions from sources such as cars and industry, and decreased when plants photosynthesize or when carbon dioxide dissolves in the oceans.

Scientists and inventors are therefore also looking for new ways of removing excess greenhouse gases from the atmosphere. One idea that some oil and gas companies are using is called **carbon dioxide sequestering**. In one version of this process, carbon dioxide gas is pumped into the ground to help extract underground oil reserves (Figure D3.20). Once the oil is removed, the gas is sealed in the empty space underground. Research is also continuing to find other methods of sequestering greenhouse gases.

*info***BIT**

Between 1988 and 1999, Syncrude Ltd has reduced the carbon dioxide emissions for the production of a barrel of oil by 26%. It is predicted that the reduction will reach 42% by 2008.

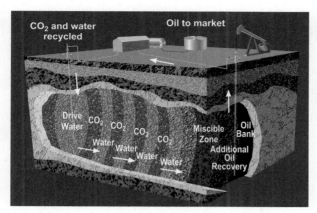

CO₂ and water recycled

Oil to market

Drive Water CO₂ CO₂ CO₂ CO₂ Miscible Zone Oil Bank

Water Water Water Water Additional Oil Recovery

FIGURE D3.20 The Weyburn CO_2 Miscible Flood Project (shown here) will extract more oil from the pool and thus extend the life of one of Canada's oldest and largest oilfields by more than 25 years. At the same time, it will reduce emissions by using CO_2 that would otherwise be vented to the atmosphere.

*re*SEARCH

By producing their goods in ways that contribute fewer greenhouse gas emissions, many companies are finding they are also saving money. Find out what companies in your area are doing to reduce their greenhouse gas emissions, and how it affects their business. Begin your search at

 www.pearsoned.ca/ school/science10

We can all contribute to this process in our personal choices. For example, you might choose to ride a bike, take mass transit, or walk to school to cut down on the use of a car. You could also plant trees in your neighbourhood. Many industries in Canada are also acting to reduce the amount of greenhouse gases they contribute. For example, the Canadian pulp and paper industry reduced its carbon dioxide emissions from 1990 to 1995 by 20%, by using wood waste to heat their facilities rather than fossil fuel oil. This change also had an economic benefit for the industry, since they no longer had to buy heating fuel.

D3.2 Check and Reflect

Knowledge

1. Describe the GCM climate model that scientists use to study climate change.

2. Explain why research on climate change requires international collaboration.

3. In one or two sentences, state the purpose of the Montreal Protocol.

4. What are CFCs, and what are they used for?

5. Explain why the United Nations Framework Convention on Climate Change was an important step in international action on climate change.

6. What is the Kyoto Protocol?

7. Explain what emission-reduction credits are, and give an example of how they might be used by Canada.

8. Describe two personal choices you could make to reduce your contribution to greenhouse gas emissions.

9. What is carbon dioxide sequestering?

Applications

10. If humans understood everything about the control of global climate, what other issues would still need to be considered in order for us to take action on climate change?

11. Explain why simpler computer climate models are used for some climate research.

12. Give an example of how an industry in Canada could reduce its contribution to greenhouse gas emissions.

13. Describe some of the problems in implementing the Kyoto Protocol.

Extensions

14. The IPCC assesses the work of over 2500 scientists from over 170 countries. State one benefit of having such a diverse group of people concerned about climate change.

15. Explain why all countries must act together to address social, political, and environmental issues that are related to climate change.

FIGURE D3.21 Climate change could increase the frequency and severity of forest fires in Alberta.

D 3.3 Assessing the Impacts of Climate Change

Canada is a relatively cold nation, so global warming might sometimes seem appealing. If global warming leads to climate change, however, there could be significant consequences to human life. Climate change might cause an increase in severe weather such as hurricanes, tornadoes, and thunderstorms. These could cause damage to property, crops, livestock, and even result in loss of life. Climate change could increase the number and intensity of droughts, which would cause crop failures and forest fires, damaging the agricultural, forestry (Figure D3.21), and tourism industries, and perhaps affecting the quality of our drinking water. Higher temperatures might cause more polar ice to melt, raising sea levels worldwide and flooding or eroding coastal communities. Climate change could also increase the intensity and length of heat waves.

Climate change would not just affect human life. If significant climate change occurs, then the biomes on our planet would also change. More northern regions would be impacted the most if the current warming trend in Earth's average temperature continues. The region of ice coverage would shrink, reducing the habitat of Arctic and Antarctic species. Figure D3.22 shows one prediction of changes to the vegetation of Canada that could result from climate change.

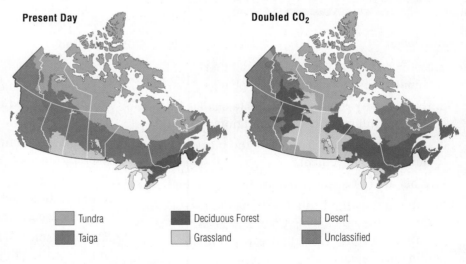

Present Day

Doubled CO$_2$

| | Tundra | | Deciduous Forest | | Desert |
| | Taiga | | Grassland | | Unclassified |

Source: Environment Canada

FIGURE D3.22 Predicted changes in Canada's forest and grassland cover as a result of a doubling of carbon dioxide levels. Note that this study used different factors to define biomes than this textbook.

As the ice receded, the albedo of Earth's polar regions would also decrease. As a result, more solar energy would be absorbed, increasing the rate at which warming of the poles occurred. Permafrost would also begin to thaw, leaving behind rotting vegetation that would increase the rate of emission of methane, a greenhouse gas, which would increase the rate of global warming even more.

Impacts of Climate Change on Alberta

The agricultural and forestry industries, and the health of Albertans, could be affected by climate change. The biomes of Alberta could also be affected, which would change the amount of suitable habitat for some species.

Droughts are predicted to become more frequent if climate change occurs. If average temperature increases, water will evaporate from soil more quickly. Without careful management, crop yields could drop by 10% to 30% as a result. To compensate, agricultural workers might have to change the crops they grow and when they plant. For example, since winter wheat can grow in dry conditions, Alberta's farmers might have to change from moisture-loving canola to this crop (Figure D3.23). Changing crops can cause an economic loss, since different crops have different worth per acre.

Agriculture in the more northern areas of Alberta might benefit from climate change. Warmer temperatures would mean longer growing seasons and increased crop yields. Frost-sensitive crops could be grown farther north. However, insect populations are also predicted to increase with warmer temperatures, so climate change could be damaging to agriculture overall.

Forests could also be affected by climate change. Drier conditions would slow the growth of forests and increase the risk of forest fires. As with crop plants, the retreat of ice cover could allow trees to grow farther north than they do now. However, warmer temperatures could also increase the population of insects that can harm forests, such as spruce budworm (Figure D3.24). These consequences of climate change could harm both the forestry industry and the wildlife that depend on forests for their habitat.

If climate change occurs too rapidly, natural ecosystems, protected areas, and wildlife in Alberta would have to adapt quickly to new climate conditions. Some species would not survive. For example, plant species that could not survive the new climate conditions would die out and other species would move in. This would shift the boundaries of Alberta's biomes. Shrinking of the tundra and taiga biomes would mean far less habitat for the organisms that live in these biomes. Animals that depend on wetlands, such as the trumpeter swan, would also be at higher risk of extinction.

Warmer temperatures could also affect the health of Albertans. If climate change caused longer and more intense heat waves, air pollution in larger urban areas would worsen. People with respiratory diseases, such as asthma, would suffer more illness. Diseases associated with insects in warmer areas would also increase in Alberta. For example, Lyme disease is spread by a species of ticks that cannot survive cold temperatures. This tick could survive in Alberta if the average temperature continues to increase, and Albertans would be at risk of this disease for the first time.

FIGURE D3.23 An increase in the number of droughts in Alberta would mean that some crops, like canola, could no longer be grown successfully.

FIGURE D3.24 Warmer temperatures are linked with increases in insect populations, many of which are harmful to the agricultural and forestry industries.

Decision-Making Investigation

Student Reference **11**

The Impact of Climate Change on a Taiga Biome

 Begin your search at
www.pearsoned.ca/school/science10

FIGURE D3.25 Many species that live in polar regions would be threatened by climate change.

The Issue

How will climate change affect tourism?

Background Information

The polar bear is a well-loved symbol of northern Canada (Figure D3.25). The Canadian Wildlife Service has been gathering data on the polar bears in Churchill, Manitoba, for over 30 years, and using this information to determine how changes in the environment due to climate change are affecting the bears. Polar bears eat only during the winter, when they are on the ice. They depend on large areas of ice cover to be able to travel the great distances needed to hunt successfully. Once temperatures increase and the ice breaks up, the bears' abilities to catch prey become very limited. Monitoring when the ice breaks is therefore an important tool in predicting the bears' chances of long-term survival.

According to Environment Canada, the average temperature in western Hudson Bay has been increasing by 0.3°C to 0.4°C every decade since 1950. As a result, the ice is breaking up 2 to 4 weeks earlier than 20 years ago, forcing bears to come ashore hungrier and leaner. The bears then do not eat until the ice freezes up again, and the warmer temperatures are also causing the ice to form later than in the past. Many female polar bears are unable to hunt long enough to gain sufficient fat to sustain themselves and their cubs over the winter. Scientists at Environment Canada have studied adult male and female bears over the same 20-year period that declines in ice cover were observed. They have concluded that there is a direct correlation between early ice break-up and a decline in the health of the polar bears, in the number of cubs in a litter, and in the survival rate of the cubs. The bears are also forced to look for food in areas close to humans, such as in garbage dumps, sometimes with tragic results.

From climate models, scientists predict that western and southern Hudson Bay could become 3°C to 5°C warmer within 50 years. Because the polar bears of this region are at the southernmost point of their range, they serve as a warning of the potential consequences of climate change to many other species. Some scientists predict the polar bear will be extinct in 50 to 100 years. For a town like Churchill, where polar bear tourism accounts for 60% of the economy, this could also mean economic and social disaster.

Analyze and Evaluate

1. Restate the issue concerning the problem of polar bears and climate change in Churchill, Manitoba.

2. List the short-term and long-term consequences related to this issue.

3. In 1991, Mount Pinatubo, a volcano in the Philippines, erupted. The gases that were released into the atmosphere cooled the planet. Use electronic and print resources to research the effect this cooling had on the polar bear habitat in the Hudson Bay area, and on the polar bear population size in that area.

4. Imagine you are a community member in the town of Churchill. Concerns have been raised about the increased number of sightings of polar bears in town. Prepare a position paper to present at a town council meeting from one of the following points of view. Remember to identify the benefits and risks associated with this issue from that point of view.
   - mayor
   - meteorologist
   - local hotel owner
   - local tourist operator
   - local parent
   - climate change scientist

Canada's Action Plan on Climate Change

Figure D3.26 shows the contribution made by different sectors of Canadian society to greenhouse gas emissions in 1998. The Government of Canada has developed an action plan to reduce greenhouse gas emissions in those sectors that impact greenhouse gas emissions the most (Table D3.3).

Emissions by Economic Sector

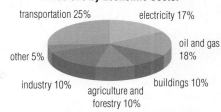

transportation 25% electricity 17%

other 5% oil and gas 18%

industry 10% agriculture and forestry 10% buildings 10%

Source: Environment Canada

FIGURE D3.26 Contribution of economic sectors in Canada to total greenhouse gas emissions in 1998

TABLE D3.3 Key Features of *The Government of Canada's Action Plan 2000 on Climate Change*

Sector	Actions to Reduce Greenhouse Gas Emissions
Transportation	• develop more fuel-efficient vehicles • increase use of fuels that produce less carbon dioxide, such as ethanol • develop technologies to reduce or eliminate emissions, such as hydrogen-powered fuel cells • encourage efficiencies in the transport of freight • encourage more use of public transit
Energy	• find and create suitable carbon dioxide capture and storage sites • work with oil and gas sector to improve energy efficiency • support the development of emerging renewable energy sources that do not emit greenhouse gases, such as solar and wind energies • educate Canadian citizens on how they can act to reduce the greenhouse gas emissions contributed by their personal actions
Buildings	• encourage businesses to make renovations that use more energy-efficient heating and cooling systems • promote construction of energy-efficient residential housing • improve energy-efficiency standards for household appliances
Agriculture and Forestry	• promote best practices in fertilizer application, and in soil and livestock management • promote the planting of trees in areas where no trees previously existed
Industry	• conduct energy-efficiency audits to identify further areas for improvement • support the use of renewable energy technologies, such as biomass, solar energy, and geothermal energy for heating

reSEARCH

Select one area of life in Alberta that could be impacted by climate change. Look for additional information, then analyze the risks and benefits of climate change on the area you chose. Begin your search at

www.pearsoned.ca/
school/science10

Balancing Environmental, Social, and Economic Goals

Although the Government of Canada has ratified the Kyoto Protocol, some Canadians think this agreement is not the best way to proceed. Some believe it will be impossible for Canada to meet the objectives of the Kyoto Protocol unless major changes are implemented soon, despite some economic costs. Others are concerned that the economic impacts of the Kyoto Protocol will be too severe, and so will not allow sustainable development of Canada's resources. In 2002, the Government of Alberta produced its own action plan against human impact on climate, called *Albertans & Climate Change*. This plan offered alternative ways to reduce greenhouse gas emissions other than those that would be required by the Kyoto Protocol.

However Canadians proceed, we will all need to be involved in decisions related to climate change. For example, oil, gas, and electricity production account for 35% of Canada's greenhouse gases. If a reduction is to be made, everyone must reduce their energy use. No one group of people, political party, or company can do it alone. It will require an effort by everyone to change their present usage of energy if emissions of greenhouse gases are to be reduced.

D3.3 Check and Reflect

Knowledge

1. Describe at least three consequences of climate change to Canada.

2. Why would tundra biomes be impacted more by climate change than other biomes?

3. Explain why climate change could change the boundaries of the planet's biomes.

4. Outline the potential consequences of climate change on the agriculture industry in Alberta.

5. Describe the potential consequences of warmer temperatures on the forests of Alberta.

6. State the sectors that the government of Canada has targeted as its focus for reduction of greenhouse gas emissions.

7. List five ways that the transportation sector could reduce greenhouse gas emissions.

8. State which sector of Canadian society could benefit from climate change, and describe the potential impacts.

Applications

9. Illustrate the data in the pie chart in Figure D3.26 in another graphical format.

10. Describe some of the changes that can be made in the day-to-day business of Canada to help us to reduce greenhouse gas emissions.

11. Different computer climate models generate different conclusions on the potential for drought in Alberta as a result of climate change. Suggest possible reasons for these conflicting conclusions.

12. Using an example, describe how climate change could impact the tourism industry.

Extensions

13. Use print and electronic resources to find the current status of Canada with respect to the Kyoto Protocol. Summarize your findings in one or two paragraphs.

14. Select one of the five sectors identified in Table D3.3 that have been targeted by the Canadian government as areas that could significantly reduce their greenhouse gas emissions. Carry out additional research to find out what has changed in this sector to address the problem of greenhouse gas emissions.

15. Use print and electronic resources to research any new predictions on the impacts of climate change on Alberta.

Knowledge

1. Describe the role of the IPCC.

2. Identify at least three human activities that add greenhouse gases to the atmosphere.

3. Describe how the concentrations of greenhouse gases on Earth are changing, according to the evidence collected by scientists.

4. According to IPCC data, what was the increase in Earth's average surface temperature during the 20th century?

5. Describe the position of the IPCC on the relationship between the increase in average surface temperature on Earth, and climate change.

6. Describe two pieces of evidence that do not support the theory that Earth is currently undergoing climate change.

7. What is global warming?

8. Carbon dioxide concentrations in the atmosphere are currently rising. Explain why this is occurring by referring to carbon sinks and carbon sources.

9. Give one example of how carbon dioxide gas is removed from the atmosphere.

10. How is the enhanced greenhouse effect thought to be connected to global warming?

11. What did the nations that signed the Montreal Protocol agree to do?

12. Describe the impact of CFCs on the environment.

13. Describe the key idea that emerged from the United Nations Framework Convention on Climate Change.

14. Describe the commitment that Canada would need to meet, according to the provisions of the Kyoto Protocol.

15. List the five areas that have been identified by the Government of Canada as targets for greenhouse gas emission reduction.

16. Explain how using renewable energy sources could help to reduce greenhouse gas emissions.

17. Describe how life in Alberta could be impacted by climate change.

18. Outline how Alberta's forests would be impacted by climate change. Include examples of social, environmental, and economic impacts.

Applications

19. In a short paragraph, describe some of the possible impacts of the enhanced greenhouse effect on the world's climate.

20. Explain why it is important to know the level of confidence that scientists give to their climate change predictions.

21. Why is sustainable development a global issue?

22. State the key international agreements dealing with issues of global climate change. Describe the goals and results of these agreements.

23. Describe the three ways that a country can earn emission-reduction credits under the Kyoto Protocol.

24. Describe how buildings contribute to greenhouse gases. Suggest some ways that the emissions of greenhouse gases from buildings can be reduced.

25. Describe how human health could be affected by climate change.

Extensions

26. Explain why the following statement is true: *The study of climate change is not a precise science.*

27. Climate change may occur so slowly that it would have little or no effect during your lifetime. If this were the case, do you think that governments, scientists, and other citizens would no longer need to be concerned about climate change? Defend your position.

28. Create a concept map of the key terms used in this section.

Risky Solutions

Background Information

Since climate change could have global consequences, some people have suggested some very innovative technologies to reduce or reverse the impact of human activity on Earth's climate. However, every new technology has the potential to create new problems, so both the positive and negative potentials must be considered in the final decision of whether or not to adopt a new technology.

Scenario

You are part of a committee that allocates research funds for studying new technologies to minimize or reverse the effects of human activity on climate. Funds are limited, so your committee can only give financial support to one project. The proposed projects are summarized below.

A) Iron Fertilization

This project would reduce carbon dioxide levels by increasing the oceans' populations of algae, which use carbon dioxide during photosynthesis. Algae growth would be stimulated by adding iron to their environment. Supertankers would travel the world, releasing millions of tonnes of iron on the oceans' surfaces.

B) Sulfuric Acid Screen

In the atmosphere, sulfur dioxide gas combines with water vapour and forms drops of sulfuric acid, which reflect sunlight back into space. In this project, large airplanes would fly throughout Earth's atmosphere each year, releasing tonnes of sulfur dioxide gas. This would produce a sulfuric acid screen, which would decrease the insolation of Earth's surface, and so decrease the average global temperature.

C) Reflecting Balloons

The authors of this proposal would release billions of large balloons into the atmosphere. These balloons would reflect some of the incoming solar energy, reducing the insolation of Earth's surface. This could change Earth's net radiation budget back to its value prior to the Industrial Revolution.

D) Burning Sulfur

This group proposes to send ships that are burning tonnes of sulfur travelling over the world's oceans. The burning sulfur would release large amounts of sulfur particles into the atmosphere, and increase the rate of cloud formation. The resulting increase in cloud cover would reduce the amount of sunlight reaching Earth's surface.

E) Sequestering Carbon Dioxide in the Ocean

Levels of carbon dioxide in Earth's atmosphere are increasing, contributing significantly to the enhanced greenhouse effect. This group proposes to remove carbon dioxide from the atmosphere and inject it directly into the deep ocean. The carbon dioxide gas would then dissolve in the water, removing it from the atmosphere and storing it in the ocean.

Research the Issue

Research the issue by referring to the following resources:

1. Look at the Web. Check the Internet for information regarding the particular technology you chose.

2. Ask the experts. Contact climate research institutes, companies involved in making or testing the technology, and environmental groups.

3. Look in magazines, newspapers, or books for information regarding the technology you chose.

Analyze the Issue

4. Summarize the information you have found in a short report or electronic presentation. Include your recommendation to the committee on whether they should support further research into this particular idea. Your report or presentation should include current information on the technology, and discuss the advantages and disadvantages of the idea.

Address the Issue

5. Present your findings to your classmates in a convincing presentation.

A Personal Plan for Reducing Carbon Dioxide Emissions

Currently, Canada contributes an average of 17 000 kg per person of carbon dioxide gas to the atmosphere every year. If each of us could reduce our emissions by only 2% a year, this amount would drop to about 15 000 kg per person in only 10 years! In this activity, you will create a personal plan to reduce the greenhouse gas emissions of you and your family.

Potential Reduction per Action

Action	Estimated CO_2 Reduction*
Wash clothes in warm or cold water	160 kg CO_2/y
Lower room temperature	140 kg CO_2/y per 1°C reduction
Use compact fluorescent bulbs	230 kg CO_2/y per 6 bulbs replaced
Reduce use of vehicle	48 kg CO_2/L of gasoline saved
Buy a more energy-efficient air conditioner	270 kg CO_2/y
Walk, bike, carpool, or use mass transit	3.32 kg CO_2/L of gasoline saved
Plant a tree near your house	6.0 kg CO_2/y per tree
Do not use heat to dry dishes in the dishwasher	45 kg CO_2/y
Lower water-heater thermostat from 60°C to 49°C	90 kg CO_2/y
Wrap water heater in thermal blanket	110 kg CO_2/y
Install low-flow shower heads	160 kg CO_2/y
Caulk and weather-strip doors and windows	290 kg CO_2/y
Insulate the attic	910 kg CO_2/y
Lower waste production by reducing, recycling, and reusing	540 kg CO_2/y per 10% reduction
Maintain furnaces and air conditioners, and clean or replace air filters	160 kg CO_2/y
Install energy-efficient windows	460 kg CO_2/y

*Values are an average figure and will not represent specific locations or situations.

Source: Environmental Defence

Criteria for Success

- Your plan must reduce your family's carbon dioxide emissions by 2% over one year, assuming that your current emissions are at the Canadian average of 17 000 kg per person per year.

- Your plan must indicate the reduction in carbon dioxide emissions you will achieve for each month of the year.

- Your plan must take into account the economic and social costs to your family, and balance them with the benefits of your plan.

Procedure

1. Identify actions, on the table provided, that you think are most likely to be possible for your family. Determine the reduction of carbon dioxide emissions that would be achieved for each action for each month and for one year.

2. Determine if the emission reductions from your plan will meet the 2% goal. Modify your plan to meet this goal if necessary.

3. Research the economic costs of implementing your plan. For example, if your plan includes replacing the bulbs in your home with compact fluorescent bulbs, find out the cost of this replacement. With your family, determine how able you are to meet these costs.

4. Consider the social costs of implementing your plan. For example, you might find out how willing your family is to forgo entertainment in order to pay for replacement light bulbs.

Analysis

1. Review the environmental, social, and economic costs of the actions on your plan. Do you need to modify your plan based on these considerations?

Reporting

2. Draw graphs or charts to illustrate the monthly carbon dioxide reductions that will be achieved by your family through your plan. Include a one-page summary of your plan, with a place for the signature of everyone who will be involved in carrying out the plan.

Unit Summary

D 1.0 Climate results from interactions among the components of the biosphere.

Key Concepts:

- social and environmental contexts for investigating climate change

Learnings

- Climate is the average weather conditions that occur in a region. Climate change is change that occurs in the climate of a region over time, usually a minimum of 30 years.

- The components of the biosphere are the lithosphere, hydrosphere, and atmosphere.

D 2.0 Global systems transfer energy through the biosphere.

Key Concepts:

- solar radiation budget

- climate zones, transfer of thermal energy by the hydrosphere and the atmosphere

- hydrologic cycle and phase change

- relationship between biomes and solar energy and climate

Learnings

- Thermal energy is the energy possessed by a substance by virtue of the kinetic energy of its molecules or atoms.

- Insolation is the amount of solar energy received by a region of Earth's surface. Insolation varies with latitude, albedo, cloud cover, and atmospheric dust.

- The net radiation budget is the difference between the amount of incoming radiation and outgoing radiation from Earth's surface and atmosphere.

- Thermal energy transfer is the movement of thermal energy from an area of high temperature to an area of low temperature.

- Global winds result from convection in the atmosphere, and are modified by the Coriolis effect, which is the deflection of any object from a straight-line path by Earth's rotation.

- Ocean currents modify the climate of coastal regions due to the high specific heat capacity of water. The specific heat capacity (c) of a substance is the amount of energy required to raise the temperature of 1 g of the substance by 1°C.

- The quantity of thermal energy, Q, is the amount of thermal energy required to change the temperature of a specific mass, m, of the substance by a certain number of degrees, Δt.

- The hydrologic cycle releases and absorbs thermal energy during phase changes. The heat of fusion, H_{fus}, of a substance is the amount of energy required to change 1 mol of the substance from solid phase to liquid phase, without a change in temperature. The heat of vaporization of a substance, H_{vap}, is the amount of energy required to change 1 mol of the substance from liquid phase to vapour phase, without a change in temperature.

- A biome is a large geographical region with a particular range of temperature and precipitation levels, and the plants and animals that are adapted to those climate conditions. Biomes are open systems.

- A climatograph is a summary of the average temperature and precipitation for each month of the year for a given location, presented as a graph.

D 3.0 Changes in global energy transfer could cause climate change, and impact human life and the biosphere.

Key Concepts:

- social and environmental contexts for investigating climate change

- human activity and climate change

Learnings

- The enhanced greenhouse effect is the change in Earth's net radiation budget caused by the increase in human-generated greenhouse gases.

- Climate change is a global issue that requires international collaboration.

- The effects of climate change are difficult to predict.

Vocabulary

1. Create a concept map with the term "climate change" at the centre, that links all the terms in the list below.

   albedo
   angle of incidence
   angle of inclination
   atmosphere
   biome
   climate
   climate zone
   convection
   energy
   enhanced greenhouse effect
   fossil fuels
   global warming
   greenhouse gases
   hydrologic cycle
   hydrosphere
   lithosphere
   natural greenhouse effect
   net radiation budget
   ozone layer
   solar energy
   specific heat capacity
   sustainable development
   thermal energy
   thermal energy transfer
   weather

Knowledge

D 1.0

2. Explain the difference between weather and climate.

3. Give an example of climate and an example of weather that illustrates the difference between these concepts.

4. Compare the composition of Earth's atmosphere to the atmospheres of Mars and Venus.

5. List the four layers of Earth's atmosphere.

6. Explain how temperature varies with altitude in Earth's atmosphere.

7. What is the ozone layer?

8. Draw a diagram to illustrate the components of the lithosphere.

9. In point form, outline the characteristics of the hydrosphere.

10. Describe two examples of the effect of climate on your daily life.

11. In a short paragraph, describe the effect of climate on the behaviour of one animal species.

12. What types of evidence are used to provide evidence of climate change?

D 2.0

13. In a sentence, identify the main source of Earth's energy.

14. Identify four different types of radiation that can be found in solar radiation.

15. What is radiant energy?

16. Define insolation.

17. Describe the relationship between Earth's angle of inclination and the seasons.

18. State the angle of inclination of Earth.

19. Relate the effect of reflection and absorption in the atmosphere to the amount of solar energy that reaches Earth's surface.

20. A small proportion of the solar energy that reaches Earth is used for a process not related to Earth's climate. Identify this other process.

21. Describe how insolation varies with latitude.

22. Compare the relative albedo of Earth's surface in an area covered with water, such as the ocean, and an area covered by grasslands.

23. Explain why a city at the equator would receive more solar energy on average than would Red Deer, Alberta.

24. State the component of the atmosphere that is the main contributor to the natural greenhouse effect.

25. Identify three greenhouse gases.

26. Explain the relationship of the net radiation budget to Earth's climate.

27. What area of Earth has a net radiation budget surplus?

28. Is convection or conduction more important in moving thermal energy in the atmosphere?

29. Identify what is transferred by global winds.

30. Describe the difference in the Coriolis effect in the Northern Hemisphere and the Southern Hemisphere.

31. Distinguish between the Coriolis effect and the jet stream.

32. Describe how convection of the gases in the atmosphere causes differences in air pressure.

33. Describe how differences in the insolation of Earth's surface are related to wind.

34. Identify the variables that must be controlled in order to determine the specific heat capacity of a substance.

35. What is the function of a calorimeter?

36. Describe how thermal energy is transferred in the hydrologic cycle.

37. In one or two sentences, distinguish between the heat of fusion and the heat of vaporization of a substance.

38. Describe how phase changes of water transfer thermal energy.

39. Distinguish between the biosphere and a biome.

40. Name at least three biomes that are found in Canada, and state one characteristic of each.

41. Describe how most energy enters a biome.

42. Give an example of a way in which matter might move in and out of a biome.

43. Identify the biomes in western Canada.

44. In one or two sentences, explain the purpose of a climatograph.

45. Describe the information that is found on a climatograph.

46. Explain how climatographs can be used to analyze thermal energy transfer in biomes.

D 3.0

47. Identify the components of the biosphere that are considered in general circulation models of climate.

48. State the name of the international organization that reports scientific information on climate change to the public.

49. Distinguish between the natural greenhouse effect and global warming.

50. Explain why greenhouse gases like methane and nitrous oxide are thought to have more effect on Earth's climate today than does water vapour.

51. Identify the human activity that contributes the highest level of greenhouse gas emissions to the atmosphere.

52. What is the enhanced greenhouse effect?

53. Explain why carbon sinks are important to the enhanced greenhouse effect.

54. Describe two pieces of evidence that support the view that climate change is occurring.

55. Explain why climatologists include the confidence level of their data and predictions when reporting the results of their investigations.

56. Create a timeline of the international agreements that address the issue of climate change.

57. In your own words, describe the main points of the Montreal Protocol.

58. Describe the emission-reduction credits of the Kyoto Protocol.

59. Describe the purpose of the work published in the government document entitled *Canada Country Study: Climate Impacts and Adaptations.*

60. Describe three potential consequences of climate change that would affect Canada.

61. In a paragraph, predict how the increase in average global temperature could affect the albedo of the Arctic in the future.

62. Outline the main points of *The Government of Canada's Action Plan on Climate Change.*

63. Describe a change you could make in your daily life that would help to reduce the emission of greenhouse gases.

Applications

64. Rewrite the following statements to correct any errors:
    a) The last two weeks of rain have made the climate miserable.
    b) This kind of weather is the reason that good crops grow here every year.

65. Relate a personal experience in which you had to modify your environment because of the weather.

66. Relate a personal experience in which you had to modify your environment because of the climate.

67. Give two examples of anecdotal evidence of climate change and two examples of scientific evidence.

68. Create a concept map using the terms: biosphere, atmosphere, lithosphere, and hydrosphere.

69. Describe one distinguishing characteristic of each layer of Earth's atmosphere.

70. Describe the effect on Earth's climate of the release of large amounts of atmospheric dust into the atmosphere.

71. Describe an example of how the components of the biosphere can interact to moderate the climate conditions of an area.

72. Why is it useful for scientists to divide the Earth into different biomes?

73. If the borders of a biome were to change, how would it affect the organisms in the area? Would it affect humans? Give examples to illustrate your answer.

74. Explain the difference between a system and its surroundings.

75. Using an example, distinguish between a closed system and an open system.

76. Compare and contrast the features that classify cells and biomes as open systems.

77. Suggest one possible change that a biome might experience if the input of solar energy into the biome were reduced.

78. Outline the relationship between variations in insolation, and the types of plants and animals in a biome.

79. How does the angle of inclination and the angle of incidence affect the insolation of your community?

80. Does Canada have a higher average albedo in summer or in winter? Why?

81. Describe the natural greenhouse effect.

82. Explain how convection moves thermal energy from one area of a fluid to another. Include a description of any changes in density that occur.

83. Describe how thermal energy is transferred from one area to another on Earth.

84. Draw a diagram to illustrate the variation of net radiation budget with latitude.

85. Calculate the quantity of thermal energy required to increase the temperature of 100.0 kg of water from 10.0°C to 20.0°C. The specific heat capacity of water is 4.19 J/g·°C.

86. Calculate the temperature change that occurs when 1290 J of thermal energy are added to 12.0 g of water and no phase change occurs. The specific heat capacity of water is 4.19 J/g·°C.

87. The temperature of a piece of iron increases from 24.0°C to 46.0°C when 148.5 J of thermal energy are applied. Given that the specific heat capacity of iron is 0.449 J/g·°C, determine the mass of the iron.

88. When 10.0 J of thermal energy are added to a 15.0-g mass of gold, the temperature of the gold increases by 5.1°C. What is the experimental specific heat capacity of gold?

89. Calculate the amount of thermal energy required to melt 200 g of ice at 0.0°C. The molar mass of ice is 18.02 g/mol, and the heat of fusion of ice is 6.01 kJ/mol.

90. Determine the amount of thermal energy required to evaporate 2.00 mol of liquid water at 100.0°C. The heat of vaporization of water is 40.65 kJ/mol.

91. Calculate the number of moles of liquid water at 100.0°C that can be evaporated by the addition of 203 kJ of thermal energy. The heat of vaporization of water is 40.65 kJ/mol.

92. If 21 kJ of thermal energy are added to ice at 0.0°C, how many grams will change to the liquid phase? The molar mass of ice is 18.02 g/mol, and the heat of fusion of ice is 6.01 kJ/mol.

93. State the change in the levels of greenhouse gases in the atmosphere that occurred in the 20th century.

94. Agree or disagree with the following statement: *Investigating climate change is a responsibility of all the countries on Earth.* Justify your answer.

95. Describe at least two economic or social factors that have influenced the implementation of the Kyoto Protocol.

96. List at least five effects that climate change would have on Alberta. Arrange your list from the largest to the smallest effect, and explain how you decided the order.

Extensions

97. Explain why some people argue that there is currently insufficient evidence to conclude that climate change is occurring or is likely to occur.

98. Imagine that farmers in an area near to your community are reporting that the growing season is longer than in the past. Write a hypothesis to explain this observation. Describe how you might use weather records to test your hypothesis.

99. Explain why a biome is considered to be an open system, using the terms: input, output, energy, and matter.

100. The atmosphere above some areas of Earth's surface is undergoing ozone depletion. The levels of what types of radiation would likely increase at Earth's surface in these areas as a result?

101. Describe the potential consequences to climate if a volcano were to erupt and release large amounts of dust into the atmosphere.

102. If a mass of cold air is approaching your town from the west during the summer, predict the direction in which the wind will be blowing.

103. Suggest one difference in Earth's climate that would result if water had a low specific heat capacity.

104. Why is the assessment of the IPCC on climate change taken more seriously than the assessment of any one individual scientist?

105. Suggest some advantages and disadvantages to climatologists reporting a confidence estimate of the data or predictions in their work.

106. Explain the following statement: *Climate change is a social, political, and environmental issue.*

Skills Practice

107. From the information presented in the climatograph on the next page, write a travel brochure that provides visitors to Caracas with information such as the best time to visit, the type of clothing they should bring, and what kind of accommodation would be appropriate for a comfortable stay in this climate.

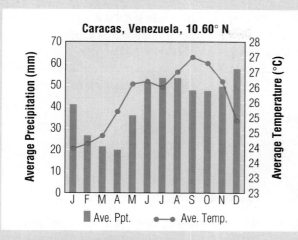

Caracas, Venezuela, 10.60° N

■ Ave. Ppt.   ●— Ave. Temp.

Source: World Climate (www.worldclimate.com)

108. The cities of Fort McMurray, Alberta, and Inverewe, Scotland, are located at similar latitudes. Construct a climatograph for both cities, using the given data. Write a paragraph describing the climates of the cities, and propose a reason for any differences.

Average Climate Conditions of Fort McMurray, Alberta, Canada, 56.4° N

Month	Average Temperature (°C)	Average Precipitation (mm)
Jan	−19.9	20.4
Feb	−14.9	16.0
Mar	−7.9	17.3
Apr	2.8	22.6
May	10.1	40.7
June	14.6	63.9
July	16.6	79.1
Aug	15.2	71.8
Sept	9.1	51.4
Oct	3.3	32.2
Nov	−9.0	26.4
Dec	−17.3	23.0

Source: Environment Canada

Average Climate Conditions of Inverewe, Scotland United Kingdom, 57.8° N

Month	Average Temperature (°C)	Average Precipitation (mm)
Jan	4.5	205.5
Feb	4.6	124.5
Mar	6.3	130.3
Apr	6.2	69.2
May	10.4	58.4
June	12.0	79.1
July	13.7	60.7
Aug	14.1	124.8
Sept	12.7	208.9
Oct	8.9	265.8
Nov	5.6	163.6
Dec	4.2	224.9

Source: Met Office, United Kingdom

Self Assessment

109. What is one thing you learned in this unit that you would like to find out more about?

110. Why is it important to consider alternative perspectives with any issue on global climate change?

111. Describe one aspect of your lifestyle you could modify or change to help reduce human impact on climate change.

112. Identify at least one personal, one social, and one environmental consequence of the change to your lifestyle that you suggested in your answer to question 111 above.

Glossary

Note: The number in parentheses at the end of each definition indicates the page number in this book where the term first appears.

A

absorb   to convert radiant energy into another form of energy, such as kinetic energy (362)

acceleration   change in velocity during a specific time interval (146)

acid   substance that produces hydrogen ions (H⁺) when dissolved in water; compound that dissolves in water to form a solution with a pH lower than 7 (at 25°C) (62)

active transport   movement of molecules or ions across a membrane against a concentration gradient; requires energy from ATP (278)

adaptation   any change in the structure or function of an organism that makes it more suited to its environment (350)

addiction   physical dependence on a drug (71)

adenosine triphosphate (ATP)   nucleotide that releases stored energy in a cell (279)

adhesion   tendency of unlike molecules to stick together (316)

albedo   percent of incoming solar radiation that a surface reflects (363)

alkali metals   soft, shiny, silvery elements, very reactive with water; group 1 in the periodic table (31)

alkaline-earth metals   shiny, silvery metals, not as soft as the alkali metals; group 2 in the periodic table (31)

altitude   the distance above Earth's surface, measured from sea level (the surface of Earth's oceans) (344)

anecdotal evidence   evidence that relies on reports from people about particular events and their interpretation of these events; anecdotal evidence has not been tested for bias or to ensure it applies to general situations (352)

angle of incidence   the angle between a ray falling on a surface and the line of the perpendicular to that surface (359)

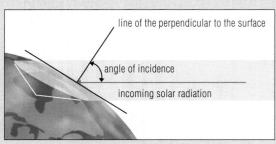

angle of inclination   the degree by which Earth's poles are tilted from the perpendicular of the plane of its orbit, or 23.5° (357)

anion   negatively charged ion (35)

area of elongation   an area of cells in the developing plant, facing away from the light source, that each elongate in a phototropic response to the light stimulus; the substance that initiates the phototropic response is auxin (326)

arm of microscope   curved portion of the microscope that holds all the optical parts at a fixed distance and keeps them aligned (478)

atmosphere   the layer of gases that surround Earth (343)

atmospheric dust   solid particles less than 0.66 mm in diameter suspended in Earth's atmosphere (343)

atmospheric pressure   the pressure exerted by the mass of air above any point on Earth's surface (372)

atom   smallest part of an element that still has the properties of the element (21)

atomic molar mass   average molar mass of an element's atoms, including those of all the element's different isotopes (34)

atomic number   number of protons in an atom; can be used to specify an element (33)

ATP   adenosine triphosphate, the nucleotide that releases stored energy in a cell (279)

auxin   type of plant hormone that promotes cell growth or elongation (327)

average speed   distance travelled in a specified time (128)

Avogadro's number   number of atoms in 1 mol; approximately 6.02×10^{23}; symbol: N_A (107)

B

base substance that produces hydroxide ions (OH⁻) in water; compound that dissolves in water to form a solution with a pH greater than 7 (at 25°C) (62)

base of microscope bears the weight of all the parts of the microscope (478)

bioindicator an animal or plant that shows a measurable response to a change in its environment (332)

biome a large geographical region with a particular range of temperature and precipitation levels, and the plants and animals that are adapted to those climate conditions (391)

biosphere a relatively thin layer of Earth that has conditions suitable for supporting life as we know it (343)

bovine spongiform encephalopathy (BSE) a chronic degenerative disease affecting the nervous system of cattle that is linked to specific infectious proteins called prions and produces large vacuoles or empty pockets in brain tissue; it is commonly known as "mad cow disease" (262)

brightfield illumination in the light microscope in which the specimen is illuminated by an unfiltered beam of white light that passes from the illumination source through the specimen, into the objective, and then to the eyepiece (253)

buffer substance that keeps the pH of a solution nearly constant despite the addition of a small amount of acid or base (62)

C

calorimeter a device used to determine the transfer of thermal energy (378)

capillary action the ability of the surface of a liquid to cling to the surface of a solid, causing the liquid to move along that solid (315)

carbohydrate sugars and related molecules formed by carbon, hydrogen, and oxygen atoms in a ratio of 1:2:1; used as a major energy source by organisms (271)

carbon dioxide sequestering a process of pumping carbon dioxide gas into the ground and storing it in sealed containers; may also refer to pumping carbon dioxide gas into the ocean bottom at very deep levels (424)

carbon sink any process that removes carbon dioxide from the atmosphere, such as photosynthesis (413)

carbon source any process that releases carbon dioxide to the atmosphere, such as burning of fossil fuels (413)

carbonic acid a weak acid produced by dissolving carbon dioxide in water (93)

carrier protein a protein present in a cell membrane that binds to a specific molecule and transports it through the membrane (278)

cation positively charged ion (34)

cell communication the ability of cells in a multicellular organism to interact with each other and to influence each other's activity (262)

cell membrane structure that surrounds a cell and regulates the passage of materials between the cell and its environment; also called plasma membrane (267)

cell theory the cornerstone of biology, which states that all living things are made up of cells, the smallest units of life, and all cells are produced from pre-existing cells (251)

cell transport the movement of materials into and out of cells (274)

cell wall a rigid frame around the cell in plants, bacteria, and some protists; provides strength and support (268)

cellular respiration breakdown of glucose molecules to release chemical energy that a cell can use (82)

$$C_6H_{12}O_{6(aq)} + 6O_{2(g)} \longrightarrow 6CO_{2(g)} + 6H_2O_{(l)} + \text{energy}$$

glucose + oxygen　　　carbon dioxide + water

centrioles paired structures found in animal cells that are important for the process of cell division (272)

channel protein a protein in the cell membrane that forms a passageway through which specific solutes can pass by diffusion; some channels open and close in response to binding of specific molecules (278)

chemical change change to a substance that always results in the formation of a different substance or substances (18)

chemical energy   potential energy stored in the chemical bonds of compounds (165)

chemical equation   record of a chemical reaction using chemical symbols and formulas; shorthand way of showing the results of a chemical reaction (86)

chemical properties   properties that describe the reactivity of a substance (13)

chemical reaction   process that occurs when a substance or substances react to form a different substance or substances (15)

chlorofluorocarbons (CFCs)   particular halocarbon compounds (70)

chlorophyll   a green pigment that makes photosynthesis possible (272)

chloroplast   a green organelle found in plants and some protists that contains chlorophyll and is the site of photosynthesis (268)

climate   average weather conditions that occur in a region over a long period of time, usually a minimum of 30 years (342)

climate change   change that occurs in the climate of a region over time, usually a minimum of 30 years (352)

climatograph   a summary of the average temperature and precipitation for each month of the year for a given location, presented as a graph (403)

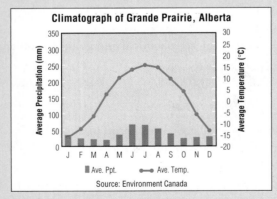

closed system   any system that exchanges energy with its surroundings but does not exchange matter (199)

coarse adjustment knob   moves the stage of the microscope up and down to bring the specimen into the focal plane of the objective lens (478)

cogeneration   using waste energy from one process to power a second process (226)

cohesion   tendency of molecules of the same kind to stick together (316)

colloid   mechanical mixture in which the suspended substance cannot be easily separated from the other substances in the mixture (14)

combustion   exothermic chemical reaction that occurs when oxygen reacts quickly with a substance to form a new substance or substances (81)

companion cells   type of small phloem cells adjacent to sieve tube cells that appear to control sugar transport in the phloem (300)

compound   chemical combination of two or more elements in a specific ratio (14)

concentration gradient   difference within a given area between the highest and lowest concentration of a particular chemical substance (275)

conclusion   the outcome of an experiment based on the agreement or disagreement of the data with the hypothesis (460)

conduction   the transfer of thermal energy by direct contact between the particles of a substance, without moving the particles to a new location (370)

confocal microscope   a microscope that uses confocal technology (257)

confocal technology   systems that use the light microscope, laser beams, and computers to produce three-dimensional images from a combination of many perfectly-focused thin sections (257)

contrast   the ability to see differences between structures due to differences in their capacity to absorb light (253)

control systems   systems within plants that produce definite responses to specific stimuli (323)

control (in an experiment)   part of the experiment in which the manipulated variable is not changed in any way from its normal condition (248)

controlled experiment   an experiment in which each variable is controlled in turn, allowing the experimenter to determine the effect of each (248)

controlled variables   conditions that are held constant throughout an experiment (248)

convection the transfer of thermal energy by the movement of particles from one location to another (371)

Coriolis effect the deflection of any object from a straight line path, caused by the rotation of Earth (372)

covalent bond bond formed when non-metallic atoms share electrons; atoms in a molecule are bound together by covalent bonds (47)

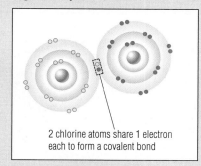

2 chlorine atoms share 1 electron each to form a covalent bond

coverslip thin piece of glass used to cover a specimen on a glass slide before examination under a microscope (480)

crystal lattice organized array of ions (40)

current flow from one place to another in one direction (371)

cuticle waxy, non-cellular, waterproof coating that covers a plant's leaves and stems (299)

cytoplasm a gel-like substance inside the cell membrane that contains nutrients and in which the organelles are suspended (267)

cytoplasmic streaming distribution of materials within cells through a circular flow of the cytoplasm (267)

cytoskeleton network of fine protein fibres that supports cells that contain a nucleus (272)

D

decomposition reaction chemical reaction in which a compound breaks apart into its elements (94)

density mass per volume of a substance (371)

dermal tissue the outermost cell layer of plants; also called epidermis (309)

desalination the removal of salt from a solution, especially from seawater (288)

dialysis tubing a seamless cellulose membrane with pores of a specific size (295)

diaphragm adjusts the diameter of an opening to control the amount of light passing through the specimen (478)

diatomic molecule molecule composed of two atoms of the same element (48)

diffusion spontaneous movement of particles from an area of higher concentration to an area of lower concentration (275)

displacement vector quantity that measures the change in distance and the change in direction or position of an object (138)

distance travelled scalar quantity that measures how far an object has travelled (137)

double replacement reaction chemical reaction between two ionic compounds in solution that often results in the formation of at least one precipitate (100)

ductile description of a substance that can be drawn or stretched into long wires (29)

E

efficiency ratio of the useful work output to the total work input; measurement of how effectively a machine converts energy input into useful energy output (216)

elastic potential energy energy stored in an object that has its shape changed by stretching, twisting, or compressing (175)

electrical energy work done by moving charges; energy produced by moving electrons (165)

electrolyte solution that conducts electricity; ionic compounds are excellent electrolytes (55)

electron negatively charged particle in the atom that occupies energy levels around the nucleus (22)

electron microscope (EM) a microscope that uses a beam of electrons to produce images of fine detail (258)

scanning electron microscope (SEM) an EM in which a three-dimensional image is formed by electrons bouncing off the surface of the specimen (259)

transmission electron microscope (TEM) an EM in which the image is formed by a beam of electrons that passes through a very thin section of a fixed and stained specimen (258)

electron-dense characteristic of a substance that does not allow electrons to pass through it, but either absorbs or scatters the electrons (258)

element pure substance that cannot be broken down into other substances; substance made up of only one type of atom (14)

emission-reduction credits (ERCs) credits given to a country under the Kyoto Protocol for actions that contribute to the global reduction of greenhouse gas emissions (422)

endocytosis uptake of particles or molecules by formation of a vesicle from the cell membrane; requires energy from ATP (281)

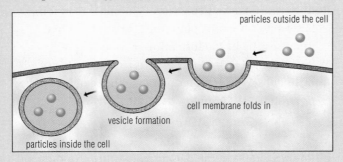

endoplasmic reticulum (ER) network of membrane tubes that branch from the nuclear envelope and circulate materials throughout the cell (268)

smooth endoplasmic reticulum ER lacking ribosomes (268)

rough endoplasmic reticulum ER studded with ribosomes (268)

endothermic energy absorbing (81)

endothermic reaction chemical reaction that absorbs energy (81)

energy ability to do work (160)

energy input energy used to do work (215)

energy level region of space near an atom's nucleus that may be empty or may contain electrons; electrons in energy levels nearest the nucleus have the lowest energy (32)

enhanced greenhouse effect the change in Earth's net radiation budget, caused by the increase in human-generated greenhouse gases (414)

epidermis the outermost cell layer of plants; also called dermal tissue (309)

equilibrium a state of balance between opposing actions (272)

equinox one of two points in Earth's orbit when the number of daylight hours is equal to the number of hours of night (359)

exocytosis release of molecules from a vesicle that fuses with the cell membrane to export the molecules from the cell; requires energy from ATP (281)

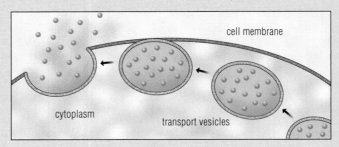

exothermic energy releasing (81)

exothermic reaction chemical reaction that releases energy, usually in the form of heat, light, or electricity (81)

extrapolation the process of estimating the value of a measurement beyond the known values of a set of data (412)

eyepiece magnifies the image from the objective lens and conveys it to your eye (478)

F

facilitated diffusion diffusion of molecules across a membrane through binding to carrier proteins; does not require energy from ATP; *see also* **diffusion** (278)

family vertical column of elements in the periodic table; numbered from 1 to 18; also called group (31)

fermentation biochemical preservation technique involving bacteria (19)

field of view area that can be seen through the microscope with a given objective lens (245)

fine adjustment knob makes subtle adjustments to produce clear sharp images (478)

first law of thermodynamics the total energy, including heat, in a system and its surroundings remains constant (200)

fluid-mosaic model   description of the arrangement of protein molecules in the fluid double layer of phospholipids that make up the cell membrane (272)

fluids   substances with no definite shape (such as gases and liquids) (371)

fluorescence microscopy   a technique to localize substances in cells by using the ability of those substances to fluoresce in the presence of ultraviolet light (256)

force   push or pull applied to an object; measured in newtons (156)

formation reaction   chemical reaction in which two elements combine to form a compound; also known as a synthesis reaction (91)

formula equation   chemical equation that uses the chemical formulas of reactants and products in a chemical equation to represent a chemical reaction (40)

formula unit   smallest amount of an ionic compound with the composition shown by the chemical formula; number of positive and negative ions in the smallest whole-number ratio that results in a neutral unit in the crystal lattice of a compound (40)

fossil fuels   carbon-based fuels formed from the remains of living organisms (191)

G

gene mapping   a technique to locate the position of specific genes within the genetic make-up of an organism (261)

general circulation model (GCM)   a climate model that incorporates the laws of physics to model climate on a global scale (419)

geotropism   directional plant growth response to gravity; may be positive or negative; also called gravitropism (323)
negative geotropism   growth against the gravitational force; also called negative gravitropism (323)
positive geotropism   growth toward the gravitational force; also called positive gravitropism (323)

GFP technology   a process that allows cell activities to be studied by attaching the green fluorescent protein (GFP) to particular parts of the cell (258)

global warming   the observed increase in Earth's average temperature over time (415)

Golgi apparatus   flat stack of membranes that receive, modify, and transport products of the endoplasmic reticulum throughout a cell (269)

gravitational potential energy   energy of an object because of its position above the surface of Earth (167)

gravitropism   directional plant growth response to gravity; may be positive or negative; also called geotropism (323)
negative gravitropism   growth against the gravitational force; also called negative geotropism (323)
positive gravitropism   growth toward the gravitational force; also called positive geotropism (323)

greenhouse gases   gases that contribute to the greenhouse effect (365)

ground tissue   parts of the plant body not included in the dermal or vascular tissue systems; function in storage, photosynthesis, and support (299)

group   vertical column of elements in the periodic table; numbered from 1 to 18; also called family (31)

guard cell   specialized epidermal cell that swells and contracts to control gas exchange through a stoma in a leaf (302)

H

halocarbons   human-made chemicals that can absorb large quantities of thermal energy (414)

halogens   non-metals in group 17 in the periodic table; fluorine, chlorine, bromine, and iodine (31)

heat   energy transferred from an object at a higher temperature to one at a lower temperature; thermal energy (169)

heat engine   device that converts heat into mechanical energy (203)

heat of condensation the amount of energy released when 1 mol of a substance changes from the vapour phase to the liquid phase, without a change in temperature (383)

heat of fusion (H_{fus}) the amount of energy absorbed when 1 mol of a substance changes from solid phase to liquid phase, without a change in temperature (383)

heat of solidification the amount of energy released when 1 mol of a substance in the liquid phase changes to the solid phase, without a change in temperature (383)

heat of vaporization (H_{vap}) the amount of energy absorbed when 1 mol of a substance changes from vapour phase to gas phase, without a change in temperature (383)

heat pump device that uses mechanical energy to transfer heat (204)

hemodialysis treatment for kidney failure in which membranes in a dialysis machine clean the blood and remove wastes and excess water from the body that would normally be removed by a healthy kidney (287)

herbaceous describes a soft plant stem with little or no woody tissue (299)

heterogeneous mixture mixture in which the different substances are visible (14)

homogeneous mixture mixture in which the different substances are not visible (14)

hormone chemical compound that travels from its production site in an organism to other sites where it produces an effect (327)

hydrocarbon compound that contains hydrogen and carbon; common hydrocarbons include the main components of gasoline (a mixture of many liquid hydrocarbons) and many plastics (95)

hydrochlorofluorocarbons (HCFCs) compounds with similar properties to CFCs, but which destroy ozone much more slowly (421)

hydrologic cycle (or water cycle) the process by which water molecules move from Earth's surface into the atmosphere and then back again (382)

hydrosphere all the water on Earth, whether present as liquid, water vapour, or ice (343)

hypertonic describes a solution that has a higher solute concentration than another solution (278)

hypothesis a way of restating a cause-and-effect question so that it gives a reasonable possible answer; possible explanation for observations; proposed answer to a question being posed (51)

hypotonic describes a solution that has a lower solute concentration than another solution (278)

I

incoming radiation all the radiant energy that reaches Earth (367)

inert unreactive with all but the most corrosive of acids (29)

insolation the amount of solar energy received by a region of Earth's surface (357)

insulin hormone that binds to a protein on the cell membrane, allowing glucose to enter the cell by facilitated diffusion (286)

Intergovernmental Panel on Climate Change (IPCC) an international group of scientists who assess information on climate change (415)

internal combustion engine device in which energy is released by burning fuel inside the engine (210)

ion electrically charged atom or group of atoms (34)

ionic bond type of bond formed when electrons transfer between metals and non-metals (41)

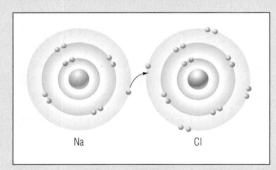

Na   Cl

One electron transfers from the sodium atom to the chlorine atom.

ionization process of an atom gaining or losing electrons (34)

isolated system system that cannot exchange either matter or energy with its surroundings (199)

isotonic describes a solution that has the same solute concentration as another solution (278)

isotopes atoms of the same element containing different numbers of neutrons (33)

J

jet stream a band of fast-moving air in the stratosphere (374)

K

kinetic energy energy of a moving object (167)

Kyoto Protocol an international agreement to reduce the emission of greenhouse gases (422)

L

lamp of microscope supplies the light required to view the specimen (478)

latitude imaginary lines that run parallel to Earth's equator; the equator has a latitude of 0°, and the poles have a latitude of 90° N and 90° S (359)

law of conservation of energy energy cannot be created or destroyed; it can only be changed from one form to another, and the total amount of energy never changes (184)

law of conservation of mass total mass of the reactants in a chemical reaction equals the total mass of the products (21)

lenticel a raised spongy region in the stem of a woody plant that allows gas exchange between the atmosphere and the interior of the plant (313)

life force a natural force postulated to produce life spontaneously (spontaneous generation); the theory of a life force was disproved by Pasteur (247)

light microscope an instrument with a system of lenses used for magnification in which the specimen is illuminated by a beam of white light (244)

lipid fats and oils formed of carbon, hydrogen, and oxygen atoms in a ratio different from 1:2:1; insoluble in water (271)

liposomes fluid-filled sacs surrounded by a phospholipid bilayer identical to the cell membrane of human cells; they can be incorporated into living cells, and are used to transport medication into diseased cells without affecting normal cells, and to insert DNA in gene therapy (285)

lithosphere solid portion of Earth, composed of rocks, minerals, and elements (343)

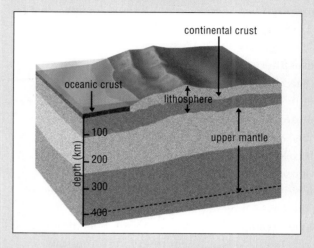

lysosome organelle containing enzymes that digest food, destroy bacteria, or break down damaged organelles in cells containing a nucleus (269)

M

magnification an increase in the apparent size of an object, calculated as the product of the magnifying powers of the objective lens and the eyepiece (244)

malleable description of a substance that can be beaten or rolled into sheets without crumbling (29)

manipulated variable condition deliberately changed in an experiment (65)

mass number integer equal to the total number of protons and neutrons in the nucleus of an atom (33)

Material Safety Data Sheet (MSDS) information sheet on a hazardous product used in workplaces, including schools; identifies the chemical and physical hazards associated with the product (9)

mechanical energy energy due to the motion and position of an object (167)

mechanical mixture mixture in which the different substances are visible (14)

membrane technologies industrial use of synthetics to mimic the action of membranes (284)

meristem growth region of the plant with tissue in which cells divide by mitosis (299)

mesophyll specialized ground tissue inside a leaf, made up of thin-walled cells containing chloroplasts (311)

mesosphere the third atmospheric layer above Earth's surface (345)

metal shiny, malleable, ductile element (29)

metalloid element with properties intermediate between metals and non-metals (29)

microscope an instrument with a lens or system of lenses for magnifying specimens (478)

microscopist (mi·cros·co·pist) a person trained in the use of the microscope (243)

mirror sometimes used in a microscope, in the place of a lamp, to direct light from the surroundings through the diaphragm (478)

mitochondria (*sing.* **mitochondrion**) organelles that perform cellular respiration in a eukaryotic cell (269)

mixture combination of pure substances (14)

molar mass mass of one mole of a substance (108)

mole quantity that chemists use to measure elements and compounds; symbol: mol; Avogadro's number is the number of particles in a mole (107)

molecular element element that forms molecules made up only of its own atoms (48)

molecule group of non-metallic atoms bound together by covalent bonds; can be made up of atoms of the same element or atoms of different elements (29)

Montreal Protocol an international agreement to phase out the production and use of CFCs (421)

motion the changing in position of an object relative to a reference point; an imaginary line joining the object to the reference point changes in length and direction or both (127)

multivalent element element with more than one stable ion (44)

N

natural greenhouse effect the absorption of thermal energy by the atmosphere (365)

net radiation budget the difference between the amount of incoming radiation and outgoing radiation from Earth's surface and atmosphere (367)

neutral description of a substance that is neither acidic nor basic; solution with a pH of 7 (at 25°C) (64)

neutralization process in which acids and bases react with each other so that the H^+ ion and OH^- ion combine to make a single water molecule; both acidic and basic properties disappear (68)

neutron neutral particle in the nucleus of an atom (25)

noble gases extremely unreactive non-metals; group 18 in the periodic table (31)

non-metal one of 17 elements with varying properties that are completely different from metals (29)

non-renewable energy source energy source that is limited and cannot be replaced (222)

nuclear energy potential energy stored in the nucleus of an atom (167)

nuclear envelope a double-layer membrane that separates the nuclear contents from the cytoplasm (270)

nucleic acid complex molecule made up of nucleotides; includes DNA and RNA (271)

nucleons subatomic particles in the nucleus of the atom; protons and neutrons (25)

nucleus (in cells) organelle that contains DNA, the genetic material, and directs all cellular activities (251)

nucleus (in atoms) positively charged centre of the atom made up of protons and neutrons (23)

O

objective lens gathers light from a specimen and forms an inverted image (478)

octet rule atoms bond in such a way as to have eight electrons in the valence energy level; also called the rule of eight (38)

ocular lens allows observation of specimen and provides part of the total magnification; is the lens nearest the eye (478)

open system a system that exchanges both matter and energy with its surroundings (199)

organ group of tissues that work together to perform a specific function (297)

organelle structure that performs a specific function within a cell (266)

osmosis diffusion of water across a selectively permeable membrane (277)

outgoing radiation the thermal radiation emitted by Earth's surface and atmosphere that is not absorbed by greenhouse gases of the atmosphere (367)

ozone a molecule made up of three atoms of oxygen (345)

ozone layer a layer in the stratosphere containing high levels of ozone gas (345)

P

palisade tissue cell column-shaped mesophyll cells in a plant leaf; responsible for photosynthesis (311)

particle model a model to explain the nature of matter, based on particle composition, attraction, and movement (274)

passive transport movement of substances along the concentration gradient; transport process that does not require ATP (275)

perfect machine hypothetical machine in which all the input energy is converted completely into mechanical energy; also called perpetual motion machine (202)

period horizontal line or row in the periodic table; periods are numbered from 1 to 7 (31)

peritoneal dialysis a process by which waste products from the blood pass by diffusion into a dialysate solution in the peritoneal cavity (286)

peritoneum a membrane that lines the abdominal cavity in humans and other vertebrates (286)

permafrost permanently frozen ground (353)

perpetual motion machine hypothetical machine in which all the input energy is converted completely into mechanical energy; also called perfect machine (202)

pH measure of the number of hydrogen ions in a solution; indicates how acidic or basic a substance is (62)

phase the state of a substance (solid, liquid, or vapour) (382)

phloem tissue vascular tissue that transports carbohydrates and water from the leaves to other parts of the plant (292)

phospholipid bilayer double layer of outward-facing phosphates and inward-facing fatty acids that form a cell membrane (272)

photosynthesis means putting together with light ("photo" = light; "synthesis" = putting together); a chemical process in which carbon dioxide from the air and water from the soil, in the presence of light energy, produce glucose and oxygen (82)

$$6H_2O_{(l)} + 6CO_{2(g)} \xrightarrow{\text{chlorophyll + light}} C_6H_{12}O_{6(aq)} + 6O_{2(g)}$$
water + carbon dioxide → glucose + oxygen

phototropism directional plant growth in response to light (323)

negative phototropism growth away from the light source (323)

positive phototropism growth toward the light source (323)

physical change change to a substance in which the composition of the substance stays the same (18)

physical properties properties that describe the physical appearance and composition of a substance (13)

plasma membrane structure that surrounds a cell and regulates the passage of materials between the cell and its environment; also called cell membrane (272)

plasmolysis shrinking of the cytoplasm and plasma membrane away from the cell wall due to outflow of water in a hypertonic environment; observed only in cells with rigid cell walls (320)

polar description of an object that has a positive electric charge at one end and a negative charge at the other; water molecules are slightly polar (60)

polyatomic ion charged particle made up of several non-metallic atoms joined together (44)

potential energy energy that is stored and held in readiness; energy that has the potential to do work; types of potential energy include gravitational, elastic, and chemical (173)

prairie a subtype of grassland biome found in regions such as North America; prairies have cooler average temperatures than the other subtype of grassland biome, savanna (397)

precipitate solid with low solubility that forms from a solution (15)

precipitation (in solutions) process of forming a solid from a solution (58)

pressure difference the difference in pressure in two areas that may cause movement of substances (321)

pressure-flow theory explanation of plant nutrient transport from leaves to other parts of the plant, driven by the pressure build-up of hypertonic solution in leaf phloem (321)

prions infectious particles composed of specifically altered proteins that occur in the brains of humans and animals and can lead to neurodegenerative diseases; some prions act as infectious agents in bovine spongiform encephalopathy (BSE) in cattle and in a new variant of Creutzfeldt-Jakob disease (nvCJD) in humans (262)

product new substance produced in a chemical reaction (79)

protein large molecule formed by amino acids; responsible for many structures and functions (271)

protein hormones protein molecules that are active in an organism at a distance from the location where they are produced (327)

protein synthesis assembly of amino acids into proteins in a cell, based on instructions encoded on a DNA molecule (269)

protist a single-celled organism with a nucleus; it does not belong to the plant, fungi, or animal groups (251)

proton positively charged particle in the nucleus of an atom (25)

pure substance substance in which all the particles are identical (14)

Q

quantity of thermal energy (Q) the amount of thermal energy absorbed or released when the temperature of a substance changes by a certain number of degrees; given by the equation $Q = mc\Delta t$ (378)

R

radiant energy energy that is transmitted as electromagnetic waves (167)

radiation emission of energy as particles or waves (370)

rate of diffusion the relative movement of a particle in response to a concentration gradient (275)

reactant substance that reacts in a chemical reaction to form another substance or substances (79)

reagent substance used for identifying, measuring, or producing other substances (37)

receptor proteins specialized molecules on the surface of the cell to which messenger molecules from other cells can bind; play an important role in cell-to-cell communication, particularly in the immune system (284)

recognition proteins protein molecules protruding from cells that allow communication between cells, such as in sperm–egg recognition in a species (284)

reflect change the direction of a ray of radiant energy (362)

renewable energy source energy source that is continually and infinitely available (222)

resolution or **resolving power** the ability to distinguish between two structures that are close together (255)

respiration process by which an organism secures oxygen from the air, distributes it, combines it with substances, and gives off carbon dioxide (82)

responding variable condition that changes in response to the manipulated variable in an experiment (65)

reverse osmosis (RO) the movement of water through a semi-permeable membrane from a high concentration of solute to a low concentration of solute (287)

revolving nosepiece rotating mount that holds many objective lenses (478)

ribosome organelle in cytoplasm that is the site of protein synthesis (269)

root part of a plant, usually below ground, that is involved in the absorption and transport of water and minerals and the storage of food materials (297)

root hair extension of a specialized dermal cell on a plant root, which absorbs water and minerals (301)

root pressure upward force exerted on water in the xylem in the roots of some plants (316)

root system the plant organ system that includes all tissues located below the ground (297)

S

salt compound produced in a neutralization reaction between an acid and a base (31)

salting method of drying food to preserve it; salt draws water out of the food (18)

savanna a subtype of grassland biome found in regions such as Africa, Central America, and Australia; has warmer average temperatures than the other subtype of grassland biome, prairie (397)

scalar quantity quantity that indicates magnitude only (137)

scale (of a drawing) the difference between the size of an object in a drawing or diagram and the actual size of the object. Scale is often expressed as a ratio, e.g., size on drawing:actual size (246)

scientific evidence evidence collected in a manner that, as much as possible, ensures it is unbiased and reflects general situations, rather than particular events; is usually collected by trained scientists and checked by other scientists (352)

second law of thermodynamics heat always flows naturally from a hot object to a cold object, never naturally from a cold object to a hot object (202)

selectively permeable membrane a natural membrane that allows certain particles to pass through it but excludes others (275)

semi-permeable membrane a type of membrane which allows certain particles to pass through while others are excluded; can be natural or synthetically produced for industrial use (275)

shoot system the plant organ system that includes all tissues located above ground (297)

sieve tube a tube formed by a stack of sieve tube cells to allow conduction of phloem in plants (300)

sieve tube cell cylindrical cells lacking nuclei and with perforated sides and end walls that allow the movement of phloem sap between cells (300)

single replacement reaction chemical reaction in which a reactive element reacts with an ionic compound (96)

sink according to the pressure-flow theory, cells that receive carbohydrates in plants (321)

skeleton equation formula equation showing the identity of each substance involved in a chemical reaction; does not show the correct proportions of the reactants and the products (87)

solar energy energy from the Sun; generated by a hydrogen–hydrogen nuclear fusion reaction (167)

solstice one of two points in Earth's orbit at which the poles are most tilted toward or away from the Sun (359)

solute the substance that is dissolved in a solution (275)

solution mixture in which the separate components are not visible (14)

solvent the substance that dissolves one or more solutes in a solution; water is the most common solvent (272)

source according to the pressure-flow theory, cells that manufacture carbohydrates in plants (321)

specific heat capacity (c) amount of energy required to raise the temperature of 1 g of a substance by 1°C (377)

spongy mesophyll tissue layer of loosely spaced mesophyll cells in a leaf; the increased distance between cells promotes diffusion (311)

spontaneous generation the idea that life could emerge spontaneously from non-living matter, widely held into the 19th century; disproved by Louis Pasteur (247)

stage clip clip that holds a microscope slide in place on the stage (478)

stage of microscope the part of the microscope on which the specimen slide is placed for examination; can be moved up and down for examination of the specimen (478)

staining techniques use of stains or colouring agents to improve the contrast between structures in cells; staining properties depend on the chemical composition of the structure (254)

stimulus (*pl.* **stimuli**) a change in the environment that causes a reaction by the organism (323)

stomata (*sing.* **stoma**) pores that allow gases to pass through the epidermis of a leaf (302)

stratosphere atmospheric layer above the troposphere, from 10 to 50 km above Earth's surface (345)

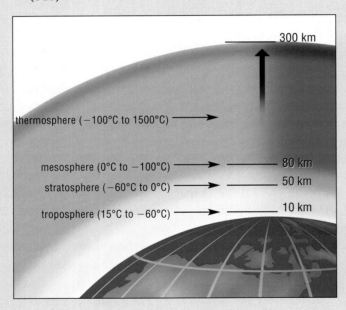

surface area total area of external surfaces of an object (289)

surface area to volume ratio the ratio between the total area of external surfaces of an object and its volume (289)

surroundings everything that is outside of a system (199)

suspension mechanical mixture in which the components are in different states (14)

sustainable description of any process that will not compromise the survival of living things or future generations while still providing for current energy needs (227)

sustainable development the use of the world's resources in a way that maintains the resources for future generations (227)

synthesis reaction chemical reaction in which two elements combine to form a compound; also known as a formation reaction (91)

system a set of interconnected parts; a system can be classified as open, closed, or isolated (199)

system (in animals and plants) a set of organs or parts that performs one or more functions as a unit (391)

T

tension a stress caused by the action of a pulling force (318)

thermal energy the amount of energy possessed by a substance by virtue of the kinetic energy of its molecules or atoms (357)

thermal energy transfer movement of thermal energy from an area of high temperature to an area of low temperature (370)

thermal power station electrical generating station that uses thermal energy to produce steam to drive turbines; sources of thermal energy include coal, natural gas, and nuclear energy (193)

thermodynamics study of the interrelationships between heat, work, and energy (169)

thermosphere furthest atmospheric layer from Earth's surface (345)

tissue group of similar cells that perform a specific function (297)

tonicity a term that relates the concentration of solute particles in solutions; *see also* **hypertonic**, **hypotonic**, and **isotonic** (319)

trace element element that an organism requires in small amounts (272)

transpiration loss of water from leaves through evaporation (309)

transpiration pull the tension or pull on water molecules in the xylem due to evaporation of water through the stomata or lenticels in a plant (318)

troposphere layer of atmospheric gases at 0 km to 10 km from Earth's surface (344)

tuber enlarged underground stem that stores food (297)

turgid firm; plant cells become turgid when water enters due to a hypotonic surrounding environment (268)

turgor pressure pressure exerted against a cell wall by the water that has entered the cell through osmosis (268)

U

uniform motion movement in a straight line at a constant speed (127)

United Nations Framework Convention on Climate Change (UNFCCC) an agreement by the world's nations to act in ways that will stabilize greenhouse gas emissions from anthropogenic sources (421)

universal indicator mixture of several indicators that change colour as the acidity of a solution changes (63)

useful energy output energy needed to do work (215)

useful work output work that a machine is supposed to do (215)

V

vacuole membrane-enclosed sac within a cell; is usually large and may be permanent (268)

valence tendency of an atom to gain or lose electrons (36)

valence electron electron in the outermost energy level of an atom (36)

valence number number of electrons an element can gain or lose to combine with other elements (36)

vascular bundle strand of xylem, phloem, and associated tissues in a plant (313)

vascular tissue transport tissue formed of cells joined into tubes that carry water and nutrients through the body of the plant (300)

vector quantity quantity that indicates magnitude and direction (137)

velocity speed and direction of an object (137)

vesicle membrane-enclosed sac that transports materials throughout a cell; structure is similar to a vacuole (268)

volume space, measured in cubic units, occupied or contained by an object (289)

W

weather conditions of temperature, air pressure, cloud cover, precipitation (rain or snow), and humidity that occur at a particular place at a particular time (342)

wind movement of cool air from an area of high atmospheric pressure to an area of low atmospheric pressure (372)

work a measure of the amount of energy transferred from one object to another when an object moves against an opposing force or the speed of an object increases; calculated by multiplying the force acting on an object by the distance the object travels (157)

Workplace Hazardous Materials Information System (WHMIS) system of easy-to-see warning symbols on hazardous materials, designed to help protect people who use hazardous materials at work (8)

X

X-ray crystallography the study of the structure of molecules by means of X-rays, special sensors that analyze patterns of X-ray scattering, and computer technology (264)

xylem tissue vascular tissue that conducts water and minerals from the roots to the leaves in plants (300)

xylem vessel tube, formed of cells that are dead at maturity, that transports water and minerals in plants (300)

Student Reference

Contents

Student Reference 1: Safety

The first step in ensuring a safe learning environment is to read over the entire procedure before you begin any activity in the science classroom. Make sure you note and understand the safety cautions. If you are unsure about any procedure or safety instruction, ask your teacher before you proceed.

Safety Icons

You will be alerted to safety hazards in *Addison Wesley Science 10* by the following symbols. Look for them at the top of the *Materials and Equipment* section of each activity.

TABLE 1.1 Safety Icons

	glassware; breakage hazard
	eye protection required
	protective clothing required, such as lab apron
	protective gloves required

Safety Symbols

Some safety information is given by standard symbols on the product label. There are two main groups of labels: those for hazardous household products and those for hazardous workplace products.

Household Hazardous Product Symbols (HHPS)

Labels on hazardous household products must include a symbol that indicates the degree and type of hazard. The shape of the symbol tells you about the degree of hazard (Figure 1.1). A red octagon shape means "danger," an orange diamond shape means "warning," and a yellow triangle means "caution." The symbol inside the shape tells you the type of danger.

| flammable | toxic | explosive | corrosive |

FIGURE 1.1 If the toxic symbol was in a yellow triangle, what would the hazard symbol mean?

Workplace Hazardous Materials Information System (WHMIS)

Hazardous materials used in the workplace (including classrooms) must be labelled according to the WHMIS. These symbols are similar to those of HHPS, but WHMIS symbols also identify additional hazards (Figure 1.2). These symbols are used in *Addison Wesley Science 10*. Look for them in the *Materials and Equipment* section of each activity. You will find the appropriate WHMIS symbol beside any hazardous material that will be used.

| compressed gas | dangerously reactive material | oxidizing material | poisonous and infectious material causing immediate and serious toxic effects |

| flammable and combustible material | biohazardous infectious material | corrosive material | poisonous and infectious material causing other toxic effects |

FIGURE 1.2 Make sure you understand the meaning of the symbol before you proceed with any activity.

Suppliers of hazardous workplace products must also provide a materials safety data sheet (MSDS). The MSDS gives detailed information about the potential hazards of a chemical. The MSDS must be stored in an accessible place. An example of an MSDS appears on page 9 of *Addison Wesley Science 10*.

Laboratory Safety Practices

This section provides general guidelines to help you work safely in the science classroom. Your teacher may provide additional instructions specific to your school.

❶ General Safety Procedures

a) Identify and locate all safety equipment.

b) Know how to operate all safety equipment.

c) Wear appropriate safety apparel, as indicated in the activity.

d) Tie back long hair. Remove or secure any loose clothing.

e) Obtain the approval of your teacher before starting any procedure, especially one you have planned independently.

f) Never work alone or without your teacher's supervision.

g) At the end of all lab activities, make sure your work space is clean.

h) Wash your hands after completing any lab work.

❷ Bunsen Burners and Hot Plates

a) Never leave a Bunsen burner or hot plate unattended.

b) Before connecting a Bunsen burner, make sure the gas supply valve is completely closed. Open the valve just slightly, then immediately light the Bunsen burner.

c) Be sure to use only heatproof containers.

d) Use tongs or holders to handle all hot objects.

❸ Glassware

a) Never use chipped, cracked, or broken glassware.

b) Place all broken glass into a marked container, as instructed by your teacher.

c) Use the glassware specified in the procedure, unless instructed otherwise by your teacher.

d) Ensure glassware is clean before and after use.

❹ Chemicals

a) Read the safety precautions provided on the label before using any chemical. Never use a chemical from an unlabelled container.

b) Never smell, taste, or touch chemicals in the laboratory without your teacher's instruction.

c) Never directly inhale fumes. To smell a substance, waft the air above it toward your nose.

d) Never return unused chemicals to stock bottles or containers.

e) Dilute acids by adding **acid to water**. Add the acid slowly, by pouring it down the side of the container.

❺ Electrical Devices

a) Keep water and wet hands away from electrical cords.

b) Never use electrical equipment that has a damaged plug or wires.

What if an accident occurs?

If an accident occurs, inform your teacher right away. Any injury, no matter how small, must be reported. Any spills or breakages must be cleaned up only under the direction of your teacher.

Student Reference 2: The Inquiry Process

Science is a way of asking questions about the world, and then answering these questions using a structured approach. This is sometimes called the inquiry process. It uses logical reasoning to find answers to questions, through observation, measurement, experimentation, research, analysis, and evaluation.

The proposed answer to a question about a scientific problem or issue is called a hypothesis. An experiment is a way of testing to see if a hypothesis should be accepted or rejected. Experiments are designed so that only one variable (a condition that can change in an experiment) is modified at a time. All other variables are controlled (kept unchanged). The effect of the variable that is modified is observed and recorded, and then the observations are analyzed and interpreted. The experimenter then decides whether the observations support the hypothesis, and then clearly communicates the results and conclusions.

STEP 1 Ask a question.

The inquiry process starts when you ask a question. In the inquiry process of science, questions are often about cause and effect. Suppose you leave a glass of ice water in sunlight. You observe that the ice seems to melt more quickly than when you leave an identical glass of ice water in the shade. If you wanted to use the inquiry process to expore this observation, you might ask a cause-and-effect question like the one below. In this example, the cause is the exposure to sunlight and the effect is the rise in temperature of ice water.

> *How does exposure to sunlight affect the temperature of ice water?*

STEP 2 State a hypothesis.

A hypothesis is one possible explanation of an observed phenomenon. When you propose a hypothesis, you are predicting the answer to the question you have asked. The hypothesis is often stated as an "if ... then" statement. To be useful, a hypothesis must be testable. A testable hypothesis will predict observable and/or measurable changes in one variable as a result of modifications to the manipulated variable. A hypothesis about the effect of sunlight on ice water could be

> *If ice water is exposed to sunlight, then its temperature will increase over time at a greater rate than it would if the ice water was kept in the shade.*

Step 1: Ask a question.
- Formulate a question about a scientific problem or issue.

Step 2: State a hypothesis.
- A hypothesis is a reasonable answer to the question.

Step 3: Design the experiment.
- Identify the variables.
- Write a design statement.
- Write a procedure that describes how to test the hypothesis by manipulating one variable.
- Identify and prepare for any safety hazards.
- Select appropriate instruments and equipment.

Step 4: Carry out the procedure.
- Carry out the procedure, ensuring that only one variable is changed at a time.
- Use suitable tools and materials appropriately and safely.
- Work as a team to address problems.

Step 5: Collect and record data.
- Observe and record the necessary data.

Step 6: Analyze and interpret the data.
- Determine the relationships between the variables. When possible, use tools such as graphing or mathematical calculations.
- Compare experimental and theoretical values, and account for any differences.
- Identify sources of error.

Step 7: State your conclusions.
- State whether the hypothesis is accepted, based on the interpretation of the results.
- Identify new questions or problems.

The hypothesis clearly states what will be tested (the rate of temperature change of ice water in sunlight versus in shade). It also must relate the cause (exposure to sunlight) to only one effect (increase in temperature over time). A hypothesis may also predict that the manipulated variable will not affect the responding variable. This would be a null hypothesis, which is a hypothesis that states there is not a relationship between the variables being tested. Since the experiment will be designed to test the hypothesis, it does not matter if the hypothesis is accurate or not. However, it should be a reasonable prediction of the expected results of the experiment.

STEP 3 Design the experiment.

An experiment is a set of changes made by an experimenter and/or specific observations that test a hypothesis. When designing an experiment, the first step is to identify all the variables that could affect the outcome of the experiment. For example, the following variables could affect the outcome of an experiment to find the effect of sunlight on ice water: exposure to sunlight, the length of time of exposure, the volume of the ice water, the proportion of ice to water, the length of time over which observations are made, the type of container in which the ice water is held, and the starting temperature of the ice water.

Once all the variables are identified, the next step is to decide which variable will be changed, which ones will remain the same, and which variable will be measured or observed in order to test the hypothesis. A manipulated variable is a condition that is deliberately changed by the experimenter. A controlled variable is a condition that could change during an experiment but does not, because of the actions of the experimenter. A responding variable is a condition that changes in response to the change in the manipulated variable. When a cause-and-effect question is being investigated, the responding variable corresponds to the effect predicted in the hypothesis.

> *Manipulated variable: exposure to sunlight*
>
> *Controlled variables: the volume of the ice water, the proportion of ice to water, the type of container in which the ice water is held, and the starting temperature of the ice water*
>
> *Responding variable: the temperature of the ice water*

Variables in an experiment may also be independent or dependent variables. An independent variable is any variable that influences the effect being studied, but is not itself affected by the experimental conditions. For example, time is the independent variable in this experiment. A dependent variable is any variable that is influenced by changes in the independent variable, under the conditions of the experiment. The dependent variable is therefore the same as the responding variable.

> *Independent variable: time*
> *Dependent variable: the temperature of the ice water*

Once all the variables have been identified, write a design statement for the experiment. The design statement outlines the general plan for testing the hypothesis and identifies all variables. It also identifies the conditions of the experimental control. An experimental control is a set-up that includes all the conditions of the experiment, except that the manipulated variable is not changed. In this example of the ice water experiment, the beaker that is left in the shade (is not exposed to sunlight) is the experimental control.

Design Statement

Identical volumes of ice water will be placed in two different locations, one of which will be in the sunlight, and the other in the shade. The temperature of both ice water samples will be recorded every 2 min. Exposure to sunlight is the manipulated variable, and the temperature of the ice water is the responding variable. The ice water that is left in the shade will be the experimental control. Controlled variables are the volume of ice water, the proportion of ice to water, the type of container used, and the starting temperature of the ice water. Time is the independent variable, and the temperature of the ice water is the dependent variable.

The procedure of an experiment describes how the manipulated variable will be changed, how the controlled variables will be kept unchanged, and how the responding variable will be observed and recorded. A procedure is usually written as a series of numbered steps that can be easily followed.

Procedure

1. *Make a data table to record the temperature of two samples of ice water every 2 min for 10 min.*
2. *Prepare 300 mL of ice water in a 500-mL beaker, by mixing approximately equal amounts of water and crushed ice.*
3. *Measure 100 mL of ice water into each of the 250-mL beakers.*
4. *Using a thermometer, measure and record the starting temperature of each sample.*
5. *Place a stirring rod into both ice water samples. Place one sample in direct sunlight, and the other in the shade. Stir each sample throughout the procedure.*
6. *Every 2 min, measure and record the temperature.*
7. *Continue to take readings for 10 min.*

The experimental design must outline any safety hazards and how they will be handled. Refer to *Student Reference 1: Safety* for more information. The experimental design must also list all the materials and equipment that will be needed. A diagram may be used to illustrate how equipment is to be set up.

Safety

Do not use the thermometer to stir the ice water.
Be careful handling any glassware.

Materials and Equipment

crushed ice	1 100-mL graduated cylinder
500 mL water	2 thermometers
1 500-mL beaker	2 stirring rods
2 250-mL beakers	timer

STEP 4 Carry out the procedure.

Put on any protective clothing, goggles, and gloves required, and collect the necessary equipment. Carefully follow the steps of the procedure, making sure that only the manipulated variable is changed. Divide tasks among your group members.

STEP 5 Collect and record data.

As the experiment progresses, observations related to the independent variable and the responding variable must be clearly recorded. Dependent on the experiment, an observation may be based on qualitative data, which is information that does not involve measurements of amounts. For example, an experiment on the rate of photosynthesis of two aquatic plants might include qualitative data on the colour of each plant (e.g., red or green). Qualitative data should be recorded in complete sentences. Qualitative data may also be recorded as a scientific diagram. Refer to *Student Reference 8: The Compound Light Microscope*, for details on how to draw a scientific diagram.

Observations may include quantitative data, which is information that involves measurements of amounts. Quantitative data must always include the units used to make the measurements. It is often organized in a data table, clearly labelled with a title. The independent variable is listed in the first column, and the units of measurement are clearly identified. The responding variable is listed in the next column. The data table below shows how one student recorded the quantitative data for the ice water experiment.

Observations

Temperature of Ice Water Samples over Time

Time (min)	Temperature (°C)	
	Beaker 1 (sunlight)	Beaker 2 (shade)
0.0	0.0	0.0
2.0	0.0	0.0
4.0	0.5	0.0
6.0	2.4	0.5
8.0	6.3	0.5
10.0	10.8	1.0

All quantitative measurements must be recorded to the correct number of significant digits. You can find more information about this in *Student Reference 5: Measurement*. An experimenter should also note any unusual or unforeseen events that occur during the course of the experiment. For example, if a thermometer breaks and you have to change thermometers, you must record this fact.

STEP 6 Analyze and interpret the data.

There are many ways of analyzing data. For example, you might compare an experimental (empirical) value to a theoretical (calculated or accepted) value and calculate the percent error. You can find more information about percent error in *Student Reference 6: Math Skills*. A common way of analyzing quantitative data is to create a graph. For example, the difference in the rate of temperature change can be seen more clearly in a scatterplot or line graph. *Student Reference 7: Graphing* provides details on drawing and interpreting graphs.

Analysis

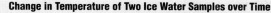
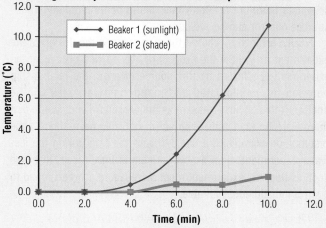

Change in Temperature of Two Ice Water Samples over Time

From the graph of the temperature data, it can be seen that after about 4 min, the temperature of a sample of ice water exposed to sunlight was always greater than that of an identical sample kept in the shade. The temperatures of both samples increased over the course of the experiment, but the temperature changed more in the ice water exposed to sunlight. The relationship between temperature and time was non-linear for both samples.

Sources of Error

Analysis of the results must also include the sources of error. One source of error is the variation that always occurs when an experiment is repeated, even though the experimenter follows a well-designed procedure carefully and works with properly functioning equipment. This error is mainly due to the limits in the precision (reproducibility) of the particular instrument used to take the measurements and in its readability. More information about precision and readability of instruments can be found in *Student Reference 5: Measurement*. Scientists always repeat an experiment several times, which helps to reduce the effect of this source of error. In the science classroom, you may not always be able to repeat your experiment. However, you can get a sense of the accuracy of your results by comparing your data with those of your classmates, or with theoretical values.

Another source of error can occur when a measuring instrument has not been properly calibrated. Calibration is the process of comparing the measurements given by the instrument against known standards, and ensuring that the two values match. If an instrument is not properly calibrated, the measurements taken with that instrument will always contain an error. Professional scientists therefore calibrate their instruments regularly. These sources of error can be avoided.

Finally, error may result if there is a flaw in the design of the experiment or in how the procedure was carried out. When an experiment is affected by this source of error, the relationship between the manipulated and responding variables will be unclear. If this occurs, re-examine the procedure and ensure that there were no unidentified variables that may have affected the results. For example, if a cloud covers the Sun during the ice-water experiment, then a new variable is introduced. In cases such as this, the experiment must be repeated, or redesigned to control the additional variable.

The sources of error in this experiment include the readability and precision of the thermometer, the graduated cylinder, and the timer used to make measurements. Between 3 min and 4 min, a cloud covered the Sun, which introduced an uncontrolled variable during this period.

STEP 7 State your conclusions.

The conclusion of an experiment states whether the hypothesis is accepted, based on the interpretation of the results. After the conclusion, outline any unresolved questions or new problems that could be investigated, based on these results.

Conclusion

These data support the hypothesis that if ice water is exposed to sunlight, then its temperature will increase more quickly than when ice water is kept in the shade. Based on this experiment, it would be interesting to test if the rate of temperature change varies according to the amount of thermal energy added to the ice water.

You may be required to communicate the results of your experiment in a lab report. Refer to *Student Reference 11: Writing Reports*, for additional information.

Student Reference 3: The Problem-Solving Process

Technology is the application of scientific knowledge to solve practical problems. For example, a pair of scissors is a piece of technology that uses scientific knowledge about wedges and levers to solve the practical problem of making clean cuts in certain substances. Developing a technology to solve a problem follows a series of general steps.

STEP 1 Recognize a practical need.

This step involves recognizing a practical need that can be addressed by a technological solution. For example, say you are about to go on a camping trip. The park service has issued an extreme fire hazard warning, so campfires are not allowed. You have to walk to the camping area, so you cannot carry in water. The need in this situation is that you must purify lake water so that it is safe to drink.

STEP 2 Identify the specific problem to be solved.

When you understand the situation, you can then restate the problem in terms of a specific task. Campers can usually purify lake water by boiling it over a campfire. In this situation, however, the problem is how to purify water without using a campfire. The task is to construct a device that will purify water by some other means.

STEP 3 Identify criteria for a successful solution to a problem.

Assessment criteria are a set of conditions that will tell you when and if you have solved the problem successfully. Establish these before you carry out any in-depth research, planning, or analysis of the problem. When you are setting criteria for success, you must consider limits to your possible solutions. Limits may include cost, time, safety, social implications, environmental impact, and feasibility. For a school assignment, the criteria may be set by you or your teacher.

For example, the criteria for the device in the water purification example would include: it will remove all harmful micro-organisms, it will not require a campfire, and it will be made of materials that can be carried into or found at a remote campsite.

STEP 4 Generate a list of potential solutions.

Brainstorming and/or conducting research are key components of this step. Brainstorming involves generating as many ideas as possible without judging them. Record your ideas clearly.

Step 1: Recognize a practical need.

Step 2: Identify the specific problem to be solved.
- Identify a particular task that would address the need.

Step 3: Identify criteria for a successful solution to a problem.
- Define the particular standards that need to be met in order to solve the problem.

Step 4: Generate a list of potential solutions.
- Come up with as many possible solutions as you can.

Step 5: Compile and organize the information.
- Gather information on all the possible solutions, and organize it clearly.

Step 6: Assess the potential solutions.
- Consider the strengths and weaknesses of each solution, and choose one to develop further.

Step 7: Plan and construct a working model or prototype for the chosen solution.
- Make diagrams to scale, troubleshoot if necessary, and then construct your model or prototype.

Step 8: Test, evaluate, and modify (if necessary) the model or prototype.
- Test your model to see if it meets the criteria for a successful solution. If not, modify your model or prototype until it meets all the criteria.

Step 9: Communicate the procedure and results of your design.
- Choose an effective format to communicate the problem you worked on, why you chose the solution you did, and how it meets the criteria for solving the problem.

Here are some of the ideas that one group of students came up with for solving the problem of purifying water without a campfire:

- a device that converts solar energy to thermal energy
- a device that converts the chemical energy in candles to thermal energy
- a device that filters out micro-organisms

STEP 5 Compile and organize the information.

Conduct research to collect information on each idea. You might need to use library and electronic research tools, interview experts, or visit business sites. Generate a list of materials and equipment needed for each solution.

As you collect the information you need, organize it in a form that allows you to clearly see any links or gaps in your information. Continue your research until you can no longer identify any gaps. Refer to *Student Reference 9: Researching Information* for more details on finding and organizing information.

STEP 6 Assess the potential solutions.

You will now need to use the information you have found to choose one idea to develop further. Decide on a method for analyzing the information you have collected. Graphic organizers can be very helpful for sorting information. *Student Reference 10: Tools for Analyzing Information* provides a number of examples you may find useful. Each of these tools can be modified to fit the specific information you are analyzing.

Based on your analysis, assess the potential strengths and weaknesses for each possible solution. Determine whether you can get all the necessary materials and equipment for each solution. If cost is part of the criteria for your potential solution, then calculate the cost of each idea as well. Finally, choose one possible solution that you think is most likely to meet all the criteria.

STEP 7 Plan and construct a working model or prototype for the chosen solution.

Start a plan for a working model or prototype for the solution you have chosen. You will likely need to create a working diagram on paper or using computer software. You may need to make several diagrams as you identify and solve problems in the design. This allows you to explore and troubleshoot your ideas early on. Your diagram should include detailed labels and a scale, similar to a blueprint. Have your teacher approve your plans before you build your model.

Models are useful for presenting a three-dimensional view and for testing the operation of the design. Your design may need to be modified at any step before the final model is constructed.

STEP 8 Test, evaluate, and modify (if necessary) the model or prototype.

Testing allows you to check how your solution works. If you find a problem during testing, you can then make modifications to your design and test the model or prototype again. Invite your classmates and your teacher to try your design. Their feedback can help you identify things that could be improved, and they may be able to offer some ideas of their own.

Finally, make sure you return to your original list of criteria for solving the problem. Check your model or prototype against the list, and make sure you have truly met your original goals.

STEP 9 Communicate the procedure and results of your design.

Choose an appropriate way to clearly communicate the problem, why you chose the solution you did, all the details of building and testing your model or prototype, and how well your solution meets the criteria for solving the problem. Possible choices include presenting your model or solution as a display, making an oral presentation that includes a demonstration of your model, or writing a report. *Student Reference 11: Writing Reports* provides more details about preparing a report.

Student Reference 4: The Decision-Making Process

Making good decisions involves gathering relevant information, considering the information, and then making a choice based on that information. In many decisions you will make, some of this information will involve scientific knowledge. Many decisions will also require consideration of the potential impact of your decision on other people or events, and that you balance your views with the perspectives of others. Decision-making can be organized into a series of steps, as shown in the flowchart on this page.

STEP 1 Define the practical problem or issue.

A practical problem is a real-world difficulty that requires action. An issue is a controversy that needs to be resolved. The first step in the decision-making process is to identify questions that arise from practical problems or issues. Based on these questions, make a clear statement that defines the problem or issue. In the example below, an issue is defined first by a question and then a statement.

Should the City of Calgary build a waste disposal site to the west of the city, near the Kananaskis Valley?

The City of Calgary is proposing that a waste disposal site be located close to the Kananaskis Valley.

STEP 2 Identify the viewpoints.

To make an informed decision, you must identify and describe all the related viewpoints. These can be scientific, technological, social, or economic. Consider the issue from the perspective of different stakeholders as well. Stakeholders are people who are affected in some way by the issue or practical problem. Viewpoints that may be considered include:

- Scientific—scientific facts and theories
- Ecological—protection of the natural environment
- Technological—design and use of technology
- Health and safety—well-being of people
- Social—human relationships, public welfare, or society
- Cultural—customs of a particular group of people
- Educational—sharing and acquiring new skills
- Ethical—beliefs about what is right and wrong
- Aesthetic—beauty in art and nature
- Historical—knowledge dealing with past events
- Recreational—leisure activities
- Political—effects of the issue on government policies
- Economic—financial and business issues

Step 1: Define the practical problem or issue.
- Ask a question about a practical problem or issue.

Step 2: Identify the viewpoints.
- List the major points that need to be considered, including who in society will be affected by the decision.

Step 3: Conduct research.
- Find information related to the major points and record it clearly.

Step 4: Analyze the information.
- Assess the information, including any limitations of data or bias in interpretation. Weigh the costs and benefits of all potential courses of action or decisions.

Step 5: Propose a course of action or a decision, and justify your choice.
- Suggest one course of action to solve the problem, or come to a decision about the issue. Use the results of your research to justify your choice.

Step 6: Communicate your decision.
- Share your decision with others, and be able to defend that decision with the information you researched.

The following example outlines some of the viewpoints that a student identified concerning the waste disposal issue:

- *Environmentalists may object to a waste disposal site on the grounds that it could have a negative impact on the ecology of the Kananaskis Valley.*
- *Business leaders may consider this proposed project to be an advantage for their businesses, since they could be involved in supplying the site with materials needed for its construction and operation.*

STEP 3 Conduct research.

Conducting research involves activities such as using library and electronic research tools, interviewing people, and taking a field trip. The aim is to get as much information as possible on each of the viewpoints you identified in Step 2. It is important to evaluate your sources of information to determine if there is a bias, and to separate fact from opinion.

Make sure you keep a record of the resources you use and the information you found in each. *Student Reference 9: Researching Information* provides additional guidance on finding and recording information and information sources.

STEP 4 Analyze the information.

Decide on a method for analyzing the information you have collected. Graphic organizers can be very helpful for sorting information. *Student Reference 10: Tools for Analyzing Information* provides a number of examples you may find useful. Each of these tools can be modified to fit the specific information and issue you are analyzing.

In the example here, the student ranked each potential consequence by its importance. Each was given a number to designate the ranking: high (3), moderate (2), low (1), or none (0). Each consequence was then designated either negative (a cost) or positive (a benefit).

Cost/Benefit Analysis of Proposed Waste Disposal Site

Potential Consequence	Importance (3,2,1,0)	Cost or Benefit?
ecosystems destroyed	2	cost
run-off	3	cost
residents affected by traffic	2	cost
disposal site well used	3	benefit
economic opportunities from construction and operation	2 to 1	benefit

STEP 5 Propose a course of action or a decision, and justify your choice.

Based on your analysis, make a decision on the issue or propose a solution to the practical problem that you believe will have the most positive and the least negative consequences. Ensure you have considered the viewpoints of all the stakeholders. (In some cases in *Addison Wesley Science 10,* you will be asked to consider the viewpoint of only one type of stakeholder.)

When proposing your course of action or decision, refer to any facts and figures you found during your research. For example, here is part of what one group of students considered in proposing a course of action regarding the waste disposal site:

Building a waste disposal site near to the Kananaskis Valley would likely cause environmental harm, and would therefore have a great deal of opposition. Instead of going ahead with this site, a study should be conducted to determine the effects of locating the waste disposal site to the east of the city.

STEP 6 Communicate your decision.

Choose an appropriate way to communicate the issue, the decision or proposal you made, and your justification. Possible choices include participating in a debate, writing a letter to a newspaper, creating a poster or Web page, or writing a report. *Student Reference 11: Writing Reports* provides more details about preparing a written report.

Student Reference 5: Measurement

Scientific investigations may involve collection of measured quantities, or quantitative data. A measurement always consists of a number and a unit. The unit tells us what is being measured.

The International System of Units

To communicate clearly, scientists use a system of units called SI (short for Système International d'Unités). SI has seven base units (Table 5.1)

TABLE 5.1 Base Units of SI

Quantity	Unit Name	Symbol
length	metre	m
mass	kilogram	kg
time	second	s
temperature	kelvin	K
electric current	ampere	A
luminous intensity	candela	cd
amount of substance	mole	mol

Derived units are units that are combinations of the base units. Table 5.2 lists four derived units that you will encounter during your Grade 10 studies.

TABLE 5.2 Derived SI Units

Quantity	Unit Name	Symbol	Definition
volume	cubic metre	m^3	$m^3 = m \cdot m \cdot m$
pressure	pascal	Pa	$Pa = kg/m \cdot s^2$
force	newton	N	$N = kg \cdot m/s^2$
energy	joule	J	$J = kg \cdot m^2/s^2$

For very large or very small quantities, all SI units are modified by decimal divisions, following the conventions of the metric system. The particular division used is indicated by adding a prefix to the base unit or derived unit. Some prefixes and their symbols are shown in Table 5.3.

TABLE 5.3 Common SI Prefixes

Prefix	Symbol	Value	Scientific Notation
giga-	G	1 000 000 000	10^9
mega-	M	1 000 000	10^6
kilo-	k	1000	10^3
hecto-	h	100	10^2
deka-	da	10	10^1
deci-	d	0.1	10^{-1}
centi-	c	0.01	10^{-2}
milli-	m	0.001	10^{-3}
micro-	μ	0.000 001	10^{-6}
nano-	n	0.000 000 001	10^{-9}
pico-	p	0.000 000 000 001	10^{-12}

Non-SI Units

Some non-SI units are commonly used along with SI units in science. Non-SI units that you may see in your Grade 10 studies are shown in Table 5.4.

TABLE 5.4 Non-SI Units

Quantity	Unit Name	Symbol	Definition
time	minute	min	1 min = 60 s
	hour	h	1 h = 3600 s
	day	d	1 d = 86 400 s
	year	y	1 y = 31 557 600 s
area	hectare	ha	1 ha = 10 000 m^2
volume	litre	L	1 L = 1000 cm^3
mass	metric ton or tonne	t	1 t = 1000 kg
temperature	degree Celsius	°C	0°C = 273.5 K

Measurement and Accuracy

Whenever you take a measurement, you are making an estimate. There is always an amount of uncertainty in measured values. In contrast, counted and defined values are exact numbers, and so have no uncertainty. For example, 32 students in a classroom is a counted number, and a length of 1 m is defined as exactly equal to 100 cm. There is no estimation in these values, and so no uncertainty.

Accuracy is the difference between a measurement and its true value. No matter how carefully you work, there will be a difference between a quantity you measure and its true value. The accuracy of any measurement is affected by the precision of the measurement. Precision refers to the degree of agreement among repeated measurements of the sample (the reproducibility). Precision is determined by your actions; how carefully you take measurements and control the variables in your experiment. Figure 5.1 illustrates the differences between precision and accuracy, using the example of a darts game.

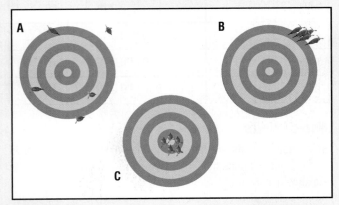

FIGURE 5.1 In this illustration, the centre of the dartboard is the true value of the measurement. Player A was neither precise nor accurate; the positions of the shots all differed and none hit the centre. Player B was precise but not accurate; all the darts hit the same area of the target, but they all were off the centre. Player C was both precise and accurate; all the darts are close to one another and in the centre of the target.

The accuracy of a measurement may be increased by carefully repeating it several times. When you repeat a measurement, you make another estimation of the true value of the quantity. Scientists often report an average (mean) of repeated measurements, since the average will usually be more accurate than only one measurement. However, it is possible to make reproducible measurements that are not accurate, as shown by Player B in Figure 5.1.

Choosing an appropriate instrument can also affect the accuracy of a measurement. All measuring instruments are limited by their readability and by their internal precision. Readability is the smallest fraction of a division on the scale of an instrument that can be read with ease, using estimation. Readability is affected by the size of the divisions on the scale, and is usually considered to be half of the smallest division.

For example, Figure 5.2 shows two rulers. Ruler A has only centimetre divisions, whereas ruler B has millimetre divisions. When ruler A is used to measure, you can see only that the length of the eraser is between the 2 cm and 3 cm marks. Using ruler A, you can therefore estimate the length to be 2.5 cm, but you know that the true value may be anywhere between 2.0 cm and 3.0 cm. If you use ruler B instead, you can see that the length of the eraser is between 2.3 cm and 2.4 cm. You can therefore estimate the length to be 2.35 cm using ruler B, and the true value of the measurement can be anywhere between 2.3 and 2.4 cm.

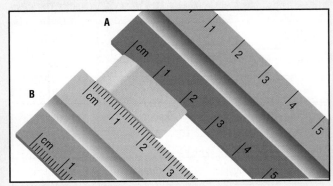

FIGURE 5.2 Which of these two rulers has a readability that would allow you to estimate a measurement of 2.35 cm for the length of the eraser?

Each measuring instrument has a certain internal precision. The precision of an instrument is the degree of agreement among repeated measurements of a single sample using that instrument. For example, a digital thermometer may be precise to within 0.2°C. This means if the thermometer reads 1.0°C, the true temperature of the substance could be anywhere between 0.8°C and 1.2°C.

Significant Digits

Significant digits are the specific number of digits used to communicate the degree of uncertainty in a measurement. The last digit indicates the uncertain (or estimated) digit. The measurement of 2.5 cm for the eraser taken with ruler A above has two significant digits, but the measurement of 2.35 cm taken using ruler B has three significant digits. When a measurement is on a division on a scale, indicate it by including a zero. For example, a length on the 3 cm mark would be recorded as 3.0 cm (two significant digits) on ruler A, and as 3.00 cm (three significant digits) on ruler B.

Student Reference 6: Math Skills

Solving problems related to science often requires you to apply math skills. In the inquiry process, math skills may be needed to analyze quantitative observations. In the problem-solving process, math skills may be needed to calculate scale or determine a budget. In the decision-making process, math skills may be needed to assess the arguments made for two sides of an issue.

Calculations with Significant Digits

Recall that significant digits are used to communicate the degree of uncertainty of a measurement. The last number in a measurement is always the digit that was estimated. When performing calculations with measured values, it is important that the uncertainty of the final result is also communicated correctly. This is done by using rules to count the number of significant digits in each number in the calculation, and to determine the correct number of significant digits in the final answer.

Rules for Counting Significant Digits

1. The *digits 1 to 9* are always significant. For example, all of the following examples have 3 significant digits: 321, 0.321, 0.000 032 1, 3.21×10^3, and 3.21.
2. The position of zeros in a number determines whether or not they count as significant digits.
   - *Leading zeros* are not significant. For example, both 0.321 and 0.003 21 have 3 significant digits.
   - All *trailing zeros* are assumed to be significant. For example, the following examples all have 3 significant digits: 500, 5.00, 0.500, and 5.00×10^3.
   - *Zeros positioned between the digits 1 to 9* are significant on either side of the decimal point. For example, 203 has 3 significant digits, 1.905 has 4 significant digits, and 100.746 has 6 significant digits.
3. For *logarithmic values*, such as pH, any digits to the left of the decimal are not significant. For example, a pH of 2.3 has only 1 significant digit, and a pH of 10 has no significant digits.
4. All digits in *exact numbers* are considered to have an infinite number of significant digits. These include counted values (7 oranges) and defined values, such as the 1 and 1000 in the statement "1 kg is 1000 g."

Rules for Performing Mathematical Operations

The number of significant digits in a calculated value can never be greater than the number of significant digits in the original data. In many cases, this requires that the final answer be rounded off to the correct number of significant digits. Note that calculators do not apply the guidelines for significant digits, so you must always determine the correct number of significant digits yourself after using a calculator.

- When the first digit to be dropped is less than or equal to 4, the preceding digit is not changed. For example, 7.4345 is rounded to 7.43, giving 3 significant digits.
- When the first digit to be dropped is greater than or equal to 5, the preceding digit is increased by one. For example, 7.4355 is rounded to 7.44, giving 3 significant digits.

1. When *adding* or *subtracting*, the calculated result has the same number of decimal places as the number with the least number of decimal places in the original data.

Example 6.1

Perform the following addition, and express the answer using the correct number of significant digits.

$$
\begin{aligned}
x &= 2.2 \text{ kg} + 8.267 \text{ kg} + 12.32 \text{ kg} \\
&= 22.787 \text{ kg} \\
&= 22.8 \text{ kg}
\end{aligned}
$$

Since 2.2 has only one decimal place, the final answer using the correct number of significant digits is 22.8 kg.

2. When *multiplying or dividing*, the calculated answer should be rounded to the least number of significant digits of the data values.

Example 6.2

Perform the following multiplication, and express the answer using the correct number of significant digits.

$$
\begin{aligned}
x &= (3.87 \text{ cm})(0.050 \text{ cm})(208 \text{ cm}) \\
&= 40.248 \text{ cm}^3 \\
&= 40 \text{ cm}^3
\end{aligned}
$$

Since 0.050 has only 2 significant digits, the final answer must be rounded off to 40 cm^3.

3. If you must perform *more than one mathematical operation* to get the final answer, carry all digits through to the final result, without any rounding. The final answer should then be rounded to the same number of significant digits as the quantity in the original data with the fewest number of significant digits.

Example 6.3

Perform the following calculation, and express the answer using the correct number of significant digits.

$$
\begin{aligned}
x &= (5.2542 \text{ m}) \div (4.56 \text{ s} - 2.31 \text{ s}) \\
&= 5.2542 \text{ m} \div 2.25 \text{ s} \\
&= 2.3352 \text{ m/s} \\
&= 2.34 \text{ m/s}
\end{aligned}
$$

Since 4.56 s and 2.31 s each have only 3 significant digits, the final answer must be rounded off to 2.34 m/s.

Scientific Notation

Scientists worldwide use the metric system to record observations. Here in Canada, we use the metric system in everyday life as well. Each place value in the metric system is based on units of 10. When a numeral contains a decimal point, the place values to the left of the decimal point increase by an order of 10, and the place values to the right decrease by an order of 10. For example, the numeral 111.11 represents 1 unit of 100, 1 unit of 10, 1 unit of 1, one unit of $\frac{1}{10}$, and 1 unit of $\frac{1}{100}$.

To write very large or very small numbers using the metric system, digits are separated into groups of 3 by spaces (not commas). For example, three million is written as 3 000 000, and $\frac{1\ 234\ 567}{10\ 000\ 000}$ is written as 0.123 456 7.

Note that a zero is always included before the decimal point for numbers less than 1. However, spaces are not used when a number contains only four digits before or after the decimal point (e.g., 6500 or 0.1234). As you can see, writing very large and very small numbers can become cumbersome. Very large or very small numbers are therefore often written using scientific notation.

In scientific notation, numbers are written with only one digit before the decimal point, and then multiplied by a power of 10. The power is a superscript to the base 10, which is called an exponent. For example, the speed of light is 299 792 458 m/s. In scientific notation, this number is written as 2.997 924 58 x 10^8 m/s. Numbers that are less than 1 are written using negative exponents. For example, the mass of a proton is 0.000 000 000 000 000 000 000 017 g; in scientific notation, this number is written as 1.7 x 10^{-24} g.

Example 6.4

The scientist Avogadro deduced that there are always 602 000 000 000 000 000 000 000 particles in 1 mol of a substance. Express Avogadro's number in scientific notation to 3 significant digits.

In scientific notation, there must be only 1 digit before the decimal place. Therefore, you need to move the decimal place over, and then multiply by 10 to the correct power to give the original number, expressed as an exponent.

Avogadro's number
= 602 000 000 000 000 000 000 000 particles/mol
= 6.02 × 100 000 000 000 000 000 000 000 particles/mol
= 6.02 × 10^{23} particles/mol

Avogadro's number in scientific notation to 3 significant digits is 6.02 x 10^{23} particles/mol.

Rules for Calculations Using Scientific Notation

Whenever a quantitative measurement is recorded, it must be written with the correct number of significant digits. Scientific notation allows you to clearly indicate the number of significant digits. When performing a calculation with numbers written in scientific notation, you must use the following mathematical rules for working with exponents. You must also remember to apply the guidelines for determining the correct number of significant digits in the final answer. The exponent of a number in scientific notation does not affect the number of significant digits.

1. To *add or subtract* numbers in scientific notation, the numbers must first be written so that they have the same exponents. The coefficients may then be added like any integer. The exponent in the final answer remains the same.

Example 6.5

Perform the following addition, and express the final answer using the correct number of significant digits.

$$
\begin{aligned}
x &= (5.4 \times 10^3 \text{ mol}) + (6.82 \times 10^2 \text{ mol}) \\
&= (5.4 \times 10^3 \text{ mol}) + (0.682 \times 10^3 \text{ mol}) \\
&= 6.082 \times 10^3 \text{ mol} \\
&= 6.1 \times 10^3 \text{ mol}
\end{aligned}
$$

Since this is an addition calculation, the number of significant digits in the final answer is determined by the number in the original data with the least number of decimal places. In this case, this is one decimal place in the number 5.4. The final answer therefore must be rounded to one decimal place, or 6.1×10^3 mol.

2. To *multiply* numbers that are written in scientific notation, the coefficients are multiplied first, and then the exponents are added.

Example 6.6

Perform the following multiplication, and express the final answer using the correct number of significant digits.

$$x = (6.02 \times 10^{23} \text{ atoms/mol})(3.2 \times 10^{24} \text{ mol})$$
$$= (6.02 \times 3.2) \times 10^{23+24} \text{ atoms}$$
$$= 19.264 \times 10^{47} \text{ atoms}$$
$$= 1.9 \times 10^{48} \text{ atoms}$$

This is a multiplication, so the number of significant digits in the final answer is determined by the smallest number of significant digits in the original data. In this case, there are 2 significant digits in the number 3.2 x 10^{24}. The final answer therefore must be rounded to 2 significant digits, or 1.9 x 10^{48} atoms.

3. To *divide* numbers written in scientific notation, the coefficients are first divided, and then the exponent of the divisor is subtracted from the exponent of the number being divided.

Example 6.7

Perform the following division, and express the final answer using the correct number of significant digits.

$$x = (6.5 \times 10^7 \text{ g}) \div (3.41 \times 10^5 \text{ L})$$
$$= (6.5 \div 3.41) \times 10^{7-5} \text{ g/L}$$
$$= 1.9061583 \times 10^2 \text{ g/L}$$
$$= 1.9 \times 10^2 \text{ g/L}$$

Since this is a division, the number of significant digits in the final answer is determined by the smallest number of significant digits in the original data. In this case, there are 2 significant digits in the number 6.5 x 10^7. The final answer therefore must be rounded to 2 significant digits, or 1.9 x 10^2 g/L.

Percents

A percent is an expression of a quantity in terms of hundredths. Percents can be calculated from any ratio of quantities by conversion to an equivalent ratio with a denominator of 100.

$$\text{percent} = \frac{\text{quantity}}{\text{total}} \times 100\%$$

Example 6.8

If you receive a score of 38 correct answers on an examination containing 40 questions, what percent of the questions did you get correct?

The ratio of correct answers to total questions can be written:

$$\frac{38}{40} = \frac{x}{100}$$

Rearranging the equation to solve for x, we get:

$$x = \frac{38 \times 100}{40}$$
$$= 95$$

Therefore, the percent of questions you got correct is $\frac{95}{100}$, or 95%.

When percents are calculated from measured quantities they must also be expressed using the correct number of significant digits, by applying the rules for calculations with significant digits.

Example 6.9

The incoming radiation to Medicine Hat on November 6, 2002 was reported as follows: 6.3% was reflected back to space, 27.9% was reflected by cloud cover, 8.9% was reflected by Earth's surface, 12.5% was absorbed by greenhouse gases, 4.7% was absorbed by clouds, and 39.7% was absorbed by Earth's surface. What is the total percent of incoming radiation that was absorbed?

Absorbed radiation includes the following: 12.5% absorbed by greenhouse gases, 4.7% absorbed by clouds, and 39.7% absorbed by Earth's surface.

$$\text{Percent absorbed} = 12.5\% + 4.7\% + 39.7\%$$
$$= 56.9\%$$

Since this is an addition, the number of significant digits in the final answer is rounded to the lowest number of decimal places in the original data. Therefore, the total percent of incoming radiation that was absorbed is 56.9%.

Percent Error

In some experiments, the results are compared with a theoretical value, which may be either a value computed for the experiment (such as the theoretical efficiency of an engine) or a standard value (such as the theoretical specific heat capacity of a substance). Percent error communicates the difference between an experimental value and the theoretical value. Percent error is the result of all the following: experimental error (variability between trials of an experiment); readability and precision of instruments; whether all instruments are functioning properly; and whether the experimenter has made any mistakes during the procedure.

Percent error is calculated using the following formula:

$$\text{percent error} = \left| \frac{\text{experimental value} - \text{theoretical value}}{\text{theoretical value}} \right| \times 100\%$$

Example 6.10

A student conducted an experiment to determine the specific heat capacity of iron. The experimental value was 0.51 J/g·°C. The theoretical value is 0.449 J/g·°C. Calculate the percent error.

$$\text{percent error} = \left| \frac{\text{experimental value} - \text{theoretical value}}{\text{theoretical value}} \right| \times 100\%$$

$$= \left| \frac{0.51 \text{ J/g·°C} - 0.449 \text{ J/g·°C}}{0.449 \text{ J/g·°C}} \right| \times 100\%$$

$$= 13.6\%$$

$$= 14\%$$

The percent error of the experimental value for the specific heat capacity of iron is 14%.

Problem-Solving Strategies

Analyzing scientific data often involves mathematical equations. All the variables that describe quantities in mathematical equations have units. Therefore, when working with equations in science, you must do two things: solve for the appropriate variables in the equation, and determine the units of the final answer.

The following steps will help you determine the variable you need to solve for and ensure that the final answer is expressed in the appropriate units.

1. Analyze the problem.
   - Read the entire problem carefully.
   - Identify and list all the given variables in the problem (those for which numerical values are given), including their units.
   - Identify the required variable (the value that needs to be calculated). This variable will be the one variable that is not on your list of given variables.
   - Write down the equation that contains all the variables and that can be used to solve the problem.
2. Use the appropriate conversion factors to make any necessary changes in the units of quantities in the problem, using unit analysis to check that your conversion is correct.
   - Determine the units in which the required variable must be expressed. Check that all the given variables are expressed in units that will allow you to compute the required value in the correct units.
   - If necessary, convert the units of any variable to the appropriate units needed to solve the equation using conversion factors.
3. Solve the equation for the required variable.
   - If necessary, isolate the required variable using formula manipulation. Formula manipulation rearranges the equation into a form that allows you to solve for the required variable.
   - Enter all the given variables in the equation, including their units.
   - Perform the calculations, using unit analysis to cancel out repeated units.
4. Evaluate your answer.
   - Does the final result make sense? If not, recheck your work.
5. Write a statement to answer the question posed in the original problem.

Conversion Factors and Unit Analysis

Suppose you are given a volume in millilitres and need to convert the units of this volume to litres. You can convert between these units by using a conversion factor. A conversion factor is a ratio that relates two quantities expressed in different units when the quantities are of the same attribute (for example, volume). It is the ratio of the required unit to the given unit.

For example, to determine the conversion factor (ratio) of millilitres (the given unit) to litres (the required unit), first determine how many litres are in 1 mL. Recall the relationship between the given unit and the required unit. In this case, 1000 mL are equal to 1 L.

$$1000 \text{ mL} = 1 \text{ L}$$

Then divide both sides of the equation by the appropriate amount to get 1 of the given units on one side of the equation (in this case, 1 mL).

$$\frac{1000 \text{ mL}}{1000 \text{ mL}} = \frac{1 \text{ L}}{1000 \text{ mL}}$$

$$1 \text{ mL} = \frac{1 \text{ L}}{1000 \text{ mL}}$$

Note that multiplying by a conversion factor does not change the value of the measurement, only its unit. Unit analysis (also called dimensional analysis) is a tool for keeping track of units in a calculation, to ensure that the final answer is expressed in the correct units. The following example shows how to use conversion factors and unit analysis to express, in litres, a quantity that was given in millilitres.

Example 6.11

Express the volume 225 mL in litres.

First, write the given variable:
volume, $V = 225$ mL

Now multiply the variable by the conversion factor, and cancel out any repeated units:

$$\text{volume in litres, } V_{(L)} = V \times \frac{1 \text{ L}}{1000 \text{ mL}}$$

$$= 225 \text{ mL} \times \frac{1 \text{ L}}{1000 \text{ mL}}$$

$$= 0.255 \text{ L}$$

The volume of 225 mL is equal to 0.255 L.

Formula Manipulation

When solving a problem, you may find that the equation is not in the correct form to solve for the variable that you need. You then need to rearrange the equation so that the variable in which you are interested is the only variable on one side of the equation, and the known quantities are on the other side. To isolate a variable, you must always perform the same mathematical operation on both sides of the equation.

Example 6.12

Iron has a specific heat capacity, c, of 0.449 J/g·°C. What was the mass, m, of a piece of iron if the temperature change, Δt, was 10.0°C when 449 kJ of thermal energy, Q, were added? Use the formula $Q = mc\Delta t$.

The given variables are:
$c = 0.449$ J/g·°C,
$\Delta t = +10.0$°C,
$Q = 449$ kJ.
The required variable is mass, m.

Because c is expressed in units of J/g·°C, you must first convert Q from kJ to J. Since 1 kJ = 1000 J, the unit conversion is:

$$Q = 449 \text{ kJ}$$

$$= 449 \text{ kJ} \times \frac{1000 \text{ J}}{1 \text{ kJ}}$$

$$= 449\,000 \text{ J}$$

Next, rearrange the formula $Q = mc\Delta t$ to solve for m. You can isolate m by dividing both sides of the equation by $c\Delta t$.

$$Q = mc\Delta t$$

$$\frac{Q}{c\Delta t} = \frac{mc\Delta t}{c\Delta t}$$

$$\frac{Q}{c\Delta t} = m$$

Therefore, $m = \dfrac{Q}{c\Delta t}$

You can now substitute the given variables with their units and work out the answer. Remember to include and cancel out units at each step.

$$m = \frac{Q}{c\Delta t}$$

$$= \frac{449\,000 \text{ J}}{(0.449 \frac{\text{J}}{\text{g·°C}})(10.0\text{°C})}$$

$$= 100\,000 \text{ g}$$

$$= 1.00 \times 10^5 \text{ g}$$

$$= 100 \text{ kg}$$

The mass of iron was 100 kg.

Student Reference 7: Graphing

Data collected during an experiment is usually recorded in a data table. You can find out more about making a data table in *Student Reference 2: The Inquiry Process*. For quantitative data, analyzing the relationship between the responding and manipulated variables in an experiment can be made easier by using the data to create a graph. A graph can be thought of as a picture, or visual representation, of the data.

Circle Graphs

A circle graph is useful when you want to display data that are part of a whole. There are no manipulated or responding variables in this kind of data. For example, this circle graph (Figure 7.1) shows the percent of different gases in Earth's atmosphere. The graph is given a title that describes the information it contains, and each section of the circle is clearly labelled. Circle graphs may be drawn by hand using paper and pencil, or using technology such as a graphing calculator or spreadsheet software.

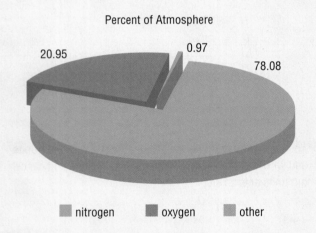

Percent of Atmosphere

20.95   0.97   78.08

■ nitrogen   ■ oxygen   ■ other

FIGURE 7.1 In this circle graph, the whole circle represents Earth's atmosphere and the parts show the percent of each specific gas.

Bar Graphs

Bar graphs are useful when you want to analyze the relationship between quantitative data in different categories. For example, Table 7.1 shows the average monthly precipitation in Jasper, Alberta. In this example, the manipulated variable is a category, a month, and the responding variable is the average precipitation. The average for each month in the table was calculated independently of the other months. The data for each month are therefore discrete (separate) from the data for all the other months. The researcher would first record the data in a table similar to the one in Table 7.1.

TABLE 7.1 Average Precipitation per Month in Jasper, Alberta from 1961 to 1990

Month	Average Precipitation (mm)
Jan	31.1
Feb	17.4
Mar	15.7
Apr	21.2
May	28.6
June	49.9
July	56.2
Aug	50.6
Sept	37.0
Oct	30.9
Nov	28.2
Dec	26.8

Data Source: Environment Canada

On a bar graph, the manipulated variable (e.g., the month) is plotted on the *x*-axis and the responding variable (e.g., the average precipitation) is plotted on the *y*-axis. The *x*-axis is the horizontal axis and the *y*-axis is the vertical axis. The maximum number on the scale of the *y*-axis is determined by the maximum value in the data set. If all the values in the data set are positive, the minimum number on the scale is usually zero. If the data set contains negative numbers, then the minimum value in the data set will be the minimum number on the *y*-axis.

Each category in the data set is drawn as a bar of equal width on the *x*-axis. The height of each bar is determined by the value of the responding variable, and it is drawn according to the scale of the *y*-axis. The graph is given a title, placed at the top of the graph, which describes the information presented. Bar graphs may be drawn by hand using paper and pencil, or using technology such as a graphing calculator or spreadsheet software. As you can see, the changes in the responding variable are a lot easier to see on the graph in Figure 7.2 than in Table 7.1.

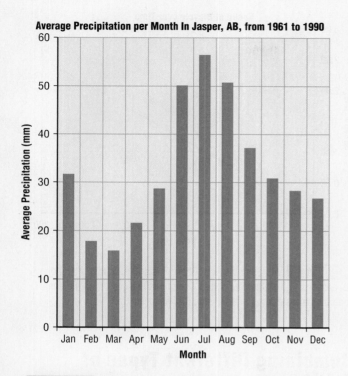

Average Precipitation per Month In Jasper, AB, from 1961 to 1990

FIGURE 7.2 It is clear that the amount of precipitation is highest from June to August and lowest from February to April from this bar graph.

Scatterplots

Scatterplots are useful for analyzing the relationship between quantitative data in which both the manipulated and responding variables continually change during an experiment. For example, if you were to measure the speed of a bicycle (fitted with a speedometer) rolling down a ramp over time, the manipulated variable (time) and responding variable (speed of the bicycle) would be continuously changing, such as in the data in Table 7.2.

TABLE 7.2 Speed of Bicycle over Time

Time t (s)	Speed v (m/s)
0	0.00
60	0.50
120	1.00
180	1.50
240	2.00
300	2.50

On a scatterplot, the manipulated variable (e.g., time) is plotted on the *x*-axis and the responding variable (e.g., speed) is plotted on the *y*-axis. Each axis must be clearly marked with a scale, which must take into account the entire range of measurements to be plotted and use up at least half the size of the graph paper used. The maximum and minimum numbers of the data determine the maximum and minimum numbers on the scales of the axes. It is not necessary for each axis to start at zero, but the axes of a scatterplot usually cross one another at the zero point.

Each piece of data in the table is then plotted by moving over to the correct position on the *x*-axis and up to the correct position on the *y*-axis. A point is placed at the intersection of these two positions. If two or more sets of data are plotted on one graph, different colours or shapes are used to plot the different data sets, and a legend is provided to explain the colours or shapes. When the scatterplot is completed, it is given a title that describes the information presented. Scatterplots may be drawn by hand using paper and pencil, or using technology such as a graphing calculator or spreadsheet software. Figure 7.3 shows a scatterplot of the data in Table 7.2.

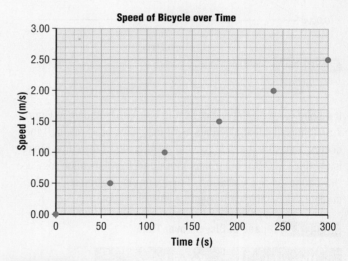

FIGURE 7.3 This scatterplot shows the relationship between the two variables, time and speed, as separate points on the graph.

Drawing the Line of Best Fit

A line of best fit drawn through the plotted data points can help an experimenter determine the relationship between variables more clearly. Scatterplots that include a line of best fit are commonly called line graphs. You can use a graphing calculator or spreadsheet software to draw a line of best fit on a scatterplot. Note that you cannot create a line of best fit by connecting or trying to draw a curve or straight line through all the data points. Figure 7.4 shows the line of best fit for the scatterplot in Figure 7.3.

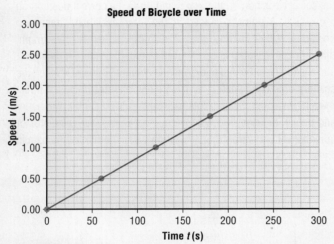

FIGURE 7.4 The line of best fit for these data goes through all the data points.

If a point is far off the line of best fit, such as is shown in Figure 7.5, it indicates that a serious error may have been made. If this occurs, measure the data for that point again. If the same result is obtained, a factor other than those under investigation may be the cause of the variation. For example, suppose another student's data table contained the entries in Table 7.3.

TABLE 7.3 Speed of Bicycle over Time

Time t (s)	Speed v (m/s)
0	0.00
60	0.50
120	0.76
180	1.83
240	2.00
300	2.50

The line of best fit for the scatterplot of these data is shown in Figure 7.5.

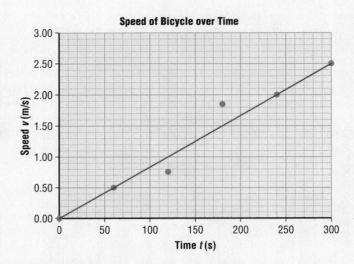

FIGURE 7.5 Although the line of best fit is still a straight line, it does not pass through all the data points. The points that are not on the line should be measured again, to ensure they are accurate.

Combining Different Types of Graphs

In some cases, two different types of data may be combined on one graph. For example, in Unit D you will create climatographs, which are graphical representations of the average climate of an area. A climatograph is composed of a bar graph showing average precipitation per month, and a line graph showing average temperature per month. There are two vertical axes, as shown in Figure 7.6. The vertical axis on the left presents the scale for the precipitation data, and the vertical axis on the right presents the scale for the temperature data.

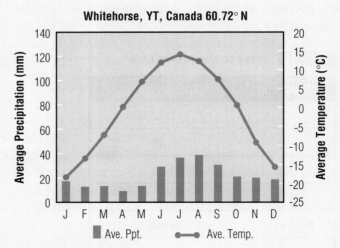

Source: Environment Canada

FIGURE 7.6 A climatograph combines a line graph with a bar graph.

Interpolation and Extrapolation

Graphing data can also allow us to estimate values for data points that we did not or cannot directly measure. Interpolation is the process of estimating a value that is between two directly measured data points of a variable. Data can often be interpolated using a line graph. For example, in Figure 7.4, you might want to interpolate the speed of the bicycle after 250 s. Figure 7.7 shows the procedure for interpolating data from a linear relationship on a line graph.

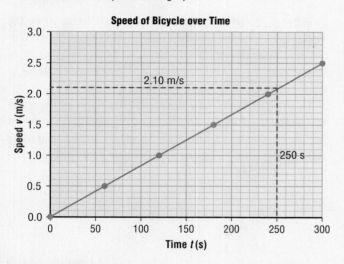

FIGURE 7.7 Values can be interpolated from a line graph when the relationship between the variables is linear.

First, locate the data point in which you are interested on the appropriate axis. In this example, this is the 250 s point on the x-axis. Next, draw a perpendicular line from this point to the line of best fit. At the point where the perpendicular line and the line of best fit intercept, draw a second line at a right angle to the first line and all the way to the second axis. In this example, this is the line from the intersection point to the y-axis. You can now read the interpolated value for the second variable using the scale of this axis (2.10 m/s in this example).

There is always some inaccuracy involved in interpolation, because we assume that the trend of the line continues between measured points. This assumption may not always be valid. There is also inaccuracy due to measurement, especially if you are working with pencil and paper.

Extrapolation is the process of estimating the values of a data point beyond the limits of the known or measured values. However, there is a considerable risk of inaccuracy, because we assume that the trend of the curve or straight line continues outside the range of the data. A dotted line is usually used to show extrapolation of a line. Figure 7.8 shows the extrapolated value for the speed of the bicycle at 400 s.

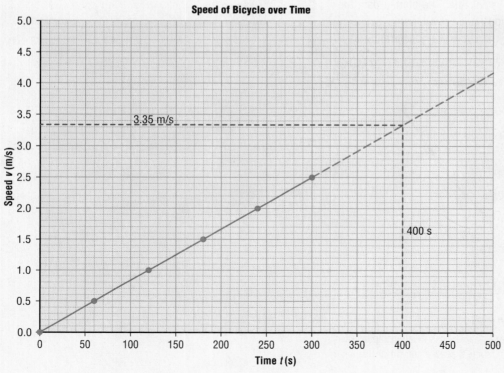

FIGURE 7.8 To extrapolate the speed of the bicycle at 400 s, extend the straight line of the graph beyond the last data point. The extrapolated line is shown as a dotted red line. The speed of the bicycle at 400 s can then be determined by drawing a straight line (horizontal blue dotted line) to the y-axis from the intersection of the 400 s point on the x-axis with the extrapolated line (vertical blue dotted line). This gives an extrapolated speed of 3.35 m/s.

Relationships between Variables

The main function of graphing is to help us to understand the relationships between variables. The previous examples have all shown linear relationships between the manipulated and responding variables. That is, a straight line defines the relationship between the variables. Line graphs (scatterplots with a line of best fit) can also tell you if a relationship between variables is non-linear. For example, consider the following data on the speed of two different bicycles as they passed markers at different distances during a race (Table 7.4).

TABLE 7.4 Speed of Two Bicycles Passing Markers

Distance d (m)	Speed of Bicycle A v_A (m/s)	Speed of Bicycle B v_B (m/s)
0.0	0.0	0.0
1.0	0.5	0.5
2.0	1.0	1.0
3.0	1.5	2.0
4.0	2.0	3.5
5.0	2.5	5.5

The line graph for these data is shown in Figure 7.9. The plotted data for bicycle A show a linear relationship between speed and distance. In other words, the cyclist is increasing speed, or accelerating, at a constant rate. The plotted data for bicycle B, however, show a non-linear relationship between speed and data. In this case, the cyclist is accelerating at a greater rate as the race continues.

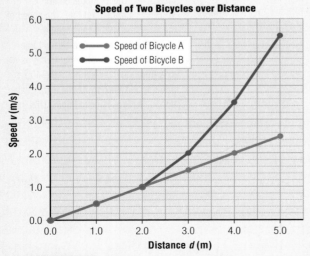

FIGURE 7.9 The data for bicycle A show a linear relationship between speed and distance, but the data for bicycle B show a non-linear relationship between these two variables.

Calculating the Slope

If the relationship between two variables is linear (i.e., the line of best fit is straight), we can use the graph to find the slope of the line. The slope of the line is defined as the ratio of the rise to the run. A run is a horizontal line drawn below the curve of the graph, touching the curve at one end. A rise is a vertical line joining the free end of the run to the curve.

$$slope = \frac{rise}{run}$$

When two variables have a linear relationship, then the manipulated variable and the responding variable increase or decrease in proportion to each other. When one variable varies by one unit, the other will always vary by a certain number of units. The slope of the graph gives us this number.

Figure 7.10 shows how to calculate the slope of the graph first shown in Figure 7.4. To find the slope, draw any convenient run on the graph. Your calculations will be simpler and more accurate if you make the run a large whole number. Then draw the corresponding rise.

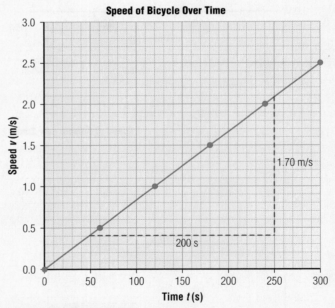

FIGURE 7.10 This graph has a run of 250 s − 50 s = 200 s and a rise of 2.10 m/s − 0.40 m/s = 1.70 m/s.

To calculate the slope for this graph, carry out the following steps:

$$\text{Slope} = \frac{\text{rise}}{\text{run}}$$

$$= \frac{y_2 - y_1}{x_2 - x_1}$$

$$= \frac{2.10 \frac{m}{s} - 0.40 \frac{m}{s}}{250\ s - 50\ s}$$

$$= \frac{1.70 \frac{m}{s}}{200\ s}$$

$$= 0.0085 \frac{m}{s^2}$$

$$= 8.5 \times 10^{-3} \frac{m}{s^2}$$

The slope of the graph is 8.5×10^{-3} m/s^2

We can therefore say a lot of things about the relationship between speed and time from this graph. We can say that speed and time have a linear relationship, i.e., the two variables are directly proportional to each other. From calculating the slope of the graph, we know that the proportion by which the speed of the bicycle increases is 8.5×10^{-3} m/s for every 1 s increase in time.

Notice that the slope has units. Examining the units will help you determine the meaning of the slope. The slope of a speed versus time graph such as Figure 7.10 is in units of m/s^2, which is the unit for acceleration. By finding the slope of the line, we have found the value for a quantity that we did not directly measure, in this case, the acceleration of the bicycle.

Calculating the Area under a Line

The area under the line of a graph of a linear relationship can also be used to find the value of a variable that was not directly measured. The relationship between variables is often described by an equation. For example, the speed (v) of any object can be calculated from the following formula:

$$v = \frac{\Delta d}{\Delta t}$$

where Δd is the change in distance and Δt is the change in time.

By formula manipulation, this formula can be rearranged to solve for Δd. That is

$$\Delta d = v\Delta t$$

The data in Table 7.2 do not include any measurement for the distance the bicycle travelled. We could use this formula to determine Δd for any time point, or we can determine Δd from the area under the line.

Note that the shaded area under the line in Figure 7.11 forms a triangle. The area under the line can therefore be determined as follows:

$$\text{area under the line} = \text{area of a triangle}$$

$$= \frac{1}{2}\ \text{base} \times \text{height}$$

$$\text{area} = \frac{1}{2}\Delta t \times v$$

$$= \frac{1}{2}\ 200\ \cancel{s} \times 1.65\ \frac{m}{\cancel{s}}$$

$$= 165\ m$$

The distance that the bicycle travelled in 200 s was 165 m.

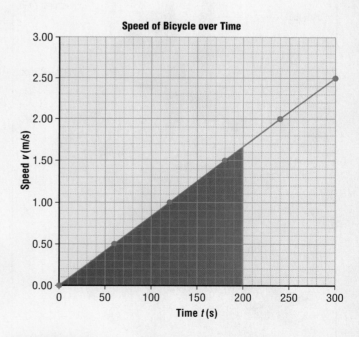

Speed of Bicycle over Time

FIGURE 7.11 The area under this line is a triangle. You therefore can use the formula for the area of a triangle to find the area.

Student Reference 8: The Compound Light Microscope

A microscope allows us to see an image of an object that is too small to see with the unaided human eye. A light microscope functions by focussing a beam of light through the object into the lens of the microscope. A compound light microscope is any light microscope that contains more than one lens. The compound light microscope you will use in the science classroom contains an eyepiece lens and a number of objective lenses. Each objective lens is a combination of two lenses made of different kinds of glass.

The Parts of the Microscope

It is important to know the location and function of the parts of the microscope in order to use it correctly. These are shown in Figure 8.1.

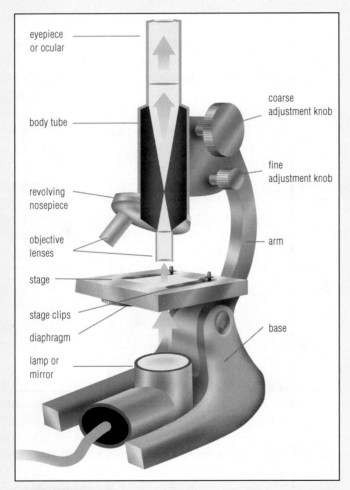

eyepiece or ocular

body tube

revolving nosepiece

objective lenses

stage

stage clips

diaphragm

lamp or mirror

coarse adjustment knob

fine adjustment knob

arm

base

FIGURE 8.1 A compound light microscope

Using the Microscope

1. Carry the microscope with two hands, grasping the arm of the microscope with one hand and holding the base of the microscope with the other. Place the microscope on the table or bench so that the arm is facing you.
2. Plug in the microscope and turn on the light.
3. Rotate the nosepiece until the objective lens with the lowest power is in place.
4. Place a microscope slide on the stage and secure with the stage clips.
5. Watch the stage from one side of the microscope and slowly lower the nosepiece with the coarse adjustment until it is as low as possible. Ensure the lens does not touch the slide.
6. Look through the eyepiece. Slowly turn the coarse adjustment so that you move the lens away from the slide. Stop when the image comes into view.
7. Use the fine adjustment to sharpen the focus of the image.
8. If you need to view the object under higher magnification, watch from the side of the microscope and rotate the nosepiece until the next higher power objective lens is in place. Ensure the lens does not touch the slide. Use only the fine adjustment knob to focus the image.

Magnification and Field of View

Each lens on the compound microscope will magnify a sample to a different degree. Magnification is calculated by multiplying the power of the ocular lens (usually 10× power) by the magnification of the objective lens you are using.

magnification = (power of ocular lens)(power of objective lens)

For example, if you are viewing a slide using a 4× power objective lens, the magnification of the image would be (10×)(4×) = 40×.

The field of view is the entire area that you see when you look through the microscope. The diameter of the field of view varies with the particular objective lens you are using. The diameters of the field of view for low-power (4×) and medium-power (10×) objective lenses can be determined by the following steps:

1. Rotate the objective lens into position.
2. Place a small, transparent, metric ruler on the stage so that it covers about half the stage. The ruler must be small enough to fit on the stage.
3. Using the coarse adjustment knob, bring the ruler into focus. Adjust the placement of the ruler so that the scale crosses the centre of the circle (the diameter), as shown in Figure 8.2.
4. Use the fine adjustment knob to get a clear, sharp image. If necessary, adjust the ruler so that one of the markings on the left side is exactly at the edge of the diameter.

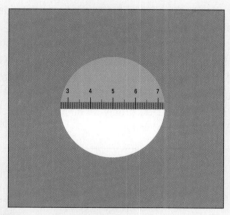

FIGURE 8.2 Move the ruler so that you are measuring the diameter (width) of the field of view from left to right.

5. Determine the diameter of the field of view in millimetres, using the scale on the ruler. Convert the millimetre reading to micrometres. This is the field of view for the magnification used.

You cannot measure the diameter of the field of view of a high-power (40×) objective lens using this method, because the field of view is less than 1 mm. However, you can estimate the diameter of the field of view of a high-power objective lens by using ratios. As you increase magnification by a certain amount, you decrease the diameter of the field of view by the inverse of that amount.

Therefore, you can determine the diameter of the field of view of a high-power (HP) objective lens by using the following ratio:

$$\frac{\text{HP field diameter}}{\text{LP field diameter}} = \frac{\text{LP magnification}}{\text{HP magnification}}$$

Example 8.1

A student measured the field diameter of a microscope using the 4× and 10× objective lenses.

Objective Lens	Magnification of Objective Lens	Field Diameter (mm)	Field Diameter (μm)
low power	4×	4.5	4500 or 4.5×10^3
medium power	10×	1.1	1100 or 1.1×10^3

Calculate the field diameter of a high-power (40×) objective lens.

$$\frac{\text{HP field diameter}}{\text{LP field diameter}} = \frac{\text{LP magnification}}{\text{HP magnification}}$$

$$\text{HP field diameter} = \text{LP field diameter} \times \frac{\text{LP magnification}}{\text{HP magnification}}$$

$$= 4500 \text{ μm} \times \frac{(4\times)}{(40\times)}$$

$$= 450 \text{ μm}$$

$$= 4.5 \times 10^2 \text{ μm}$$

The field diameter of the high-power (40×) objective lens is 4.5×10^2 μm.

Note that when the magnification increases by a factor of 10, such as from 4× to 40×, the field diameter decreases by the same factor (10×), from 4500 μm to 450 μm.

Once you have estimated the diameter of the field of view of an objective lens, you can estimate the size of any structure you are viewing with that lens. Compare the size of the structure with the diameter of the field of view. For example, if a cell component takes up one-tenth of a field of view that has a diameter of 400 μm, then the cell component is about one-tenth of 400 μm, or 40 μm.

Preparing a Wet Mount

1. Obtain a clean microscope slide and coverslip. In a wet mount, the coverslip serves three functions: it flattens the sample, it prevents the sample from drying out, and it protects the objective lens from contamination.
2. Place your sample in the centre of the slide. The specimen must be thin enough for light to pass through.
3. With an eyedropper, place a drop of water on the sample, as shown in Figure 8.3.

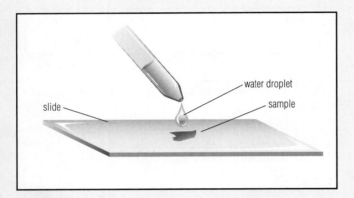

FIGURE 8.3   Step 3

4. Place the coverslip at an angle at one end of the drop of water (Figure 8.4(a)). Carefully lower the coverslip to cover the sample, being careful not to trap any air. It may be helpful to use a probe or toothpick to lower the coverslip.
5. If you do get air bubbles, gently tap the slide with a probe to release them (Figure 8.4(b)).

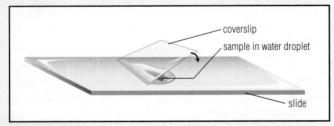

FIGURE 8.4   (a) Lower the coverslip slowly to avoid trapping air.

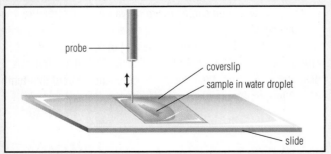

(b) Tapping gently on the coverslip can release any air bubbles that do occur.

Staining Samples

The parts of a cell are composed of various substances, and the different cell components react differently to many chemicals. Stains are chemicals that react in specific ways to different cell components. Stains therefore make it easier to distinguish the components of a cell. Some stains will dye only certain parts of the cell. Others change colour depending on the substances that comprise the different cell components.

There are many ways to stain cells, but one of the most common is the flow technique. This technique may be used to stain cells with, for example, iodine or methylene blue. The flow technique consists of the following steps:

1. Prepare a wet mount slide, as described at left.
2. Place a drop of stain at the edge of one side of the coverslip.
3. Obtain a small piece of paper towel or tissue paper. Place the paper against the edge of the coverslip on the side opposite to the stain, as shown in Figure 8.5(a).
4. Allow the paper to wick the fluid from under the coverslip and draw the stain into the sample, as shown in Figure 8.5(b).
5. Remove the paper when the stain has travelled to the other side of the coverslip.
6. If the stain is too dark, it may be diluted by repeating steps 2 to 5 with a drop of water.

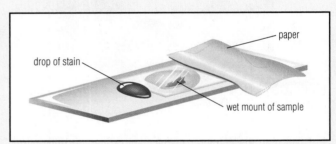

FIGURE 8.5   (a) Place the paper next to the coverslip, being careful not to disturb your sample.

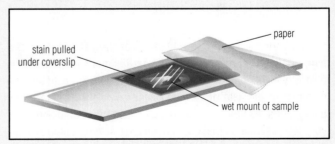

(b) Do not remove the paper until the stain is spread evenly under the coverslip.

Drawing Scientific Diagrams

To record what you observe under a microscope, you will often draw a scientific diagram. Scientific diagrams can also be used to record observations not made with a microscope. For example, they may also be used to show how equipment is set up for an experiment or to record objects observed with the unaided eye. A scientific diagram is different from other types of drawings in that it represents "the real thing." In other words, it is a record of exactly what was observed, with all features accurately drawn and identified.

Guidelines for Drawing Scientific Diagrams

1. Give a title for your diagram at the top of the page. The title should include information about the object shown (Figure 8.6).
2. Use pencil. Do not colour diagrams. Shade areas if necessary.
3. Draw only one diagram on a page. (There are sometimes exceptions to this rule, for example, if you were drawing only very simple diagrams.)
4. Label the parts or structures of the object on the diagram. Use a ruler to draw lines to connect the label to the part or structure.
5. Record the scale of the drawing at the side of the diagram.

Cross Section of Plant Stem

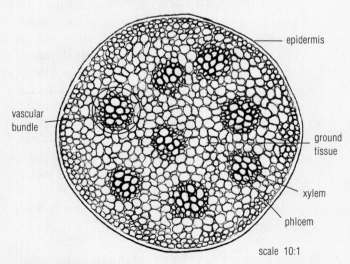

scale 10:1

FIGURE 8.6 This example of a scientific diagram shows the features of a cross-sectional view of a plant stem.

When samples have been dissected (cut apart), it is important to note how they were prepared in the title of the diagram. A sample can be prepared as a cross section (across the width), as in Figure 8.6, or as a longitudinal section (lengthwise), as in Figure 8.7.

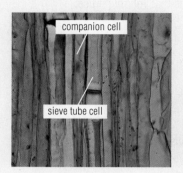

FIGURE 8.7 This longitudinal view of a plant stem shows different features of the plant stem from those shown in a cross section.

Diagrams may be drawn larger, smaller, or the same size as the actual object. The scale of a diagram is the difference between the size of the diagram and the size of the actual object. Scale is often expressed as a ratio, such as in the examples in Table 8.1.

TABLE 8.1 Actual Size, Diagram Size, and Scale

Actual Size	Diagram Size	Scale
1.1 mm	11 cm (110 mm)	100:1 (or × 100)
2.6 m	2.6 cm	1:100 (or × 0.01)

When using a microscope, the actual size of the object is usually estimated by comparing it to the diameter of the field of view.

To calculate actual size and scale for a scientific diagram, you must first measure the field diameter (if you are using a microscope) and the size of the finished diagram. Actual size and scale can then be calculated using the following relationships:

$$\text{actual size of object} = \frac{\text{field diameter}}{\text{number of objects estimated to fit across field of view}}$$

$$\text{scale} = \frac{\text{diagram size of objects (units)}}{\text{actual size (units)}}$$

Student Reference 9: Researching Information

Research involves finding and recording accurate information about a topic or subject. Information can be found just about anywhere. Here are a few ideas that you might use:

- library catalogues
- books, encyclopedias
- journals
- posters, brochures
- newspapers, magazines
- films, videos, CD-ROMs, DVDs
- Internet sites
- community professionals or experts
- government agencies (local, provincial, and federal)
- non-profit organizations

Using Library Resources

Library computer catalogues are a fast way to find books on the subjects you are researching. Most of these electronic catalogues have four ways to search: author, title, subject, and key words. If you know the author or title of a book, just type it in. Otherwise, use the subject and key word searches to find books on your topic.

- If you are doing a subject search, type in the main topic you are researching. For example, if you are searching for information on solar energy, type in "solar energy." If there are no books on that topic, try again using a more general category, like "renewable resources" or just "energy."
- If you are doing a key word search, type in any combination of words that have to do with your topic. To research solar energy, you might type words such as "renewable energy," "Sun," or "solar panels."

The library may also have a way to search for magazine articles, called a periodical search. A periodical is any publication that is published regularly, such as newspapers, magazines, and journals. Periodical searches may be done using a computer or by using special periodical indexes. Periodicals are especially useful for finding information on recent events. Ask your librarian how to do a periodical search.

Your library will also probably have a reference section where encyclopedias, atlases, and other reference books that must be used in the library are kept. These resources can provide you with accurate information on more general concepts and facts, such as the parts of the cell or the structure of an atom.

Using the Internet

The Internet is useful for finding information on many subjects. Make sure you know your school's policy about acceptable use of the Internet, and follow this policy whenever you use the Internet at school.

To find information quickly on the Internet, make use of special programs called search engines. A search engine scans the Internet for Web sites containing specific information. To find a search engine, ask your teacher or click on the search icon found at the top of your Internet browser. Here are some suggestions on how to search the Internet:

- In the appropriate place on the search engine Web page, type in key words or phrases that relate to your topic. For example, to find information on solar energy, you might use the following key words or phrases: "solar energy," "solar panels," or "renewable resources."
- When you click on the appropriate button (usually labelled "go" or "search"), the search engine will scan the Internet and then display a list of Web sites that contain your key words or phrases. You can then click on any Web site on the list to go directly to that site.
- If your initial search gives you a very long list, you may need to make your search more specific. Start your search again, but add other key words to your initial search terms. Some search engines allow you to search within the first list for additional terms without starting over. For example, if you were looking for examples of solar energy in Canada and your initial key words were "solar energy," you could add the key word "Canada" to your search to reduce the length of the list of sites.
- You might find you want to check a previously viewed site, so remember to record the addresses of any useful Web sites. Your Internet browser should have a way for you to keep a file of sites you want to visit again (these may be called either "bookmarks" or "favourites"). Check with your teacher or librarian to find out how to save Web site addresses.

Be aware that some Web sites may be strongly biased toward a specific point of view. Educational or government Web sites are generally reliable.

Note-Taking Charts

When researching, you need to record the information you collect in an organized manner. One way you could do this is to use a note-taking chart.

In both printed and electronic information sources, information is usually organized under headings. For example, the information you are reading now is under the heading "Note-Taking Charts." Use these headings as a tool for recording relevant information. Before you begin any in-depth reading, look at each heading and turn it into a question. Try to use "how," "what," or "why" to begin each question. Write your questions in your chart. Leave enough space between questions to record information as you read.

For example, a student was asked to prepare a report on the scientific meaning of work. She found a section in a book that had the following headings:

- The Meaning of Work
- Calculating Work
- Energy and Work

Figure 9.1 shows the student's note-taking chart:

Questions from Headings	Answers from Reading
What is the meaning of the word "work"?	— work is done when a force acts on an object to make the object move — If there's no movement, no work is done — just trying to push something isn't work—it's only work if the object moves
How do you calculate work?	
How are energy and work related?	

FIGURE 9.1 A note-taking chart keeps all your information organized as you work. It is similar to a data table used during a lab activity.

Recording Information Sources

As you do your research, you will look at many different sources. Whatever sources you use, you need to record and communicate them clearly. This allows you or anyone else to go back and recheck the information. If you do not present the reference sources you use, you may be committing plagiarism, which is taking or using someone else's words or ideas as your own.

Your teacher may want you to list your information sources in a specific format. Check this format before you begin your research so that you can collect the details you need. Your record should include at least the following:

- the title or name of the source
- the author's name, if known
- the name of the publisher
- the date the material was published
- the specific page numbers you consulted

Most lists of information sources are presented alphabetically, according to the name of the author (or editor). If there is no author or editor, alphabetize by the first word of the title (other than "a," "an," or "the.") Here are some examples of commonly accepted styles for presenting reference sources.

a) Books with one or more authors:
   Trentsky, Ola, and Frank O'Brien. *The Life of Plants*. Edmonton: Glacier Press, 2001.
b) Books with one or more editors:
   Singh, Vijay, ed. *Machines in Motion*. Calgary: Advance Press, 2000.
c) Books with no author or editor:
   The Canadian Atlas of Climate. Vancouver: Three Spokes, 1999.
d) Encyclopedia
   Lee, Hu. "Chemical Reactivity" *Encyclopedia of High School Chemistry*. 1999 ed.
e) Government publications:
   Government of Alberta. Alberta Learning. *Science Data Booklet*. Edmonton, 1999.
f) Periodical publications:
   Kampa, Bisasu. "The Efficient Engine." *Everyday Technology* 14 Jan. 2003: 12–15.
g) Web sites:
   Canadian Forestry Organization. *Sustaining Canada's Forests*. Aug. 2001. 12 Sept. 2003. <http://www.canfor.org/sustain.html>.

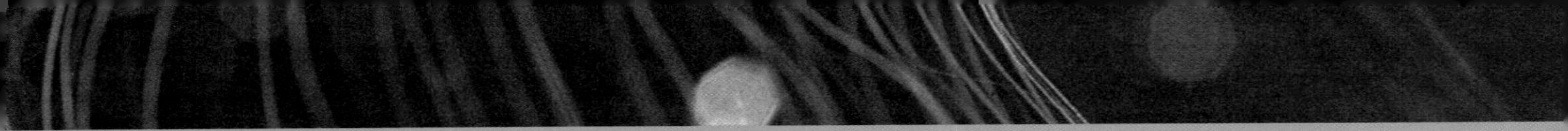

Student Reference 10: Tools for Analyzing Information

Visual organizers are effective tools that can help you learn. They enable you to problem-solve and think critically by analyzing similarities and differences, inferring sequences, and establishing cause-and-effect relationships. They generate discussion and negotiation of ideas, extend comprehension of a concept, theme, or topic, and lead to organized representation and presentation of understandings. You can use them to brainstorm, to demonstrate what you know, and to organize your thoughts before writing a report or essay, or planning a presentation. The following chart outlines a number of graphic organizers, their intended purposes, and how to use them as you study science.

Type of Graphic Organizer	Purpose	Method
Concept Map or Web Diagram 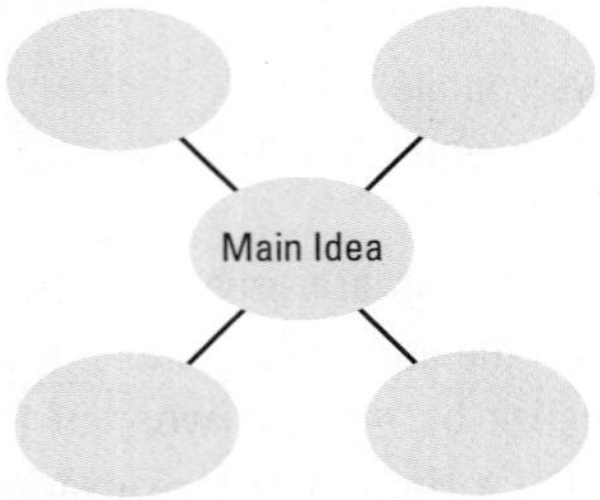	Used to clarify relationships and linkages between concepts, events, or ideas	Brainstorm ideas and link together from "big to small" with arrows or lines linking words. Cluster information around a central concept or idea.
Venn Diagram 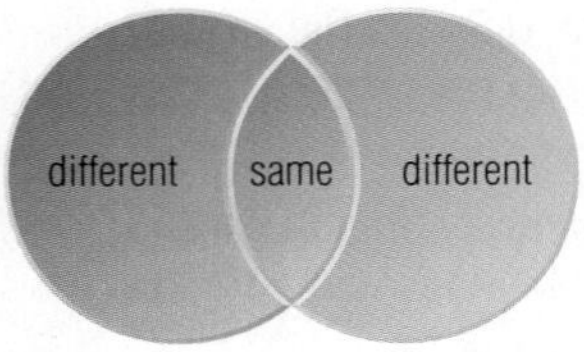	Used to visualize similarities and differences between two or more ideas, topics, or concepts	Brainstorm similarities, and list these in the overlapping section of the two circles. Then brainstorm differences and list these in the non-overlapping sections.
Flowchart or Sequence Chart 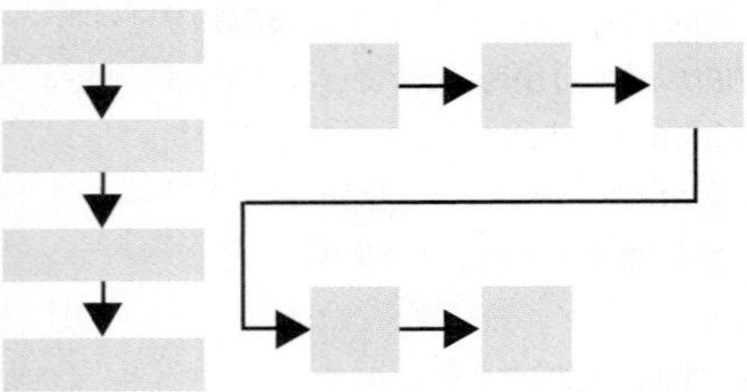	Used to map out your thinking about an issue or to organize ideas for an essay or report	Brainstorm aspects of the whole event or concept. Select important aspects and put them into sequential order.
Ranking Ladder 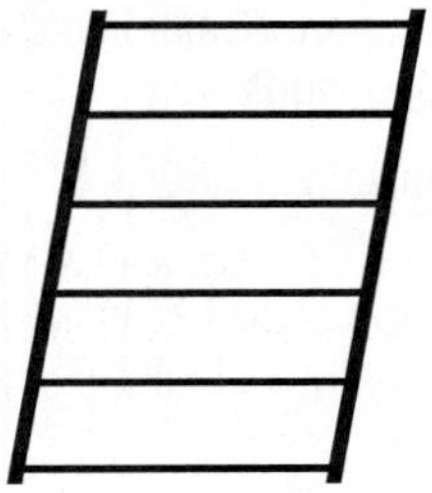	Used to rank ideas in order of importance	Brainstorm ideas and rank them in order from most important (bottom rung) to least important (top rung).

Type of Graphic Organizer	Purpose	Method
Fishbone Diagram	Used to analyze cause-and-effect relationships	List the effect at the head of the "fish." Brainstorm possible causes and list them in each "bone." Rank the causes and circle the most probable ones, justifying your choice.
Right-Angle Diagram	Used to explore the consequences of an idea and the impact of its application	Briefly describe the idea you are exploring on the horizontal arrow. Brainstorm consequences of the idea, and list these to the right of the horizontal arrow. Expand on one consequence, and list details about it along the vertical arrow. Describe social impacts of that trait below the vertical arrow.
Target Diagram	Used to weigh the importance of facts and ideas	Brainstorm facts and ideas. Rank their importance and place the most important facts or ideas centrally, and the least important toward the outer ring.
Agree/Disagree Chart	Used to organize data to support a position for or against an idea or decision	List a series of statements relating to a topic or issue. Survey agreement and disagreement before discussion. Survey again after discussion and research.
Cost/Benefit Chart	Used to summarize the negative (costs) and positive (benefits) aspects of a topic or issue	List ideas or information relating to the topic or issue. Sort the ideas or information in a chart that includes the headings "Costs" and "Benefits."
Concept-Hierarchy Diagram	Used to identify and sequence the subordinate concepts needed to understand a higher-order concept	Place the higher-order concept at the top of the page. Then consider the question, "What concepts need to be understood before the higher-order concept above can be grasped?" The same question is then asked for each of the subordinate concepts and a hierarchy of connected concepts is created.

Student Reference 11: Writing Reports

Whether your work in science involves the inquiry process, the problem-solving process, or the decision-making process, the final step is always to effectively communicate your results. There are many different ways you may communicate results: you might give an oral presentation, create an electronic presentation, or make a video. Many times, however, you will be required to write a report.

The list below summarizes all the things you need to do when communicating scientific information in a written report.

- Give your report a title.
- Tell your readers why you did the work.
- State your hypothesis, describe the design challenge, or outline the scope of the issue.
- List the materials and equipment you used.
- Describe all the steps you took when you did your experiment; designed, made, and tested your product; or researched the issue.
- Communicate your experimental data, the results of testing your product, or the background information on the issue.
- Analyze and interpret the results of your experiment, product test, or research on the issue.
- Describe your conclusions.

If you are writing a report on an experiment or a product design, you will need to follow all eight of these steps.

Give your report a title.

Write a brief title at the top of the first page of your report. Your title may be one or two words or a short sentence, but it should describe the experiment you performed, the product you designed and made, or the issue you investigated.

Tell your readers why you did the work.

Use a heading such as "Introduction" or "Purpose" for this section. Describe your reasons for doing a particular experiment, designing and making a particular product, or considering a specific issue. If you are writing about an experiment, state the question you investigated. If you designed a product, explain why this product is needed, what it will do, who might use it, and who might benefit from its use. If you considered an issue, state the issue and explain why you found it important or interesting enough to research.

State your hypothesis and design statement, describe the design challenge, or outline the scope of the issue.

If your report is about an experiment, state your hypothesis and your design statement. Your hypothesis must indicate the relationship between the manipulated and responding variables. A design statement is an outline of the general plan for testing the hypothesis, and identifies all the variables. Refer to *Student Reference 2: The Inquiry Process* for more information.

If your report is about a product you designed, describe the reasons behind your design. Explain how and why you chose your design over other possible designs, including features such as the materials you used.

If your report is about an issue, briefly outline the scope of the issue, such as who is affected, the locations that are affected, and any other related information. You may wish to include this information in the introduction to your report.

List materials and equipment.

List all the materials and equipment you used for your experiment or design project. Your list can be in point form, or set in a table or chart. Include the exact amounts of materials used (e.g., the masses of substances used in an experiment or the number of nails used to build a model). Include the proper units and exact measurements for all materials used. Also include in this section any diagrams that show how you set up your equipment or prepared your materials. You may wish to use the heading "Materials and Equipment" for this section. If you are writing a report about an issue you have researched, you do not need to complete this step.

Describe the steps you took.

If you performed an experiment, describe in detail all the steps you carried out in order to complete it. If you made a product, outline what you did to design and make your product, and how you tested it. If you had to alter your design based on your testing, describe how you did this as well. If you researched an issue, briefly describe the kinds of sources you used, such as reference books, government sites, or interviews with experts. You may wish to use the heading "Procedure" or "Method" for this section.

Show your experimental data, results of testing, or background information.

In this section of your report, show the data or information you collected while performing the experiment, testing your product, or researching an issue. Use data tables and diagrams to clearly communicate the results of an experiment or of tests of a product. If you performed your experiment more than once, include the results for each trial. If you tested several designs of your product, give results for each design. If your report is about an issue, this section should be a concise description of only the information that is essential for a reader to understand the issue and all the related viewpoints. Diagrams or pictures can also help you to communicate the background information on an issue. Give this section a heading such as "Data," "Observations," or "Background Information."

Analyze and interpret the results of your experiment, product testing, or research.

This section must communicate how you analyzed the data or information you collected, and the interpretations you made based on that analysis. Include any calculations or graphs you used in analyzing your data. Refer to *Student Reference 6: Math Skills* and *Student Reference 7: Graphing* for more information on analyzing data. If your report concerns an issue, describe the results of your analysis. For example, if you analyzed the costs and benefits of an issue, you would describe whether the costs outweighed the benefits (or vice versa). If you used a particular tool to analyze your information, describe the tool. *Student Reference 10: Tools for Analyzing Information* describes several such tools. You may wish to use the heading "Analysis and Interpretation" for this section.

Describe your conclusions.

The last section of your report can be called "Conclusions." In one or two paragraphs, explain what your tests and experiments showed, or what decision you made as a result of your research.

If you performed an experiment, state whether your results supported your hypothesis. If the results do not fully support your hypothesis, describe how you might adjust the hypothesis based on your results, and how you might test this new hypothesis. Describe the practical application your experimental results might have for the world outside the classroom.

If you made a product, explain whether your design worked the way you intended. If you changed the design of your product after testing, explain why one design is better than another. Describe the practical application your product might have for the world outside the classroom.

If you considered an issue, explain why you made the decision that you did. Briefly summarize the supporting evidence for your decision. If necessary, explain how your decision responds to different viewpoints on the issue.

A. Periodic Table

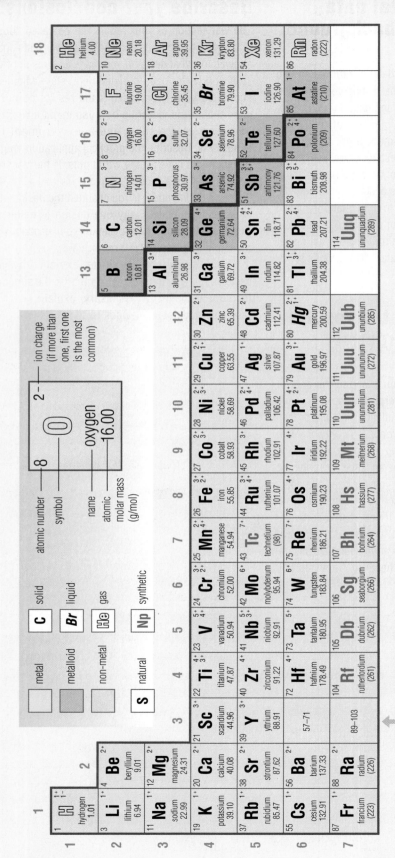

B. Some Common Chemical Compounds

Chemical Name	Common Name	Formula	Description and Uses
ammonia	ammonia	$NH_{3(g)}$	• used in the manufacture of fertilizers, explosives, and synthetic fibres, and as a refrigerant • produced during nitrogen cycle by plants
benzene	benzene	$C_6H_{6(l)}$	• used in the production of nylon and polystyrene, and as a solvent • is a component of gasoline
carbon dioxide	carbon dioxide	$CO_{2(g)}$	• produced by cellular respiration of living things and by combustion of fossil fuels • used by plants for photosynthesis • is a greenhouse gas
ethanol	grain alcohol	$CH_3CH_2OH_{(l)}$ $C_2H_5OH_{(l)}$	• used as a solvent, in the manufacture of medicines, and as a gasoline additive
glucose	glucose	$C_6H_{12}O_{6(s)}$	• is a simple sugar, produced by plants during photosynthesis from carbon dioxide and water
methane	methane	$CH_{4(g)}$	• produced by the decomposition of organic matter • is a major component of natural gas • is a greenhouse gas
methanol	wood alcohol	$CH_3OH_{(l)}$	• used in the production of wood adhesives and plastics, as a solvent for paints and dyes, and as gas-line anti-freeze
nicotine	nicotine	$C_{10}H_{14}N_{2(s)}$	• addictive substance in tobacco products
water	water	$H_2O_{(l)}$	• is the universal solvent • is a vital component of all living cells • liquid water covers over 70% of Earth's surface

C. Solubility of Some Common Ionic Compounds in Water at 298.15 K

Ion	Group 1 NH_4^+ H_3O^+ (H^+)	ClO_3^- NO_3^- ClO_4^-	CH_3COO^-	Cl^- Br^- I^-	SO_4^{2-}	S^{2-}	OH^-	PO_4^{3-} SO_3^{2-} CO_3^{2-}
solubility ≥ 0.1 mol/L (very soluble)	all	all	most	most	most	Group 1 Group 2 NH_4^+	Group 1 NH_4^+ Sr^{2+} Ba^{2+} Tl^+	Group 1 NH_4^+
solubility < 0.1 mol/L (slightly soluble)	none	none	Ag^+ Hg^+	Ag^+ Pb^{2+} Hg^+ Cu^+ Tl^+	Ca^{2+} Sr^{2+} Ba^{2+} Ra^{2+} Pb^{2+} Ag^+	most	most	most

Group 1: Li^+, Na^+, K^+, Rb^+, Cs^+, Fr^+
Group 2: Be^{2+}, Mg^{2+}, Ca^{2+}, Sr^{2+}, Ba^{2+}, Ra^{2+}

D. Diagnostic Tests for Some Common Substances

Substance Detected	Description of Test
oxygen gas	Collect a small amount of gas in a test tube. Insert a glowing wooden splint into the test tube. If oxygen gas is present, the splint will ignite and you will see a flame.
hydrogen gas	Collect a small amount of gas in a test tube. Insert a burning wooden splint into the test tube. If hydrogen gas is present, you will hear a popping sound.
carbon dioxide gas	Collect a small amount of gas in a test tube. Insert a burning wooden splint into the test tube. If carbon dioxide gas is present, the flame will be extinguished (go out). Since other gases can also extinguish the flame, the presence of carbon dioxide must be confirmed by testing it with limewater (a solution of calcium hydroxide). Place a few drops of limewater into the test tube. If the gas is carbon dioxide, the limewater will turn milky.
bases	Dip a piece of red litmus paper into the solution. If the solution is a base (i.e., it has a pH > 7), the litmus paper will turn blue.
acids	Dip a piece of blue litmus paper into the solution. If the solution is an acid (i.e., it has a pH < 7), the litmus paper will turn red.

E. Common Polyatomic Ions

Polyatomic Ion	Formula
acetate (ethanoate)	CH_3COO^-
ammonium	NH_4^+
benzoate	$C_6H_5COO^-$
borate	BO_3^{3-}
carbide	C_2^{2-}
carbonate	CO_3^{2-}
hydrogencarbonate (bicarbonate)	HCO_3^-
chlorate	ClO_3^-
chlorite	ClO_2^-
hypochlorite	ClO^- or OCl^-
chromate	CrO_4^{2-}
dichromate	$Cr_2O_7^{2-}$
cyanide	CN^-
hydroxide	OH^-
iodate	IO_3^-
nitrate	NO_3^-
nitrite	NO_2^-
oxalate	$OOCCOO^{2-}$
hydrogenoxalate	$HOOCCOO^-$
perchlorate	ClO_4^-
permanganate	MnO_4^-
peroxide	O_2^{2-}
persulfide	S_2^{2-}
phosphate	PO_4^{3-}
hydrogenphosphate	HPO_4^{2-}
dihydrogenphosphate	$H_2PO_4^-$
silicate	SiO_3^{2-}
sulfate	SO_4^{2-}
hydrogensulfate	HSO_4^-
sulfite	SO_3^{2-}
hydrogensulfite	HSO_3^-
hydrogensulfide	HS^-
thiocyanate	SCN^-
thiosulfate	$S_2O_3^{2-}$

F. Thermodynamic Properties of Selected Substances

Name	Formula	Heat of Fusion (kJ/mol)	Heat of Vaporization (kJ/mol)	Specific Heat Capacity (J/g·°C)
aluminium	$Al_{(s)}$	10.79	294	0.897
copper	$Cu_{(s)}$	12.93	300.4	0.385
gold	$Au_{(s)}$	12.72	324	0.129
iron	$Fe_{(s)}$	13.81	340	0.449
nickel	$Ni_{(s)}$	17.04	377.5	0.444
silver	$Ag_{(s)}$	11.28	258	0.235
zinc	$Zn_{(s)}$	7.07	123.6	0.388
ice	$H_2O_{(s)}$	6.01	—	2.00
water	$H_2O_{(l)}$	—	40.65	4.19
steam	$H_2O_{(g)}$	—	—	2.02
methanol	$CH_3OH_{(l)}$	3.22	35.21	2.53

Answers to Numerical Questions

page 39

A2.1 Check and Reflect

10. a) phosphorus will gain 3 electrons

b) sodium will lose 1 electron

c) chlorine will gain 1 electron

d) magnesium will lose 2 electrons

e) iodine will gain 1 electron

11.

Element Name	Mass Number	Number of Protons	Number of Neutrons
calcium	41	20	21
uranium	238	92	146
aluminium	27	13	14
beryllium	9	4	5
neon	19	10	9
iron	53	26	27

12.

Atom or Ion Name	Overall Charge	Number of Protons	Number of Electrons	Symbol	Number of Electrons Lost or Gained
oxygen atom	0	8	8	O	0
oxide ion	2-	8	10	O^{2-}	gained 2
potassium ion	1+	19	18	K^+	lost 1
magnesium ion	2+	12	10	Mg^{2+}	lost 2
fluoride ion	1-	9	10	F^-	gained 1
calcium ion	2+	20	18	Ca^{2+}	lost 2
aluminium ion	3+	13	10	Al^{3+}	lost 3

page 43

Practice Problem

1. a) $MgCl_{2(s)}$

b) $Na_2S_{(s)}$

c) $Ca_3P_{2(s)}$

d) $K_3N_{(s)}$

e) $CaF_{2(s)}$

page 44

Practice Problem

2. a) iron(III) chloride

b) lead(IV) oxide

c) nickel(III) sulfide

d) copper(II) fluoride

e) chromium(III) sulfide

page 46

Practice Problems

3. a) $Ba(OH)_{2(s)}$

b) $Fe_2(CO_3)_{3(s)}$

c) $CuMnO_{4(s)}$

4. a) gold(III) nitrate

b) ammonium phosphate

c) potassium dichromate

page 49

Practice Problem

5. a) carbon dioxide

b) dinitrogen monoxide

c) phosphorus trichloride

d) $OF_{2(g)}$

e) $N_2S_{4(s)}$

f) $SO_{3(g)}$

page 50

A2.2 Check and Reflect

3. a) Na^+

b) Ca^{2+}

c) Ag^+

d) Cu^{2+}

e) Pb^{4+}

f) Cl^-

g) ClO_3^-

h) ClO_2^-

i) CH_3COO^-

j) NH_4^+

4. a) aluminium ion

b) potassium ion

c) zinc ion

d) nickel(III) ion

e) iron(II) ion

f) iron(III) ion

g) hydrogencarbonate ion

h) hydroxide ion

i) thiocyanate ion

j) sulfite ion

5. a) methane
b) ammonia
c) water

d) hydrogen sulfide
e) hydrogen fluoride

8. a) aluminium chloride
b) calcium sulfide
c) sodium nitride
d) potassium sulfate
e) lithium oxide
f) iron(III) iodide
g) lead(IV) nitrate
h) copper(I) phosphate
i) ammonium nitrite
j) sodium acetate (or sodium ethanoate)

9. a) $NaOH_{(s)}$
b) $(NH_4)_2SO_{3(s)}$
c) $Mg(SCN)_{2(s)}$

d) $CaHPO_{4(s)}$
e) $Al(CH_3COO)_{3(s)}$
f) $CrCl_{3(s)}$

10. a) $N_2O_{4(g)}$
b) $PCl_{5(g)}$
c) $NI_{3(s)}$
d) $CO_{(g)}$
e) $P_4O_{10(s)}$

f) $CS_{2(g)}$
g) $SO_{3(g)}$
h) $CH_{4(g)}$
i) $NH_{3(g)}$
j) $C_6H_{12}O_{6(s)}$

11. a) carbon tetrabromide
b) nitrogen monoxide
c) oxygen difluoride
d) iodine monobromide
e) selenium dibromide
f) phosphorus trichloride
g) dinitrogen trioxide
h) sulfur dichloride

12. a) hydrogen peroxide
b) iron(III) thiocyanate
c) $C_2H_5OH_{(l)}$

d) $Na_2SiO_{3(s)}$
e) $NH_4ClO_{4(s)}$
f) sulfur hexafluoride

page 69
A2.4 Check and Reflect

4. a) $HNO_{3(aq)}$
b) $CsOH_{(s)}$
c) $CH_3COOH_{(aq)}$
d) $Ca(OH)_{2(s)}$
e) $HCl_{(aq)}$

f) $H_3PO_{4(aq)}$
g) potassium hydroxide
h) hydrobromic acid
i) sulfuric acid
j) magnesium hydroxide

page 76–77
A2.0 Section Review

23. a) sodium will lose 1 electron
b) fluorine will gain 1 electron
c) calcium will lose 2 electrons
d) nitrogen will gain 3 electrons
e) oxygen will gain 2 electrons

24. a) cesium chloride
b) potassium nitride
c) sodium oxide
d) aluminium nitride
e) magnesium sulfide
f) lithium phosphide
g) aluminium oxide
h) silver fluoride
i) iron(II) bromide
j) lead(IV) chloride
k) nickel(III) oxide
l) gold(III) nitride

25. a) ammonium sulfide
b) ammonium sulfate
c) calcium nitrate
d) aluminium hydrogencarbonate
e) sodium silicate
f) chromium(II) chlorite
g) lead(IV) hydrogenphosphate
h) potassium permanganate
i) sodium dichromate
j) aluminium acetate or ethanoate
k) cobalt(II) benzoate
l) ammonium thiocyanate

26. a) $NaBr_{(s)}$
b) $Ca_3N_{2(s)}$
c) $MgO_{(s)}$
d) $AlCl_{3(s)}$
e) $RbI_{(s)}$
f) $Li_3P_{(s)}$

g) $FeS_{(s)}$
h) $Cr_3N_{2(s)}$
i) $Cu_2O_{(s)}$
j) $TiBr_{4(s)}$
k) $PbF_{2(s)}$
l) $CoN_{(s)}$

27. a) $Li_2CO_{3(s)}$
b) $Be(NO_3)_{2(s)}$
c) $Na_3PO_{4(s)}$
d) $NH_4CN_{(s)}$
e) $NaHCO_{3(s)}$
f) $AlBO_{3(s)}$

g) $Mn(ClO_4)_{2(s)}$
h) $Fe(OH)_{3(s)}$
i) $Cu(C_6H_5COO)_{2(s)}$
j) $Au(SCN)_{3(s)}$
k) $Pb(CrO_4)_{2(s)}$
l) $CrPO_{3(s)}$

28. a) dinitrogen monoxide
b) sulfur trioxide
c) phosphorus pentachloride
d) $CBr_{4(l)}$
e) $SCl_{6(g)}$
f) $OF_{2(g)}$
g) nitrogen triiodide
h) water
i) ammonia
j) $CH_{4(g)}$
k) $P_4O_{10(s)}$
l) $XeF_{2(g)}$

31. a) hydrofluoric acid

b) nitric acid

c) sodium hydroxide – base

d) methanoic acid or formic acid

e) ammonium hydroxide – base

f) ethanoic acid or acetic acid

g) phosphoric acid

h) calcium hydroxide – base

36. a) $Ca(NO_3)_{2(s)}$ g) tin(II) chloride

b) $Al(OH)_{3(s)}$ h) strontium chloride

c) $CH_3OH_{(l)}$ i) $NaCH_3COO_{(s)}$

d) $PBr_{3(g)}$ j) $Pb(CH_3COO)_{4(s)}$

e) ammonium carbonate   k) $H_2O_{2(l)}$

f) sulfur dichloride   l) $C_6H_{12}O_{6(s)}$

page 85
A3.1 Check and Reflect
10. 14.5 g

11. 6.7 g

12. a) 57.4 g

b) 42.6 g

page 89
Practice Problem
1. a) $N_{2(g)} + 3 H_{2(g)} \longrightarrow 2 NH_{3(g)}$

b) $CaC_{2(s)} + 2 H_2O_{(l)} \longrightarrow Ca(OH)_{2(s)} + C_2H_{2(g)}$

c) $SiCl_{4(s)} + 2 H_2O_{(l)} \longrightarrow SiO_{2(s)} + 4 HCl_{(aq)}$

d) $2 H_3PO_{4(aq)} + 3 CaSO_{4(s)} \longrightarrow$
$$Ca_3(PO_4)_{2(s)} + 3 H_2SO_{4(aq)}$$

page 90
A3.2 Check and Reflect
7. a) $2 Al_{(s)} + 3 F_{2(g)} \longrightarrow 2 AlF_{3(s)}$

b) $4 K_{(s)} + O_{2(g)} \longrightarrow 2 K_2O_{(s)}$

c) $C_6H_{12}O_{6(s)} + 6 O_{2(g)} \longrightarrow 6 CO_{2(g)} + 6 H_2O_{(g)}$

d) $H_2SO_{4(aq)} + 2 NaOH_{(s)} \longrightarrow Na_2SO_{4(aq)} + 2 H_2O_{(l)}$

e) $Mg(CH_3COO)_{2(aq)} + 2 AgNO_{3(aq)} \longrightarrow$
$$Mg(NO_3)_{2(aq)} + 2 AgCH_3COO_{(s)}$$

f) $2 H_2O_{2(aq)} \longrightarrow O_{2(g)} + 2 H_2O_{(l)}$

8. a) $CH_{4(g)} + 2 O_{2(g)} \longrightarrow CO_{2(g)} + 2 H_2O_{(g)}$

b) $2 NaCl_{(s)} \longrightarrow 2 Na_{(s)} + Cl_{2(g)}$

c) $Ca(NO_3)_{2(aq)} + Na_2SO_{4(aq)} \longrightarrow 2 NaNO_{3(aq)} + CaSO_{4(s)}$

d) $H_{2(g)} + CO_{(g)} \longrightarrow C_{(s)} + H_2O_{(g)}$ (balanced)

e) $2 Na_{(s)} + 2 H_2O_{(l)} \longrightarrow 2 NaOH_{(aq)} + H_{2(g)}$

f) $2 CaCO_{3(s)} + 2 SO_{2(g)} + O_{2(g)} \longrightarrow 2 CaSO_{4(s)} + 2 CO_{2(g)}$

g) $S_{8(s)} + 8 O_{2(g)} \longrightarrow 8 SO_{2(g)}$

h) $Ca_3(PO_4)_{2(s)} + 3 H_2SO_{4(aq)} \longrightarrow 2 H_3PO_{4(aq)} + 3 CaSO_{4(s)}$

i) $2 KClO_{3(s)} \longrightarrow 2 KCl_{(s)} + 3 O_{2(g)}$

9. a) $Ca_{(s)} + 2 HCl_{(aq)} \longrightarrow CaCl_{2(aq)} + H_{2(g)}$

b) $Mg_3N_{2(s)} + 6 H_2O_{(l)} \longrightarrow 3 Mg(OH)_{2(aq)} + 2 NH_{3(g)}$

c) $H_2SO_{4(aq)} + 2 NaOH_{(s)} \longrightarrow Na_2SO_{4(aq)} + 2 H_2O_{(l)}$

d) $2 NO_{2(g)} \longrightarrow N_2O_{4(g)}$

e) $CuCl_{2(aq)} + 2 NaOH_{(aq)} \longrightarrow Cu(OH)_{2(s)} + 2 NaCl_{(aq)}$

page 92
Practice Problems
2. skeleton: $Li_{(s)} + O_{2(g)} \longrightarrow Li_2O_{(s)}$

balanced: $4 Li_{(s)} + O_{2(g)} \longrightarrow Li_2O_{(s)}$

3. skeleton: $Pb_{(s)} + Br_{2(l)} \longrightarrow PbBr_{4(s)}$

balanced: $Pb_{(s)} + 2 Br_{2(l)} \longrightarrow PbBr_{4(s)}$

page 93
Practice Problem
4. a) calcium nitride, $Ca_3N_{2(s)}$

b) silver oxide, $Ag_2O_{(s)}$

c) aluminium fluoride, $AlF_{3(s)}$

page 93
Skill Practice: Formation Reactions
1. a) potassium iodide

b) magnesium phosphide

c) cesium chloride

d) calcium oxide

e) aluminium sulfide

2. a) $Na_{(s)} + Br_{2(l)} \longrightarrow NaBr_{(s)}$

b) $Mg_{(s)} + F_{2(g)} \longrightarrow MgF_{2(s)}$

c) $Al_{(s)} + Cl_{2(g)} \longrightarrow AlCl_{3(s)}$

d) $K_{(s)} + N_{2(g)} \longrightarrow K_3N_{(s)}$

e) $Ca_{(s)} + P_{4(s)} \longrightarrow Ca_3P_{2(s)}$

3. a) $4 Li_{(s)} + O_{2(g)} \longrightarrow 2 Li_2O_{(s)}$

b) $2 Al_{(s)} + 3 Br_{2(l)} \longrightarrow 2 AlBr_{3(s)}$

c) $Hg_{(l)} + I_{2(s)} \longrightarrow HgI_{2(s)}$

d) $2 Na_{(s)} + Cl_{2(g)} \longrightarrow 2 NaCl_{(s)}$

e) $3 Mg_{(s)} + N_{2(g)} \longrightarrow Mg_3N_{2(s)}$

f) $Ni_{(s)} + F_{2(g)} \longrightarrow NiF_{2(s)}$

page 94
Practice Problem
5. a) $8 MgS_{(s)} \longrightarrow 8 Mg_{(s)} + S_{8(s)}$

b) $2 KI_{(s)} \longrightarrow 2 K_{(s)} + I_{2(s)}$

c) $2 Al_2O_{3(s)} \longrightarrow 4 Al_{(s)} + 3 O_{2(g)}$

d) $NiCl_{2(s)} \longrightarrow Ni_{(s)} + Cl_{2(g)}$

Practice Problem

6. a) $CH_{4(g)} + 2\ O_{2(g)} \longrightarrow CO_{2(g)} + 2\ H_2O_{(g)}$
   b) $2\ C_2H_{6(g)} + 7\ O_{2(g)} \longrightarrow 4\ CO_{2(g)} + 6\ H_2O_{(g)}$
   c) $C_3H_{8(g)} + 5\ O_{2(g)} \longrightarrow 3\ CO_{2(g)} + 4\ H_2O_{(g)}$
   d) $2\ C_6H_{6(l)} + 15\ O_{2(g)} \longrightarrow 12\ CO_{2(g)} + 6\ H_2O_{(g)}$

Practice Problems

7. Word equation: chlorine + nickel(III) bromide →
   nickel(III) chloride + bromine
   Skeleton equation: $Cl_{2(g)} + NiBr_{3(aq)} \longrightarrow$
   $NiCl_{3(aq)} + Br_{2(l)}$
   Balanced equation: $3\ Cl_{2(g)} + 2\ NiBr_{3(aq)} \longrightarrow$
   $2\ NiCl_{3(aq)} + 3\ Br_{2(l)}$

8. Word equation: zinc + silver nitrate $\longrightarrow$
   zinc nitrate + silver
   Skeleton equation: $Zn_{(s)} + AgNO_{3(aq)} \longrightarrow$
   $Zn(NO_3)_{2(aq)} + Ag_{(s)}$
   Balanced equation: $Zn_{(s)} + 2\ AgNO_{3(aq)} \longrightarrow$
   $Zn(NO_3)_{2(aq)} + 2\ Ag_{(s)}$

Skill Practice: Decomposition and Single Replacement Reactions

Activity Notes

1. a) magnesium phosphide $\longrightarrow$
   magnesium + phosphorus
   b) sodium chloride $\longrightarrow$ sodium + chlorine
   c) strontium oxide $\longrightarrow$ strontium + oxygen
   d) zinc + iron(II) chloride $\longrightarrow$ iron + zinc chloride
   e) aluminium + copper(II) iodide $\longrightarrow$
   copper + aluminium iodide
   f) magnesium + gold(III) nitrate $\longrightarrow$
   gold + magnesium nitrate

2. a) $CaO_{(s)} \longrightarrow Ca_{(s)} + O_{2(g)}$
   b) $NaF_{(s)} \longrightarrow Na_{(s)} + F_{2(g)}$
   c) $Mg_3N_{2(s)} \longrightarrow Mg_{(s)} + N_{2(g)}$
   d) $Fe_{(s)} + Cu(NO_3)_{2(aq)} \longrightarrow Cu_{(s)} + Fe(NO_3)_{3(aq)}$
   e) $Cl_{2(g)} + NaI_{(aq)} \longrightarrow I_{2(s)} + NaCl_{(aq)}$
   f) $Pb_{(s)} + AgNO_{3(aq)} \longrightarrow Ag_{(s)} + Pb(NO_3)_{2(aq)}$

3. a) $2\ FeCl_{3(s)} \longrightarrow 2\ Fe_{(s)} + 3\ Cl_{2(g)}$
   b) $2\ Cu_2O_{(s)} \longrightarrow 4\ Cu_{(s)} + O_{2(g)}$
   c) $2\ LiBr_{(s)} \longrightarrow 2\ Li_{(s)} + Br_{2(l)}$
   d) $3\ Br_{2(l)} + 2\ CrI_{3(aq)} \longrightarrow 2\ CrBr_{3(aq)} + 3\ I_{2(s)}$
   e) $2\ AgNO_{3(aq)} + Cu_{(s)} \longrightarrow 2\ Ag_{(s)} + Cu(NO_3)_{2(aq)}$

4. a) bromine + iron(III) iodide $\longrightarrow$
   iron(III) bromide + iodine
   $Br_{2(l)} + FeI_{3(aq)} \longrightarrow FeBr_{3(aq)} + I_{2(s)}$
   $3\ Br_{2(l)} + 2\ FeI_{3(aq)} \longrightarrow 2\ FeBr_{3(aq)} + 3\ I_{2(s)}$
   b) magnesium + gold(III) fluoride $\longrightarrow$
   magnesium fluoride + gold
   $Mg_{(s)} + AuF_{3(aq)} \longrightarrow MgF_{2(aq)} + Au_{(s)}$
   $3\ Mg_{(s)} + 2\ AuF_{3(aq)} \longrightarrow 3\ MgF_{2(aq)} + 2\ Au_{(s)}$

Activity A10 Inquiry Lab

Analyzing and Interpreting

4. $4\ Fe_{(s)} + 3\ O_{2(g)} \longrightarrow 2\ Fe_2O_{3(s)}$
8. a) $Mg_{(s)} + 2\ AgNO_{3(aq)} \longrightarrow 2\ Ag_{(s)} + Mg(NO_3)_{2(aq)}$
   b) $Cu(NO_3)_{2(aq)} + Mg_{(s)} \longrightarrow Mg(NO_3)_{2(aq)} + Cu_{(s)}$
   c) $2\ AgNO_{3(aq)} + Cu_{(s)} \longrightarrow 2\ Ag_{(s)} + Cu(NO_3)_{2(aq)}$

Practice Problem

9. a) Word equation:
   copper(I) nitrate + potassium bromide $\longrightarrow$
   copper(I) bromide + potassium nitrate
   Skeleton equation: $CuNO_{3(aq)} + KBr_{(aq)} \longrightarrow$
   $CuBr_{(s)} + KNO_{3(aq)}$
   Balanced equation: $CuNO_{3(aq)} + KBr_{(aq)} \longrightarrow$
   $CuBr_{(s)} + KNO_{3(aq)}$
   b) Word equation:
   aluminium chloride + sodium hydroxide $\longrightarrow$
   aluminium hydroxide + sodium chloride
   Skeleton equation: $AlCl_{3(aq)} + NaOH_{(aq)} \longrightarrow$
   $Al(OH)_{3(s)} + NaCl_{(aq)}$
   Balanced equation: $AlCl_{3(aq)} + 3\ NaOH_{(aq)} \longrightarrow$
   $Al(OH)_{3(s)} + 3\ NaCl_{(aq)}$

Activity A11 Quicklab

1–3. a) sodium iodide + silver nitrate $\longrightarrow$
   sodium nitrate + silver iodide
   $NaI_{(aq)} + AgNO_{3(aq)} \longrightarrow NaNO_{3(aq)} + AgI_{(s)}$
   b) iron(III) chloride + sodium hydroxide $\longrightarrow$
   sodium chloride + iron(III) hydroxide
   $FeCl_{3(aq)} + 3\ NaOH_{(aq)} \longrightarrow 3\ NaCl_{(aq)} + Fe(OH)_{3(s)}$
   c) sodium carbonate + calcium chloride $\longrightarrow$
   sodium chloride + calcium carbonate
   $Na_2CO_{3(aq)} + CaCl_{2(aq)} \longrightarrow 2\ NaCl_4 + CaCO_{3(s)}$
   d) no precipitate
   e) silver nitrate + sodium carbonate $\longrightarrow$
   sodium nitrate + silver carbonate
   $2\ AgNO_{3(aq)} + Na_2CO_{3(aq)} \longrightarrow$
   $2\ NaNO_{3(aq)} + Ag_2CO_{3(s)}$

page 103

Practice Problem

10. a) $C_4H_{10(g)} + O_{2(g)} \longrightarrow CO_{2(g)} + H_2O_{(g)}$

b) $Ca(NO_3)_{2(aq)} + Na_3PO_{4(aq)} \rightarrow Ca_3(PO_4)_{2(s)} + NaNO_{3(aq)}$

c) $Ca_{(s)} + AgNO_{3(aq)} \longrightarrow Ca(NO_3)_{2(aq)} + Ag_{(s)}$

d) $Mg_{(s)} + O_{2(g)} \longrightarrow MgO_{(s)}$

e) $AlCl_{3(s)} \longrightarrow Al_{(s)} + Cl_{2(g)}$

page 104

Activity A12 Quicklab

1. copper(II) chloride + aluminium $\longrightarrow$
aluminium chloride + copper

$3\,CuCl_{2(aq)} + 2\,Al_{(s)} \longrightarrow 2\,AlCl_{3(aq)} + 3\,Cu_{(s)}$

4. calcium chloride + sodium carbonate $\longrightarrow$
calcium carbonate + sodium chloride

$CaCl_{2(aq)} + Na_2CO_{3(aq)} \longrightarrow CaCO_{3(s)} + 2\,NaCl_{(aq)}$

page 105

Practice Problems

11. Word equation: lead(IV) nitrate + zinc $\longrightarrow$
zinc nitrate + lead

Skeleton equation: $Pb(NO_3)_{4(aq)} + Zn_{(s)} \longrightarrow$
$Zn(NO_3)_{2(aq)} + Pb_{(s)}$

Balanced equation: $Pb(NO_3)_{4(aq)} + 2\,Zn_{(s)} \longrightarrow$
$2\,Zn(NO_3)_{2(aq)} + Pb_{(s)}$

12. $3\,Ag_{(s)} + Au(NO_3)_{3(aq)} \longrightarrow 3\,AgNO_{3(aq)} + Au_{(s)}$

page 106

A3.3 Check and Reflect

1. a) $CaCl_{2(s)} \longrightarrow Ca_{(s)} + Cl_{2(g)}$ (balanced)

b) $Mg(ClO_4)_{2(s)} + 2\,Na_{(s)} \longrightarrow 2\,NaClO_{4(s)} + Mg_{(s)}$

c) $2\,NaN_{3(s)} \longrightarrow 2\,Na_{(s)} + 3\,N_{2(g)}$

d) $Ca(NO_3)_{2(aq)} + Cu_2SO_{4(aq)} \longrightarrow$
$CaSO_{4(s)} + 2\,CuNO_{3(aq)}$

e) $2\,C_5H_{10(l)} + 15\,O_{2(g)} \longrightarrow 10\,CO_{2(g)} + 10\,H_2O_{(g)}$

f) $Li_4C_{(s)} + 2\,Ca_{(s)} \longrightarrow 4\,Li_{(s)} + Ca_2C_{(s)}$

g) $PbO_{2(s)} \longrightarrow Pb_{(s)} + O_{2(g)}$ (balanced)

h) $CH_{4(g)} + 2\,O_{2(g)} \longrightarrow CO_{2(g)} + 2\,H_2O_{(g)}$

i) $2\,Li_{(s)} + Cl_{2(g)} \longrightarrow 2\,LiCl_{(s)}$

j) $3\,NaI_{(aq)} + AlCl_{3(aq)} \longrightarrow 3\,NaCl_{(aq)} + AlI_{3(s)}$

2. a) $Na_2SO_{4(aq)} + CaCl_{2(aq)} \longrightarrow 2\,NaCl_{(aq)} + CaSO_{4(s)}$

b) $3\,Mg_{(s)} + N_{2(g)} \longrightarrow Mg_3N_{2(s)}$

c) $Sr(OH)_{2(aq)} + PbBr_{2(aq)} \longrightarrow SrBr_{2(aq)} + Pb(OH)_{2(s)}$

d) $2\,Ni(NO_3)_{3(aq)} + 3\,Ca_{(s)} \longrightarrow 3\,Ca(NO_3)_{2(aq)} + 2\,Ni_{(s)}$

e) $CH_{4(g)} + 2\,O_{2(g)} \longrightarrow CO_{2(g)} + 2\,H_2O_{(g)}$

f) $4\,Na_{(s)} + O_{2(g)} \longrightarrow 2\,Na_2O_{(s)}$

g) $N_{2(g)} + 3\,H_{2(g)} \longrightarrow 2\,NH_{3(g)}$

h) $2\,HCl_{(aq)} \longrightarrow H_{2(g)} + Cl_{2(g)}$

i) $2\,AlI_{3(aq)} + 3\,Br_{2(l)} \longrightarrow 2\,AlBr_{3(aq)} + 3\,I_{2(s)}$

---

j) $2\,H_2O_{(l)} + 2\,Na_{(s)} \longrightarrow 2\,NaOH_{(aq)} + H_{2(g)}$

3. a) $Li_2O_{(s)}$

b) $Cu_{(s)}$ and $Cl_{2(g)}$

c) $Al_2(SO_4)_{3(aq)}$ and $Cu_{(s)}$

d) $Ca(NO_3)_{2(aq)}$ and $PbBr_{2(s)}$

e) $CO_{2(g)}$ and $H_2O_{(g)}$

f) $AgCl_{(s)}$ and $KNO_{3(aq)}$

g) $N_{2(g)}$ and $I_{2(s)}$

h) $S_{8(s)}$ and $LiCl_{(aq)}$

i) $Al_2S_{3(s)}$

j) $CO_{2(g)}$ and $H_2O_{(g)}$

4. $3\,Zn_{(s)} + N_{2(g)} \longrightarrow Zn_3N_{2(s)}$

5. $2\,HgO_{(s)} \longrightarrow 2\,Hg_{(l)} + O_{2(g)}$

6. $2\,C_6H_{6(l)} + 15\,O_{2(g)} \longrightarrow 12\,CO_{2(g)} + 6\,H_2O_{(g)}$

7. $Br_{2(l)} + CaI_{2(aq)} \longrightarrow CaBr_{2(aq)} + I_{2(s)}$ (balanced)

8. $Pb(NO_3)_{2(aq)} + 2\,NaI_{(aq)} \longrightarrow 2\,NaNO_{3(aq)} + PbI_{2(s)}$

9. $HCl_{(aq)} + NaOH_{(s)} \longrightarrow NaCl_{(aq)} + H_2O_{(l)}$

10. $C_{12}H_{22}O_{11(s)} + 12\,O_{2(g)} \longrightarrow 12\,CO_{2(g)} + 11\,H_2O_{(g)}$

page 108

Practice Problems

13. 32.05 g/mol

14. 142.05 g/mol

15. 44.01 g/mol

16. 149.12 g/mol

page 109

Practice Problems

17. 2.0×10^2 g

18. 2.00 mol

19. 85.2 mol

20. 0.135 mol

page 112

A3.4 Check and Reflect

5. a) 6.0×10^{23} gold atoms

b) 1.5×10^{24} helium atoms

c) $6.02 \times 10^{24}\ H_{2(g)}$ molecules

d) $3.78 \times 10^{23}\ CO_{2(g)}$ molecules

6. a) 1.2 mol   d) 1.711 mol

b) 0.50 mol   e) 0.928 mol

c) 2.29 mol

7. a) 59 g   d) 3.50 kg

b) 44 g   e) 0.191 g

c) 90 g

8. a) 1 mol

b) 6 g

c) 1.20×10^{25} molecules

9. 31.8 g

10. 3.34×10^{25} molecules of water

11. 2.4×10^{24} atoms

13. $CH_{4(g)} + 2\,O_{2(g)} \longrightarrow CO_{2(g)} + 2\,H_2O_{(g)}$
30 moles of water

page 113

A3.0 Section Review

9. a) 3.00 mol

   b) 55.49 mol

   c) 0.500 mol

   d) 0.2824 mol

   e) 0.0102 mol

10. a) 0.20 kg

   b) 0.36 kg

   c) 202 g

   d) 36.7 g

   e) 427 g

12. a) $3 Br_{2(l)} + 2 Al_{(s)} \longrightarrow 2 AlBr_{3(s)}$

   b) $(NH_4)_2CO_{3(s)} + Ca(NO_3)_{2(aq)} \longrightarrow$
   $$2 NH_4NO_{3(aq)} + CaCO_{3(s)}$$

   c) $NaOH_{(s)} + HCl_{(aq)} \longrightarrow NaCl_{(aq)} + H_2O_{(l)}$ (balanced)

13. a) $2 KBrO_{3(s)} \longrightarrow 2 KBr_{(s)} + 3 O_{2(g)}$

   b) $2 C_2H_{2(g)} + 5 O_{2(g)} \longrightarrow 4 CO_{2(g)} + 2 H_2O_{(g)}$

   c) $4 AuCl_{3(aq)} + 3 Pb_{(s)} \longrightarrow 3 PbCl_{4(aq)} + 4 Au_{(s)}$

   d) $6 K_{(s)} + N_{2(g)} \longrightarrow 2 K_3N_{(s)}$

   e) $Sn(NO_3)_{4(aq)} + 2 Ca(OH)_{2(s)} \longrightarrow$
   $$2 Ca(NO_3)_{2(aq)} + Sn(OH)_{4(s)}$$

14. a) $F_{2(g)} + Ca_{(s)} \longrightarrow CaF_{2(s)}$ (balanced)

   b) $3 Cl_{2(g)} + 2 NiBr_{3(aq)} \longrightarrow 2 NiCl_{3(aq)} + 3 Br_{2(l)}$

   c) $2 C_5H_{10(g)} + 15 O_{2(g)} \longrightarrow 10 CO_{2(g)} + 10 H_2O_{(g)}$

   d) $2 KBr_{(s)} \longrightarrow 2 K_{(s)} + Br_{(l)}$

   e) $AlF_{3(aq)} + Na_3PO_{4(aq)} \longrightarrow AlPO_{4(s)} + 3 NaF_{(aq)}$

16. 4.60 g

17. $9.03 \times 10^{23} CO_{2(g)}$ molecules

page 115

Unit A Project

1. magnesium + hydrochloric acid
   $$\longrightarrow \text{magnesium chloride + hydrogen}$$
   $Mg_{(s)} + 2 HCl_{(aq)} \longrightarrow MgCl_{2(s)} + H_{2(g)}$

2. magnesium sulfate + sodium carbonate $\longrightarrow$
   sodium sulfate + magnesium carbonate
   $MgSO_{4(aq)} + Na_2CO_{3(aq)} \longrightarrow Na_2SO_{4(aq)} + MgCO_{3(s)}$

3. magnesium carbonate $\longrightarrow$
   magnesium oxide + carbon dioxide
   $MgCO_{3(s)} \longrightarrow MgO_{(s)} + CO_{2(g)}$

pages 117–121

Unit A Unit Review

14.

Element	Mass Number	Protons	Neutrons
carbon	13	6	7
bromine	79	35	44
bromine	81	35	46
chlorine	36	17	19
iron	57	26	31
sodium	33	11	22

15.

Atom or Ion	Overall Charge	Protons	Electrons	Symbol
sulfur atom	0	16	16	S
sulfide ion	2–	16	18	S^{2-}
lithium ion	1+	3	2	Li^+
oxide ion	2–	8	10	O^{2-}
chloride ion	1–	17	18	Cl^-
iron(II) ion	2+	26	24	Fe^{2+}
nitride ion	3–	7	10	N^{3-}

22. a) $Cl_{2(g)} + 2 KBr_{(aq)} \longrightarrow 2 KCl_{(aq)} + Br_{2(l)}$

   b) $4 Li_{(s)} + O_{2(g)} \longrightarrow 2 Li_2O_{(g)}$

   c) $2 C_2H_{6(g)} + 7 O_{2(g)} \longrightarrow 6 H_2O_{(g)} + 4 CO_{2(g)}$

   d) $6 Na_{(s)} + N_{2(g)} \longrightarrow 2 Na_3N_{(s)}$

   e) $2 (NH_4)_3PO_{4(aq)} + 3 Ca(NO_3)_{2(aq)} \longrightarrow$
   $$6 NH_4NO_{3(aq)} + Ca_3(PO_4)_{2(s)}$$

   f) $CaCO_{3(s)} \longrightarrow CaO_{(s)} + CO_{2(g)}$ (balanced)

33. a) $LiCl_{(s)}$

   b) $Ba_3N_{2(s)}$

   c) $ZnO_{(s)}$

   d) $Ag_2CO_{3(s)}$

   e) $Ca(NO_2)_{2(s)}$

   f) $RbHSO_{4(s)}$

   g) $Cd_3(PO_4)_{2(s)}$

   h) $Co(OH)_{3(s)}$

   i) $Cu(MnO_4)_{2(s)}$

   j) $CrO_{3(s)}$

   k) $Fe(ClO_3)_{3(s)}$

34. a) sodium phosphide

   b) magnesium sulfide

   c) beryllium chloride

   d) ammonium sulfide

   e) cesium nitride

   f) zinc iodide

   g) iron(II) fluoride

   h) iron(III) hydrogen sulfide

   i) gold(I) nitrate

   j) lead(IV) permanganate

   k) sodium acetate or sodium ethanoate

35. a) $N_2S_{(g)}$ d) $H_2S_{(g)}$

b) $SBr_{2(g)}$ e) $CH_{4(g)}$

c) $ClF_{(g)}$ f) $PCl_{5(g)}$

36. a) tetraphosphorus decaoxide

b) nitrogen dioxide

c) nitrogen trichloride

d) xenon hexafluoride

e) hydrogen peroxide

f) ammonia

46. a) $I_{2(s)} + Hg_{(l)} \longrightarrow HgI_{2(s)}$

b) $2\ K_3PO_{4(aq)} + 3\ Sr(OH)_{2(aq)} \longrightarrow$

$$6\ KOH_{(aq)} + Sr_3(PO_4)_{2(s)}$$

c) $Mg_{(s)} + 2\ HCl_{(aq)} \longrightarrow MgCl_{2(aq)} + H_{2(g)}$

47. a) $CaI_{2(s)} + 2\ AgNO_{3(aq)} \longrightarrow Ca(NO_3)_{2(aq)} + 2\ AgI_{(s)}$

b) $2\ C_6H_{14(l)} + 19\ O_{2(g)} \longrightarrow 12\ CO_{2(g)} + 14\ H_2O_{(g)}$

c) $MgCO_{3(s)} \longrightarrow MgO_{(s)} + CO_{2(g)}$ (balanced)

d) $3\ Li_2SO_{3(aq)} + 2\ Au(NO_3)_{3(aq)} \longrightarrow$

$$6\ LiNO_{3(aq)} + Au_2(SO_3)_{3(s)}$$

e) $16\ Cs_{(s)} + S_{8(s)} \longrightarrow 8\ Cs_2S_{(s)}$

f) $2\ Al_{(s)} + 3\ CuSO_{4(aq)} \longrightarrow Al_2(SO_4)_{3(aq)} + 3\ Cu_{(s)}$

48. a) Skeleton equation: $CaF_{2(aq)} + I_{2(s)} \longrightarrow$

$$CaI_{2(aq)} + F_{2(g)}$$

Balanced equation: $CaF_{2(aq)} + I_{2(s)} \longrightarrow$

$$CaI_{2(aq)} + F_{2(g)}$$

b) Skeleton equation: $RbI_{(s)} \longrightarrow Rb_{(s)} + I_{2(s)}$

Balanced equation: $2\ RbI_{(s)} \longrightarrow 2\ Rb_{(s)} + I_{2(s)}$

c) Skeleton equation: $C_3H_{8(g)} + O_{2(g)} \longrightarrow$

$$CO_{2(g)} + H_2O_{(g)}$$

Balanced equation: $C_3H_{8(g)} + 5\ O_{2(g)} \longrightarrow$

$$3\ CO_{2(g)} + 4\ H_2O_{(g)}$$

d) Skeleton equation: $Cu(ClO_4)_{2(aq)} + Li_3PO_{4(aq)} \longrightarrow$

$$LiClO_{4(aq)} + Cu_3(PO_4)_{2(s)}$$

Balanced equation:

$3\ Cu(ClO_4)_{2(aq)} + 2\ Li_3PO_{4(aq)} \longrightarrow$

$$6\ LiClO_{4(aq)} + Cu_3(PO_4)_{2(s)}$$

e) Skeleton equation: $Zn_{(s)} + FeBr_{3(aq)} \longrightarrow$

$$ZnBr_{2(aq)} + Fe_{(s)}$$

Balanced equation: $3\ Zn_{(s)} + 2\ FeBr_{3(aq)} \longrightarrow$

$$3\ ZnBr_{2(aq)} + 2\ Fe_{(s)}$$

49. a) 2.00 moles d) 0.00177 moles

b) 0.5002 moles e) 83 moles

c) 4.000 moles

50. a) 216 g d) 736 g

b) 1.0×10^2 g e) 83.3 g

c) 3.2×10^2 g

54. a) sodium oxide

b) aluminium oxalate

c) methanol

d) $NH_4HOOCCOO_{(s)}$

e) $C_3H_{8(g)}$

f) $Ru(H_2PO_4)_{4(s)}$

g) dinitrogen tetroxide

h) tungsten(VI) dichromate

i) osmium(VIII) oxide

j) $C_6H_{12}O_{6(s)}$

k) $Pt(CN)_{4(s)}$

l) $Na_2S_2O_{3(s)}$

56. a) 1.2×10^{24} Al atoms

b) 2.17×10^{25} $SO_{3(g)}$ molecules

c) 1.4×10^{22} $He_{(g)}$ atoms

57. a) 0.155 mol

b) 2.71 mol

c) 0.65 mol

page 128
Practice Problems

1. 1.1×10^2 m/s

2. 5.76×10^4 s

3. 28 m

page 130
Practice Problem

4. b) 5.0×10^2 m/s

page 132
Skill Practice: Using Significant Digits

1. a) 5 d) 2

b) 6 e) 2

c) 5

2. a) 5.3 cm c) 3.55 km^2

b) 3.0 km d) 21 km/h

3. a) 6.83×10^{-4} c) 6.2×10^4

b) 122 d) 0.06

page 133
Practice Problem

5. b) 0 m/s^2

c) 50 m

page 135–136
B1.1 Check and Reflect

8. 4.17 m/s **10.** 4.06×10^3 km

9. 1.50 s **11.** 5.00 h

12. a) 5 m/s

13. a) 0

14. c) 9.0 cm/s

15. c) 6.3 cm

16. 1.80 m/s

17. 1.78 m/s

page 139
Practice Problem
6.

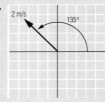

page 140
Practice Problem
7.

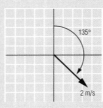

page 141
Practice Problems
8. a) 22.0 m [E]

b) 1.47 m/s [E]

9. 112 m [N]

10. 0.444 h

page 143
Practice Problem
11. b) 25 m/s [E]

page 145
B1.2 Check and Reflect
3. vector 1 = [60°]

vector 2 = [215°]

4. vector 1 = [30°]

vector 2 = [245°]

5. a) 25.0 m

b) 5.0 m [N]

c) 1.56 m/s

d) 0.313 m/s [N]

6. b) slope$_1$ = 52 cm/s [E]

slope$_2$ = −52 cm/s [W]

page 147
Practice Problems
12. 13 m/s^2 [up]

13. 50 m/s^2

14. 333 m/s^2

15. −2.50 m/s^2 [E]

page 154
B1.3 Check and Reflect
5. −5.0 m/s^2 [N]

6. −3.75 m/s^2 [W]

7. 0.250 m/s^2

8. 7.80 m/s [N]

9. 5.01 s

10. c) 2.00 cm/s^2

page 160
Practice Problems
18. 9.75 × 10^5 J

19. 2.3 × 10^3 N

page 160
Practice Problem
20. 2.2 × 10^4 J

page 161
B1.4 Check and Reflect
6. a) 147 J

b) 50.0 J

c) 0.200 J

7. 13.4 N

8. 16.7 m

9. 39.0 J

10. a) 5.0 × 10^3 J

page 162–163
B1.0 Section Review
8. a) 15.0 J

9. 1.62 m/s

10. 292 m

11. 5.25 h

12. b) 0.00 m/s^2

c) about 100 m

13. a) 7.0 m

b) −3.0 m [W]

14. a) vector A = 75°

vector B = 140°

b) vector A = 15°

vector B = 310°

15. a) 800 m

b) 200 m [N]

c) 3.20 m/s

d) 0.800 m/s [N]

16. b) 3.00 m/s [N]

17. 0.563 m/s^2

18. −12.0 m/s [W]

19. 3.00 s

21. 20 N [E]

22. 600 J

23. 1.1 × 10^2 J

24. 35.0 N

27. 103 km/h [E]

page 174
Practice Problem
1. 981 J

page 175
Practice Problems
2. 5.99 m

3. 49.9 kg

page 178
B2.2 Check and Reflect
4. a) 96.0 J
   b) 96.0 J
5. 129 N
6. 1.48 m

7. 375 J
8. 3.20×10^3 N
9. 2.06×10^3 J

page 179
Practice Problems
4. 1.82×10^{-20} J

5. 7.4 kg

page 181
Practice Problems
6. 45.0 m/s

7. 2.2 m/s

page 182
B2.3 Check and Reflect
5. a) 36.0 J
   b) 6.00×10^4 J
   c) 39.2 J
6. 20.0 kg

7. a) 4.00 m/s
   b) 0.470 m/s
10. a) 80.0 J
    b) 160 J

page 183
Practice Problems
8. 97.9 J
9. 1.09×10^3 J

10. 899 J

page 184
Practice Problems
11. 15.3 m/s

12. 0.130 m

page 185
Practice Problems
13. 0.313 J

14. 1.40 m/s

pages 186–187
Activity B9 Inquiry Lab
7. 2.40 m/s
9. 2.88 J
10. 2.88 J

15. 2.40 m/s
17. 2.88 J
18. 2.88 J

page 189
B2.4 Check and Reflect
5. a) 4.00 J
   d) 4.00 J
   e) 28.3 m/s
   f) 4.00 J
   g) 40.8 m

6. 4.23 m/s
7. 4.16 J
9. a) 29.4 J
   b) 5.42 m/s

page 197
B2.0 Section Review
20. 45.0 J
21. 9.81 J

23. 800 J
25. 5.7 m/s

page 216
Practice Problem
1. 34.9%

page 217
Practice Problem
2. 13 J

page 217
Practice Problem
3. 3.13%

page 220
B3.3 Check and Reflect
5. a) 1000 J
   b) 800 J
   c) 800 J
   d) 200 J
   e) 80%

7. 65.7%
8. 4.20×10^3 J
9. 2.80×10^5 J

page 228
B3.0 Section Review
14. a) 3.5×10^2 J

pages 232–237
Unit B Unit Review
8. 26.0 J
31. 2.00 h
32. a) 20.0 m
    b) 0 m
    c) 5.0 m/s
    d) 0.0 m/s
33. 8.33 m/s^2 [N]
34. 2.0 J
36. 500 J
39. 7.19×10^{-3} J
40. 20.0 m/s

41. 1.96×10^3 J
42. 988 m
43. 17.2 m/s
46. 2.19×10^3 m
53. 35.0%
54. 9.33×10^3 J
67. 0.650 m
75. d) 7.5×10^{-3} m/s
76. e) 0
    g) 5.3×10^{-2} m
77. 25 J

page 244
Skill Practice
a) 25×
b) 1000×

page 246
C1.1 Check and Reflect
6. 1500 μm
7. 375 μm
8. 50 : 1

page 265
C1.0 Section Review
14. 400 μm
15. 100×

page 289
Practice Problems
1. a) 1.7; b) 1.1
2. $\dfrac{2lw + 2lh + 2wh}{lwh}$; 3.8
3. $\dfrac{3}{r}$; a) 1.4 b) 0.70

page 293
C2.4 Check and Reflect
8. a) 96 cm^2; b) 64 cm^3; c) 64 cm^2;
   d) 128 cm^2; e) 32 cm^3; 64 cm^3
   f) surface area increases from 96 cm^2 to 128 cm^2; volume remains the same; surface area: volume increases from 1.5 to 2.0.

page 294

Cell #	Length (cm)	Width (cm)	Height (cm)	Surface Area (A) cm^2	Volume (v) m^3	Surface Area to Volume ratio (A/v)
1	5	3	2	62	30	2.1
2	12	5	1	154	60	2.6
3	40	27	20	4840	21 600	0.22

17. Cell #2

page 335
Unit C Unit Review
39. 300 μm

page 367
Activity D9 QuickLab
2. 30%
3. 100%
4. 70%

page 379
Practice Problems
1. 15.1 kJ
2. 32.3 kJ
3. 1.26 kJ
4. 30.2 kJ

page 380
Practice Problems
5. 20°C
6. water 0.119°C, iron 1.11°C
7. 0.897 J/g·°C
8. 0.130 J/g·°C

page 386
Practice Problems
9. 6.01 kJ/mol
10. 19.2 kJ
11. 2.50 mol
12. 0.385 kJ/mol

page 387
Practice Problems
13. 3.48 kJ/mol
14. 40.7 kJ/mol
15. 1.13×10^3 kJ

page 390
D2.3 Check and Reflect
14. 1.6×10^2 kJ
15. 168 kJ
16. 36.0°C
17. 15.0 g
18. 40.7 kJ/mol
20. 15.0 kJ
21. 12.0 mol

pages 408-409
D2.0 Section Review
32. 37.3°C
33. 14 J
34. 110 g
35. 2.3×10^2 kJ
36. 40.7 J/mol
37. 1.02×10^3 kJ
38. 3.34 kJ

pages 435-439
Unit D Unit Review
85. 4.19×10^6 J or 4.19×10^3 kJ
86. 25.7°C
87. 15.0 g
88. 0.13 J/g·°C
89. 66.7 J
90. 81.3 J
91. 4.99 mol
92. 63 g

Index

Photo Credits and Acknowledgements

The publisher wishes to thank the following sources for photographs, illustrations, and other materials used in this book. Care has been taken to determine and locate ownership of copyright material used in this text. We will gladly receive information enabling us to rectify any errors or omissions in credits.

Photography

Cover image: Miguel S. Salmeron/Getty Images/Taxi; Unit Opener pp.2-3 Colin Cuthbert/SPL/Photo Researchers, Inc.; p.4 (top) J. Pinkston and L Stern/USGS; p.6 CP Picture Archive (Leah Hennel); p.8 Richard Kellaway/PC Services; p.12 Cheryl A. Ertelt/Visuals Unlimited; p.13 (top) Harry Taylor/Dorling Kindersley; p.13 (bottom) Richard Megna/Fundamental Photographs, NYC; p.14 Billy Hustace/Stone/Getty Images; p.18 (top) Patrick J. Endres/Visuals Unlimited; p.18 (bottom) Wally Eberhart/Visuals Unlimited; p.19 Canadian Museum of Civilization, catalogue no. NaPi-2:50-3, photographer Merle Toole, image no. S95-24915; p.20 Glenbow Archives NA-1700-62; p.21 Edgar Fahs Smith Collection/University of Pennsylvania Library; p.24 Department of Physics, Imperial College/SPL/Publiphoto; p.26 Mike Wysocki; p.28 Peter Adams/Taxi/Getty Images; p.31 (top and bottom) Richard Megna/Fundamental Photographs, NYC; p.31 (middle) Tom Bochsler Photography Limited/Prentice Hall Inc., Ltd.; p.35 Richard Megna/Fundamental Photographs, NYC; p.40 Richard Kellaway/PC Services; p.45 Mark S. Skalny/Visuals Unlimited; p.54 Albert Copley/Visuals Unlimited; p.59 Dorling Kindersley; p.61 Nuridsany & Perennou/Photo Researchers, Inc.; p.62 Richard Megna/Fundamental Photographs, NYC; p.63 Tom Bochsler Photography Limited/Prentice Hall, Inc.; p.72 E.H. Gill/Custom Medical Stock Photo; p.74 Richard Kellaway/PC Services; p.78 NASA; p.79 (far left) EyeWire/Getty Images; p.79 (middle left) Dorling Kindersley; p.79 (middle right) Richard Megna/Fundamental Photographs, NYC; p.79 (far right) Richard Kellaway/PC Services; p.80 Benelux Press/Photo Researchers, Inc.; p.81 (top inset) Spike Mafford/PhotoDisc/Getty Images; p.81 (bottom) Tom Bochsler Photography Limited/Prentice Hall, Inc.; p.82 Lester V. Bergman/Corbis/Magma; p.84 Tom Bochsler Photography Limited/Prentice Hall, Inc.; p.86 (top) Donald Clegg & Roxie Wilson/Prentice Hall, Inc.; p.86 (bottom) Richard Megna/Fundamental Photographs, NYC; p.87 (top) Tom Bochsler Photography Limited/Prentice Hall, Inc.; p.87 (bottom) Ballard Power Systems; p.88 Richard Kellaway/PC Services; p.91 Richard Megna/Fundamental Photographs, NYC; p.92 Tom Bochsler Photography Limited/Prentice Hall, Inc.; p.93 Dorling Kindersley; p.95 Lucidio Studio, Inc./SuperStock; p.100 Richard Megna/Fundamental Photographs, NYC; p.102 Richard Kellaway/PC Services; p.103 Carey B. Van Loon; p.107 Tom Pantages; 122 PhotoDisc/Getty Images; 124 bottom © NASA; 126 Associated Press/Pascall Pavani; 127 © Michael S. Yamashita/CORBIS/MAGMA; 164 © David Samuel Robbins/CORBIS/MAGMA; 167 © DK Images; 171 Courtesy of Perry Ambrose.; 173 Photo by Mike Sturk. Courtesy of the Calgary Stampede.; 175 © Kevin Fleming/CORBIS/MAGMA; 190 CP Picture Archive/Jacques Boissinot; 198 Rube Goldberg is the ® and © of Rube Goldberg Inc.; 204 left © Francis Lepine/VALAN PHOTOS; 204 right © J.A. Wilkinson/VALAN PHOTOS; 207 top © Bettmann/CORBIS/MAGMA; 208 middle © DK Images; 209 © Bettmann/CORBIS/MAGMA; 211 © Bettmann/CORBIS/MAGMA; 215 © John Fowler/VALAN PHOTOS; 216 © Guido Alberto Rossi/Getty Images; 221 © Phillip Norton/VALAN PHOTOS OR © Wayne Lankinen/VALAN PHOTOS; 222 © Lone Pine Photo; 224 top Associated Press, AP/Franck Prevel; 224 bottom © Phillip Norton/VALAN PHOTOS; 225 Associated Press, AP; 238-239 Photo by Wernher Krutein/photovault.com; 238 inset © Eye of Science/Photo Researchers, Inc.; 240 Courtesy of EPCOR.; 242 top © Photo Researchers, Inc.; 242 middle © Photo Researchers, Inc.; 242 bottom © Dr Ryder/Jason Burns/Phototake USA; 242 bottom © Science Photo Library/Publiphoto; 244 left © Science VU/Visuals Unlimited; 244 right © Bettmann/CORBIS/MAGMA; 248 right Courtesy of the Institute Pasteur, Paris.; 251 left Courtesy of Brian J. Ford, Research Biologist, email: bjford@science.demon.co.uk; 251 middle © Science Photo Library/Photo Researchers Inc.; 251 right © Science Photo Library/Photo Researchers Inc.; 254 left Visuals Unlimited/David M. Phillips; 254 right © ISM/J.C.Revy/Phototake USA; 255 top left © Carolina Biological/Visuals Unlimited; 255 top middle left © Carolina Biological/Visuals Unlimited; 255 top middle right © G.W. Willis MD/Visuals Unlimited; 255 top right © Cabisco/Visuals Unlimited; 255 bottom left Corel; 255 bottom right Corel; 256 bottom left © Science Photo Library/Publiphoto; 256 bottom right © M.I. Walker/Photo Researchers, Inc.; 257 © Science Photo Library/Publiphoto; 258 left © Science Photo Library/Publiphoto; 258 right © Science Photo Library/Publiphoto; 259 top © Science Photo Library/Publiphoto; 259 bottom left © Science Photo Library/Publiphoto; 259 bottom right © Pascal Geotgheluck/Science Photo Library/Publiphoto; 260 left © K.G. Murti/Visuals Unlimited; 260 middle left © Don W.Fawcett/Visuals Unlimited; 260 middle right © Don W.Fawcett/Visuals Unlimited; 260 right © RMF/Visuals Unlimited; 261 top © Science Photo Library/Publiphoto; 261 bottom © Science Photo Library/Publiphoto; 264 © Kenneth Eward/Biografx/Photo Researchers, Inc.; 266 © Victor Last/Geographical Visual Aids; 267 © Biophoto Associates/Photo Researchers, Inc.; 268 fig. C2.3 © R.Calentine/Visuals Unlimited; 268 fig. C2.4 © Martha Powell/Visuals Unlimited; 268 fig. C2.5 a © K.G.Murti/Visuals Unlimited; 268 fig. C2.5 b © D.M.Phillips/Visuals Unlimited; 269 fig. C2.6 © Don W. Fawcett/Visuals Unlimited; 269 fig. C2.7 © David M. Phillips/Visuals Unlimited; 269 fig. C2.8 © D.Fawcett/Visuals Unlimited; 269 fig. C2.9 © Don W.Fawcett/Visuals Unlimited; 272 Pearson Dorling-Kindersley; 273 © Harold N. Edwards/Visuals Unlimited; 281 right L.A.Hufnagel,"Ultrastructural Aspects of Chemoreception in Ciliated Protists ciliophoral." Journal of Electron Microscopy Technique,1991. Photomicrograph by Jurgen Bohmer and Linda

Hufnagel, University of Rhode Island.; 281 left cRobert Brons/Biological Photo Service; 284 © Hans Golderbloom/Visuals Unlimited; 293 left © TH Foto-Werbung/Phototake USA; 293 right © Mark Gibson/Visuals Unlimited; 296 © Ken Wagner/Phototake USA; 297 top © M.Abbey/Visuals Unlimited; 297 bottom © Walt Anderson/Visuals Unlimited; 298 top left (c) Cabisco/Visuals Unlimited; 298 bottom left (c) John D. Cunningham/Visuals Unlimited; 298 top right (c) Biophoto Associates, Photo Researchers, Inc.; 298 middle right Biodisc/Visuals Unlimited; 298 bottom right (c) Andrew Syred/Photo Researchers, Inc.; 299 top © Adam Hart-Davis/Photo Researchers, Inc.; 299 bottom left © Biophoto Associates/Photo Researchers, Inc.; 299 bottom right © John D. Cunningham/Visuals Unlimited; 300 top left © Jack M.Bostrack/Visuals Unlimited; 300 middle left © George Wilder/Visuals Unlimited; 300 bottom © Cabisco/Visuals Unlimited; 301 top left © Biodisc/Visuals Unlimited; 301 top right © V.A.Wilmot/Visuals Unlimited; 301 bottom left © David M.Phillips/Visuals Unlimited; 301 bottom right © VU/Gustav Verderber/Visuals Unlimited; 303 © R.Calentine/Visuals Unlimited; 305 left Courtesy of Brian J. Ford, Research Biologist, email: bjford@science.demon.co.uk; 305 right © Science Photo Library/Publiphoto; 309 © Biodisc/Visuals Unlimited; 312 © John D. Cunningham/Visuals Unlimited; 313 Dr. Jeremy Burgess/Science Photo Library/Publiphoto; 314 left © John D. Cunningham/Visuals Unlimited; 314 right © Andrew Syred/Science Photo Library; 315 © Parks Canada, Banff National Park; 317 left © Valerie Price/Dorling Kindersley Media Library; 317 right © Clive Streeter/Dorling Kindersley Media Library; 320 left © Kevin & Betty Collins/Visuals Unlimited; 320 right © Jack Bostrack/Visuals Unlimited; 323 © Dr. Jeremy Burgess/Photo Researchers; 329 Courtesy of Dr. Olga Kovalchuk; Unit Opener pp.338-339 Corbis, Magma/ p.340 Galen Rowell, Corbis, Magma/ p.341 photo courtesy of Science Museum of Minnesota, painting by Jerome Connolly/ p.342 Andries Blouw, Fisheries and Oceans Canada/ p.346 (top) Frans Brouwers, Take Stock Inc./ p.346 (bottom) PhotoDisc, Inc./ p.349 (top) Charles O. Cecil, Visuals Unlimited/ p.349 (bottom) Dr. A. Farquhar, Take Stock Inc./ p.350 (left) F. Brouwers, Take Stock Inc./ p.350 (right) Richard Kellaway, PC Services/ p.351 (top and centre) PhotoDisc, Inc./ p.351 (bottom left) Erwin Nielsen, Visuals Unlimited/ p.351 (bottom centre) Michael S. Quinton, Visuals Unlimited/ p.351 (bottom right) Bill Beatty, Visuals Unlimited/ p.353 courtesy of U.S. Geological Survey, Denver/ p.356 Craig Popoff, Take Stock Inc./ p.362 (top) Brian Stablyk, Take Stock Inc./ p.362 (bottom) PhotoDisc, Inc./ p.363 (top left and right) Lyle Korytar, Take Stock Inc./ p.363 (bottom map)NASA, http://earthobservatory.nasa.gov/ and Crystal Schaaf, http://modis.gsfc.nasa.gov/ / p.377 (bottom and inset) PhotoDisc, Inc./ p.383 (centre and bottom) PhotoDisc, Inc./ p.389 CP Picture Archives (Calgary Herald – Leah Hennel)/ p.394 James L. Amos, Corbis, Magma/ p.395 Jacob Taposchaner, Taxi, Getty Images/ p.396 T. Kitchin, firstlight.ca/ p.397 Lowell Georgia, Corbis, Magma/ p.398 Wolfgang Kaehler, Corbis, Magma/ p.399 SuperStock, Inc./ p.400 (top right) Wolfgang Kaehler, Corbis, Magma/ p.400 (centre right) T. Kitchin, firstlight.ca/ p.400 (bottom right) Jacob Taposchaner, Taxi, Getty Images/ p.400 (top left) SuperStock, Inc./ p.400 (bottom left) James L. Amos, Corbis, Magma/ p.400 (centre) Lowell Georgia, Corbis, Magma/ p.403 Joe McDonald, Visuals Unlimited/ p.410 (top diagram) Dai, A., T.M.L. Wigley, G.A. Meehl, and W.M. Washington, 2001: Effects of stabilizing atmospheric CO2 on global climate in the next two centuries. Geophys. Res. Lett., vol.28, pp. 4511-4514/ p.411 Kim Stallknecht, Take Stock Inc./ p.413 Glenbow Archives NA-1873-1/ p.414 Richard Kellaway, PC Services/ p.415 PhotoDisc, Inc./ p.417 CP Photo Archives (The Calgary Sun – Carlos Amat)/ p.419 (top) Bill Beatty, Visuals Unlimited/ p.419 (bottom) Richard Kellaway, PC Services and courtesy of Intergovernmental Panel on Climate Change/ p.420 University of Victoria Photographic Services/ p.421 (top) Joe Waters, Nasa Jet Propulsion Laboratory, NASA/ p.421 (bottom) UN-DPI Photo/ p.424 Reuters NewMedia Inc., Corbis, Magma/ p.425 (top diagram) PanCanadian Energy/ p.426 PhotoDisc, Inc./ p.427 (top) Dave Reede, Take Stock Inc./ p.427 (bottom) Natural Resources Canada, Canadian Forest Service/ p.428 PhotoDisc, Inc./ p.429 (top) Honda Canada Inc./ p.429 (second from top) courtesy of Vision Quest Windelectric Inc./ p.429 (third from top) Rick Rudnicki, Take Stock Inc./ p.429 (fourth from top) PhotoDisc, Inc/ p.429 (bottom) PanCanadian Energy.

The publisher wishes to thank the following sources for diagram reference or reproduction. Page 4 (bottom map) Reproduced from http://www.oilandgasinternational.com with permission, Oil and Gas International.
p.9 (MSDS sheet) Courtesy of Agrium Inc.

Illustrations
AMID Studios
Kevin Cheng
Crowle Art Group
François Escamel
Dave McKay
Mike Opsahl
Dave Mazierski
NSV Productions
Dusan Petricic
Cynthia Watada

Hay may pagkain ka? gutom na ako as in!
ang ingay ng tummy ko hahaha XD

Nasa locker ko :"
may saging ato

hndi na nay. hahaha. kainin
mo na yun! #healthyliving
hohoha XD

Ahh
Laus!
Ge na. aral na
tuo!

ayy okay okay
bibili nlng ako
ng food sa
caf. or inumin
at least.

ge. bigay ko
na rin yung
saging

PIANO · VOCAL · GUITAR

W9-CTA-845

Christian Christmas Hits

ISBN 0-634-08239-6

HAL•LEONARD®
CORPORATION
7777 W. BLUEMOUND RD. P.O. BOX 13819 MILWAUKEE, WI 53213

Visit Hal Leonard Online at
www.halleonard.com

contents

ANGELS WE HAVE HEARD ON HIGH

Traditional French Carol
Arranged by RICK HEIL,
TOM MICHAEL and TODD SHAY

(An - gels ___ we have ___ heard on ___ high.)

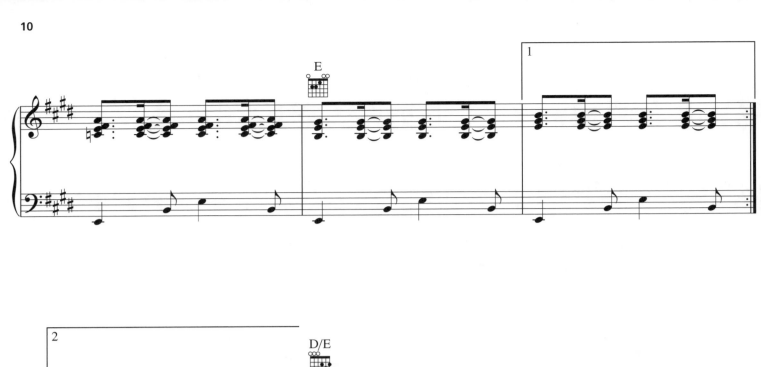

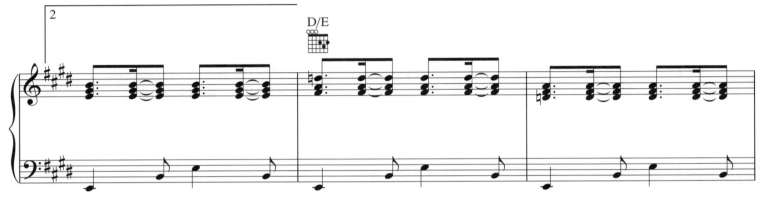

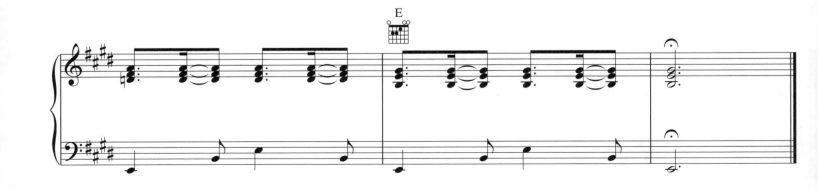

BABE IN THE STRAW

Words and Music by STEVE HINDALONG
and DERRI DAUGHERTY

BREATH OF HEAVEN
(Mary's Song)

Words and Music by AMY GRANT
and CHRIS EATON

CHILD OF LOVE

Words and Music by STEVE HINDALONG,
MARK D. LEE and MATTHEW WEST

THE CHRISTMAS STAR

Words and Music by KIMMIE RHODES
and KEVIN SAVIGAR

Easy four

On a mag - ic night __ in __ Beth -

- le - hem, __ on the birth - day of __ a Boy, __ the __

To Coda ⊕

souls who search ___ for peace _____ on earth, _____ it's the

Christ - mas star ___ that ___ lights _____ the way.

For the

way. There's a light ev - 'ry - one can see, a song for ev - 'ry

bright-er, _____ oh, _____ ev-'ry day. _____

Christ-mas star, _____ ooh, _____ light the way. _____

Christ-mas star _____ that _____ lights _____ the way.

rit.

CHRISTMASTIME

Words and Music by MICHAEL W. SMITH
and JOANNA CARLSON

Ring Christ- mas bells, ring them loud with a mes- sage bring- ing peace on the earth, tid- ings of good cheer! ___

Come, car- ol- ers, come and join with the an- gels sing- ing, "Joy to the world!" Christ- mas-

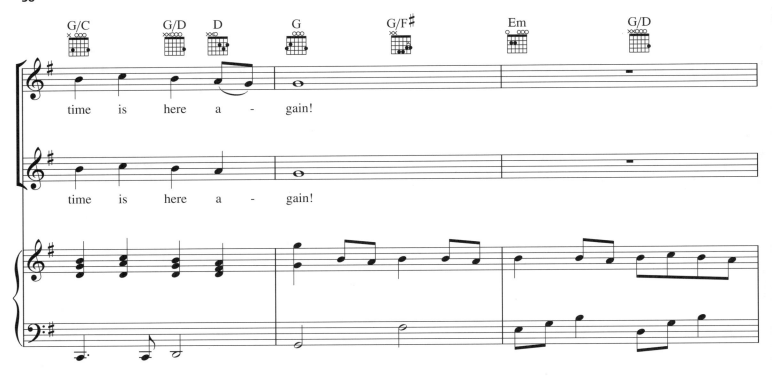

time is here a - gain!

time is here a - gain!

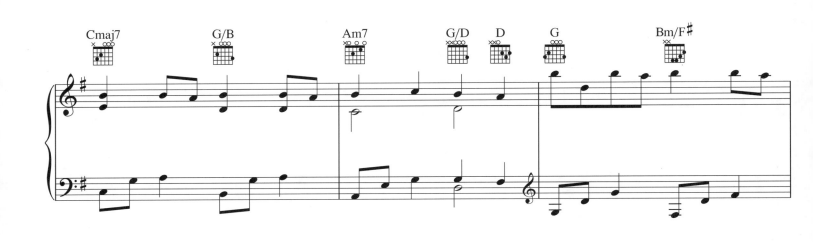

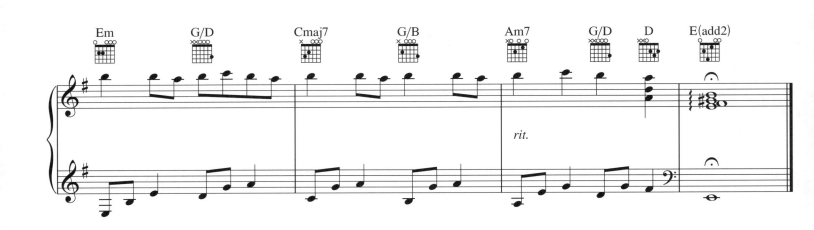

rit.

A CRADLE PRAYER

Words and Music by REBECCA ST. JAMES
and CHARLES GARRETT

DON'T SAVE IT ALL
FOR CHRISTMAS DAY

Words and Music by CELINE DION,
PETER ZIZZO and RIC WAKE

Don't get so bus-y that you miss

* Key of recording: Db

48

EMMANUEL

Words and Music by
MICHAEL W. SMITH

LIGHT A CANDLE

Words and Music by JOEL LINDSEY
and WAYNE HAUN

GOING HOME FOR CHRISTMAS

Words and Music by STEVEN CURTIS CHAPMAN
and JAMES ISAAC ELLIOT

though our hearts _ still ache, __ we know _ that as we cel - e - brate, __

_ she's sing - in' with the her - ald an - gels and heav-en's

glow - in' on __ her face. _____

And now _____ she's home for Christ -

HALLELUJAH

Words and Music by
DARLENE ZSCHECH

IT'S THE THOUGHT

Words and Music by
TWILA PARIS

lov - ing
And a lov - ing

thought   sends   us   out   to   find   some - thing
thought   sent   a   snow   white   Lamb   to   a

LIGHT OF THE STABLE

Words and Music by STEVE RHYMER
and ELIZABETH RHYMER

Hail, hail ___ to the new - born ___ King; ___ let our
Come now, ___ let it shine so ___ bright ___ to the

voic - es sing ___ Him our prais - es. ___
know - ing light ___ of the sta - ble. ___

*Recorded a half step lower.

LOVE HAS COME

Words and Music by AMY GRANT,
SHANE KEISTER and MICHAEL W. SMITH

MANGER THRONE

Words and Music by
JULIE MILLER

Moderately slow, in 2

With pedal

mf

What kind of king _____ would
left the sound _____ of

leave _ His throne _____ in _____ Heav - en to make _____ this earth His home? _____ While
an - gels' praise _____ to _____ come _____ for men _____ with un - kind ways. _____ And

men seek fame _____ and great re - nown, _____ in _____ low - li - ness, _____ our
by this ba - by's help - less - ness, _____ the _____ pow'r of _____ na - tions is

NOT THAT FAR FROM BETHLEHEM

Words and Music by JEFF BORDERS,
GAYLA BORDERS and LOWELL ALEXANDER

Bm

D/A

Ev - er drawn, ev - er close to the on - ly love ___ that
(Ev - er drawn, ev - er close.)

E9/G♯   G   G/A

lasts. ___ And though two thou - sand ___ years ___ have passed, ___ we're ___

cresc.

D   A/C♯   G/B   D/A   G(add2)   D/F♯

not that far ___ from Beth - le - hem, ___ where all our hope ___ and

f

G(add2)   G/A   D   A/C♯   G/B   D/A

joy be - gan. ___ For ___ when our hearts ___ still cher - ish Him, ___ we're

OH HOLY NIGHT

Words and Music by BART MILLARD
and PETER KIPLEY

In a slow two

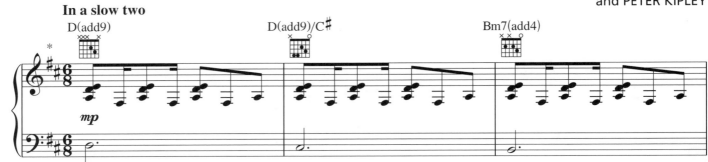

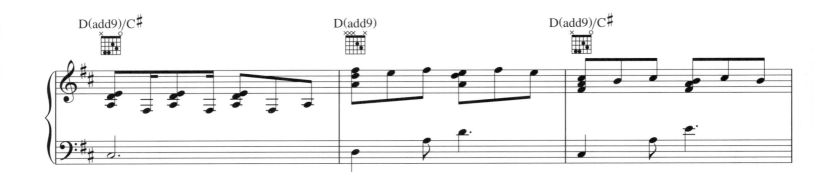

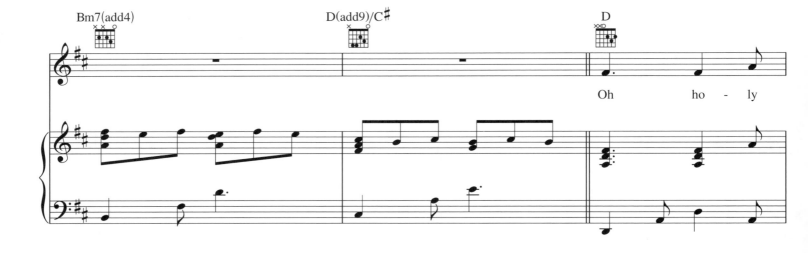

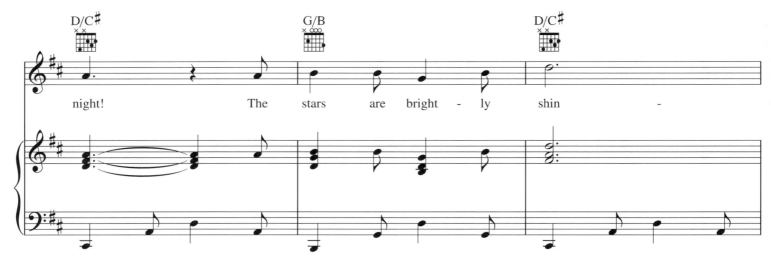

Oh ho-ly night! The stars are bright-ly shin -

* *Recorded a half step lower.*

OUR GOD IS WITH US

Words and Music by STEVEN CURTIS CHAPMAN
and MICHAEL W. SMITH

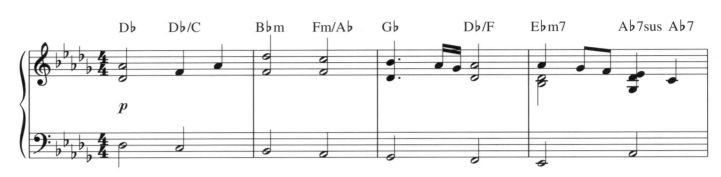

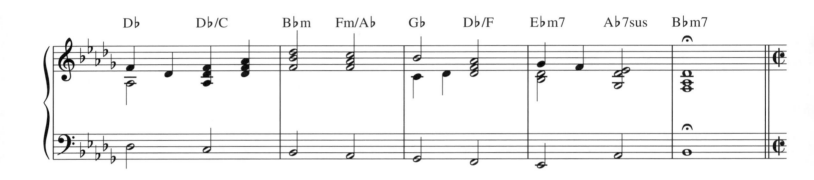

ROSE OF BETHLEHEM

Words and Music by
LOWELL ALEXANDER

SAVIOUR OF THE WORLD

Words and Music by
KATIA BOWLEY

THIS BABY

Words and Music by
STEVEN CURTIS CHAPMAN

Gently

What child is this, __ who, laid to rest, __ on Mar-y's lap __ is sleep - ing? Whom an - gels greet ____ with an - thems sweet, ____ while

Rhythmically

shep - herds watch __ are keep - ing?

2000 DECEMBERS AGO

Words and Music by JOEL LINDSEY
and REGIE HAMM

Moderately slow

(Bum, bum, bum, bah, bum, bum, bum, bah, bum, bum, bum, bah,

bum, bum, bum, bah.)

Did it feel like a night _____ an-y dif-f'rent _____ than at
sheep as a-mazed _____ as the shep-herds _____ at the
walls of the barn _____ start to trem-ble _____ with a

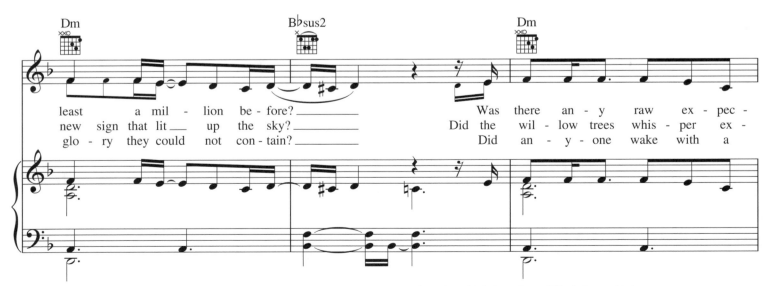

least a mil-lion be-fore? _____ Was there an-y raw ex-pec-
new sign that lit _____ up the sky? _____ Did the wil-low trees whis-per ex-
glo-ry they could not con-tain? _____ Did an-y-one wake with a

ta - tion, __ like there was some kind - a some - thin' in store? ___ Did the
cite - ment __ to the riv - ers and streams __ pass - ing by? ___ Did the
feel - ing __ of peace that they could __ not ex - plain? ___ Oh, the

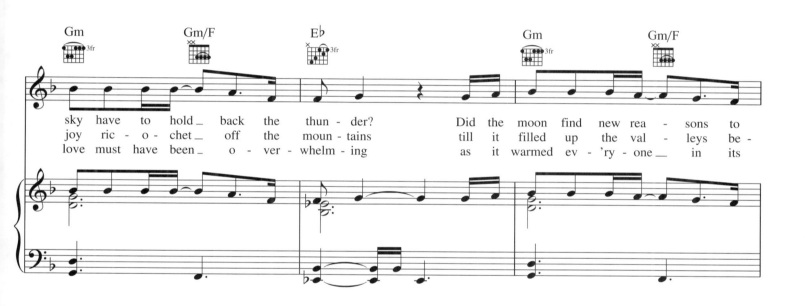

sky have to hold __ back the thun - der? Did the moon find new rea - sons to
joy ric - o - chet __ off the moun - tains till it filled up the val - leys be -
love must have been __ o - ver - whelm - ing as it warmed ev - 'ry - one __ in its

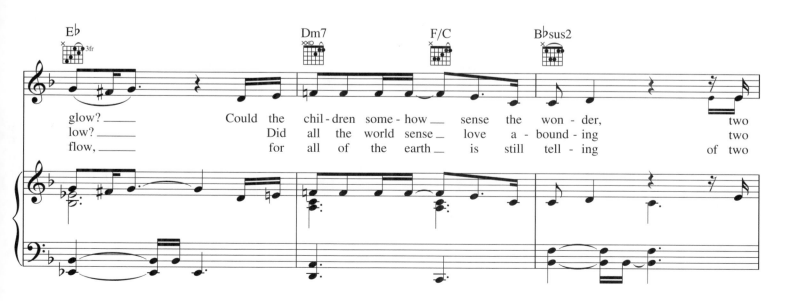

glow? ___ Could the chil - dren some - how __ sense the won - der, two
low? ___ Did all the world sense __ love a - bound - ing two
flow, ___ for all of the earth __ is still tell - ing of two

WELCOME TO OUR WORLD

Words and Music by
CHRIS RICE